# Using Geometry

*Wells / Dalton / Brunner*

USING GEOMETRY is a comprehensive high school geometry textbook in the successful Laidlaw Brothers series of mathematics publications. This book is colorful, readable, and designed for flexible use by providing three suggested course levels. USING GEOMETRY motivates students with a practical approach to geometry that emphasizes applications, especially career and consumer uses.

## Special Features

**Colorful, easy-to-follow format and functional illustrations** aid learning.

**Concrete models** promote understanding and show practical applications of geometry. (Pp. 44-45, 60, 123-124, 136, etc.)

**Abundant exercises** are grouped for oral classwork, individual written practice, and extension or student discovery. These are clearly marked *A, B,* and *C.* (Pp. 7-8, 19-21, 36-37, etc.)

**Comprehensive geometry content** including . . .

Proof (Pp. 90-92, 102-105, etc.)
Constructions (Pp. 35-37, 58, etc.)
Solid geometry (Pp. 266-283, 446-514)

Transformations (Pp. 38-39, 72-76, etc.)
Coordinates (Pp. 516-552)

**Mini-chapters** on topics such as repeating geometric designs and rubber-sheet geometry provide enrichment. (Pp. 200-203, 320-323, etc.)

**Special topics** offer a change of pace through interesting features . . .

*Geometry at Work* (Pp.136, 349, 503, etc.)

*Geometry Around You* (Pp. 76, 328, 509, etc.)

**Effective review and testing provisions** . . .

*Quick Quiz* (Pp. 17, 34, 59, etc.)
*Chapter Review* (Pp. 40-41, 77-78, 118-119, etc.)
*Chapter Test* (Pp. 42, 79, 120, etc.)

*Cumulative Review* (Pp. 121-122, 261-264, 373-374, etc.)
*Algebra Review* (Pp. 21, 47, 55, etc.)

**Convenient Teacher's Edition** contains the annotated student's textbook and a teacher's manual. Included are . . .

Answers to exercises, including proofs
Suggested class times and assignment
  guides for three course levels
Notes to the teacher

List of performance objectives
Chapter and cumulative tests
  with answers

*(For further information on these features, see the description of the textbook beginning on page T2 of this Teacher's Edition.)*

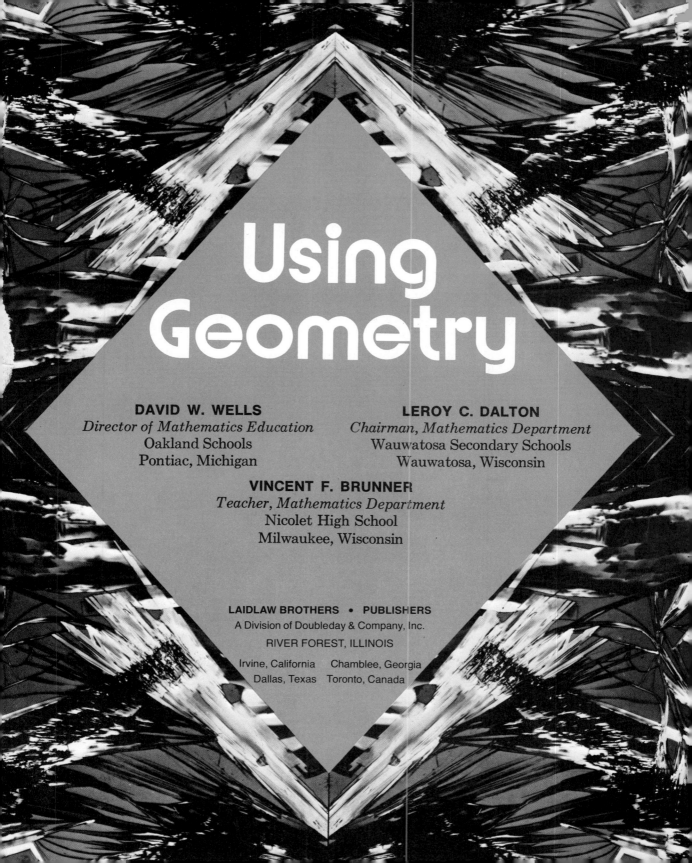

# Using Geometry

**DAVID W. WELLS**
*Director of Mathematics Education*
Oakland Schools
Pontiac, Michigan

**LEROY C. DALTON**
*Chairman, Mathematics Department*
Wauwatosa Secondary Schools
Wauwatosa, Wisconsin

**VINCENT F. BRUNNER**
*Teacher, Mathematics Department*
Nicolet High School
Milwaukee, Wisconsin

**LAIDLAW BROTHERS • PUBLISHERS**
A Division of Doubleday & Company, Inc.
RIVER FOREST, ILLINOIS

Irvine, California    Chamblee, Georgia
Dallas, Texas    Toronto, Canada

**About the cover:** The cover design was made from a photograph of a highly magnified view of sulfathiozole crystals, a sulfa drug used in veterinary medicine.

EDITORIAL STAFF

**Project Director:** Eugene M. Malecki

**Staff Editors:** Joan M. Davidson,  Gene S. Kuechmann,
Max V. Lyles,  Carol A. Papke

**Production Associate:** Nora Gubbins-Kawa

**Art Director:** Gloria Muczynski

**Photo Researcher:** William A. Cassin

ILLUSTRATORS

**Cover and Title Page:** Donald C. Meighan

**Text:** John D. Firestone & Associates,  Paul Hazelrigg,
Donald C. Meighan

Teacher's Edition ISBN 0–8445–1963–4

ISBN 0–8445–1962–6

Printed in the United States of America

2 3 4 5 6 7 8 9 10 11 12 13 14 15     6 5 4 3 2 1 0 9 8

1 2 3 4 5 6 7 8 9 10 11 12 13 14 15     7 6 5 4 3 2 1 0 9 8

# CONTENTS

This section is in the student's text only. It includes answers for the odd-numbered items in the "B" exercises, the Chapter Reviews, and the Algebra Reviews, as well as answers for all items in each Quick Quiz and Chapter Test.

# SPECIAL TOPICS

# ALGEBRA REVIEWS

# GEOMETRY: WHAT AND WHY?

## 1

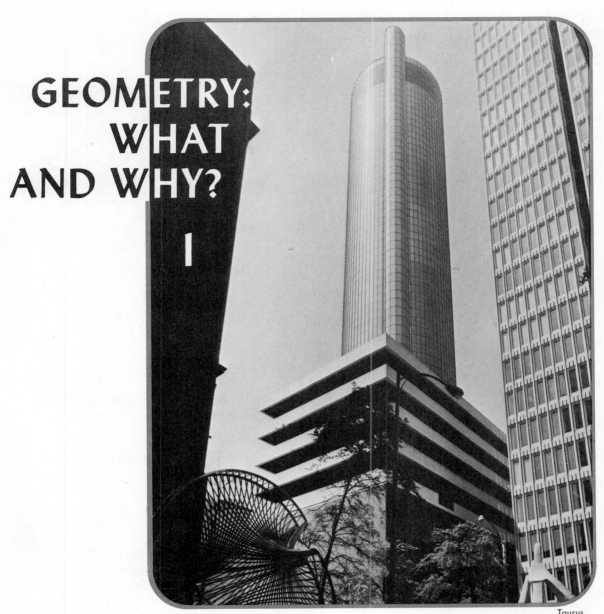

Taurus

Geometry may be thought of in two ways:

- It is the study of size, shape, position, and other properties of the objects around us.

- It is a mathematical system in which a few basic statements or ideas are agreed to and then used to discover results by logical reasoning.

Throughout this book, geometry will be studied in both ways.

# 1.1 Figures—Sets of Points

**Suggested Class Time**

| Course | Min. | Reg. | Max. |
|--------|------|------|------|
| Days   | 1    | 1    | 1    |

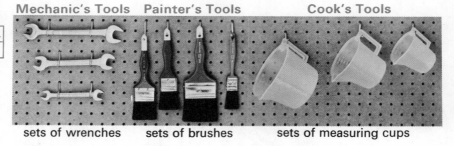

**Mechanic's Tools**    **Painter's Tools**    **Cook's Tools**

sets of wrenches    sets of brushes    sets of measuring cups

Different sets of tools are used in different kinds of work. Different kinds of mathematics use different sets of ideas.

| Arithmetic | Algebra | Geometry |
|------------|---------|----------|
| $1, 2, 3, 4, \cdots$ | $1, \frac{3}{2}, 2, \frac{9}{4}, -3, \cdots$ | $1, \frac{5}{4}, \sqrt{2}, \frac{3}{2}, \sqrt{3}, \cdots$ |
| $\frac{1}{2}, \frac{2}{3}, \frac{3}{4}, \frac{1}{5}, \frac{7}{3}, \cdots$ | $\sqrt{2}, \sqrt{3}, -\sqrt{5}, \cdots$ | |
| $1\frac{1}{2}, 2\frac{1}{3}, 4\frac{2}{7}, 8\frac{3}{5}, \cdots$ | $a, b, c, x, y, \cdots$ | |
| sets of numbers | sets of numbers sets of variables | sets of numbers sets of points |

Geometry deals mostly with points and sets of points. Here is how we draw and name them.

| Model | Picture | Names | Important Notes |
|-------|---------|-------|-----------------|
| a spot of light | $\bullet P$ | point $P$ <br> $P$ | A point has no size at all—it involves position or location only. |
| an endless light beam | | line $\ell$ <br> line $AB$ <br> $\overleftrightarrow{AB}$ | A line extends without end in both directions. <br><br> Points $A$ and $B$ are two points in the set. <br><br> Think of a line as *straight* and as having absolutely no width or thickness. |

Lick Observatory, University of California

| Model | Picture | Names | Important Notes |
|---|---|---|---|
| 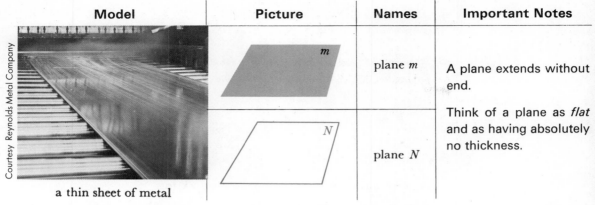 a thin sheet of metal | *m* | plane *m* | A plane extends without end. |
| | *N* | plane *N* | Think of a plane as *flat* and as having absolutely no thickness. |

Courtesy Reynolds Metal Company

A set of points (like a line or a plane) is also called a **figure.** Objects (like lengths of thread or sheets of plastic) that help us think about geometric figures are **models.** In fact, the drawings we make of figures are also models.

Here are some basic figures and the terms we use in talking about them.

Points *A* and *B* are *on* (or *in*) line $\ell$.

Line $\ell$ *contains* points *A* and *B*.

$\ell = \overleftrightarrow{AB}$ means that $\ell$ and $\overleftrightarrow{AB}$ are two names for the same line

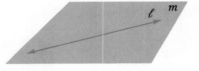

Line $\ell$ is *in* plane *m*.

Each point of line $\ell$ is *in* plane *m*.

Plane *m* *contains* line $\ell$.

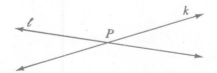

Lines *k* and $\ell$ *intersect* at point *P*.

Their *intersection* is point *P*.

Lines *m* and *n* do not intersect.

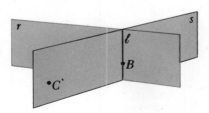

Planes *r* and *s* *intersect* at line $\ell$.

Their *intersection* is line $\ell$.

Point *B* on line $\ell$ is in both planes *r* and *s*.

Point *C* is in plane *s* but not in plane *r*.

**Assignment Guide**
*Oral:* 1–18
*Written:*
Min. 19–32
Reg. 19–34
Max. 19–33 odd; 35–45

The set of all points is called **space**. We say that space contains all points and that every point is in space.

A point is said to have *no dimensions*, a line *one dimension*, a plane *two dimensions*, and space *three dimensions*.

## Exercises 1.1 |||||||||||||||||||||||||||||||||||||||||||||||||||||||||||||||||||||||||||

(A) **1–4.** For what geometric figure is the object a model?

**1.** a beam of light   Line

**2.** a desk top   Plane

**3.** the tip of a pin   Point

**4.** a flagpole   Line

**5–18.** Using the walls, floor, and ceiling of your classroom and their intersections, describe a model of the figure.   *Typical answers*

**5.** a line   "Line" where 2 walls meet

**6.** a point   Any corner

**7.** two intersecting lines

**8.** two lines that do not intersect

**9.** a line and a point on that line

**10.** a line and a point not on that line

**11.** three lines that intersect at one point

**12.** three lines, none of which intersect

**13.** a plane

**14.** a plane and a line in that plane

**15.** a plane and a line that intersects that plane at one point

**16.** a plane and a point not in that plane

**17.** two intersecting planes

**18.** two planes that do not intersect

(B) **19–28.** Refer to the drawing. From the list, choose a word or phrase that correctly completes the statement.

**a.** point

**b.** line

**c.** plane

**d.** contains

**e.** is on (or in)

**f.** is not in

**g.** intersect(s)

7. Two "lines" where 2 adjacent walls meet the floor
8. "Lines" where 2 opposite walls meet the floor
9. "Line" where a wall meets the floor and a corner on that "line"
10. "Line" where a wall meets the floor and a corner at the ceiling
11. Three "lines" where 2 adjacent walls meet and where these walls meet the floor
12. "Lines" where 2 opposite walls meet the floor and where a wall meets the ceiling
13. Any wall (or floor or ceiling)
14. A wall and the "line" where that wall meets the floor
15. Floor and "line" where 2 adjacent walls meet
16. Floor and a corner at the ceiling
17. Floor and wall (or adjacent walls)
18. Floor and ceiling (or opposite walls)

**19.** $P$ is a ___a___ .

**20.** $n$ is a ___c___ .

**21.** $b$ is a ___b___ .

**22.** $Q$ is a ___a___ .

**23.** Point $T$ ___e___ line $b$.

**24.** Line $d$ ___d___ point $T$.

**25.** Lines $d$ and $b$ ___g___ .

**26.** Point $Q$ ___f___ plane $n$.

**27.** Point $R$ ___e___ line $d$ and plane $n$.

**28.** Line $d$ ___e___ plane $n$.

**29–42.** Draw and label the figure described.

**29.** Line $\ell$ intersects $\overleftrightarrow{DP}$ at $P$.

**30.** $\overrightarrow{SR}$ intersects line $n$ at $R$.

**31.** $\overleftrightarrow{BC}$ is in plane $m$.

**32.** Plane $r$ contains $\overrightarrow{AD}$.

**33.** Plane $n$ contains lines $\ell$ and $m$, but lines $\ell$ and $m$ do not intersect.

**34.** Lines $a$ and $b$ are in plane $w$, but lines $a$ and $b$ do not intersect.

© **35.** Points $A$, $B$, and $C$ are in plane $n$, but point $D$ is not.

**36.** Plane $r$ contains $\overleftrightarrow{EF}$ but not points $M$ and $N$.

**37.** Planes $m$ and $n$ intersect at $\overleftrightarrow{AB}$.

**38.** Plane $t$ contains line $GH$ but not $\overleftrightarrow{CH}$.

**39.** Planes $a$, $b$, and $c$ intersect at line $\ell$.

**40.** $\overleftrightarrow{AB}$, $\overleftrightarrow{AC}$, $\overleftrightarrow{AD}$, and $\overleftrightarrow{AE}$ intersect.

**41.** Line $\ell$ does not intersect plane $n$.

**42.** Planes $x$ and $y$ do not intersect.

**43.** Does geometric space extend indefinitely?  Yes

**44.** What could be used as a model of a small portion of geometric space?  Any solid object

**45.** Show how you think space might be represented by a drawing.

# 1.2 The Real Numbers

**Suggested Class Time**

| Course | Min. | Reg. | Max. |
|--------|------|------|------|
| Days   | 1    | 1    | 1    |

In geometry, distance and size are described using real numbers. A **real number** is any number for which there is a decimal expansion.

Integers ($\cdots$, $-4$, $-3$, $-2$, $-1$, 0, 1, 2, 3, 4, $\cdots$) have decimal expansions.

$$2 = 2.000 \cdots$$
$$-5 = -5.000 \cdots$$

Rational numbers (ratios of integers) have repeating decimal expansions.

$$\tfrac{3}{2} = 1.5000 \cdots$$
$$-\tfrac{1}{3} = -0.333 \cdots$$

Irrational numbers (numbers that are not ratios of integers) have nonrepeating decimal expansions.

$$\sqrt{2} = 1.414213 \cdots$$
$$-\sqrt{5} = -2.236 \cdots$$

Every integer is a rational number, since $2 = \tfrac{2}{1}$ and $-5 = \tfrac{-5}{1}$.

Every real number is either a rational number or an irrational number.

To find a rational number between any two distinct (different) rational numbers, you can take their average (one half their sum).

$$\tfrac{1}{2}(2 + 3) = 2\tfrac{1}{2}$$
$$\tfrac{1}{2}(2 + 2\tfrac{1}{2}) = 2\tfrac{1}{4}$$
$$\tfrac{1}{2}(2 + 2\tfrac{1}{4}) = 2\tfrac{1}{8}$$
$$\vdots$$

The averaging can be continued indefinitely.

So between any two distinct rational numbers there is another rational number. (In fact, between any two distinct rational numbers there is also an irrational number.) So the set of rational numbers, and consequently the set of real numbers, is an **infinite set**. No matter how many real numbers are named, more can be named.

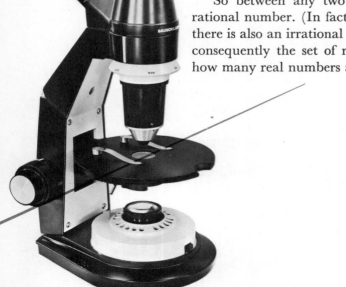

Now let's look at a line through an imaginary "geomicroscope." No matter how much we magnify the line, between every two points we can see more points. (Remember, a point doesn't "use up" any space.) That is, the set of all points on a line is also an infinite set. In fact, there are exactly as many points on a line as there are real numbers!

By matching each point on a line with a real number, we can make a **real number line**. The number matched with a point is its **coordinate**. In a diagram, we label only a few of the points with their coordinates, using whatever part of the line we need, as shown below.

Examples:   a.
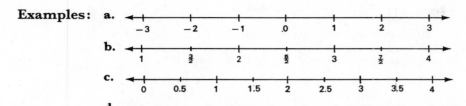
b.

c.

d.

One of the ways in which real numbers are related is their **order**.

| In words | In symbols | On the real number line |
|---|---|---|
| 2 *is less than* 3. | $2 < 3$ | 2 is to the left of 3. |
| 3 *is greater than* 2. | $3 > 2$ | 3 is to the right of 2. |

The real numbers also have the following properties.

| Let *a*, *b*, and *c* stand for any real numbers. | | **Examples:** |
|---|---|---|
| $a < b, a = b,$ or $a > b$  ◀ Exactly one of these is true. | | • $3 < 2, 3 = 2,$ or $3 > 2$ <br> • $\frac{1}{2} < 0.5, \frac{1}{2} = 0.5,$ or $\frac{1}{2} > 0.5$ |
| If $a < b$ and $b < c$, then $a < c$. | | $2 < 5$ and $5 < 6$, so $2 < 6$ |
| If $a < b$, then $b > a$. | | $4 < 7$, so $7 > 4$ |

# Exercises 1.2

(A)  **1–7.** True or False?

**Assignment Guide**
*Oral:* 1–16
*Written:* Min. 17–39 odd
　　　　　Reg. 17–43 odd
　　　　　Max. 17–49 odd

**1.** All integers are rational numbers.  T

**2.** Every irrational number is a real number.  T

**3.** Some rational numbers are not real numbers.  F

**4.** Between any two points in a line there is another point.  T

**5.** There are more points on a line than there are real numbers.  F

**6.** *Is less than* is used to express order.  T

**7.** There is a smallest integer.  F

**8–16.** Tell how to read each statement. Then tell whether it is true.

**8.** $3 < 5$ T    **9.** $-4 > -2$ F    **10.** $0 < -3$ F    **11.** $2 > 0$ T

**12.** $-2 < -3$, $-2 = -3$, or $-2 > -3$ T    **13.** $-1 < 1$ T    **14.** $4 > -1$  T

**15.** If $n < 2$ and $2 < 3$, then $n < 3$. T    **16.** If $x < 5$, then $5 < x$.  F

Ⓑ **17–28.** Name a rational number that is between the two given numbers.

**17.** 5, 6 $5\frac{1}{2}$    **18.** 7, 8 $7\frac{1}{2}$    **19.** $-3, -4$ $-3\frac{1}{2}$    **20.** $-6, -7$ $-6\frac{1}{2}$

**21.** $1\frac{1}{2}, 2$ $1\frac{3}{4}$    **22.** $3, 3\frac{1}{2}$ $3\frac{1}{4}$    **23.** $3\frac{1}{4}, 3\frac{1}{2}$ $3\frac{3}{8}$    **24.** $5\frac{1}{2}, 5\frac{3}{4}$ $5\frac{5}{8}$

**25.** 1.2, 1.3 1.25    **26.** 2.4, 2.5 2.45    **27.** $0, -\frac{1}{3}$ $-\frac{1}{6}$    **28.** $-\frac{1}{4}, 0$ $-\frac{1}{8}$

**29–36.** Draw a real number line and label the points described.

**29.** integers from 3 to 10    **30.** integers from 5 to 12

**31.** integers from $-8$ to 0    **32.** integers from $-12$ to $-4$

**33.** $0, \frac{1}{2}, \frac{2}{2}, \frac{3}{2}, \frac{4}{2}, \frac{5}{2}, \frac{6}{2}, \frac{7}{2}$    **34.** $0, \frac{1}{3}, \frac{2}{3}, \frac{3}{3}, \frac{4}{3}, \frac{5}{3}, \frac{6}{3}, \frac{7}{3}$

**35.** 0.1, 0.2, 0.3, 0.4, 0.5, 0.6    **36.** 1.0, 1.1, 1.2, 1.3, 1.4, 1.5

**37–48.** Which symbol, $<$, $=$, or $>$, should replace the ▨ ?

**37.** 13 ▨ 11 $>$    **38.** 27 ▨ 33 $<$    **39.** $4 + 1$ ▨ 5 $=$    **40.** $6 + 3$ ▨ 10 $<$

**41.** $\frac{17}{3}$ ▨ 5 $>$    **42.** $\frac{14}{3}$ ▨ $4\frac{1}{3}$ $>$    **43.** 2.6 ▨ $2\frac{3}{5}$ $=$    **44.** $13 + 4$ ▨ $24 - 6$ $<$

Ⓒ **45.** $\sqrt{5}$ ▨ 2 $>$    **46.** $\sqrt{5}$ ▨ 3 $<$    **47.** 1 ▨ $\sqrt{3}$ $<$    **48.** $\sqrt{3}$ ▨ 2 $<$

$A$    $B$ $C$ $D$    $E$ $F$ $G$    $H$

**49.** Match each point with its coordinate.

$3, \sqrt{5}, 1, 2\sqrt{2}, 4, 2, \sqrt{3}, \sqrt{11}$

$F$   $D$   $A$   $E$   $H$ $C$   $B$   $G$

Copy the puzzle onto graph paper. Then use the numbered clues to solve it. If a result is negative, write the negative sign with the first digit. (So if either the ACROSS or the DOWN clue gives a negative result, both clues should give a negative result.)

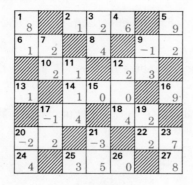

## ACROSS

**1.** $3 + 5$     **9.** $-4 - 8$     **16.** $(-3)^2$     **22.** $3(13 - 4)$

**2.** $21 \cdot 6$     **10.** $1 \cdot 21$     **17.** $(-2)(7)$     **24.** $\sqrt{16}$

**5.** $13 - 4$     **12.** $27 + (-4)$     **18.** $-7 - (-49)$     **25.** $1 \cdot 350$

**6.** $48 \div 4$     **13.** $\frac{1}{3} \cdot 3$     **20.** $-44 \div 2$     **27.** $2^3$

**8.** $-3 + 7$     **14.** $10^2$     **21.** $-1 \cdot 3$

## DOWN

**1.** $9^2$     **7.** $5^2 - 3$     **15.** $17 \cdot 0$     **21.** $5 \cdot (-7)$

**2.** $-1(3 - 4)$     **9.** $-9 + (-4)$     **16.** $(-45) \div (-5)$     **23.** $3(-13)(-2)$

**3.** $(-4)(-6)$     **11.** $111 - (-3)$     **17.** $72 \div (-6)$     **25.** $\frac{1}{3} \cdot 9$

**4.** $(-54) \div (-9)$     **12.** $4 \cdot 51$     **19.** $-11(-2)$     **26.** $-7 + 7$

**5.** $23 \cdot 2^2$     **13.** $\frac{5}{2} \cdot \frac{2}{5}$     **20.** $-26 - (-2)$

⊖⊖⊖⊖⊖⊖ Geometry Around the World ⊖⊖⊖⊖⊖⊖

In ancient Greece, the word *geōmetrein* meant "to measure the earth." From that word came the Greek word *geōmetria* for the subject we call *geometry*.

In France it is *géométrie*.      In Germany it is *geometrie*.
In Mexico it is *geometría*.      And in Russia it is Геометрия.

See if you can find out what geometry is called in some language other than the ones shown here.

# 1.3 Distance

**Suggested Class Time**

| Course | Min. | Reg. | Max. |
|--------|------|------|------|
| Days | 1 | 1 | 1 |

The edge of a ruler represents a real number line. To measure the distance between points *A* and *B*, you could

**1** Lay a ruler so its edge touches both points and the end is at *A*, as shown below.

**2** Count the number of marks between *A* and *B* that are labeled with whole numbers.

**3** Use the additional marks on the ruler to estimate the distance between the last mark counted and point *B*.

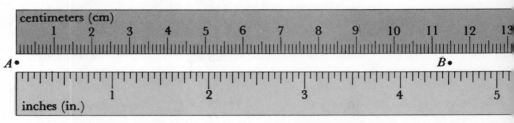

But the whole-number marks are not the same distance apart on all rulers! To state the distance between *A* and *B*, you must tell which ruler you used. That is, you must name the *unit of measure*. On one of the rulers above, the whole-number marks are one inch apart, so the unit of measure is the *inch*. On the other ruler, the unit of measure is the *centimeter*.

The distance between points *A* and *B* is about $4\frac{1}{2}$ inches or about 11.5 centimeters. (Why do we say *about*?)

Inches and centimeters belong to the two most commonly used systems of measurement. Here are some units of distance in these systems.

| Customary (English) System | Metric (SI) System |
|---|---|
| 12 inches (in.) = 1 foot (ft) | 0.001 meter (m) = 1 millimeter (mm) |
| 3 feet (ft) = 1 yard (yd) | 0.01 meter (m) = 1 centimeter (cm) |
| 5280 feet (ft) = 1 mile (mi) | 1000 meters (m) = 1 kilometer (km) |

Most ideas in geometry apply to any system of measurement. So we do not always state a unit of measure. But if no units are stated, we do assume that the same unit is used for all measurements in the same problem.

Two rulers are used to measure the distance between $M$ and $N$ below. This distance, written $MN$ or $NM$, can be found in each case by subtracting.

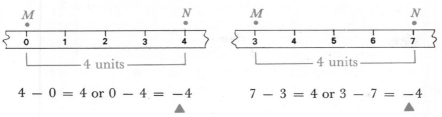

$$4 - 0 = 4 \text{ or } 0 - 4 = -4 \qquad\qquad 7 - 3 = 4 \text{ or } 3 - 7 = -4$$

To state distance, disregard the negative sign.

Another way to say *disregard the negative sign* is to say *take the absolute value*. The symbol $|\quad|$ is used to indicate absolute value.

Harrison Forman

## Examples

If a number is nonnegative, it equals its absolute value.

▶ If $n \geq 0$, $|n| = n$.
  { **a.** $|4| = 4$
  { **b.** $|0| = 0$

If a number is negative, its absolute value is its opposite.

▶ If $n < 0$, $|n| = -n$.
  { **a.** $|-4| = -(-4) = 4$
  { **b.** $|5 - 9| = |-4| = -(-4) = 4$

Since any real number has only one absolute value, we say its absolute value is **unique.**

The important ideas in this section and the preceding section are summarized in the following statements. We call these statements *postulates*. A **postulate** is a statement that is accepted as true without proof. We will say more about postulates in later sections.

**Distance Postulate**

For every pair of points there is a unique nonnegative number, called the **distance** between them.

**Ruler Postulate**

The points of a line can be matched with the real numbers so that

1. for every point on the line there is exactly one real number coordinate;

2. for every real number there is exactly one point on the line;

3. the distance between any two points is the absolute value of the difference of their coordinates.

**Ruler Placement Postulate**

> For any two points $P$ and $R$ on a line, a ruler can be placed so that the coordinate of $P$ is zero and the coordinate of $R$ is a positive number.

Two points that are the same distance from a third point are **equidistant** from the third point.

$A \bullet \underrightarrow{\quad 2.5\ cm \quad}$
$B \bullet \underrightarrow{\quad 2.5\ cm \quad} \bullet P$

## Exercises 1.3

**Assignment Guide**
*Oral:* 1–16
*Written:* Min. 17–45 odd
Reg. 17–47 odd
Max. 17–59 odd

(A) **1–10.** Complete each sentence.

1. A statement that is accepted as true without proof is a ___. Postulate

2. According to the ___ Postulate, for every point on a line there is exactly one real number coordinate. Ruler

3. The most commonly used systems of measurement are the customary (English) system and the ___ system. Metric

4. The ___ of $-3$ is written $|-3|$. Absolute value

5. The ___ between two points is the absolute value of the difference of their coordinates. Distance

6. The distance between two points cannot be $-5$ because, according to the Distance Postulate, distance is ___. Nonnegative

7. If the same unit of measure is used, the distance between two points cannot be both 6 and 7 because the distance is ___. Unique

8. According to the ___ Postulate, if the coordinate of $R$ is zero, a positive coordinate can always be assigned to another point $S$. Ruler Placement

9. $AB$ and $BA$ both mean the ___ points $A$ and $B$. Distance between

10. If $MR$ is 3.2 and $MS$ is 3.2, then $R$ and $S$ are ___ from $M$. Equidistant

**11–28.** Find the absolute value.

11. $|6|$  6      12. $|8|$  8      13. $|-9|$  9

14. $|-10|$  10      15. $|6-2|$  4      16. $|3-1|$  2

ⓑ **17.** $|12 - 5|$  7 **18.** $|17 - 6|$  11 **19.** $|23 - 9|$  14

**20.** $|21 - 7|$  14 **21.** $|5 - 13|$  8 **22.** $|4 - 7|$  3

**23.** $|13 - 13|$  0 **24.** $|24 - 24|$  0 **25.** $|2 - 18|$  16

**26.** $|5 - 12|$  7 **27.** $|0 - 27|$  27 **28.** $|0 - 19|$  19

**29–55.** The coordinates of $P$ and $R$ are listed. Find $PR$.

**29.** $P: 0$   $R: 7$  7 **30.** $P: 0$   $R: 9$  9 **31.** $P: 0$   $R: 15$  15

**32.** $P: 0$   $R: 18$  18 **33.** $P: 12$   $R: 0$  12 **34.** $P: 6$   $R: 0$  6

**35.** $P: 4$   $R: 15$  11 **36.** $P: 7$   $R: 13$  6 **37.** $P: 18$   $R: 3$  15

**38.** $P: 21$   $R: 14$  7 **39.** $P: 15$   $R: 6$  9 **40.** $P: 7$   $R: 3$  4

**41.** $P: 7$   $R: 13$  6 **42.** $P: 8$   $R: 15$  7 **43.** $P: 18$   $R: 112$  94

**44.** $P: 19$   $R: 113$ 94 **45.** $P: 23$   $R: 12$  11 **46.** $P: 25$   $R: 16$  9

ⓒ **47.** $P: 5$   $R: 5$  0 **48.** $P: 3$   $R: 3$  0 **49.** $P: 72$   $R: -16$  88

**50.** $P: 56$   $R: -18$ 74 **51.** $P: -37$   $R: 44$  81 **52.** $P: -23$   $R: 52$  75

**53.** $P: -12$   $R: -51$ 39 **54.** $P: -13$   $R: -72$ 59 **55.** $P: -7$   $R: -7$  0

**56–59.** Express as an integer.

**56.** $2 + |-7| - |3|$  6 **57.** $|-5| + |5 - 2| - |-7 + 4|$  5

**58.** $||-2 - 3| + (-5) - 7|$  7 **59.** $9 - |3 + |-2 - 3| - 8|$  9

===== **Highway Coordinates** =====

Many highways are marked with mileposts that tell motorists how far they have traveled from some point of reference (often the state line).

A stalled car is reported at milepost 56. There is an emergency service truck parked at milepost 8 and another one parked at milepost 123. How far would each truck have to travel to reach the stalled car? 48 mi and 67 mi

The truck closer to the stalled car goes to the aid of the motorist. It then immediately answers another call at milepost 31. How far has the truck traveled from its original location? 73 mi

Gene Kuechmann

# Defining Terms

© King Features Syndicate Inc. 1977

Beetle Bailey accepts *greenstuff* as an undefined term. In geometry we also accept some terms, such as *point*, *line*, and *plane*, as undefined terms. This is done to avoid circular definitions.

If we tried to define *point*, for example, we would eventually come back to the term *point*.

The terms we leave undefined are used, however, in defining other geometry terms. Here are some of those definitions.

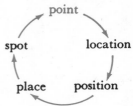

| DEFINITION (The word being defined is in heavy type.) | EXAMPLE |
|---|---|
| **Collinear** points are points on the same line.<br><br>**Noncollinear** points are points not all on the same line. | 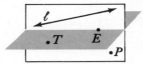<br>*A*, *B*, and *C* are *collinear*.<br><br>*A*, *B*, and *E* are *noncollinear*. |
| **Coplanar** points are points in the same plane.<br><br>**Noncoplanar** points are points not all in the same plane. | 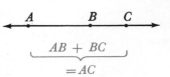<br>*P*, *E*, and line *ℓ* are *coplanar*.<br><br>*P*, *ℓ*, and *T* are *noncoplanar*. |
| Let *A*, *B*, and *C* be distinct collinear points.<br><br>*AB* + *BC* = *AC* means<br><br>    *B* is **between** *A* and *C*.<br><br>    *A* and *C* are **on opposite sides of** *B*.<br><br>    *B* and *C* are **on the same side of** *A*. | $A \qquad B \quad C$<br><br>$\underbrace{AB + BC}_{= AC}$ |

| | |
|---|---|
| **Segment** *DE* (symbol: $\overline{DE}$) is the figure that contains *D*, *E*, and all points between *D* and *E*.<br><br>Points *D* and *E* are the **endpoints** of $\overline{DE}$.<br><br>The **length** of a segment is the distance between its endpoints. | *D* ———————— *E*<br><br>segment *DE* (or $\overline{DE}$)<br>with length *DE* |
| $\overline{DE}$ and $\overline{ED}$ name the same segment.<br><br>$\overline{DPE}$ means *P* is on $\overline{DE}$ between *D* and *E*.<br><br>$\overline{DRE}$ means *R* is on $\overline{DE}$ between *D* and *E*.<br><br>$\overline{DPRE}$ means *P* is between *D* and *R* on $\overline{DE}$. | *D    P    R    E*<br><br>$\overline{DE} = \overline{ED}$<br>$= \overline{DPE} = \overline{DRE} = \overline{DPRE}$ |
| The **midpoint** of a segment is the point that is between the endpoints and equidistant from them.<br><br>Any figure that intersects a segment only at its midpoint **bisects** the segment. | *D ——————— M ———— E*  ℓ<br><br>$DM = ME$<br><br>*M* is the midpoint of $\overline{DE}$.<br>Line ℓ bisects $\overline{DE}$. |
| **Ray** *FG* (symbol: $\overrightarrow{FG}$) is the figure that contains *F* and every point on the same side of *F* as *G*.<br><br>Point *F* is the **endpoint** of $\overrightarrow{FG}$. | *F        G* ——————→<br><br>ray *FG* (or $\overrightarrow{FG}$) |
| **Opposite rays** are two distinct rays that are collinear and have a common endpoint. | ←—— *B    P    A* ——→<br><br>$\overrightarrow{PB}$ and $\overrightarrow{PA}$ are opposite rays. |

Notice that these definitions make use of

*1.* ordinary (dictionary-defined) words.

*2.* undefined (or primitive) terms, such as *point* and *contains*.

*3.* geometry terms already defined.

For example, consider the definition of **ray**.

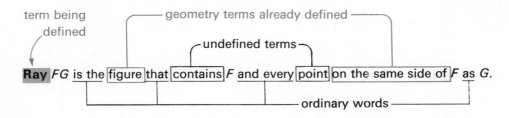

# Exercises 1.4

**Assignment Guide**
*Oral:* 1–20
*Written:*
Min. 21–34; Quiz, p. 17
Reg. 21–36; Quiz, p. 17
Max. 21–41; Quiz, p. 17

Ⓐ **1–12.** Tell whether the term, as used in the definitions on pages 14–15, is an *ordinary word*, and *undefined term*, or a *defined geometry term*.

**1.** ray   Defined    **2.** every   Ordinary    **3.** line   Undefined

**4.** same side of Defined   **5.** and   Ordinary    **6.** bisects   Defined

**7.** plane   Undefined    **8.** endpoint   Defined    **9.** contains   Undefined

**10.** point   Undefined    **11.** collinear   Defined    **12.** segment   Defined

**13–18.** Each of these terms has been defined earlier in this chapter. Give the number of the page on which each definition can be found.

**13.** figure   Page 3    **14.** postulate   Page 11    **15.** distance   Page 11

**16.** coordinate   Page 7    **17.** equidistant   Page 12    **18.** absolute value
                                                                        Page 11

**19.** What term in the definition of *ray* tells you that the points on a ray are collinear?   On the same side of

**20.** What term in the definition of *midpoint of a segment* tells you that the midpoint is on the segment?   Between

Ⓑ **21–34.** Using the choices listed below the figure, match the word or phrase with an example from the figure.

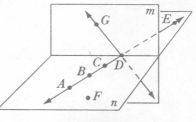

**21.** the endpoint of $\overrightarrow{BA}$   c

**22.** an endpoint of $\overline{AD}$   a

**23.** the midpoint of $\overline{AE}$   a

**24.** a point on $\overrightarrow{AC}$   c

$$AD = DE$$

**25.** three collinear points   g

**26.** a point between $A$ and $D$   c

**27.** a point between $B$ and $E$   a

**28.** another name for $\overline{AE}$   i

**29.** another name for $\overrightarrow{EC}$   e

**a.** $D$        **f.** $A, C, G$

**b.** $E$        **g.** $A, C, E$

**c.** $B$        **h.** $A, F, C$

**d.** $A, E$      **i.** $\overline{ACE}$

**e.** $\overline{CE}$

**30.** a point on the same side of $C$ as $D$    b

**31.** two points on opposite sides of $C$    d

**32.** the endpoint of the ray opposite $\overrightarrow{DC}$    a

**33.** three points not all in plane $n$    f

**34.** three coplanar, noncollinear points    h (or f)

© **35–40.** Refer to the figure for Exercises 21–34. Name the following.

**35.** two points equidistant from $D$    **36.** a point on $\overleftrightarrow{AD}$ but not on $\overline{AD}$    E
$$A, E$$

**37.** the intersection of $\overline{AC}$ and $\overline{BD}$    **38.** the intersection of $\overline{FD}$ and $\overline{DB}$    D
$$BC$$

**39.** the intersection of $\overleftrightarrow{FD}$ and $\overleftrightarrow{AC}$    **40.** a line that bisects $\overline{AE}$    $\overrightarrow{DG}$
$$D$$

**41.** Name the segment whose endpoints are $M$ and $N$ to show that $C$ and $D$ are on the segment and that $C$ is between $D$ and $N$.    $\overline{MDCN}$

⏱ ⏱ ⏱ ⏱  **Time Out**  ⏱ ⏱ ⏱ ⏱

If the hands of the clock are opposite rays when the clock strikes the hour, what time is it?    6 o'clock

---

**1.** Name three undefined geometric terms.    Any 3 of point, line, plane, contains

**2–7.** Refer to the figure. Name an example of:

**2.** a line
$$\overline{AP} \text{ (or } \overline{AB} \text{ or } \overline{PB})$$
**3.** three noncollinear points
$$C, A, P \text{ (or } C, A, B \text{ or } C, P, B)$$
**4.** a segment
$$\overline{AB} \text{ (or } \overline{PB} \text{ or } \overline{AP})$$
**5.** a ray with endpoint $A$
$$\overrightarrow{AP} \text{ (or } \overrightarrow{AB})$$
**6.** a ray opposite $\overrightarrow{PA}$    $\overrightarrow{PB}$    **7.** a point between $A$ and $B$    P

**8.** $\frac{2}{3}$ is (a rational, an irrational) number.

**9.** If $0 < 3$ and $3 < x$, then $0$ ($\underline{<}$, $=$, $>$) $x$.

**10.** A (figure, postulate) is accepted as true without proof.

**11.** The (coordinate, absolute value) of $-7$ is 7.

**12.** An endless light beam is a (model, figure) of a line.

*Quick Quiz for Sections 1.1 to 1.4*

# 1.5 Reaching Conclusions

We've checked more than 30 of these footprints, and they've been fakes. They're all fakes.

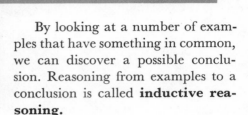

By looking at a number of examples that have something in common, we can discover a possible conclusion. Reasoning from examples to a conclusion is called **inductive reasoning.**

■ Sometimes we can check every example. Then we know that the conclusion reached by inductive reasoning is correct.

■ If we cannot check every example, we cannot be sure a conclusion reached by inductive reasoning is correct.

■ If we can find **one** example that does not agree with the conclusion, we know the conclusion is *not* correct.

Pictures can also suggest a possible conclusion. But again the conclusion is not necessarily correct. Most people looking at the *optical illusions* shown here reach conclusions that do not agree with the facts.

*A*

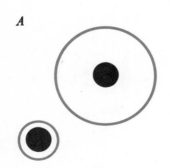

Which black spot is larger?

*B*

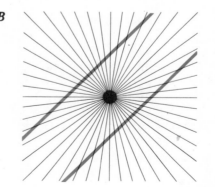

*C*

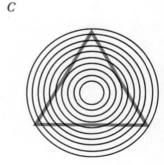

Are the heavy lines curved or straight?

If appearances and reasoning from examples do not always lead to correct conclusions, what does? In geometry, conclusions are accepted as true if they can be reached by *deductive reasoning*.

**Deductive reasoning** follows this pattern.

1. Start with agreed - upon statements (postulates and definitions).

2. Set up conditions (the hypothesis).

3. Use logical reasoning.

4. Find a result (the conclusion).

The statement of a hypothesis (step 2 above) and its logical conclusion (step 4) is called a **theorem**.

In deductive reasoning, different postulates can lead to different conclusions.

| | |
|---|---|
| **Postulate:** The rights of the majority should rule. | **Postulate:** The majority must protect the rights of the minority. |

**Hypothesis:** The majority of people in this country are more than 21 years old.

| | |
|---|---|
| **Conclusion:** The rights of people over 21 should rule. | **Conclusion:** Those over 21 must protect the rights of those under 21. |

| | |
|---|---|
| **Theorem:** If the majority of people in this country are more than 21 years old, their rights should rule. | **Theorem:** If the majority of people in this country are more than 21 years old, they must protect the rights of those under 21. |

## Exercises 1.5

Ⓐ 1. Reaching a conclusion on the basis of a number of examples is called _____ reasoning.   Inductive

2. How many examples that disagree with a conclusion are needed to show that the conclusion is not true?   1

3. Reaching a conclusion on the basis of postulates, definitions, and a hypothesis is called _____ reasoning.   Deductive

4. In geometry, a conclusion reached by _____ reasoning is accepted as true.   Deductive

**Assignment Guide**
*Oral:* 1–6
*Written:*
Min. 7–17 odd; Alg.
Rev., p. 21, odd
Reg. 7–21 odd; Alg.
Rev., p. 21, odd
Max. 7–24

**5.** A hypothesis and its logical conclusion are stated in a(n) <u>Theorem</u>.

**6.** Using the same hypothesis but different <u>Postulates</u> can lead to different conclusions.

Ⓑ **7–10.** What would have to happen to show that the conclusion is not true?

**7.** The first 39 Presidents of the United States were men.

*Conclusion:* A woman cannot be President of the United States.

A woman be President

Grant Heilman

**8.** The first 36 Presidents of the United States were born east of the Rocky Mountains.

*Conclusion:* A person born west of the Rocky Mountains cannot be elected President of the United States.

A person born west of the Rocky Mts. be elected President

**9.** The Passenger Pigeon, a bird once common to North America, was last seen in 1914.

*Conclusion:* The Passenger Pigeon is extinct.

A live passenger pigeon exist

**10.** Every map that has ever been drawn can be colored with four colors so that no two regions colored alike touch at more than one point.

*Conclusion:* Every map can be colored with four colors.

Someone draw a map that cannot

Camerique

**11–14.** Use one of the postulates below and the given hypothesis to reach a conclusion by deductive reasoning.

**Postulate a:** An effective punishment deters crime.

**Postulate b:** To be protected, an animal should belong to an endangered species.

**11.** *Hypothesis:* Capital punishment deters crime.

Capital punishment is effective.

**12.** *Hypothesis:* Bengal tigers belong to an endangered species.

Bengal tigers should be protected.

Grant Heilman

**13.** *Hypothesis:* Capital punishment does not deter crime.

Capital punishment is not effective.

**14.** *Hypothesis:* Field mice do not belong to an endangered species.

Field mice should not be protected.

**15–18.** Let $x$ and $y$ stand for real numbers. Give an example from the real numbers that contradicts the conclusion.

**15.** $x \cdot \dfrac{1}{x} = 1$   $x = 0$   **16.** $\sqrt{y^2} = y$

Any number less than 0

**17.** $x^2 > x$

$x = 1$ or $x = 0$ or any number between 0 and 1

**18.** $\dfrac{0}{y} = 0$   $y = 0$

**19–22.** Tell which postulate, **a** or **b**, leads to the given conclusion.

**Postulate a:** No line intersects line $\ell$.

**Postulate b:** Some line intersects line $\ell$ at point $P$.

**19.** $P$ is on line $\ell$.   b

**20.** Every line through $P$ intersects line $\ell$.   b

**21.** If $\ell$ and $m$ are not the same line and point $A$ is on line $m$, point $A$ is not on line $\ell$.   a

**22.** If point $T$ is on line $\ell$, point $T$ is not on any other line.   a

© **23.** Find an example that contradicts this conclusion:
If $n$ is a positive integer, then $n^2 - n + 41$ is a prime integer. (That is, the only positive integers that divide into it without a remainder are 1 and $n^2 - n + 41$.)   The smallest counterexample is 41.

**24.** Do library research to find an example that contradicts the conclusion in Exercise 8.   Richard Nixon (37th President) was born in California.

---

Solve.

**1.** $x + 2 = 7$   $x = 5$

**2.** $5 + y = 13$   $y = 8$

**3.** $12 = 3 + x$   $x = 9$

**4.** $n - 3 = 1$   $n = 4$

**5.** $10 - t = 4$   $t = 6$

**6.** $3 = y - 6$   $y = 9$

**7.** $4a = 12$   $a = 3$

**8.** $18 = 3n$   $n = 6$

**9.** $\frac{1}{3}y = 2$   $y = 6$

**10.** $8 = \frac{4}{7}x$   $x = 14$

**11.** $7y = \frac{2}{3}$   $y = \frac{2}{21}$

**12.** $\frac{1}{2}n = \frac{1}{3}$   $n = \frac{2}{3}$

**13.** $\frac{7}{2} = \frac{3}{4}a$   $a = \frac{14}{3}$

**14.** $x + \frac{2}{5} = 3$   $x = 2\frac{3}{5}$

**15.** $2.4 = 0.6 + n$   $n = 1.8$

**16.** $a - 2.3 = 15.6$   $a = 17.9$

**17.** $9\frac{1}{2} - y = 4$   $y = 5\frac{1}{2}$

**18.** $0.5x = 12$   $x = 24$

**19.** $3 = \dfrac{a}{7}$   $a = 21$

**20.** $\dfrac{5}{n} = 1$   $n = 5$

*Algebra Review*

**Review this skill:**

● *solving equations using one operation*

# 1.6 Reasoning in Algebra

**Suggested Class Time**

| Course | Min. | Reg. | Max. |
|--------|------|------|------|
| Days | 1 | 1 | 1 |

The properties of real numbers on page 7 are postulates of algebra. (In algebra, the synonym *axiom* is usually used for the word *postulate*.) Here are some more postulates of algebra.

| | Property of Addition | Property of Multiplication |
|---|---|---|
| **Closure** | The sum of two real numbers is a unique real number. | The product of two real numbers is a unique real number. |
| **Commutative** | Any two real numbers may be added in either order. | Any two real numbers may be multiplied in either order. |
| **Associative** | Any three real numbers may be added by grouping the first two or the last two numbers. | Any three real numbers may be multiplied by grouping the first two or the last two numbers. |
| **Identity** | The sum of 0 and any real number is the real number. (0 is the **additive identity**.) | The product of 1 and any real number is the real number. (1 is the **multiplicative identity**.) |
| **Inverse** | The sum of a real number $a$ and its **opposite** $-a$ is 0. | The product of a nonzero real number $b$ and its **reciprocal** $\frac{1}{b}$ is 1. |

**Distributive Property** (multiplication over addition)

When the sum of two real numbers is multiplied by a third real number, to find the result either

- add first, then multiply.  ▶ $3(2 + 5) = 3 \cdot 7 = 21$
- multiply each addend, then add.  ▶ $3(2 + 5) = 3 \cdot 2 + 3 \cdot 5 = 21$

There are four properties of equality that are also postulates.

| | |
|---|---|
| Any number equals itself. | $3 = 3$ |
| If two numbers are equal, the equation may be written with either number first. | If $2 + 1 = 3$, then $3 = 2 + 1$. |
| If two numbers are both equal to a third number, they are equal to each other. | If $x = 3$ and $3 = y$, then $x = y$. |
| If two numbers are equal, either one may be substituted for the other. | If $x + y = 6$ and $x = 2$, then $2 + y = 6$. |

Many theorems in algebra result from these postulates and deductive reasoning. The Multiplication Property of Zero is one such theorem.

**Multiplication Property of Zero**    If $n$ is a real number, $0 \cdot n = 0$.

| Chain of equivalent expressions | The reason each expression is equivalent to the preceding one |
|---|---|
| $0 \cdot n = 0 \cdot n + 0$ | Identity Prop. of Addition |
| $\quad = 0 \cdot n + [n + (-n)]$ | $0 = n + (-n)$ by the Inverse Prop. of Add. |
| $\quad = [0 \cdot n + n] + (-n)$ | Associative Prop. of Add. |
| $\quad = [0 \cdot n + 1 \cdot n] + (-n)$ | $n = 1 \cdot n$ by the Identity Prop. of Mult. |
| $\quad = [0 + 1]n + (-n)$ | $[0 \cdot n + 1 \cdot n] = [0 + 1]n$ by the Distrib. Prop. |
| $\quad = 1 \cdot n + (-n)$ | $0 + 1 = 1$ by the Identity Prop. of Add. |
| $\quad = n + (-n)$ | $1 \cdot n = n$ by the Identity Prop. of Mult. |
| $\quad = 0$ | $n + (-n) = 0$ by the Inverse Prop. of Add. |

Each reason in the right-hand column above is a postulate. But now that the Multiplication Property of Zero has been shown to result from the postulates, it can be used as a reason later. Definitions can also be used as reasons.

Deductive reasoning can also be used in solving equations. Usually, reasons are not written, and some steps are combined. But the solution *can be* written in as much detail as we wish. There are four properties of equality that are especially useful in solving equations.

$$a = b \qquad \blacktriangleleft \text{Given an equation, you can:}$$

**Addition Property of =**        $a + c = b + c$    ◀ add the same number to both sides

**Subtraction Property of =**      $a - c = b - c$    ◀ subtract the same number from both sides

**Multiplication Property of =**       $ca = cb$    ◀ multiply both sides by the same number

**Division Property of =**    If $c \neq 0, \dfrac{a}{c} = \dfrac{b}{c}$    ◀ divide both sides by the same number (not 0)

$\qquad\qquad\qquad$ └── is not equal to

We will solve $4x = 12$.

| | |
|---|---|
| $4x = 12$ | Given |
| $\frac{1}{4}(4x) = \frac{1}{4}(12)$ | Multiplication Property of $=$ |
| $\frac{1}{4}(4x) = 3$ | Substitution of 3 for $\frac{1}{4}(12)$ |
| $(\frac{1}{4} \cdot 4)x = 3$ | Associative Property of Multiplication |
| $1x = 3$ | $\frac{1}{4} \cdot 4 = 1$ by the Inverse Prop. of Mult. |
| $x = 3$ | $1x = x$ by the Identity Prop. of Mult. |

# Exercises 1.6 ▌▌▌▌▌▌▌▌▌▌▌▌▌▌▌▌▌▌▌▌▌▌▌▌▌▌▌▌▌▌▌▌▌▌▌▌▌▌▌▌

**Assignment Guide**
*Oral:* 1–24
*Written:*
Min. 25–39 odd; 41–51
Reg. 25–39 odd; 41–52
Max. 25–39 odd; 41–52;
    53–57 odd

Ⓐ **1.** The additive identity is ___0___.   **2.** The reciprocal of $\frac{1}{2}$ is ___2___.

**3.** The multiplicative identity is ___1___.   **4.** The opposite of $-3$ is ___3___.

**5.** The property expressed $0 \cdot n = 0$ is the ___Mult. Prop. of Zero___.

**6.** In algebra, postulates are usually called ___Axioms___.

**7–16.** Let *a*, *b*, and *c* be any real numbers. Then each statement below expresses a property of addition or multiplication. Identify that property.

**7.** $(a + b) + c = a + (b + c)$
   Assoc. Prop. of Add.

**8.** $a \cdot \frac{1}{a} = \frac{1}{a} \cdot a = 1$ if $a \neq 0$
   Inverse Prop. of Mult.

**9.** $a + 0 = 0 + a = a$
   Identity Prop. of Add.

**10.** $ab = ba$  Comm. Prop. of Mult.

**11.** $a \cdot 1 = 1 \cdot a = a$
   Identity Prop. of Mult.

**12.** $a(b + c) = ab + ac$
   Distrib. Prop.

**13.** $ab$ is a unique real number.
   Closure Prop. of Mult.

**14.** $a + b = b + a$
   Comm. Prop. of Add.

**15.** $(ab)c = a(bc)$
   Assoc. Prop. of Mult.

**16.** $a + (-a) = (-a) + a = 0$
   Inverse Prop. of Add.

**17–42.** Which property is illustrated? (Letters stand for any real numbers.)

17. If two numbers are equal, the equation may be written with either number first.

**17.** If $4 = n$, then $n = 4$.

**18.** If $x = 4$, then $2x = 8$.
   Mult. Prop. of =

**19.** $7 + 1 = 1 + 7$
   Comm. Prop. of Add.

**20.** If $3y = 9$, then $y = 3$.
   Div. Prop. of =

**21.** If $x - 2 = 9$, then $x = 11$.
   Add. Prop. of =

**22.** $7 + a$ is a unique real number.
   Closure Prop. of Add.

**23.** $x + 1 = x + 1$
   Any number equals itself.

**24.** $0 \cdot x = 0$  Mult. Prop. of Zero

Ⓑ **25.** $3n + 6 = 3(n + 2)$
   Distrib. Prop.

**26.** $8 + (x + 2) = (8 + x) + 2$
   Assoc. Prop. of Add.

**27.** $x \cdot 7y = 7yx$
   Comm. Prop. of Mult.

**28.** $(n + 3) = (n + 3) + 0$
   Identity Prop. of Add.

**29.** $(4 + x) + 0 = 4 + x$
   Identity Prop. of Add.

**30.** $12 + 4a = 4(3 + a)$
   Distrib. Prop.

**31.** $(9 + a) + 0 = 9 + (a + 0)$
   Assoc. Prop. of Add.

**32.** $3 = 1 \cdot 3$
   Identity Prop. of Mult.

**33.** $\frac{1}{2 + n}(2 + n) = 1, n \neq -2$
   Inverse Prop. of Mult.

**34.** $(x + 6)\frac{1}{x + 6} = 1, x \neq -6$
   Inverse Prop. of Mult.

**35.** $p = 1 \cdot p$
      Identity Prop. of Mult.

**36.** $a \cdot 2b = 2ba$
      Comm. Prop. of Mult.

**37.** $4(2n) = 8n$
      Assoc. Prop. of Mult.

**38.** $6(3a) = 18a$
      Assoc. Prop. of Mult.

**39.** $-(a + 1) + (a + 1) = 0$
      Inverse Prop. of Add.

**40.** $-(p + 3) + (p + 3) = 0$
      Inverse Prop. of Add.

**41.** If $x = a + b + 3$ and $y = a + b + 3$, then $x = y$. If two numbers are both equal to a third number, they are equal to each other. (or Substitution)

**42.** If $m + n + x = 180$ and $m + n = 120$, then $120 + x = 180$.
      Substitution

**43–50.** Give a reason for each step. Let $a$ be any real number.

**43.** $\quad -1a = -1a + 0$        Identity Prop. of Add.

**44.** $\qquad = -1a + [a + (-a)]$        Inverse Prop. of Add.

**45.** $\qquad = [-1a + a] + (-a)$        Assoc. Prop. of Add.

**46.** $\qquad = [-1a + 1a] + (-a)$        Identity Prop. of Mult.

**47.** $\qquad = [-1 + 1]a + (-a)$        Distrib. Prop.

**48.** $\qquad = 0a + (-a)$        Inverse Prop. of Add.

**49.** $\qquad = 0 + (-a)$        Mult. Prop. of Zero

**50.** $\qquad = -a$        Identity Prop. of Add.

**51–52.** Give a reason for each step.

**51.**
$$x + (-9) = 3$$
$$[x + (-9)] + 9 = 3 + 9$$
$$[x + (-9)] + 9 = 12$$
$$x + [-9 + 9] = 12$$
$$x + 0 = 12$$
$$x = 12$$

**52.**
$$y + (-2) = -5$$
$$[y + (-2)] + 2 = -5 + 2$$
$$[y + (-2)] + 2 = -3$$
$$y + [-2 + 2] = -3$$
$$y + 0 = -3$$
$$y = -3$$

**51.** Given
Add. Prop. of $=$
Substitution of 12 for $3 + 9$
Assoc. Prop. of Add.
Inv. Prop. of Add.
Ident. Prop. of Add.

**52.** Given
Add. Prop. of $=$
Substitution of $-3$ for $-5 + 2$
Assoc. Prop. of Add.
Inv. Prop. of Add.
Ident. Prop. of Add.

© **53–56.** Solve as in Exercises 51–52.

**53.** $5 + x = 18$
    $x = 13$

**54.** $8n = -320$
    $n = -40$

**55.** $13 = 9 - y$
    $y = -4$

**56.** $\frac{3}{5}r = 12$
    $r = 20$

**57.** The properties of equality on page 22 are called the *reflexive property*, the *substitution property*, the *transitive property*, and the *symmetric property*. Find out which is which.
      In order: reflexive, symmetric, transitive, substitution

# SYMBOLS

Imagine how thick this book would be if no symbols other than words were used! Look at these equations from the Algebra Review on page 21.

1. $x + 2 = 7$ | **One.** When two is added to some number, the result is seven.

5. $10 - t = 4$ | **Five.** The difference when some number is subtracted from ten is four.

7. $4a = 12$ | **Seven.** Four times some number is twelve.

You can see why a word or phrase that is used over and over again in mathematics is usually replaced by a shorter symbol. Here are some symbols used in geometry. Can you read them?

$$\overrightarrow{AB} \quad \overrightarrow{DE} \quad \triangle ABC \quad \odot P \quad \ell \perp \overrightarrow{AB} \quad \overleftrightarrow{DE} \parallel \overleftrightarrow{EF} \quad \angle A \quad m \angle C$$

If you travel in a foreign country, the words you see may look strange. But many of the symbols will look familiar. What do these symbols, all found on signs in many countries, mean?

Drinking water · · · No smoking · · · Access for the handicapped · · · Poison

Here are some symbols found on shipping cartons. Can you figure out what they mean?

Keep dry · · · This way up · · · Fragile · · · Keep frozen

Chemists, architects, stenographers, and people in many other occupations use symbols with special meanings in those occupations. In fact, even hobos have their own symbols.

This is not a safe place. · · · OK, All right · · · Good place for a handout · · · Good road to follow

# Reasoning in Geometry 1.7

Some parts of the system of geometry have already been given.

**Suggested Class Time**

| Course | Min. | Reg. | Max. |
|--------|------|------|------|
| Days | 1 | 1 | 1 |

| undefined terms | defined terms | | postulates |
|-----------------|---------------|--|------------|
| point | collinear | coplanar | Distance Postulate |
| line | between | segment | Ruler Postulate |
| plane | midpoint | ray | Ruler Placement Postulate |
| | distance | equidistant | |
| | opposite rays | absolute value | |

We can use the ideas above and logical reasoning to decide that the following theorem is true.

 On ray *AB* there is exactly one point *P* whose distance from *A* is a given positive number *n*.

**Point Plotting Theorem**

Reasoning:  (A drawing is usually helpful.)

Think of ray *AB* as part of line *AB*. By the Ruler Placement Postulate (p. 12), let the coordinate of *A* be zero and let the coordinate of *B* be a positive number.

By parts 1 and 2 of the Ruler Postulate (p. 11), the positive number $n$ corresponds to exactly one point $P$ on $\overrightarrow{AB}$, and $P$ corresponds to exactly one positive number, which therefore must be $n$.

By part 3 of the Ruler Postulate, the distance between $A$ and $P$ is the absolute value of the difference of their coordinates: $AP = |0 - n|$. By subtraction and the definition of absolute value: $AP = |-n| = n$. So on $\overrightarrow{AB}$ there is exactly one point $P$ whose distance from $A$ is $n$.

The Point Plotting Theorem now becomes a part of the geometric system that we are developing. It can be used to help decide that the next theorem is true.

 Every segment has exactly one midpoint.

**Midpoint Theorem**

Reasoning:

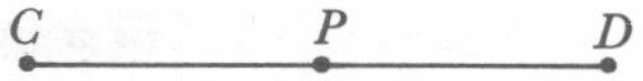

By definition of *midpoint*, the midpoint $P$
of any segment $CD$ is between $C$ and $D$ and $\qquad CP = PD$

By definition of *between*, $\qquad\qquad\qquad CP + PD = CD$

Using algebra $\begin{cases} \text{Substitute} & CP + CP = CD \\ \text{Add on the left side} & 2CP = CD \\ \text{Multiply both sides by } \tfrac{1}{2} & CP = \tfrac{1}{2}CD \end{cases}$

By the Point Plotting Theorem, there is exactly one point on $\overrightarrow{CD}$ whose distance from $C$ is $\tfrac{1}{2}CD$. So $\overline{CD}$ has exactly one midpoint.

Before considering any more theorems, we must state some more postulates. These postulates are needed to guarantee that lines, planes, and space will have properties that we want them to have.

| | |
|---|---|
| **Straight Line Postulate** | For any two points, exactly one line contains both of them. |
| **Number-of-Points Postulate** | A plane contains at least three noncollinear points. Space contains at least four noncoplanar points. |
| **Plane Postulate** | Any three points are in at least one plane. Three noncollinear points are in exactly one plane. |
| **Plane Intersection Postulate** | If two planes intersect, they intersect at exactly one line. |
| **Flat Plane Postulate** | If two points are in a plane, the line through them is in the plane. |

two points $P$ and $Q$

$P \bullet$

$\bullet Q$

points $P$ and $Q$

$P \bullet$

$\bullet Q$

or

$P \bullet$

$\bullet Q$

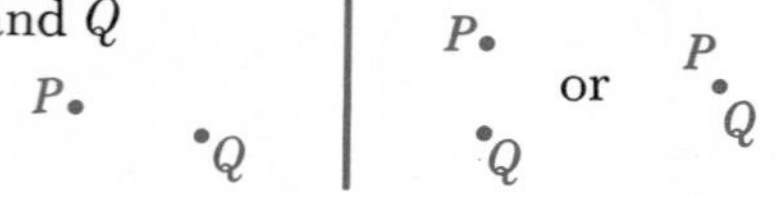

When we refer, as above, to two points, three points, four points, or two planes, we mean that there are that many *distinct* figures. If no number is named, the figures may or may not be distinct.

| We state this postulate | to get this | and not this. |
|---|---|---|
| Straight Line Postulate | A ———— B | *A ... B (curved lines intersecting)* |
| Number-of-Points Postulate | **Planes with width and length:** *(shaded parallelogram with 3 dots)* <br> **Space with width, length, and depth:** *(3D box)* | **Planes that are just like lines:** *(line with dots)* <br> **Space that is just like a plane:** *(shaded parallelogram with 3 dots)* |
| Plane Postulate | *A B C on a line in a plane* <br> *•B C• •A in a plane* | *A B C on line, C off in curved space* <br> *B• •C A• in curved plane* |
| Plane Intersection Postulate | *(two planes intersecting in a line)* | *(curved surfaces)* |
| Flat Plane Postulate | *A B ℓ / n (line in flat plane)* | *A --- B ℓ / n (line on curved plane)* |

# *Exercises 1.7*

Ⓐ **1.** Give three undefined terms of geometry we have considered.
3 of point, line, plane, contains

**2.** Give five terms we have defined.    *See page 27.*

**Assignment Guide**
*Oral:* 1–12
*Written:* Min. 13–22
Reg. 13–22
Max. 13–27

**3–12.** Refer to the figure. Which definition, postulate, or theorem shows that the given conclusion is false?

**3.** No plane contains $A$, $B$, and $D$.
Plane Post.

**4.** $B$ is on $\ell$.
Straight Line Post.

**5.** Two planes contain $A$, $B$, and $C$.
Plane Post.

**6.** $D$ is on $\overline{AB}$.
Def. of segment

**7.** $A$ and $F$ are midpoints of $\overline{DB}$.
Midpoint Thm.

**8.** $AB = AE$
Point Plotting Thm.

**9.** $A$ is the midpoint of $\overline{DB}$, and $DA$ is greater than $AB$.
Def. of midpoint

**10.** Planes $r$ and $n$ intersect at $\ell$ and $m$.
Plane Intersection Post.

**11.** $\overrightarrow{FD}$ and $\overrightarrow{AF}$ are opposite rays.
Def. of opp. rays

**12.** $F$ is not coplanar with $D$ and $E$.
Plane Post.

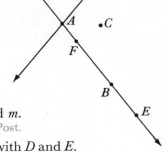

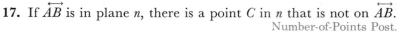

**13.** $D$, $R$, and $S$ are coplanar.
Plane Post.

**14.** If $AP = 3$, then $AQ \neq 3$.
Point Plotting Thm.

**15.** If $P$ is the midpoint of $\overline{AB}$, then $Q$ is not the midpoint of $\overline{AB}$.
Midpoint Thm.

**16.** $A$, $B$, and $D$ are coplanar.
Plane Post.

**17.** If $\overleftrightarrow{AB}$ is in plane $n$, there is a point $C$ in $n$ that is not on $\overleftrightarrow{AB}$.
Number-of-Points Post.

**18.** If planes $m$ and $n$ intersect at $\overleftrightarrow{RS}$, they do not intersect at $\ell$.
Plane Intersection Post.

**19.** If $A$ and $B$ are in plane $n$, $\overleftrightarrow{AB}$ is in plane $n$.
Flat Plane Post.

23. Plane Intersection Post. and def. of collinear

**20.** On $\overrightarrow{AP}$, there is exactly one point $B$ such that $AB = 2PB$.
Point Plotting Thm.

**21.** Since $A$ and $B$ are on line $\ell$, $A$ and $B$ are not on line $t$.
Straight Line Post.

**22.** If $A$, $B$, and $C$ are in plane $n$, there is a point $D$ not in $n$.
Number-of-Points Post.

Ⓒ **23.** If $R$, $S$, and $T$ are in the intersection of planes $m$ and $n$, $R$, $S$, and $T$ are collinear.

**24.** If planes $m$ and $n$ both contain $R$ and $S$, they intersect at $\overleftrightarrow{RS}$.
Plane Intersection Post. and Straight Line Post.

**25–27.** What postulate explains why?

**25.** The sand yacht doesn't rock from wheel to wheel.
Plane Post.

**26.** A string stretched between two stakes marks a straight row.
Straight Line Post.

**27.** The string lies flat on the board.
Flat Plane Post.

Grant Follis

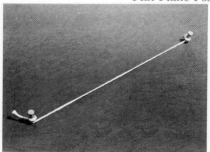

Camerique

# More About Reasoning

The five postulates stated in the preceding section can be used to answer the four questions below.

If two lines intersect, what is their intersection like?

If a line and a plane intersect, what is their intersection like?

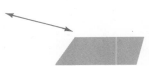

How many planes contain a line and a point not on that line?

How many planes contain two intersecting lines?

 If two lines intersect, they intersect at exactly one point.  **Line Intersection Theorem**

**Reasoning:**

The fact that the lines intersect tells us that they intersect at *at least one* point $P$.

Suppose the lines intersect at two points, $P$ and $Q$. Then there are two lines, each of which contains both $P$ and $Q$. But, according to the Straight Line Postulate, this can't happen. So the lines do *not* intersect at *more than one* point.

Since the two lines intersect at *at least one* point but *not more than one* point, they intersect at *exactly one* point.

If you can show { there is at least one / there is not more than one ▶ then there is exactly one.

<table>
<tr><td>**Line-Plane Intersection Theorem**</td><td></td><td>If a plane and a line not in that plane intersect, they intersect at exactly one point.</td><td></td></tr>
</table>

Reasoning:

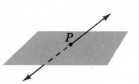

The fact that the plane and the line intersect tells us that they intersect at *at least one* point $P$.

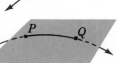

Suppose the plane and line intersect at two points, $P$ and $Q$. Then two points of $\overleftrightarrow{PQ}$ are in the plane, and $\overleftrightarrow{PQ}$ is not in the plane. But, according to the Flat Plane Postulate, this can't happen. So the plane and line do *not* intersect at *more than one* point.

Since the plane and line intersect at *at least one* point but *not more than one* point, they intersect at *exactly one* point.

In stating postulates and theorems, the term *determine* can often be used instead of the term *exactly one*.

| This postulate | that was stated this way | can be restated this way. |
|---|---|---|
| Straight Line Postulate | For any two points, **exactly one** line contains both of them. | Two points **determine** a line. |
| Plane Postulate | Three noncollinear points are in **exactly one** plane. | Three noncollinear points **determine** a plane. |

The next theorem is stated using *determine* instead of *exactly one*.

<table>
<tr><td>**Plane Theorem**</td><td></td><td>**a.** A line and a point not on the line determine a plane.<br>**b.** Two intersecting lines determine a plane.</td><td></td></tr>
</table>

Reasoning:

**a.**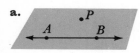

**Part a.** Let $A$ and $B$ be two points on any line $\ell$. The given point $P$ is not on $\ell$, so we now have three noncollinear points. According to the Plane Postulate, these three points determine a plane. This plane contains line $\ell$ because it contains points $A$ and $B$.

**b.**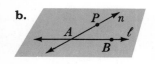

**Part b.** Let lines $\ell$ and $n$ intersect at point $A$. Then let $B$ be any other point on $\ell$ and let $P$ be any other point on $n$. These three noncollinear points determine a plane that contains lines $\ell$ and $n$.

Ⓐ **1.** The intersection of two lines is a ___Point___.

**Assignment Guide**
*Oral:* 1–6
*Written:*
Min. 7–21 odd; Quiz, p. 34
Reg. 7–20; Quiz, p. 34
Max. 7–24; Quiz, p. 34

**2.** The intersection of a plane and a line not in the plane is a ___Point___.

**3.** If there is at least one figure, but not more than one, then there is _____. Exactly one

**4.** A statement using *exactly one* can often be restated using ___Determine___.

**5.** A line and a point not on the line determine ___A plane___.

**6.** Two intersecting lines determine ___A plane___.

Ⓑ **7–8.** Restate using *determine*.

**7.** If two lines intersect, they intersect at exactly one point.
    Two intersecting lines determine a point.

**8.** If a plane and a line not in that plane intersect, they intersect at exactly one point.
    If a plane and a line not in it intersect, they determine a point.

**9–12.** Restate using *exactly one*.

**9.** Two intersecting planes determine a line.

**10.** Two intersecting lines determine a plane.

**11.** A line and a point not on the line determine a plane.

**12.** Two noncollinear rays with a common endpoint determine a plane.

9. Two planes that intersect, intersect at exactly one line.
10. Two intersecting lines are in exactly one plane.
11. A line and a point not on it are in exactly one plane.
12. Two noncollinear rays with a common endpoint are in exactly one plane.

**13–18.** Tell which theorem lets us reach the stated conclusion.

**13.** Two lines ℓ and m do not intersect at two points P and Q.
    Line Intersection Thm.

**14.** Intersecting lines r and s are not in two planes m and n.
    Plane Thm., part b

**15.** Plane p and line ℓ not in p do not intersect at two points A and B.
    Line-Plane Intersection Thm.

**16.** If point P is not in line t, then P and t are not both in two planes m and n.
    Plane Thm., part a

**17.** Two lines ℓ and m intersect; point P is on ℓ and m; a second point Q is on ℓ.
    *Conclusion:* Q is not on m.
    Line Intersection Thm.

**18.** Two lines ℓ and m intersect; plane P contains ℓ and m; a second plane Q contains ℓ.
    *Conclusion:* m is not in Q.
    Plane Thm., part b

**19–22.** Draw the figure described.

**19.** Lines $m$ and $n$ intersect only at point $A$.

**20.** Line $s$ and plane $T$ intersect only at point $D$.

**21.** Line $t$ and point $R$ determine plane $n$.

**22.** Intersecting lines $k$ and $r$ determine plane $M$.

Ⓒ **23–24.** Which theorem explains why the picture frame sits firmly?

**23.**

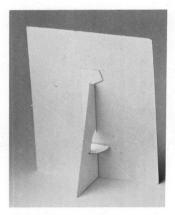

Plane Thm., part b

**24.**

Plane Thm., part a

Alfa

**Quick Quiz**

for Sections 1.5 to 1.8

**1.** Reasoning from postulates and definitions leads to conclusions in (inductive, <u>deductive</u>) reasoning.

**2.** A statement that includes a hypothesis and its logical conclusion is a (postulate, <u>theorem</u>).

**3.** The additive identity is ($\underline{0}$, 1, $x$).

**4.** The reciprocal of 2 is ($-2$, $|2|$, $\underline{\frac{1}{2}}$).

**5–8.** In the figure shown, which of these would determine a plane?

**5.** $\overleftrightarrow{AM}$ and $\overleftrightarrow{BP}$ Yes

**6.** $A$, $P$, and $M$ No

**7.** $B$, $P$, and $C$ Yes

**8.** $\overleftrightarrow{AP}$ and $C$ Yes

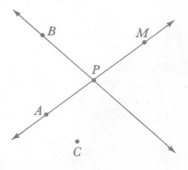

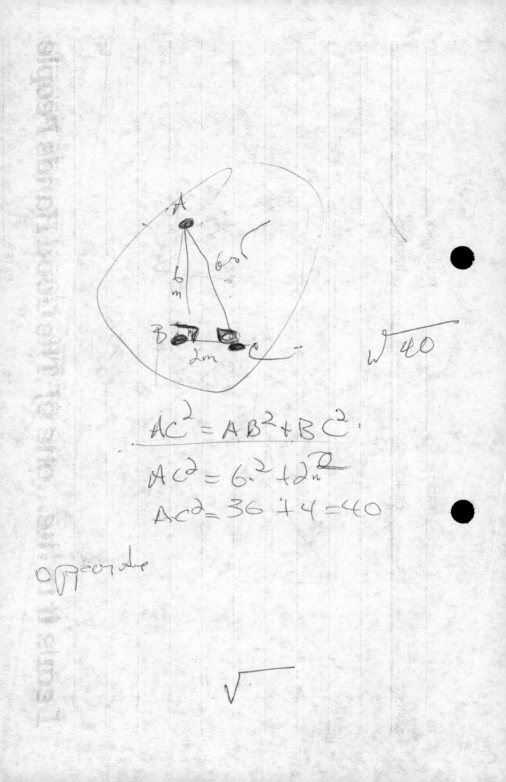

A

6
m

6m

B

2m

C

√40

$$AC^2 = AB^2 + BC^2$$

$$AC^2 = 6^2 + 2_m^2$$

$$AC^2 = 36 + 4 = 40$$

opposite

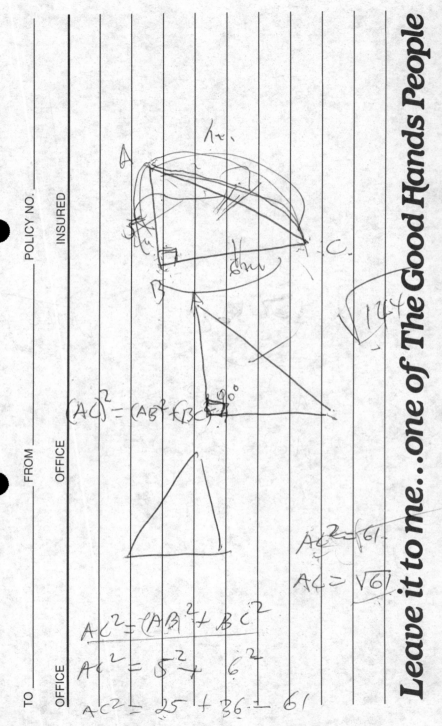

TO ____ FROM ____

OFFICE ____

OFFICE ____

$(AC)^2 = (AB)^2 + (BC)^2$

$90°$

$\sqrt{124}$

$AC^2 = 61$

$AC = \sqrt{61}$

$AC^2 = (AB)^2 + BC^2$

$AC^2 = 5^2 + 6^2$

$AC^2 = 25 + 36 = 61$

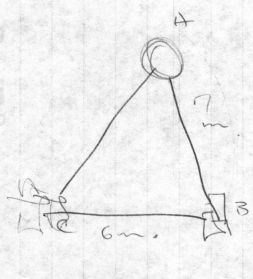

A

7 m

C    6 m.    B

3

AB = CB
CB = BA.

______ FROM ______ POLICY NO. ______

OFFICE ______ OFFICE ______ INSURED ______

**Leave it to me...one of The Good Hands People**

G 110-5 PRINTED IN U.S.A.

DATE ____ / ____ / ____

| Suggested Class Time | | | |
|---|---|---|---|
| Course | Min. | Reg. | Max. |
| Days | 1 | 1 | 1 |

Basketball players must not only get the ball through the hoop—they must do it according to the rules of the game. Doing a geometric construction is like playing basketball. If you don't do it by the rules, it isn't the same game.

There are two ways to make diagrams in geometry. To **draw** a geometric figure, you can use any device or instrument. But to **construct** a geometric figure, you can use only two tools besides pencil and paper. The first of these two tools is the *straightedge*.

A **straightedge** is used to construct a line through two points.

The straightedge most commonly used is the edge of a ruler. But never use the marks along the edge of the ruler. A straightedge is not used for measuring.

The second construction tool is the *compass*.

A **compass** is used to construct a circle with a given center and given radius.

Chicago Tribune Photo

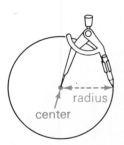

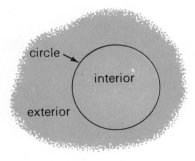

Notice that the circle contains *only* the points drawn by the compass. All other points in the plane, including the center of the circle, are either in the **interior** of the circle or in its **exterior**. Only part of a circle, called an **arc**, is actually drawn in most constructions.

# Exercises 1.9 ▐▌▌▐▐▌▐▐▌▌▌▐▐▌▐▐▐▌▐▐▌▐▐▐▌▐▐▌▐▐▐▌▌▐▐▐▌▐▐▌▐▐▐▌▐▐▌▐▐▐▌▐

**Assignment Guide**
*Oral:* 1–22
*Written:*
Min. 23–36
Reg. 23–45 odd
Max. 23–45 odd; 47–48

Ⓐ **1.** What tools can be used to draw geometric figures?　　Anything

**2.** What tools can be used to construct geometric figures?
Straightedge, compass

**3.** Give three examples of a straightedge besides the edge of a ruler.
*Answers will vary.*

**4.** In constructions, a ruler must not be used for <u>Measuring</u>.

**5.** A compass is used to construct a <u>Circle</u>.

**6.** The radius of a circle is the distance between any point on the circle and the <u>Center</u> of the circle.

**7.** If the tips of a compass are set 3 inches apart, the compass will construct a circle whose <u>Radius</u> is 3 inches.

**8.** The center of a circle is in the <u>Interior</u> of the circle.

**9.** If the radius of a circle is 3 inches, any point 4 inches from the center of the circle is in the <u>Exterior</u> of the circle.

**10.** Part of a circle is called an <u>Arc</u>.

**11–22.** Refer to the construction below.

## construction: segment of a given length

| 1. Given: Any segment *MN* | 2. Construct line ℓ and point *S* on ℓ |
|---|---|
| M————————N | S ←————————————→ ℓ |
| 3. | 4. |
| M ⟋⟍ N | ←——— S ⟋⟍ T ———→ ℓ |

11. Set one end of compass on *M* and the other on *N*.

12. Set the point of compass on *S* and make an arc on ℓ. Label the intersection *T*.

**11.** Describe step 3.

**12.** Describe step 4.

**13.** What segment is a copy of $\overline{MN}$? $\overline{ST}$

**14.** Is it true that $ST = MN$? Yes

A step 5 might follow step 4 above. Here are two possibilities.

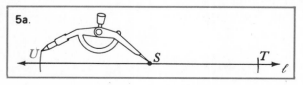

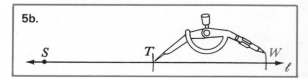

**15.** Describe step 5a.     **16.** Describe step 5b.

**17.** Is the compass setting changed between step 4 and step 5a? Between step 4 and step 5b?  No; no

**18.** What two segments in 5a would be copies of $\overline{MN}$? In 5b?

$US,\ ST;\ ST,\ TW$

**19.** What segments in 5a and 5b would be twice as long as $MN$?

$\overline{UT},\ \overline{SW}$

**20.** What segment has length $US + ST$? Is it true that $US + ST = 2MN$?

$\overline{UT};$ yes

**21.** What segment has length $ST + TW$? Is it true that $ST + TW = 2MN$?

$\overline{SW};$ yes

**22.** What is the midpoint of $\overline{UT}$? Of $\overline{SW}$?   $S;\ T$

**15.** Make another arc on $\ell$ on the other side of $S$. Label the intersection $U$.

**16.** Move the point of compass to $T$ and make another arc on $\ell$ on the same side of $S$. Label the intersection $W$.

Ⓑ **23–36.** Use the given segments and the methods shown on page 36 to construct a segment of the length called for.

P————————————————— Q

R —————————— V  W——————————— X

**23.** $PQ$     **24.** $RV$

**25.** $2RV$   **26.** $2PQ$   **27.** $PQ + RV$   **28.** $WX + PQ$

**29.** $2RV + WX$   **30.** $2PQ + RV$   **31.** $3RV$   **32.** $3WX$

**33.** $PQ - RV$   **34.** $PQ - WX$   **35.** $2RV - WX$   **36.** $2WX - RV$

**37–46.** Draw four noncollinear points $A$, $B$, $C$, and $D$. Then construct the following.

**37.** $\overleftrightarrow{AB}$     **38.** $\overrightarrow{BC}$     **39.** $\overrightarrow{DC}$     **40.** $\overrightarrow{CA}$

**41.** $\overline{BD}$     **42.** $\overline{AB}$     **43.** $\overrightarrow{AC}$     **44.** $\overrightarrow{CD}$

**45.** the ray opposite $\overrightarrow{CB}$     **46.** the ray opposite $\overrightarrow{BD}$

Ⓒ **47–48.** Ruler and compass constructions can be used to make designs for tiles, quilt blocks, fabrics, and other decorative items. See if you can make patterns for the designs shown here. Then make up some designs of your own.

**47.**

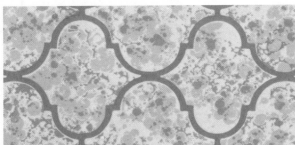

Flooring by Armstrong Cork Co.

**48.**

Frank Kuechmann

SECTION 1.9   CONSTRUCTIONS   37

# Transformations—An Introduction

The fun-house mirror has transformed the little dog into a very big dog. Geometric figures can also be transformed. Here are a few of the ways this can be done.

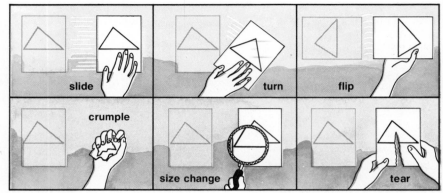

Notice that the entire plane is transformed at once. However, we usually talk about the effect of the transformation on just one figure.

The figure resulting from a transformation is called the **image** of the original figure. We often show the original figure and one or more images in the same diagram. (The original figure, like the little dog in the fun-house, is not changed by the transformation.)

Only four of the transformations shown above are important to us here. Their names describe them.

- reflection (or flip)    • slide    • turn    • size change

These transformations, and combinations of them, can be used to make many geometric ideas easier to understand. Simple paper folding shows a relation between the midpoint of a segment and a reflection.

Drawing by F. Modell; © 1960
The New Yorker Magazine, Inc.

1. Draw a line segment on thin paper.

2. Fold the paper so that the endpoints of the segment match. Now the part of the segment on one side of the fold is the flip or reflection image of the other part.

3. Open the paper. Why does the fold mark the midpoint of the segment?

Ⓐ **1–2.** Refer to the paper-folding example on page 38.

**Assignment Guide**
*Oral:* 1–6
*Written:* Min. 7–18
　　　　Reg. 7–18
　　　　Max. 7–22

**1.** Are there other ways the paper could be folded once to match the endpoints of the segment? Would the fold cross the segment at the same place? What theorem about midpoints does this suggest?

Yes; yes; Midpoint Thm.

**2.** The figure resulting from a transformation is called the <u>Image</u>.

**3–6.** Match each transformation named below with a picture at the right.

**3.** slide  c　　**4.** turn  d　　**a.** 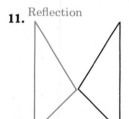　**b.** 　**c.** 　**d.**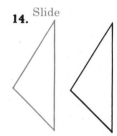

**5.** reflection
　　　　a
**6.** size change  b

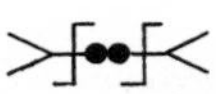

Ⓑ **7–18.** Name the transformation illustrated. The image is shown in color.

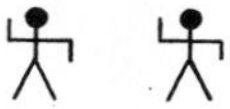

**7.** Slide

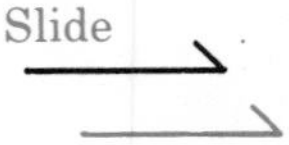

**8.** Size change

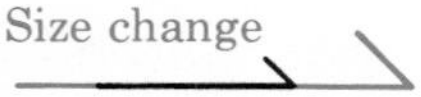

**9.** Turn

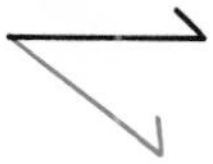

**10.** Reflection

**11.** Reflection

**12.** Size change

**13.** Turn

**14.** Slide

**15.** Slide

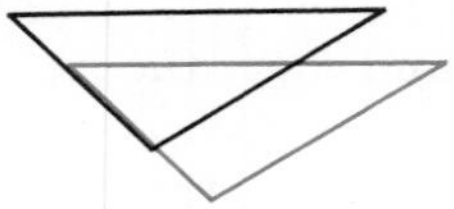

**16.** Size change

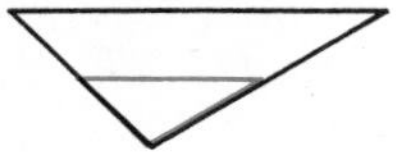

**17.** Reflection

**18.** Turn

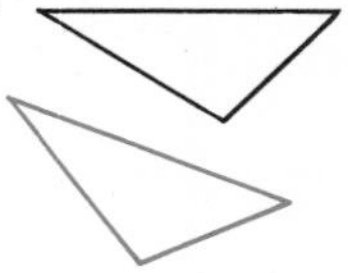

Ⓒ **19–22.** Two transformations are applied to each figure below, one after the other. The final image is shown in solid color. Name the transformations in the correct order.

**19.** Slide, turn

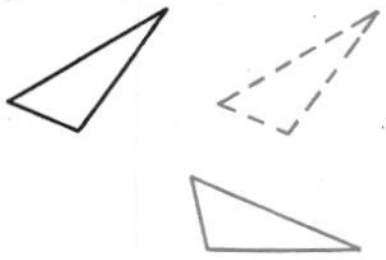

**20.** Turn, slide

**21.** Slide, reflection

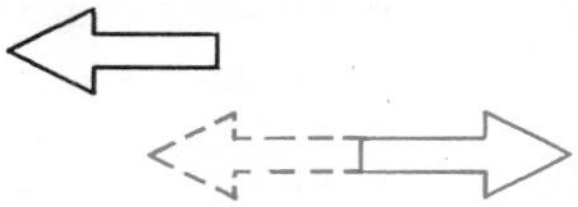

**22.** Reflection, turn

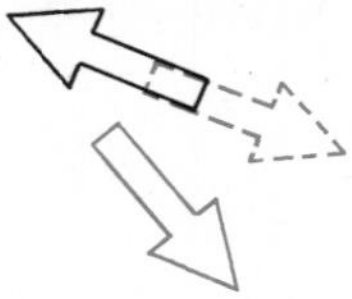

# ■ Chapter 1 Review ■

**1.1**

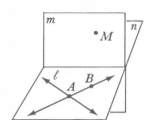

**1–3.** Name the geometric figure represented by the model.

**1.** grain of sand
Point

**2.** endless light beam
Line

**3.** endless sheet of film
Plane

**4–7.** Refer to the figure to complete each sentence.

**4.** Line $\ell$ contains point ___$A$___.

**5.** Point $M$ is not in plane ___$n$___.

**6.** ___$\overrightarrow{AB}$___ and $\ell$ intersect at $A$.

**7.** Points $A$ and ___$B$___ are on $\overleftrightarrow{AB}$.

**1.2**

**Assignment Guide**
*Oral:* 1–42
*Written:* 43–60

**8.** Any number that has a decimal expansion is a(n) _____.
Real number

**9.** The symbols $<$ and $>$ are used to show the ___Order___ of numbers.

**10.** On the real number line, each point is matched with its ___Coordinate___.

**11–13.** Which symbol, $<$, $=$, or $>$, should replace the ▨? Let $x$ and $y$ be any real numbers.

**11.** $5 < x$, $5 = x$, or $5$ ▨ $x$.  $>$

**12.** If $y > 3$, then $3$ ▨ $y$.  $<$

**13.** If $-2 < x$ and $x < y$, then $-2$ ▨ $y$.  $<$

**1.3**

**14.** A(n) ___Postulate___ is accepted as true without proof.

**15.** $|-5|$ is the _____ of $-5$.
Absolute value

**16.** $|-18| = $ ___18___

**17.** $|7 - 2| = $ ___5___

**18.** If the coordinates of $P$ and $Q$ are 12 and 3, then $PQ = $ ___9___. .

**1.4**

**19.** Points on the same line are said to be ___Collinear___.

**20.** $\overline{AD}$ is named ___$\overline{APD}$___ to show that $P$ is between $A$ and $D$.

**21.** $AD + DM = AM$ means $D$ is ___Between___ $A$ and $M$.

**22.** Points $I$ and $F$ are the ___Endpoints___ of $\overline{IF}$.

**23.** If $AH = HE$ on $\overline{AE}$, then $H$ is the ___Midpoint___ of $\overline{AE}$.

**24.** If $\overleftrightarrow{PS}$ intersects $\overline{QR}$ at its midpoint, then $\overleftrightarrow{PS}$ ___Bisects___ $\overline{QR}$.

**25.** If $A$ is between $B$ and $C$, then $\overrightarrow{AB}$ and $\overrightarrow{AC}$ are opposite ___Rays___.

**1.5**

**26.** A conclusion suggested by a number of examples is reached by _____ reasoning.  Inductive

**27.** A conclusion reached by reasoning from postulates and definitions is reached by _____ reasoning.  Deductive

**28.** Name the steps in the pattern of deductive reasoning.
*See page 19.*

**29.** What two things are included in a theorem?
Hypothesis and logical conclusion

**30–42.** Of what property is each statement an example?

**30.** $5(a + 2) = 5a + 10$
Distrib. Prop.

**31.** $(n + 2) + 3 = n + (2 + 3)$
Assoc. Prop. of Add.

**32.** If $x = 2$, then $2x = 4$.
Mult. Prop. of =

**33.** If $x + 1 = 2$, then $2 = x + 1$.

**34.** $4 \cdot 2n = (4 \cdot 2)n$
Assoc. Prop. of Mult.

**35.** $a + 3 = 3 + a$
Comm. Prop. of Add.

**36.** $3 \cdot 4 = 4 \cdot 3$
Comm. Prop. of Mult.

**37.** $0 + x = x$

**38.** $\frac{1}{2} \cdot 2 = 1$

**39.** $9 + (-9) = 0$
Inverse Prop. of Add.

**40.** $1 \cdot 5 = 5$

**41.** $0 \cdot y = 0$

**42.** If $n + x = 12$ and $n = 3$, then $3 + x = 12$.
Substitution

**33.** If two numbers are equal, the equation can be written with either number first.

**37.** Identity Prop. of Add.

**38.** Inverse Prop. of Mult.

**40.** Identity Prop. of Mult.

**41.** Mult. Prop of Zero

**43–51.** Refer to the figure. What postulate or theorem explains the given conclusion?

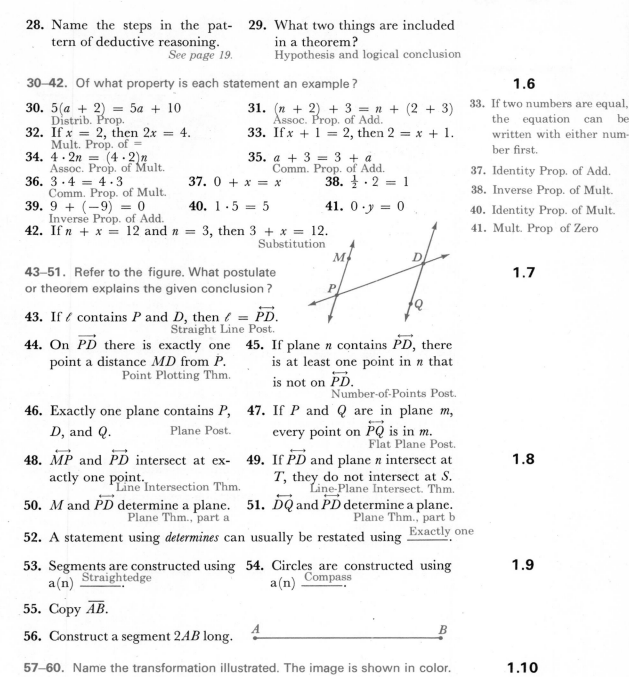

**43.** If $\ell$ contains $P$ and $D$, then $\ell = \overleftrightarrow{PD}$.
Straight Line Post.

**44.** On $\overrightarrow{PD}$ there is exactly one point a distance $MD$ from $P$.
Point Plotting Thm.

**45.** If plane $n$ contains $\overleftrightarrow{PD}$, there is at least one point in $n$ that is not on $\overleftrightarrow{PD}$.
Number-of-Points Post.

**46.** Exactly one plane contains $P$, $D$, and $Q$.
Plane Post.

**47.** If $P$ and $Q$ are in plane $m$, every point on $\overleftrightarrow{PQ}$ is in $m$.
Flat Plane Post.

**48.** $\overleftrightarrow{MP}$ and $\overleftrightarrow{PD}$ intersect at exactly one point.
Line Intersection Thm.

**49.** If $\overleftrightarrow{PD}$ and plane $n$ intersect at $T$, they do not intersect at $S$.
Line-Plane Intersect. Thm.

**50.** $M$ and $\overleftrightarrow{PD}$ determine a plane.
Plane Thm., part a

**51.** $\overleftrightarrow{DQ}$ and $\overleftrightarrow{PD}$ determine a plane.
Plane Thm., part b

**52.** A statement using *determines* can usually be restated using ___Exactly one___.

**53.** Segments are constructed using a(n) ___Straightedge___.

**54.** Circles are constructed using a(n) ___Compass___.

**55.** Copy $\overline{AB}$.

**56.** Construct a segment $2AB$ long.

$A$ ———————————————— $B$

**57–60.** Name the transformation illustrated. The image is shown in color.

**57.**

Size change

**58.**

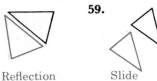

Reflection

**59.**

Slide

**60.**

Turn    CHAPTER 1 REVIEW    41

**Assignment Guide**
*Written:* 1–25

**1–8.** Refer to the figure. Name an example of

1. three collinear points  $A, B, C$

2. a line that intersects $\overleftrightarrow{AB}$  $\overleftrightarrow{PC}$

3. the intersection of line $\ell$ and plane $n$  $D$

4. three points coplanar with $A$ and $D$  $P, B, C$

5. the endpoints of $\overline{ACB}$  $A, B$

6. a segment with one endpoint at $P$  $\overline{PC}$

7. a ray opposite $\overrightarrow{CA}$  $\overrightarrow{CB}$

8. two points on opposite sides of $C$  $A, B$

9. $2 < 7$ is an example of the __Order__ of real numbers.

10. A real number is the __Coordinate__ of a point on the real number line.

11. $|-3|$ is the _____ of $-3$. __Absolute value__

12. $MN$ is the __Distance__ between $M$ and $N$.

13. If $A$, $B$, and $C$ are collinear and $AC = BC$, then $C$ is the __Midpoint__ of $\overline{AB}$.

14. If line $\ell$ intersects $\overline{PQ}$ at its midpoint, then $\ell$ __Bisects__ $\overline{PQ}$.

15. __Inductive__ reasoning reaches a conclusion from examples.

16. Reasoning from postulates and definitions is called __Deductive__ reasoning.

17. A hypothesis and its logical conclusion are stated in a __Theorem__.

18. A statement accepted as true without proof is a __Postulate__

19. Many statements using *exactly one* can be restated using __Determine__.

20. The tool used to construct circles is the __Compass__

21. Slides and flips are two kinds of __Transformations__

**22–25.** Refer to the figure for Exercises 1–8. What theorem or postulate leads to the given conclusion?

22. No line other than $\overleftrightarrow{AB}$ contains $A$ and $B$.  Straight Line Post.

23. No plane other than $n$ contains $A$, $P$, and $D$.  Plane Post.

24. No plane other than $n$ contains both $\overleftrightarrow{AB}$ and $\overleftrightarrow{PC}$.  Plane Thm., part b

25. $\overleftrightarrow{AB}$ and $\overleftrightarrow{PC}$ intersect only at $C$.  Line Intersect. Thm.

# Z

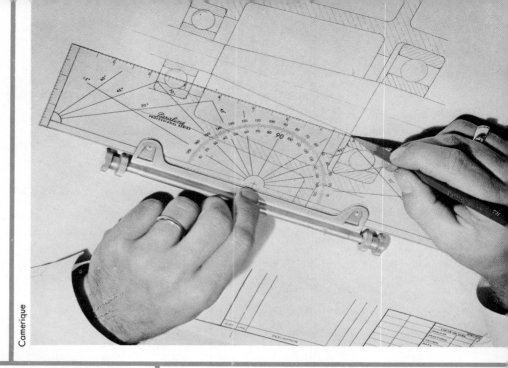

Camerique

George Franzen

# ANGLES

An angle is formed by two rays that meet at a point. Models of angles can be found in designs, buildings, and various kinds of plans and instructions, as in these photos.

# Convex Sets and Separation

**Convex Objects**

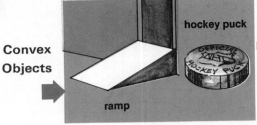

hockey puck

ramp

**Nonconvex Objects**

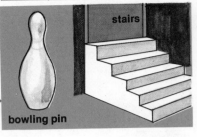

stairs

bowling pin

Notice that convex objects always "bend outward," but objects that are nonconvex "bend inward" in some places.

A **convex set** is a set of points with this property: For every two points of the set, the entire segment joining the points is in the set.

### Convex Sets

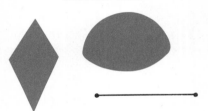

### Nonconvex Sets

The segment joining at least one pair of points does not lie entirely inside the set.

### Physical Model

Chicago Bears Football Club

The 50-yard line separates a football field into two convex sets.

### Geometric Figure

A line separates a plane into two convex sets called *half planes*.

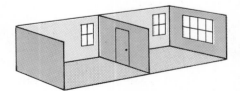

A wall separates a two-room apartment into two convex rooms.

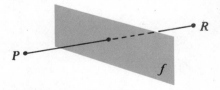

A plane separates space into two convex sets called *half spaces*.

Let *e* be a line in a given plane. The points of the plane that are not on line *e* form two **half planes** such that:
1. Each half plane is a convex set, and
2. If point *P* is in one half plane and point *R* is in the other, then segment *PR* intersects line *e*.

Line *e* is the *edge* of each half plane. The half planes do not contain the edge, and they are on *opposite sides* of the edge.

Let *f* be any plane in space. The points of space that are not on plane *f* form two **half spaces** such that:
1. Each half space is a convex set, and
2. If point *P* is in one half space and point *R* is in the other, then segment *PR* intersects plane *f*.

Plane *f* is the *face* of each half space. The half spaces do not contain the face, and they are on *opposite sides* of the face.

A line is the only one-dimensional figure that can separate a plane into *two* convex sets. A plane is the only two-dimensional figure that can separate space into *two* convex sets.

**Assignment Guide**
*Oral:* 1–16
*Written:*
Min. 17–32; Alg. Rev., p. 47
Reg. 17–32; Alg. Rev., p. 47
Max. 17–37

## *Exercises 2.1*

Ⓐ **1–4.** Is each object convex?

1. No    2. Yes    3. Yes    4. No

Alfa

**5–12.** Is each figure a convex set?

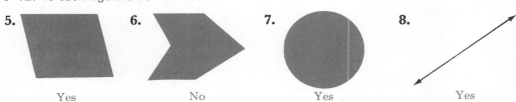

5. Yes    6. No    7. Yes    8. Yes

**9.** space   Yes        **10.** a line with a point removed   No

**11.** a plane with a point removed   No        **12.** a ray   Yes

**13.** Define *convex set.*   *See page 44.*

**14–16.** Complete each statement using the terms given.

    **a.** line        **b.** plane        **c.** space

    **d.** half planes        **e.** half spaces

**14.** A ___a___ separates a plane into two convex sets, called ___d___.

**15.** The face of a half space is a ___b___.

**16.** A ___b___ separates space into two convex sets, called ___e___.

Ⓑ **17–24.** Line $\ell$ is in plane $p$ and is the edge of two half planes $p_1$ and $p_2$. Points $A$ and $B$ are in $p_1$, and points $C$ and $D$ are in $p_2$.

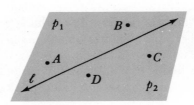

**True or False?**

**17.** $\overline{BC}$ intersects line $\ell$.   T        **18.** $\overline{CD}$ is in $p_2$.   T

**19.** $\overline{DC}$ intersects line $\ell$.   F        **20.** $\overline{AC}$ intersects line $\ell$.   T

**21.** $\overline{AD}$ is in $p_1$.   F        **22.** $\overline{BA}$ intersects line $\ell$.   F

**23.** $A$ and $B$ are on opposite sides   **24.** $B$ and $C$ are on opposite sides
of line $\ell$.   F                            of line $\ell$.   T

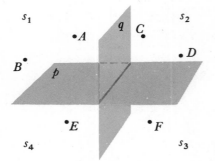

**25–32.** Planes $p$ and $q$ separate space into four sets, $s_1$, $s_2$, $s_3$, and $s_4$.

| points | $A, B$ | $C, D$ | $F$ | $E$ |
|---|---|---|---|---|
| are in set | $s_1$ | $s_2$ | $s_3$ | $s_4$ |

$s_1$ and $s_2$ are on opposite sides of $p$ from $s_3$ and $s_4$.
$s_1$ and $s_4$ are on opposite sides of $q$ from $s_2$ and $s_3$.
**True or False?**

**25.** $\overline{AC}$ intersects plane $q$.   T        **26.** $\overline{EC}$ intersects plane $q$.   T

**27.** Points $A$ and $C$ are on the same side of plane $q$.    F

**28.** Points $E$ and $F$ are on opposite sides of plane $q$.    T

**29.** Points $B$ and $D$ are on opposite sides of plane $p$.    F

**30.** Points $B$ and $C$ are on the same side of plane $p$.    T

**31.** $A$, $B$, and $E$ are on the same side of plane $q$.    T

**32.** $A$, $B$, $C$, and $D$ are on opposite sides of plane $p$.    F

© **33–37.** Lenses are used in eyeglasses, TV picture tubes, cameras, projectors, and car headlights. See if you can match each type of lens (shown in cross section below) with its name.

**a.** plano-convex        **b.** biconvex        **c.** plano-concave

**d.** biconcave        **e.** concavo-convex

**33.** a    **34.** c

**35.** d    **36.** e

**37.**  b

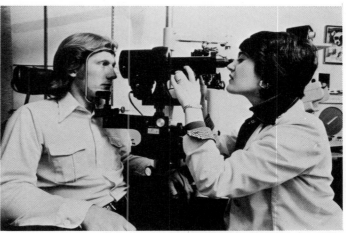

---

Solve.

**1.** $4a + 7 = 35$        **2.** $-4n + 8 = 12$        **3.** $5m - 9 = 0$
$\quad a = 7$                    $\quad n = -1$                    $\quad m = 1\frac{4}{5}$

**4.** $21 = 5 - 4b$        **5.** $\frac{1}{2}d + 4 = 8$        **6.** $\frac{2}{5}q - 4 = 10$
$\quad b = -4$                    $\quad d = 8$                    $\quad q = 35$

**7.** $3x + 2x = 90$        **8.** $5y - 2y = 180$        **9.** $14z + z = 180$
$\quad x = 18$                    $\quad y = 60$                    $\quad z = 12$

**10.** $d + 2d + 10 = 100$  $d = 30$        **11.** $5g - 10 + g = 90$    $g = 16\frac{2}{3}$

*Algebra Review*

**Review these skills:**

- *solving equations using two operations*
- *solving equations by combining like terms*

# 2.2 Angles and Triangles

**Suggested Class Time**

| Course | Min. | Reg. | Max. |
|--------|------|------|------|
| Days   | 1    | 1    | 1    |

An **angle** is formed by two noncollinear rays with the same endpoint. Each ray is a *side* of the angle. The common endpoint is the *vertex* of the angle.

angle

triangle

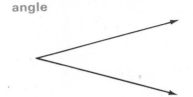

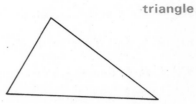

A **triangle** is formed by three segments that have three noncollinear points as their endpoints. The segments are the *sides* of the triangle. The endpoints of the sides are the *vertices* (plural of "vertex") of the triangle.

### Ways of Naming Angles and Triangles

| Figure | Names | Comments |
|--------|-------|----------|
| | angle $ABC$ or $\angle ABC$ <br> angle $CBA$ or $\angle CBA$ | $\angle$ is the symbol for "angle." The vertex letter is always in the middle. |
| | angle $B$ or $\angle B$ | The vertex letter may be used only when there is no chance of confusion. |
| | $\angle DOT$ or $\angle TOD$ <br> $\angle DOE$ or $\angle EOD$ <br> $\angle EOT$ or $\angle TOE$ | $\angle O$ cannot be used, since point $O$ is the vertex of three angles. |
| | $\angle O_1$ (for $\angle DOE$) <br> $\angle O_2$ (for $\angle EOT$) <br> $\angle O_{12}$ (for $\angle DOT$) | The small numbers used in the name are called subscripts. |
| | $\angle 1$ (for $\angle DOE$) <br> $\angle 2$ (for $\angle EOT$) | Numbers may be used to name angles. |
| | $\triangle FAM$ (or triangle $FAM$), $\triangle FMA$, $\triangle MAF$, $\triangle MFA$, $\triangle AFM$, $\triangle AMF$ | $\triangle$ is the symbol for "triangle." There are six different names for the same triangle. |

An angle separates the plane that contains it into two sets (neither of which contains the angle). One set is convex and is called the *interior* of the angle. The other set is nonconvex and is called the *exterior* of the angle.

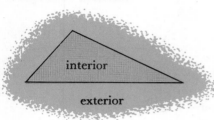

Similarly a triangle separates the plane into a convex interior and a nonconvex exterior.

$\triangle ABC$ determines $\angle BAC$, $\angle ABC$, and $\angle ACB$.

A triangle *determines* three angles called the *angles of the triangle*. Each angle has a vertex of the triangle as its own vertex and contains two sides of the triangle.

**Assignment Guide**
*Oral:* 1–16
*Written:*
Min. 17–39 odd
Reg. 17–39 odd
Max. 17–39 odd; 41–47

## Exercises 2.2

Ⓐ **1–4.** Complete each statement.

**1.** Each side of an angle is a __Ray__.

**2.** Each side of a triangle is a __Segment__.

**3.** Each vertex of a triangle is a __Point__.

**4.** The vertex of an angle is a __Point__.

**5.** Define *angle*. *See page 48.*

**6.** Define *triangle*. *See page 48.*

**7–8.** Is the figure a convex set?

**7.** interior of an angle  Yes

**8.** exterior of a triangle  No

**9–12.** Use the angle at the right.

**9.** Give a one-letter name for the angle. $\angle B$

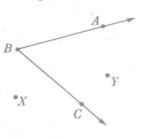

**10.** Give two three-letter names for the angle.
$\angle ABC$, $\angle CBA$

**11.** Name (**a**) its sides and (**b**) its vertex.
a. $\overrightarrow{BA}$, $\overrightarrow{BC}$; b. $B$

**12.** Name a point (**a**) in its interior and (**b**) in its exterior.  a. $Y$; b. $X$

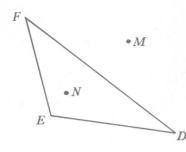

**13–16.** Use the triangle at the left.

**13.** Give six different names for the triangle.
$\triangle FED, \triangle EDF, \triangle DFE, \triangle DEF, \triangle EFD, \triangle FDE$

**14.** Name (**a**) its sides and (**b**) its vertices.
a. $\overline{DE}, \overline{EF}, \overline{FD}$; b. $D, E, F$

**15.** Name a point (**a**) in its interior and (**b**) in its exterior.
a. $N$; b. $M$

**16.** Name the angles determined by the triangle.
$\angle D, \angle E, \angle F$

Ⓑ **17–26.** Use the appropriate figures.

**17.** Give two other names for $\angle B_1$.
Any two of $\angle CBA, \angle ABC, \angle 1$

**18.** Give two other names for $\angle ABD$.
$\angle DBA, \angle B_{12}$

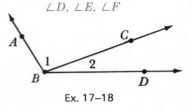

Ex. 17–18

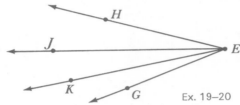

Ex. 19–20

**19.** Name all the angles in the figure.
HINT: There are more than 3. $\angle HEJ,$
$\angle JEK, \angle KEG, \angle HEK, \angle JEG, \angle HEG$

**20.** Name 3 angles having $\overrightarrow{EK}$ as a side.
$\angle KEG, \angle HEK, \angle JEK$

**21.** Name all the triangles in this figure. $\triangle RAS, \triangle RAT, \triangle RST$

**22.** Does $\triangle ART$ contain point $S$?
No

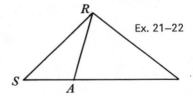

Ex. 21–22

**23.** Name all the points in the interior of $\angle SMG$.
$P, N$

**24.** Name all the points in the exterior of $\angle GMB$.
$S, W, P, N$

**25.** Name all the points in the exterior of $\angle SMG$.
$W, V, U, B$

**26.** Is $M$ on $\angle SMG$? Yes

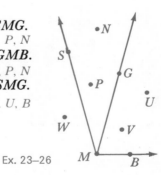

Ex. 23–26

**27–30.** True or False? Use the figure.

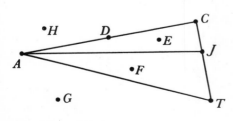

**27.** Points $D$ and $E$ are in the interior of $\triangle ACJ$. F

**28.** Points $E$ and $F$ are in the interior of $\triangle ACT$. T

**29.** Points $H, G, D,$ and $C$ are in the exterior of $\triangle JAT$. T

**30.** $D$ is in the exterior of $\triangle JAC$. F

**31–32.** Use the figure at the right.

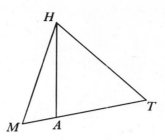

**31.** How many angles are determined by the triangles in this figure? 7

**32.** How many angles can be named by only the vertex letter? 2

**33–40.** True or False? △*PDC* determines the given angle.

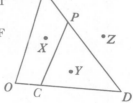

**33.** ∠*PDC*   T      **34.** ∠*OPD*   F      **35.** ∠*EDO*   T

**36.** ∠*EDC*   T      **37.** ∠*XDC*   F      **38.** ∠*XYZ*   F

**39.** ∠*O*     F      **40.** ∠*ODP*   T

© **41.** Can a point be in the exterior of a triangle and in the interior of one of the angles of the triangle? Draw a figure to show why.

**41.** Yes (In the figure for Ex. 33–40, *Z* is in the interior of ∠*O* and in the exterior of △*EOD*.)

**42.** Can a point be in the exterior of a triangle, but not in the interior of any angles of the triangle? Draw a figure to show why.

**42.** Yes (In the figure for Ex. 33–40, *O* is in the exterior of △*PCD* but not in the interior of any of its angles.)

**43–45.** Draw △*YOU*. Place point *W* so that *W* is on the same side of $\overleftrightarrow{YU}$ as *O*, on the same side of $\overleftrightarrow{OU}$ as *Y*, and on the same side of $\overleftrightarrow{OY}$ as *U*.

**43.** Is *W* in the interior of ∠*OUY*?   Yes

**44.** Is *W* in the interior of △*YOU*?   Yes

**45.** Use these ideas to state another definition of the *interior* of a triangle.   The interior of a triangle is the part of the plane that is in the interiors of all angles of the triangle.

**46–47.** If we pick a point on a straight line as a vertex, we could define *straight angle* as a figure formed by opposite rays.

**46.** Could we define the interior and exterior of a straight angle as we did for angles? Why?
No; a straight angle separates the plane into two convex sets.

**47.** We will not use "straight angle" in this text. What term can we use instead?   Opposite rays (or line)

# Measures of Angles

Angles are measured in units called *degrees*. Protractors are used to find the number of degrees in an angle as shown below.

**Examples:**

**1.**

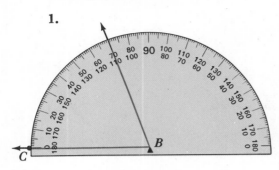

Read "measure of $\angle B$ equals 70". ⟶ $m\angle B = 70$

Use the top scale of the protractor to measure $\angle B$ because side $\overrightarrow{BC}$ intersects the top scale at 0.

**2.**

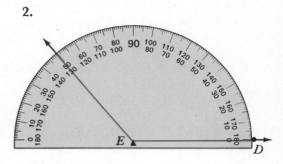

$m\angle E = 130$

Use the bottom scale of the protractor to measure $\angle E$ because side $\overrightarrow{ED}$ intersects the bottom scale at 0.

**3.**

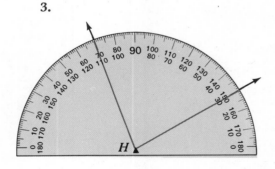

$m\angle H = 80$

The sides of the angle intersect both the top and the bottom scales. We can use either pair of numbers to measure the angle.

$$m\angle H = 150 - 70 = 80$$
$$m\angle H = 110 - 30 = 80$$

Using absolute value, we can subtract in either order.

$$m\angle H = |70 - 150| = 80$$
$$m\angle H = |30 - 110| = 80$$

NOTE: All angle measures in this book are in degrees. So we will not have to name the unit of measure or use the degree symbol (°), unless we want to make sure that a number is understood to be an angle measure.

**Angle Measure Postulate**

> For every angle, there is a unique real number between 0 and 180 called its degree measure.

Line $AB$ separates the plane into two half planes $s_1$ and $s_2$. Ray $AB$ is the side of two 35° angles, $\angle PAB$ and $\angle QAB$. With respect to each half plane, we can draw only one 35° angle having $\overrightarrow{AB}$ as a side. Would this be true for an angle of any measure? Consider the next postulate.

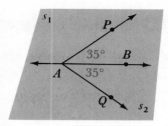

**Angle Construction Postulate**

Let ray $AB$ be on the edge of half plane $s_1$. For every number $r$ between 0 and 180 there is exactly one ray $AP$ with $P$ in $s_1$ such that $m\angle PAB = r$.

Two **adjacent angles** have a common side, but no points in the interior of one angle are in the interior of the other.

| adjacent angles | nonadjacent angles |
|---|---|
| $\angle ADB$, $\angle BDC$ | $\angle ADB$, $\angle ADC$ |
| | or |
| | $\angle ADC$, $\angle BDC$ |

The next postulate refers to adjacent angles.

**Angle Addition Postulate**

If $B$ is in the interior of $\angle ADC$, then $m\angle ADC = m\angle ADB + m\angle BDC$.

We can use the Angle Addition Postulate as in the examples.

**Examples:**

1.

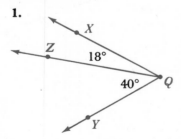

$$m\angle XQY = m\angle XQZ + m\angle ZQY$$
$$= \quad 18 \quad + \quad 40$$
$$= \quad 58$$

2.

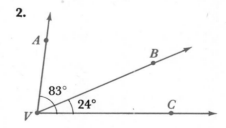

$$m\angle AVC = m\angle AVB + m\angle BVC$$
$$83 \quad = m\angle AVB + \quad 24$$
$$\underline{-24 \qquad\qquad\qquad -24}$$
$$59 \quad = m\angle AVB$$

# Exercises 2.3

**Assignment Guide**
*Oral:* 1–6
*Written:*
Min. 7–25 odd; Alg.
    Rev., p. 55
Reg. 7–25 odd; Alg.
    Rev., p. 55
Max. 7–31 odd

Ⓐ **1.** The measure of an angle is between __0__ and __180__.

**2–3.** $\overleftrightarrow{PC}$ separates plane $t$ into half planes $t_1$ and $t_2$.

**2.** Is $\overrightarrow{PS}$ the only ray that can be drawn in half plane $t_1$ so that $m\angle SPC = 110$?  Yes

**3.** Is $\angle CPR$ the only angle in plane $t$ having a measure of 27 and $\overrightarrow{PC}$ as a side?  No

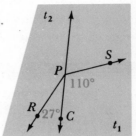

**4–6.** Choose the best word, number, or symbol. Use the figure at the left. (Do not use a protractor.)

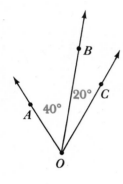

**4.** __$\angle AOB$__ and __$\angle BOC$__ are adjacent angles.

**5.** $m\angle AOC =$ __60__

**6.** The __Angle Addition__ Postulate states that if $B$ is in the interior of $\angle AOC$, then $m\angle AOC = m\angle AOB + m\angle BOC$.

Ⓑ **7–8.** Measure each angle with a protractor.

**7.**    144

**8.**   36

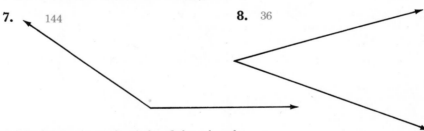

**9–10.** Measure each angle of the triangle.

**9.**   30; 135; 15

**10.**    57; 53; 70

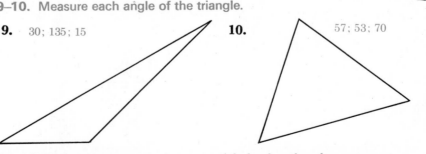

**11–14.** Using a protractor, draw an angle having the given measure.

**11.** 36        **12.** 120        **13.** 76        **14.** 155

**15–18.** Use the figure at the right.

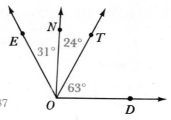

**15.** Name two angles adjacent to $\angle TON$.
∠EON, ∠DOT

**16.** Are $\angle NOT$ and $\angle NOD$ adjacent?   No

**17.** Find $m\angle TOE$.   55      **18.** Find $m\angle NOD$.   87

**19–22.** Choose the best symbol.

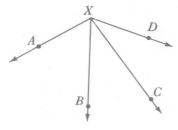

**19.** $m\angle AXB + m\angle BXC = m\angle$ _AXC_

**20.** $m\angle DXC + m\angle BXC = m\angle$ _DXB_

**21.** $m\angle BXD - m\angle BXC = m\angle$ _CXD_

**22.** $m\angle DXA - m\angle CXA = m\angle$ _CXD_

Ex. 19–26

**23–26.** $m\angle AXD = 131$, $m\angle BXA = 59$, and $m\angle BXC = 34$. Find:

**23.** $m\angle AXC$   93     **24.** $m\angle CXD$   38     **25.** $m\angle DXB$   72     **26.** $m\angle DXA$   131

Ⓒ **27–32.** $m\angle OGE = 100$, $m\angle CGM = 42$, $m\angle AGE = 37$, and $m\angle MGA = 72$. Find:

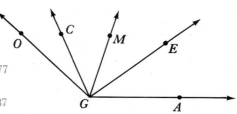

**27.** $m\angle CGA$   114     **28.** $m\angle MGE$   35     **29.** $m\angle CGE$   77

**30.** $m\angle OGC$   23     **31.** $m\angle OGM$   65     **32.** $m\angle OGA$   137

---

**1–4.** Represent each number by using a variable.

**1.** 20 more than a number
$x + 20$

**2.** 30 less than a number   $x - 30$

**3.** 2 times a number        $2x$

**4.** $\frac{1}{3}$ a number   $\frac{1}{3}x$

**5–6.** Set up the equation you would use to find each pair of numbers.

**5.** One number is 6 more than another, and their sum is 180.
$x + x + 6 = 180$

**6.** One number is 5 times the other, and their sum is 90.
$x + 5x = 90$

**7–8.** Find each pair of numbers in Exercises 5–6.   7. 87; 93
8. 15; 75

*Algebra Review*

**Review these skills:**

● *translating English to algebra*

● *setting up equations to solve problems*

# 2.4 Bisectors and Supplements of Angles

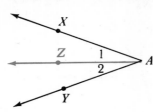

The **bisector** of $\angle XAY$ is ray $AZ$, where $Z$ is in the interior of $\angle XAY$ and $m\angle XAZ = m\angle YAZ$.

We use the Angle Measure, the Angle Construction, and the Angle Addition postulates to show why the next theorem is true.

**Theorem**   Every angle has exactly one bisector.

Reasoning:   (See figure above.)

From the Angle Measure Postulate we know that any $\angle XAY$ has exactly one measure. Call it $r$. So

▶ $m\angle XAY = r$

By the Angle Construction Postulate there is *exactly one* ray $AZ$ on the same side of $\overleftrightarrow{AY}$ as point $X$ so that

▶ $m\angle 2 = \frac{1}{2}r$

By the Angle Addition Postulate,

▶ $m\angle XAY = m\angle 1 + m\angle 2$

Use algebra  { Substitute ▶    Subtract $\frac{1}{2}r$ ▶

$$r = m\angle 1 + \frac{1}{2}r$$
$$\underline{-\frac{1}{2}r \qquad\qquad -\frac{1}{2}r}$$
$$\frac{1}{2}r = m\angle 1$$

Since $m\angle 1 = \frac{1}{2}r$ and $m\angle 2 = \frac{1}{2}r$,

▶ $m\angle 1 = m\angle 2$

Therefore $\overrightarrow{AZ}$ is the only bisector of $\angle XAY$.

**Supplementary angles** are two angles whose measures have the sum of 180.

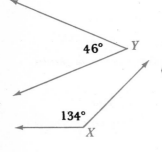

$\angle X$ and $\angle Y$ are supplementary.
$\angle X$ is the supplement of $\angle Y$.
$\angle Y$ is the supplement of $\angle X$.

$\overrightarrow{SR}$ and $\overrightarrow{ST}$ at right are opposite rays.
Notice that $m\angle VSR + m\angle VST = 180$.

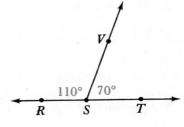

**Supplement Postulate**

If the noncommon sides of two adjacent angles are opposite rays, then the angles are supplementary.

Ⓐ **1–2.** Use the figure at the right. $\overrightarrow{ST}$ bisects $\angle RSV$.

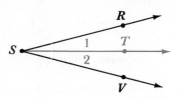

    **1.** What is true about $m\angle 1$ and $m\angle 2$?
                 $m\angle 1 = m\angle 2$

    **2.** If $m\angle 2 = 27$, find $m\angle 1$.    27

**3–5.** Complete each statement. (Do not use a protractor.)

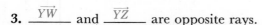

    **3.** <u> $\overrightarrow{YW}$ </u> and <u> $\overrightarrow{YZ}$ </u> are opposite rays.

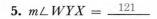

    **4.** <u>$\angle WYX$</u> and <u>$\angle XYZ$</u> are supplementary angles.

    **5.** $m\angle WYX = $ <u> 121 </u>

    **6.** State the Supplement Postulate. *See page 56.*

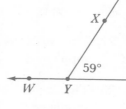

**Assignment Guide**
*Oral:* 1–6
*Written:*
Min. 7–23 odd; Quiz, p. 59
Reg. 7–23 odd; Quiz, p. 59
Max. 7–29 odd; 30;
    Quiz, p. 59
*Constructions:* 31–34

Ⓑ **7–8.** Use the figure.

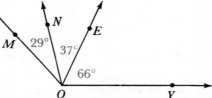

    **7.** Is $\overrightarrow{ON}$ the bisector of $\angle MOE$?   No

    **8.** Is $\overrightarrow{OE}$ the bisector of $\angle MOY$?   Yes

    **9.** Ray $AX$ bisects $\angle CAY$, and $m\angle CAY = 161$. Find $m\angle CAX$ and $m\angle XAY$.   80.5

   **10.** Ray $AG$ bisects $\angle TAP$, and $m\angle TAP = 78$. Find $m\angle TAG$ and $m\angle GAP$.   39

**11–18.** For the given angle measure, find the measure of the supplement.

**11.** 31     149      **12.** 147    33      **13.** 128    52      **14.** 41       139

**15.** 152.3   27.7     **16.** $131\frac{1}{2}$   $48\frac{1}{2}$     **17.** $n$   $180 - n$     **18.** $(180 - n)$   $n$

**19–28.** Find the measure of each angle and its supplement.

**19.** The supplement is 3 times the measure of the angle.   45; 135

    HINT: Let $x =$ the measure of the angle.

      Then $3x =$ the measure of the supplement.

     So, $x + 3x = 180$ because the two angles are supplementary.

**20.** The supplement is 5 times the measure of the angle.   30; 150

**21.** The supplement is 30 more than the measure of the angle.  75; 105

**22.** The supplement is 72 less than the measure of the angle.  126; 54

**23.** The supplement is $\frac{1}{3}$ the measure of the angle.  135; 45

**24.** The angle and its supplement have the same measure.  90; 90

© **25.** The supplement is 60 less than $\frac{1}{2}$ the measure of the angle. 160; 20

**26.** The supplement is 48 more than 5 times the measure of the angle.
22; 158

**27.** The angle has a measure of 5 more than $\frac{1}{4}$ the measure of its supplement.  40; 140

**28.** The angle has a measure 30 less than twice the measure of its supplement.  110; 70

**29–30.** $\angle ABC$ and $\angle CBD$ are adjacent supplementary angles.

**29.** Is $m\angle ABC + m\angle CBD = 180$? Why?
Yes; Supplement Post.

**30.** What is the measure of straight angle $ABD$?
*Straight angle* is defined in the instructions
before Exercise 46 on page 51.  180

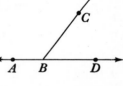

---

## construction: **the bisector of a given angle**

**1.** Given: $\angle A$

**2.**

same opening

**3.**

---

**31–34.** Use a protractor to draw an angle of the given measure. Construct its bisector. (Use a protractor to check your answer.)

**31.** 70          **32.** 85          **33.** 148          **34.** 115

## In Other Words

Students in other countries study about angles and triangles. See if you can say their words for these terms. Pronunciations are taken from *Webster's New Collegiate Dictionary*, eighth edition.

|         | angle | (pronunciation) |         | triangle | (pronunciation) |
|---------|-------|-----------------|---------|----------|-----------------|
| Russian | Угол  | ('ü–gəl)        | French  | triangle | (trē–'än–gəl)   |
| Italian | angolo | (än–'gō–lō)    | Japanese | 三角形 | (san–kä–kā)     |
| Polish  | kąt   | (känt)          | Spanish | triangulo | (trē–'än–gü–lō) |
| Hebrew  | זָוִית | (zȯ–'vēt)      | Slovak  | trojholnik | (trō–yü–'hōl–nik) |

**True or False?**

**1.** This figure is not a convex set.  T

**2.** Points $A$, $B$, and $C$ lie in half plane $t_1$.  F

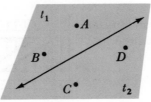

**3.** An angle is formed by two segments that intersect.  F

**4.** Point $M$ is in the interior of $\angle ABC$.  T

Ex. 4

**5.** Another name for $\angle FGK$ is $\angle G$.  F

**6.** $\angle FGH$ and $\angle FGK$ are adjacent angles.  F

**7.** $m\angle FGK = 52$  T

**8.** $\overrightarrow{GH}$ is the bisector of $\angle KGF$.  F

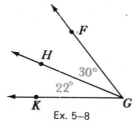

Ex. 5–8

**9.** If an angle's measure is 73, then the measure of its supplement is 107.  T

# 2.5 Angles and Perpendicular Lines

| Definition | Model | Figure |
|---|---|---|

A **right angle** is an angle whose measure is 90.

An **acute angle** is an angle whose measure is less than 90.

An **obtuse angle** is an angle whose measure is greater than 90.

**Complementary angles** are two angles whose measures have the sum of 90.

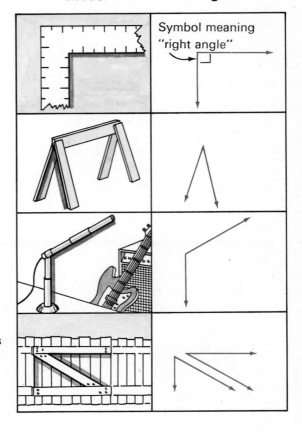

Lines, segments, and rays that meet to form a 90°, or right, angle are **perpendicular**. (⊥ means "is perpendicular to.")

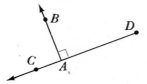

$\overrightarrow{AB}$ is perpendicular to $\overrightarrow{DC}$.

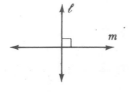

$\ell \perp m$

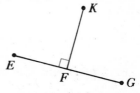

$\overline{EG}$ is perpendicular to $\overline{FK}$.

**Perpendicular Line Postulate**

In any plane containing a given line and point, there is exactly one line through the point perpendicular to the given line.

According to the postulate, if $\ell$ and $P$ are the given line and point, then:

For $P$ on $\ell$

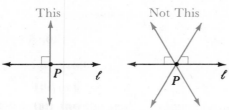

For $P$ not on $\ell$

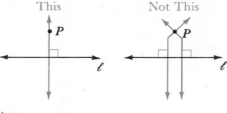

In a plane, the **perpendicular bisector** of a segment is the line that is perpendicular to the segment at its midpoint. Line $\ell$ is the perpendicular bisector of segment $AB$.

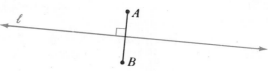

## Exercises 2.5

Ⓐ **1–6.** Use acute, obtuse, or right to complete each statement.

**1.** $\angle MOP$ is a(n) <u>Acute</u> angle.

**2.** $\angle TOP$ is a(n) <u>Right</u> angle.

**3.** $\angle HOP$ is a(n) <u>Obtuse</u> angle.

Ex. 1–3

**4.** A(n) <u>Right</u> angle has a measure of 90.

**5.** A(n) <u>Acute</u> angle has a measure less than 90.

**6.** A(n) <u>Obtuse</u> angle has a measure greater than 90.

**7.** What is the sum of the measures of two complementary angles? 90

**8.** Define *perpendicular lines*. *See page 60.*

**9.** In a plane, how many lines are perpendicular to line $\ell$ through $P$? 1

**10.** Define *perpendicular bisector*. *See above.*

Ⓑ **11–16.** $m\angle HCE = 90$, $m\angle ECL = 25$, $\overrightarrow{SL}$ contains $C$. Name the following.

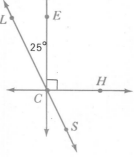

**11.** two obtuse angles
        $\angle LCH$, $\angle SCE$

**12.** two acute angles
        $\angle LCE$, $\angle HCS$

**13.** two supplementary angles
$\angle LCE$, $\angle SCE$ (or $\angle LCH$, $\angle HCS$)

**14.** two complementary angles
        $\angle LCE$, $\angle HCS$

**15.** two perpendicular lines
        $\overleftrightarrow{CE}$, $\overleftrightarrow{CH}$

**16.** two opposite rays
        $\overrightarrow{CL}$, $\overrightarrow{CS}$

**Assignment Guide**
*Oral:* 1–10
*Written:* Min. 11–30; 39–42
       Reg. 11–30; 35–42
       Max. 11–30; 35–44
*Constructions:* 31–34; 45–46

**17–20.** What type of angle is formed by the hands of a clock at

**17.** 10:00? Acute    **18.** 4:00? Obtuse    **19.** 9:00? Right    **20.** 4:30? Acute

**21–26.** Find the complement of the angle with the given measure.

**21.** 80    10    **22.** 6    84    **23.** $28\frac{1}{3}$    $61\frac{2}{3}$

**24.** 30.5    59.5    **25.** $n$    $90 - n$    **26.** $(90 - n)$    $n$

Ex. 29–30

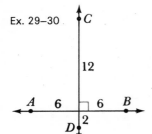

**27.** If two adjacent angles are complementary, their noncommon sides are (opposite, collinear, <u>perpendicular</u>) rays.

**28.** $\angle ABC$ and $\angle DBC$ are adjacent complementary angles. Find $m\angle ABD$.    90

**29–30.** True or False? $\overleftrightarrow{DC}$ is the perpendicular bisector

**29.** of $\overline{AB}$.    T    **30.** of $\overleftrightarrow{AB}$.    F

**construction: perpendicular bisector of a segment**

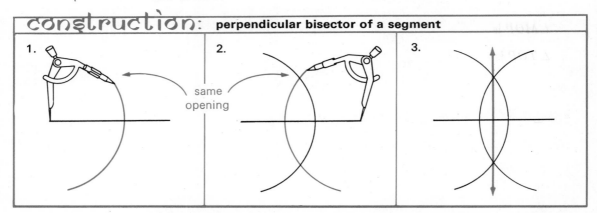

1.    2.    same opening    3.

**31–34.** Draw a segment of the length given. Construct its perpendicular bisector.

**31.** 6 cm    **32.** 12 cm    **33.** 8 cm    **34.** 70 mm

**35–37.** Choose one term (acute, obtuse, right) to describe each angle.

**35.** either of two complementary angles    Acute

**36.** the supplement of an obtuse angle    Acute

**37.** the supplement of a right angle    Right

**38.** Can an obtuse angle have a complement? Why?

No; the angle already has measure greater than 90.

**39–44.** Find the measure of each angle and its complement.

**39.** The complement is 10 more than the measure of the angle. 40; 50

    HINT: Let $x$ = the measure of the angle. Then $x + 10$ = the measure of the complement, and $x + x + 10 = 90$.

**40.** The complement is 52 less than the measure of the angle. 71; 19

**41.** The complement is twice the measure of the angle. 30; 60

**42.** The complement is equal to the measure of the angle. 45; 45

© **43.** The complement is 8 more than 3 times the measure of the angle. 20.5; 69.5

**44.** The complement is 24 less than twice the measure of the angle. 38; 52

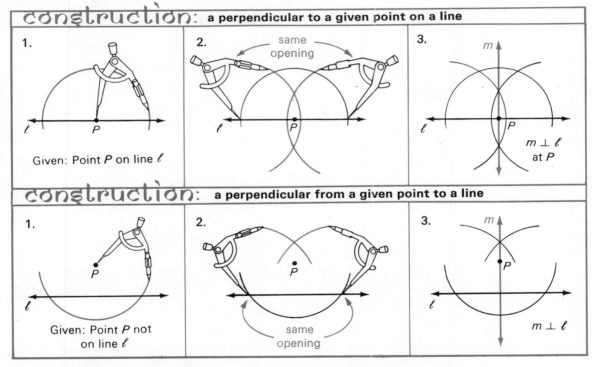

**construction:** a perpendicular to a given point on a line

**1.** Given: Point $P$ on line $\ell$

**2.** same opening

**3.** $m \perp \ell$ at $P$

**construction:** a perpendicular from a given point to a line

**1.** Given: Point $P$ not on line $\ell$

**2.** same opening

**3.** $m \perp \ell$

**45–46.** Copy. Construct perpendiculars to line $\ell$ at $P$ and from $M$.

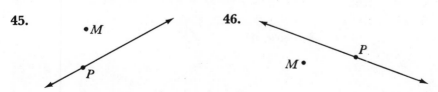

**45.** • $M$    $P$

**46.** $M$ •    $P$

# 2.6 Congruent Segments and Angles

| | Angles | | Segments |
|---|---|---|---|

**Congruent angles** are angles that have the same measure.

**Congruent segments** are segments that have the same measure.

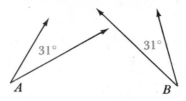

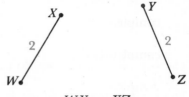

| $m\angle A = m\angle B$ | $WX = YZ$ |
|---|---|
| $\angle A$ is congruent to $\angle B$ | $\overline{WX}$ is congruent to $\overline{YZ}$ |
| $\angle A \cong \angle B$ | $\overline{WX} \cong \overline{YZ}$ |

≅ means
is congruent to

Notice that the geometric figures (segments or angles) are congruent, while their measures, which are numbers, are equal.

$m\angle A = m\angle B$ ◄ The top and bottom statements ► $WX = YZ$

$\angle A \cong \angle B$ ◄ are equivalent. One can be replaced by the other at any time. ► $\overline{WX} \cong \overline{YZ}$

The properties at the bottom of page 22 can be used to show that similar properties carry over to congruent segments and angles.

| Property of Equal Numbers | Property of Congruent Angles | Property of Congruent Segments |
|---|---|---|
| $m\angle A = m\angle A$ | $\angle A \cong \angle A$ | |
| $XW = XW$ | | $\overline{XW} \cong \overline{XW}$ |
| If $m\angle A = m\angle B$, then $m\angle B = m\angle A$. | If $\angle A \cong \angle B$, then $\angle B \cong \angle A$. | |
| If $XW = YZ$, then $YZ = XW$. | | If $\overline{XW} \cong \overline{YZ}$, then $\overline{YZ} \cong \overline{XW}$. |
| If $m\angle A = m\angle B$ and $m\angle B = m\angle C$, then $m\angle A = m\angle C$. | If $\angle A \cong \angle B$ and $\angle B \cong \angle C$, then $\angle A \cong \angle C$. | |
| If $XW = YZ$ and $YZ = PR$, then $XW = PR$. | | If $\overline{XW} \cong \overline{YZ}$ and $\overline{YZ} \cong \overline{PR}$, then $\overline{XW} \cong \overline{PR}$. |

These ideas are now stated as theorems.

An angle is congruent to itself.

Congruence of two angles can be stated in either order.

Two angles congruent to the same angle are congruent to each other.

**Congruent
Angles
Theorems**

A segment is congruent to itself.

Congruence of two segments can be stated in either order.

Two segments congruent to the same segment are congruent to each other.

**Congruent
Segments
Theorems**

If $\angle J$ and $\angle G$ are right angles, then $m\angle J = 90$ and $m\angle G = 90$, making $m\angle J = m\angle G$ and $\angle J \cong \angle G$.

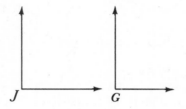

This is why we can state the next theorem.

Any two right angles are congruent.

**Theorem**

## Exercises 2.6

Ⓐ **1.** Define *congruent angles*.
   See page 64.

**2.** Define *congruent segments*. *See page 64.*

**3–10.** Complete each statement with the best symbol possible.

**3.** $\angle A \cong$ ___$\angle A$___

**4.** $\overline{AB} \cong$ ___$\overline{AB}$___

**5.** If $\angle C \cong \angle D$, then $\angle D \cong$ ___$\angle C$___.

**6.** If $\overline{KD} \cong \overline{JC}$, then $\overline{JC} \cong$ ___$\overline{KD}$___.

**7.** If $\angle A \cong \angle C$ and $\angle C \cong \angle D$, then $\angle A \cong$ ___$\angle D$___.

**8.** If $\overline{JC} \cong \overline{HD}$ and $\overline{HD} \cong \overline{BA}$, then $\overline{JC} \cong$ ___$\overline{BA}$___.

**9.** If $\overline{CG} \cong \overline{CJ}$ and $\overline{CJ} \cong \overline{DK}$, then ___$\overline{CG}$___ $\cong \overline{DK}$.

**10.** If $\angle D$ and $\angle C$ are right angles, then $\angle D \cong$ ___$\angle C$___.

**Assignment Guide**
*Oral:* 1–10
*Written:* Min. 11–18
Reg. 11–18
Max. 11–19
*Constructions:* 20–24

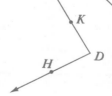

**11.** Congruence of two angles can be stated in either order.
If $\angle A \cong \angle B$, then $\angle B \cong \angle A$.

**12.** Two segments congruent to the same segment are congruent to
each other. If $\overline{AB} \cong \overline{CD}$ and $\overline{CD} \cong \overline{EF}$, then $\overline{AB} \cong \overline{EF}$.

13–16. Complete each statement with the best number or symbol.

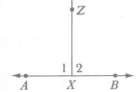

**13.** If $\angle X_1 \cong \angle Y_1$ and $m\angle X_1 = 93$, then $m\angle Y_1 = \underline{\ \ 93\ \ }$.

**14.** If $AX = 8$ and $CY = 8$, then $\underline{\ \ \overline{AX}\ \ } \cong \underline{\ \ \overline{CY}\ \ }$.

**15.** If $AX = 5$, $CY = 5$, and $\overline{BX} \cong \overline{AX}$, then $\overline{BX} \cong \underline{\ \ \overline{CY}\ \ }$.

**16.** If $\angle X_1 \cong \angle Y_1$, $\angle Y_1 \cong \angle X_2$, and $m\angle X_1 = 90$, then $m\angle Y_1 = \underline{\ \ 90\ \ }$ and $m\angle X_2 = \underline{\ \ 90\ \ }$.

17–18. Fill in the blank with $=$ or $\cong$.

**17.** $\angle Y_1 \underline{\ \ \cong\ \ } \angle Y_1$

**18.** $XB \underline{\ \ =\ \ } XB$

19. In order: reflexive, symmetric, transitive

Ⓒ **19.** The three properties in the Congruent Angles Theorems are called
the symmetric, reflexive, and transitive properties. Find out which
is which. HINT: It might help to refer to Exercise 57, page 25.

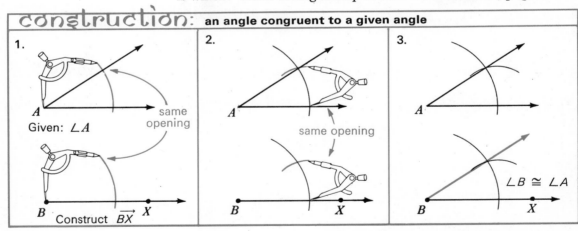

construction: **an angle congruent to a given angle**

20–23. Use the angles at the left to construct an angle of the given measure.

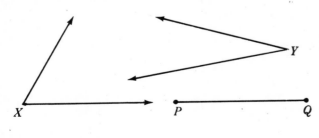

**20.** $m\angle X$

**21.** $m\angle Y$

**22.** $m\angle X + m\angle Y$

**23.** $m\angle X - m\angle Y$

**24.** Construct $\triangle ABC$ with $\angle A \cong \angle X$,
$\angle B \cong \angle Y$, and $\overline{AB} \cong \overline{PQ}$

**2.7**

| Suggested Class Time | | | |
|---|---|---|---|
| Course | Min. | Reg. | Max. |
| Days | 1 | 1 | 1 |

∠1 ≅ ∠3 because they are made to be 150° angles. Angles 1 and 2 as well as angles 3 and 4 are supplementary. Therefore, ∠2 and ∠4 are 30° angles. ∠2 ≅ ∠4

Angles 5 and 7 as well as angles 6 and 8 are complementary angles. If ∠5 and ∠8 are 15° angles, then ∠6 and ∠7 will both be 75° angles, and ∠6 ≅ ∠7.

These relationships suggest the next two theorems.

Artstreet

 Supplements of congruent angles are congruent.

Congruent
Supplements
Theorem

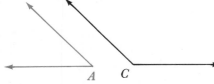 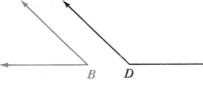

If ∠A ≅ ∠B, $m\angle A + m\angle C = 180$, and $m\angle B + m\angle D = 180$, then ∠C ≅ ∠D.

**Reasoning:**

Since $m\angle A + m\angle C = 180$ and $m\angle B + m\angle D = 180$, ▶ $m\angle A + m\angle C = m\angle B + m\angle D$

Since ∠A ≅ ∠B, $m\angle A = m\angle B$ and we can substitute $m\angle A$ for $m\angle B$

▶
$$m\angle A + m\angle C = m\angle A + m\angle D$$
$$\underline{-m\angle A \qquad\qquad -m\angle A}$$

Subtracting $m\angle A$, we get ▶ $m\angle C = m\angle D$

Since two angles with equal measure are congruent, ▶ ∠C ≅ ∠D

Since an angle is congruent to itself, the theorem above lets us say that *two angles supplementary to the same angle are congruent.* This will be useful later.

Complements of congruent angles are congruent.

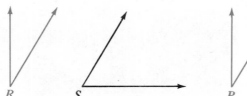

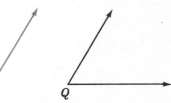

If $\angle R \cong \angle P$, $m\angle R + m\angle S = 90$, and $m\angle P + m\angle Q = 90$, then $\angle S \cong \angle Q$.

**Reasoning:**

Since $m\angle R + m\angle S = 90$ and $m\angle P + m\angle Q = 90$, ▶ $m\angle R + m\angle S = m\angle P + m\angle Q$

Since $\angle R \cong \angle P$, $m\angle R = m\angle P$ and we can substitute $m\angle R$ for $m\angle P$ ▶

$$m\angle R + m\angle S = m\angle R + m\angle Q$$
$$\underline{-m\angle R \qquad\qquad -m\angle R}$$

Subtracting $m\angle R$, we get ▶ $m\angle S = m\angle Q$

Since two angles with equal measure are congruent, ▶ $\angle S \cong \angle Q$

Since an angle is congruent to itself, the theorem above lets us say that *two angles complementary to the same angle are congruent.*

  If two angles are congruent and supplementary, then they are right angles.

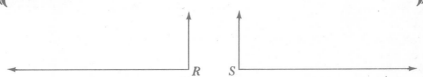

If $\angle R \cong \angle S$ and $m\angle R + m\angle S = 180$, then $\angle R$ and $\angle S$ are right angles.

**Reasoning:**

Since $m\angle R = m\angle S$, we can substitute $m\angle R$ for $m\angle S$ in the equation above to obtain $m\angle R + m\angle R = 180$. Simplifying, $2m\angle R = 180$, and $m\angle R = 90$. Therefore, $m\angle S = 90$ and $m\angle R = 90$, and both $\angle R$ and $\angle S$ are right angles.

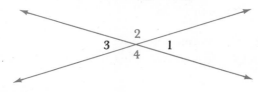

**Vertical angles** are two non-adjacent angles formed by two intersecting lines. Notice that $\angle 2$ and $\angle 4$ are both supplements of $\angle 1$.

Vertical angles are congruent.

 Vertical Angles Theorem

Reasoning:

$\angle 2$ and $\angle 4$ are supplements of $\angle 1$, and $\angle 1$ and $\angle 3$ are supplements of $\angle 2$. Angles supplementary to the same angle are congruent, so $\angle 2 \cong \angle 4$ and $\angle 1 \cong \angle 3$.

 Two perpendicular lines meet to form four right angles.

 Four Right Angles Theorem

Exercise 41 gives the reasoning for this theorem.

**Assignment Guide**
*Oral:* 1–12
*Written:* Min. 13–31 odd
Reg. 13–37 odd
Max. 13–41 odd

## Exercises 2.7

Ⓐ **1–10.** Use the appropriate figures at the right.

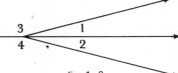

Ex. 1–2

**1.** If $\angle 1 \cong \angle 2$, then $\angle 3 \cong \angle \underline{\quad 4 \quad}$.

**2.** $\angle 1$ and $\underline{\angle 3}$ as well as $\angle 4$ and $\underline{\angle 2}$ are supplementary.

**3.** $\angle ABC$ and $\underline{\angle CBD}$ as well as $\angle EBF$ and $\underline{\angle DBE}$ are complementary.

**4.** If $\angle CBA \cong \angle FBE$, then $\angle \underline{\quad CBD \quad} \cong \angle \underline{\quad DBE \quad}$.

**5.** Find $m\angle DBF$. 90

**6.** Name 4 right angles.

**7.** Name 4 congruent angles.

$\left.\begin{array}{l}\phantom{x}\end{array}\right\}$ $\angle ABD, \angle DBF,$ $\angle FBG, \angle GBA$

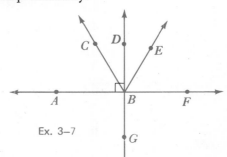

Ex. 3–7

**8.** $\angle 11$ and $\angle \underline{\quad 13 \quad}$ are vertical angles.

**9.** $\angle 12 \cong \underline{\angle 14}$  **10.** $\angle 13 \cong \underline{\angle 11}$

**11.** Vertical angles are ( supplementary, <u>congruent</u> ).

**12.** If two angles are congruent and <u>supplementary</u>, then they are right angles.

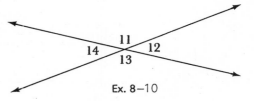

Ex. 8–10

Ⓑ **13–18.** $\angle A_1 \cong \angle B_1$. Lines $t$ and $v$ intersect at point $A$. Lines $s$ and $u$ intersect at point $B$. True or False?

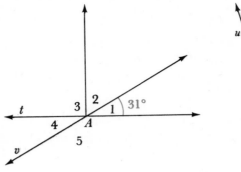

**13.** $\angle A_{23} \cong \angle B_2$  T

**14.** $\angle A_{23} \cong \angle B_4$  T

**15.** $\angle A_3 \cong \angle B_2$  F

**16.** $\angle A_4 \cong \angle B_3$  T

**17.** $\angle A_5 \cong \angle B_2$  T

**18.** $\angle A_2 \cong \angle B_3$  F

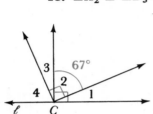

**19–28.** $\angle C_2 \cong \angle D_1$. Point $C$ is on $\ell$. True or False?

**19.** $\angle C_1 \cong \angle D_2$    T      **20.** $\angle C_3 \cong \angle D_1$    F

**21.** $\angle C_4 \cong \angle C_2$    T      **22.** $\angle C_4 \cong \angle C_1$    F

**23.** $\angle C_4 \cong \angle D_2$    F      **24.** $\angle C_3 \cong \angle D_2$    T

**25.** $\angle C_{34} \cong \angle C_{12}$    T      **26.** $\angle D_{12} \cong \angle C_{12}$    T

**27.** $\angle C_{23} \cong \angle D_{12}$    T      **28.** $\angle C_{23} \cong \angle C_{34}$    T

**29–38.** State the theorem that supports each conclusion.

29. Supplements of congruent angles are congruent.
30. Complements of congruent angles are congruent.
31. If two angles are congruent and supplementary, they are right angles.
32. *Same as Ex. 30*

**29.**

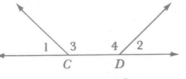

$\overleftrightarrow{CD}$ with $\angle 1 \cong \angle 2$
*Conclusion:* $\angle 3 \cong \angle 4$

**30.**

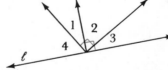

$\angle 1 \cong \angle 3$
*Conclusion:* $\angle 2 \cong \angle 4$

**31.**

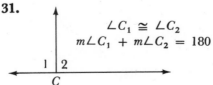

$\angle C_1 \cong \angle C_2$
$m\angle C_1 + m\angle C_2 = 180$

*Conclusion:* $\angle C_1$ and $\angle C_2$ are right angles.

**32.**

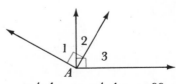

$m\angle A_{12} = m\angle A_{23} = 90$
*Conclusion:* $\angle 1 \cong \angle 3$

**70**      CHAPTER 2      ANGLES

**33.**

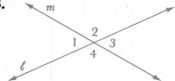

*Conclusion*: $\angle 1 \cong \angle 3$

**34.**

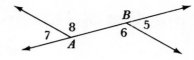

$\overleftrightarrow{AB}$ with $\angle 8 \cong \angle 6$
*Conclusion*: $\angle 5 \cong \angle 7$

**33.** Vertical angles are congruent.
**34.** *Same as Ex. 29*
**35.** *Same as Ex. 31*
**36.** Two perpendicular lines meet to form four right angles.
**37.** *Same as Ex. 33*
**38.** *Same as Ex. 36*

**35.**

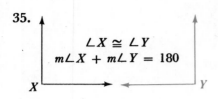

$\angle X \cong \angle Y$
$m\angle X + m\angle Y = 180$

*Conclusion*: $\angle X$ and $\angle Y$ are right angles.

**36.**

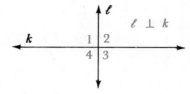

$\ell \perp k$

*Conclusion*: $\angle 1, \angle 2, \angle 3,$ and $\angle 4$ are right angles.

**37.**

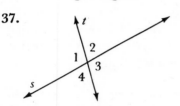

*Conclusion*: $\angle 2 \cong \angle 4$

**38.**

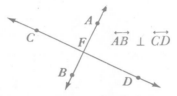

$\overleftrightarrow{AB} \perp \overleftrightarrow{CD}$

*Conclusion*: $m\angle AFD = m\angle DFB = m\angle AFC = m\angle BFC = 90$

© **39–40.** Solve for the variable.

**39.** $x = 36$

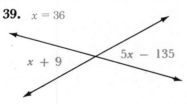

**40.** $y = 14\frac{8}{11}$

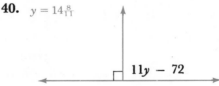

**41.** Show that the Four Right Angles Theorem, page 69, is true by answering why in steps 2–6.

   *1.* Draw $\ell \perp k$, forming $\angle 1, \angle 2, \angle 3,$ and $\angle 4$.

   *2.* $m\angle 1 = 90$. Why?

   *3.* $m\angle 3 = m\angle 1 = 90$. Why?

   *4.* $m\angle 2 + m\angle 3 = 180$, so $m\angle 2 = 90$. Why?

   *5.* $m\angle 4 = m\angle 2 = 90$. Why?

   *6.* $\angle 1, \angle 2, \angle 3,$ and $\angle 4$ are right angles. Why?

**41.** *2.* Definition of perpendicular lines
*3.* Vertical angles are congruent.
*4.* Supplement Postulate and Subtraction
*5.* Vertical angles are congruent.
*6.* Definition of right angle

## 2.8 **Some Properties of Transformations**

Remember three of the transformations from Chapter 1?

slide    turn    flip

The original and the image look the same. Let's explore why.

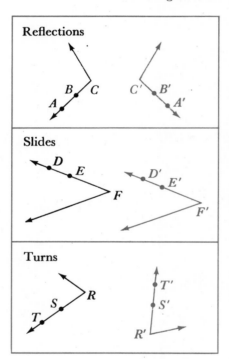

At the left, $\angle C'$ (read "$C$ prime") is the reflection image of $\angle C$, $\angle F'$ is the slide image of $\angle F$, and $\angle R'$ is the turn image of $\angle R$.

Look at the corresponding points of each figure and its image. These drawings suggest that if a point is between two points in the original, then its image is between the images of those two points. Also, if these points are collinear, their images are collinear.

Using a protractor, check that the measure of an angle is the same as the measure of its image. With a ruler, check that the distance between two points is the same as the distance between their images.

We describe these properties of reflections, slides, and turns as follows.

> Reflections, slides, and turns preserve
> 1. betweenness of points
> 2. collinearity of points
> 3. distance between points
> 4. angle measure

**Orientation** helps describe how triangles or other figures lie in a plane. To find the orientation of △*XYZ*, trace a path from *X* to *Y* to *Z*. Your finger moves in a clockwise direction, making the orientation of △*XYZ* *clockwise*. The orientation of △*YXZ* is *counterclockwise*. Consider △*ABC* and its reflection image △*A'B'C'*.

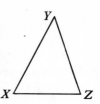

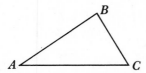  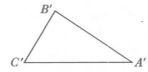

△*ABC*: clockwise orientation     △*A'B'C'*: counterclockwise orientation

Reflections reverse orientation.

Let's look again at a figure and its reflection image.

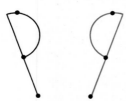  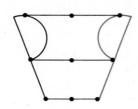  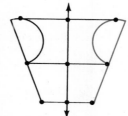

Pick three corresponding points on the original figure and its image.

Connect these points. Then find the midpoints of these segments.

Draw line ℓ through the midpoints.

Line ℓ is called the **reflecting line.** Notice that it is the *perpendicular bisector* of each segment connecting a point to its image.

We can use this relationship to draw the reflection image of a point. Each point when it is reflected over a line has exactly one image.

  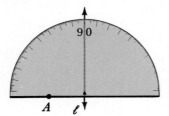  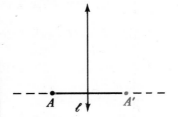

Here is point *A* and reflecting line ℓ.

Place your protractor like this one. Draw a segment along the base of the protractor.

Measure the distance from point *A* to line ℓ along the segment. Point *A'* is the same distance away from line ℓ.

You can find the reflection image of a set of points by using this method for finding the reflection image of a point.

To find the image of $\overleftrightarrow{AB}$, find $A'$ and $B'$.

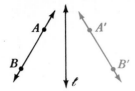

$\overleftrightarrow{A'B'}$ is the image of $\overleftrightarrow{AB}$.

To find the image of $\triangle RST$, find $R'$, $S'$, and $T'$.

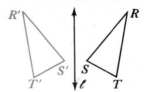

$\triangle R'S'T'$ is the image of $\triangle RST$.

# Exercises 2.8

**Assignment Guide**
*Oral:* 1–16
*Written:*
Min. 17–26; 27–35 odd
Reg. 17–26; 27–35 odd
Max. 17–26; 27–37 odd

Ⓐ **1–15.** Answer yes or no to tell whether the transformation preserves each property.

| property | transformation | | |
|---|---|---|---|
| | Reflection | Slide | Turn |
| Betweenness | **1.** Yes | **2.** Yes | **3.** Yes |
| Collinearity | **4.** Yes | **5.** Yes | **6.** Yes |
| Distance | **7.** Yes | **8.** Yes | **9.** Yes |
| Angle measure | **10.** Yes | **11.** Yes | **12.** Yes |
| Orientation | **13.** No | **14.** Yes | **15.** Yes |

**16.** The reflection image of point $A$ over line $\ell$ is $A'$. Describe the reflecting line. The perpendicular bisector of $\overline{AA'}$

Ⓑ **17–20.** Write *true* if the statement is always true. Otherwise write *false*.

**17.** $\overline{A'B'}$ is the reflection image of $\overline{AB}$. If $A'B' = 9$, then $AB = 8$. F

**18.** $\angle C'$ is the slide image of $\angle C$. If $m\angle C = 41$, $m\angle C' = 41$. T

**19.** If $G$, $H$, and $J$ are collinear, their reflection and turn images will be collinear. T

**20.** $L$ is between $M$ and $N$. Only under reflections will $L'$ be between $M'$ and $N'$. F

**21–26.** What is the orientation of each triangle?

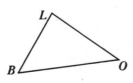

**21.** $\triangle BLO$
Clockwise

**22.** $\triangle NUF$
Counterclockwise

**23.** $\triangle LOB$
Clockwise

**24.** $\triangle UNF$
Clockwise

**25.** $\triangle BOL$
Counterclockwise

**26.** $\triangle FUN$
Clockwise

**27–30.** Copy these drawings. Draw the reflecting line so that the red figure is the image of the black figure.

**27.**

**28.**

**29.**

**30.**

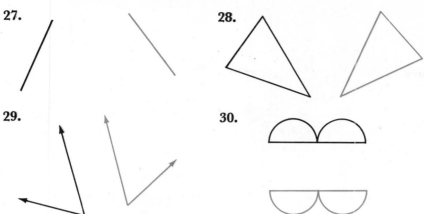

**31–36.** Copy the drawings. Reflect each figure over line $\ell$.

**31.**

**32.**

**33.**

**34.**

**35.**

**36.**

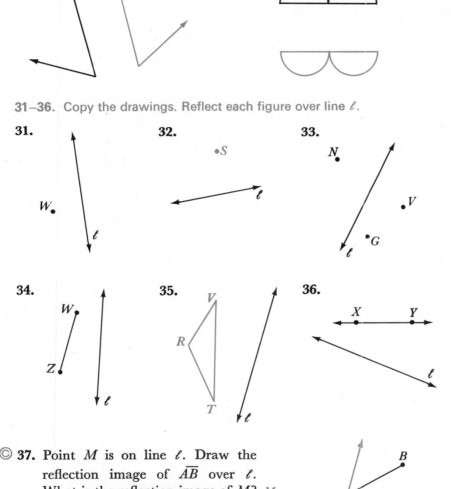

© 1975, Universal Press Syndicate.

© **37.** Point $M$ is on line $\ell$. Draw the reflection image of $\overline{AB}$ over $\ell$. What is the reflection image of $M$?

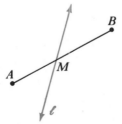

Brent Jones

# REFLECTIONS AND MINIATURE GOLF

In miniature golf the object is to use the fewest number of strokes to get the ball into the hole. It is not always possible to aim the ball at the hole. Look at the photo.

Where should you aim the ball? Knowing about reflections will be helpful. *First*, reflect the hole over the side wall that the ball must bounce off. (When you're actually playing miniature golf, visualize where the reflection image of the hole would be.)

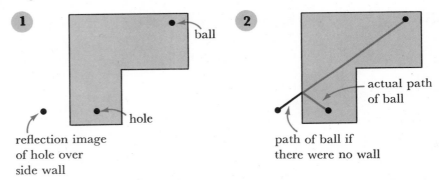

*Second*, aim for the reflection image of the hole. The ball will bounce off the side and into the hole.

Now look at diagram 2 more closely. Notice the actual path of the ball and the path of the ball if there were no side wall. With the side as the reflecting line, they are reflection images of each other.

Copy each drawing. Draw a path that will get the ball into the hole in 1 stroke.

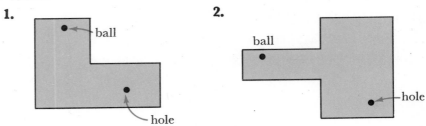

# ■ Chapter 2 Review ■

**1.** Define *convex set.*   *See page 44.*

**2.1**

**2–4.** Is each figure a convex set?

**2.** No      **3.**      Yes      **4.** No

**Assignment Guide**
*Oral:* 1–14
*Written:* 15–37

**5–7.** Complete each statement with the best word(s) possible.

**5.** A plane is separated by a _____ into two _____.   Line; half planes

**6.** Space is separated by a _____ into two _____.   Plane; half spaces

**7.** A half plane does not contain its __Edge__.

**8.** Define *angle.*  *See page 48.*     **9.** Define *triangle.*  *See page 48.*

**2.2**

**10–14.** Use the figures at the right.

**10.** State three other names for ∠1.
∠B, ∠ABC, ∠CBA

**11.** State five other names for △DEF.
△DFE, △EFD, △EDF, △FED, △FDE

**12.** Name the sides of the angle.  $\vec{BA}$, $\vec{BC}$

**13.** Name the vertices of the triangle.
D, E, F

**14.** Which of the following is a convex set?  b

    **a.** ∠ABC   **b.** the interior of ∠ABC   **c.** the exterior of △DEF

**15–16.** Measure each angle.

**2.3**

**15.**   18      **16.**   142

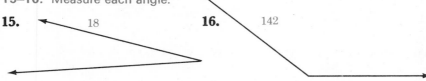

**17–18.** Point *B* is on $\overleftrightarrow{EC}$. Find the following:

**17.** *m*∠*ABC*   65

**18.** *m*∠*ABE*   115

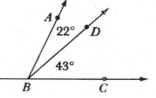

**19–21.** $\overrightarrow{AY}$ is the bisector of $\angle XAZ$.
$m\angle XAZ = 72$. Find:

**19.** $m\angle XAY$  36    **20.** $m\angle ZAW$  108

**21.** $m\angle YAZ$  36

**22–25.** Complete each statement.

**22.** The sum of the measures of two supplementary angles is _180_.

**2.5**

**23.** The measure of a right angle is _90_.

**24.** The measure of an acute angle is _____ 90.  Less than

**25.** The measure of an obtuse angle is _____ 90.  Greater than

**26.** $m\angle A = 23$ and $m\angle C = 77$. Are $\angle A$ and $\angle C$ complementary? Why?  No; $m\angle A + m\angle C$ is not 90.

**27.** When are two lines *perpendicular*?  When they form right angles

**28.** When is line $\ell$ the *perpendicular bisector* of $\overline{AB}$?
When it is perpendicular to $\overline{AB}$ at its midpoint

**2.6**
**29.** When are two segments congruent?
When they have the same measure

**30–34.** Complete each statement with the best symbol possible.

**30.** $\angle A_2 \cong$ _$\angle A_2$_

**2.7**
**31.** If $\angle A_2 \cong \angle B_2$, then $\angle A_1 \cong$ _$\angle B_3$_.

**32.** If $\angle A_1 \cong \angle B_3$, then $\angle B_{21} \cong$ _$\angle A_{23}$_.

**33.** $\angle$ _$A_1$_ and $\angle$ _$A_4$_ are vertical angles.

**34.** $\angle A_1 \cong$ _$\angle A_4$_

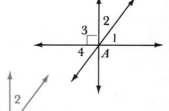

**2.8**
**35.** Name three properties preserved by slides, turns, and reflections.
Any 3 of betweenness, collinearity, distance, angle measure

**36–37.** Use the figure at the right.

**36.** What is the orientation of $\triangle ABC$?  Clockwise

**37.** Copy the figure and draw $\triangle A'B'C'$, the reflection image of $\triangle ABC$ over line $\ell$.

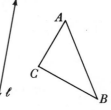

**1–5.** Write *true* if the statement is always true. Otherwise write *false*.

**1.** A segment can separate a plane.  F

**Assignment Guide**
*Written:* 1–20

**2.** An angle and its interior form a convex set of points.  T

**3.** If $m\angle A = m\angle B$, then $\angle A \cong \angle B$.  T

**4.** A line has exactly one perpendicular bisector.  F

**5.** In a plane, exactly one line can be drawn perpendicular to $\overleftrightarrow{XY}$ at point $X$.  T

**6–9.** Complete each statement with the best word or number.

**6.** Complements of ___Congruent___ angles are congruent.

**7.** If $\angle A \cong \angle B$ and $\angle A$ and $\angle B$ are supplementary, then $\angle A$ and $\angle B$ are __Right__ angles.

**8.** Every angle has a measure between __0__ and __180__.

**9.** The supplement of a $25°$ angle has a measure of __155__.

**10–17.** Use the appropriate figure.

**10.** Name two complementary angles.
$\angle EAD, \angle EAF$ (or $\angle CAB$)
**11.** Name two vertical angles.
$\angle CAB, \angle EAF$ (or $\angle BAF, \angle CAE$)
**12.** Name two angles supplementary to $\angle CAB$.
$\angle EAC, \angle FAB$
**13.** Name a line and a ray that are perpendicular.
$\overleftrightarrow{AD} \perp \overrightarrow{FC}$ (or $\overrightarrow{FA}$ or $\overrightarrow{AC}$)
**14.** Find $m\angle EAF$.  65  **15.** Find $m\angle FAB$.  115

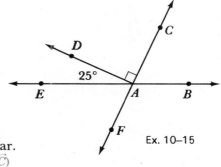

Ex. 10–15

**16.** If $m\angle RST = 110$, then $m\angle WST =$ __58__.

**17.** $m\angle RSW =$ __52__

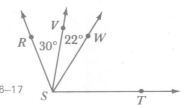

Ex. 16–17

**18.** Draw an angle whose measure is 161.

**19.** Is orientation preserved by reflections?  No

**20.** Copy this figure. Reflect $\overline{AB}$ over line $\ell$.

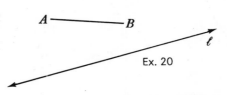

Ex. 20

# MINI-CHAPTER: MOD ART

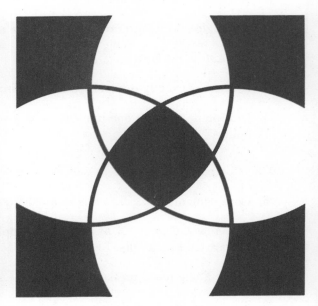

These designs contain geometric figures. Study the designs closely.
Can you pick out figures that are images of each other under reflections,
slides, or turns?

The designs on the next page are closely related to a mathematical
system. They are keyed to an addition table, mod 4.

Mod 4 Addition Table

| + | 0 | 1 | 2 | 3 |
|---|---|---|---|---|
| 0 | 0 | 1 | 2 | 3 |
| 1 | 1 | 2 | 3 | 0 |
| 2 | 2 | 3 | 0 | 1 |
| 3 | 3 | 0 | 1 | 2 |

To obtain this table, we can think of a clock with 4 numbers on it.

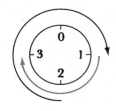

**To find 1 + 2**

Start at 1

Move clockwise
2 spaces to 3

**To find 2 + 3**

Start at 2

Move clockwise
3 spaces to 1

To make a design, give each number in the table a pattern.

0      1      2     3

Then on grid paper, place the patterns according to the numbers in the table.

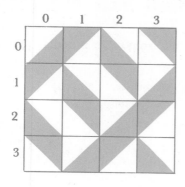

The rows of the design correspond to the rows of the table.

You can use this design, which is 4 squares by 4 squares, to get more elaborate designs. The example below is just one of the many possible designs that are 8 squares by 8 squares.

original design

design reflected over right border

design reflected over bottom border

design reflected over the bottom border and then over the right border

Instead of reflecting, as on page 81, you could use slides, turns, or some combination.

You can make original designs by:

1. using different patterns

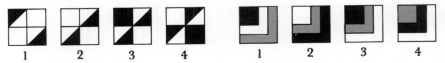

2. using addition or multiplication tables from other modular (clock) arithmetics

|   | 1 | 2 | 3 | 4 |
|---|---|---|---|---|
| 1 | 1 | 2 | 3 | 4 |
| 2 | 2 | 4 | 1 | 3 |
| 3 | 3 | 1 | 4 | 2 |
| 4 | 4 | 3 | 2 | 1 |

Mod 5 (excluding 0)
multiplication table

3. placing the patterns on different grids

kaleidoscope
grid

"curve grid"

This is the design from page 81 placed on the "curve" grid.

This is the design from page 81 placed on the kaleidoscope grid.

This row
corresponds
to the
bottom row
of the original
design.

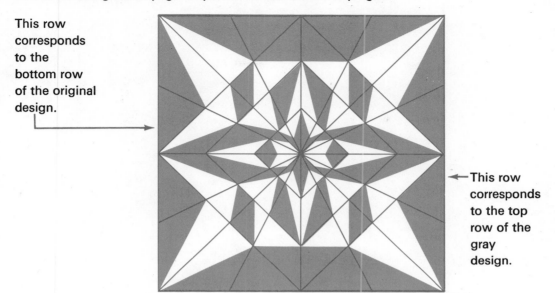

← This row
corresponds
to the top
row of the
gray
design.

## *Exercises*

1. Make a design similar to one on page 80 that has images of figures under reflections, slides, or turns.

2. Choose patterns for 0, 1, 2, and 3. Then use the mod 4 addition table to make a design that is 4 squares by 4 squares.

3. Choose patterns for 1, 2, 3, and 4. Then use the mod 5 (excluding 0) multiplication table to make a design that is 4 squares by 4 squares.

4. Use the design that you made for Exercise 2. Reflect, slide, or turn it to make a poster that is 8 squares by 8 squares.

5. Use the design that you made for Exercise 3. Reflect, slide, or turn it to make a poster that is 8 squares by 8 squares.

6. Make a design using the "curve" grid or the kaleidoscope grid.

7. Make a table for addition in mod 5. Use this table to make a design.

8. Create an original poster. Use a modular arithmetic table. Choose a pattern for each number and a grid. Reflect, slide, or turn the design that you get from the table. Experiment with colors. Most important, use your imagination.

3

Michael James Hruby

Photo Trends

# CONGRUENT TRIANGLES

In order to make a triangle that will coincide with another triangle, a carpenter will measure the sides only, not the angles. On the other hand, a surveyor might measure only one side and two angles. Why do both methods work? This chapter will answer that question.

# If-Then Statements

Many statements have the form "If ..., then ...." Sometimes the word *then* is omitted (but still understood) in these statements.

"If you were a horse, we could have shot yer!"

If you utter insults, you will also hear them. [Plautus]

If wishes were horses, beggars would ride. [Anonymous]

If you go away on this summer day, then you might as well take the sun away. [from "If You Go Away," English lyrics by Rod McKuen]

© 1977, Universal Press Syndicate.

If-then statements are very important in geometry. Every if-then statement has two clauses. The clause that follows *if* is the **hypothesis**. The clause that follows *then* is the **conclusion**.

|    | hypothesis |      | conclusion |
|----|------------|------|------------|
| If | $B$ is on $\overline{AC}$, | then | $AB + BC = AC.$ |
| If | $a + c = b + c$, | then | $a = b.$ |
| If | $2x + y = 5$ and $y = 1$, | then | $2x + 1 = 5.$ |
| If | $ab = 0$, | then | $a = 0$ or $b = 0.$ |

A statement can contain a hypothesis and a conclusion that are not stated explicitly. It is then helpful to change the statement to if-then form. You will have to introduce extra words to do this.

**Examples:**

1. *Statement:* All squares are rectangles.
   *If-then form:* If a figure is a square, then it is a rectangle.

2. *Statement:* A Volkswagen is a foreign car.
   *If-then form:* If a car is a Volkswagen, then it is a foreign car.

3. *Statement:* No elephant can fly.
   *If-then form:* If an animal is an elephant, then it cannot fly.

Diagrams can be used to picture the preceding if-then statements. These diagrams are called Euler (oil-er) diagrams after a Swiss mathematician named Leonard Euler.

**1.** rectangles / squares  **2.** foreign cars / Volkswagens  **3.** nonflying animals / elephants

To picture any if-then statement with an Euler diagram, draw two rings, one inside the other. The smaller ring stands for the hypothesis. The larger ring stands for the conclusion. In general,

Any if-then statement     Its Euler diagram

If $a$, then $b$.

## Exercises 3.1

**Assignment Guide**
*Oral:* 1–6
*Written:* Min. 7–27 odd
Reg. 7–33 odd
Max. 7–43 odd

Ⓐ  **1.** The clause that follows *if* in an if-then statement is the ⎯Hypothesis⎯.

**2.** The clause that follows *then* in an if-then statement is the ⎯Conclusion⎯.

**3.** In an Euler diagram, the smaller ring stands for the ⎯Hypothesis⎯.

**4.** In an Euler diagram, the larger ring stands for the ⎯Conclusion⎯.

**5–6.** True or False?

**5.** In an if-then statement, the word *then* can be omitted.  T

**6.** A statement can be changed from some other form to if-then form.  T

Ⓑ **7–18.** State the hypothesis and conclusion of each statement.

7–18. Hypothesis
Conclusion

**7.** If there were two birds sitting on a fence, he would bet you which one would fly first. [Mark Twain]

**8.** When poverty comes in the door, love flies out the window. [Anonymous]

**9.** If you brush your teeth with Superwhite, you will be popular.

**10.** If you keep a thing for seven years, you are sure to find a use for it. [Sir Walter Scott]

**11.** If $x = 3$, then $x^2 = 9$.

**12.** If $a \cdot 5 = 0$, then $a = 0$.

**13.** If $x^2 = 9$, then $x = 3$ or $x = -3$.

**14.** If $a = b$ and $b = c$, then $a = c$.

**15.** If $\overline{AB} \cong \overline{CD}$ and $\overline{EF} \cong \overline{CD}$, then $\overline{AB} \cong \overline{EF}$.

**16.** If $A$, $B$, $C$, and $D$ are four points in order on a line and $AB = CD$, then $AC = BD$.

**17.** Two angles are complementary if the sum of their measures is 90.
  HINT: The hypothesis is the clause that follows *if*.

**18.** An angle is acute if its measure is less than 90.

**19–26.** Change each statement to if-then form. (The statement may or may not be true!) Remember that you will have to introduce extra words.

**19.** All birds can fly.  If an animal is a bird, then it can fly.

**20.** All triangles have three sides.  If a figure is a triangle, then it has three sides.

**21.** No triangle has four sides.  If a figure is a triangle, then it does not have four sides.

**22.** No wise man ever wished to be younger. [Jonathan Swift]
  If a man is wise, then he does not wish to be younger.

**23.** A salamander is an amphibian.
  If an animal is a salamander, then it is an amphibian.

**24.** A Datsun is a Japanese car.
  If a car is a Datsun, then it is a Japanese car.

**25.** Every segment has exactly one midpoint.
  If a figure is a segment, then it has exactly one midpoint.

**26.** Every Texan is tall.
  If a person is a Texan, then that person is tall.

**27–28.** Pick the best Euler diagram for each statement.

**27.** All left-handed people are geniuses.  a

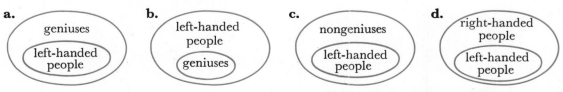

**28.** No baboon can play a guitar.  d

**a.**
not guitar players
guitar players

**b.**
guitar players
baboons

**c.**
baboons
guitar players

**d.**
not guitar players
baboons

**29.**
integers
whole numbers

**29–32.** Draw an Euler diagram to illustrate each statement.

**29.** If a number is a whole number, it is an integer.

**30.** All whales are mammals.

**30.**
mammals
whales

**31.** No planet is a star.

**32.** Every mogabump is a walapede.

**31.**
nonstars
planets

**33–34.** What if-then statement does each Euler diagram represent?

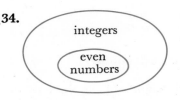

**33.**
figures contained in exactly one plane
triangles

**34.**
integers
even numbers

**32.**
walapedes
mogabumps

© **35.** Draw an Euler diagram to illustrate this statement:
All fish can swim.

**36.** Several if-then statements are listed below. Which of them seem to be true if the diagram you drew in Exercise 35 is correct?  a, d

**33.** If a figure is a triangle, then it is contained in exactly one plane.

**34.** If a number is even, then it is an integer.

**a.** If an animal is a fish, it can swim.

**b.** If an animal is not a fish, it cannot swim.

**c.** If an animal can swim, it is a fish.

**d.** If an animal cannot swim, it is not a fish.

**35.**
swimmers
fish

**37–38.** Decide if the following arguments are correct or incorrect. If incorrect, give a reason.

**37.** If you live in Chicago, you live in Illinois.
Martine does not live in Illinois.
Therefore, Martine does not live in Chicago.  Correct

**38.** If you can vote in Kentucky, you must be 18 or older.
Joe cannot vote in Kentucky.
Therefore, Joe is not yet 18. *Incorrect; there may also be other requirements for voting in Kentucky, such as living in the state.*

**39–40.** Sometimes two or more if-then statements form a *chain*. Use deductive reasoning to draw a conclusion from each set of statements.

**39.** If a number is a whole number, then it is an integer.
If a number is an integer, then it is a rational number.
If a number is a rational number, then it is a real number.
0 is a whole number.
Therefore, <u>0 is a real number.</u>

**40.** If a dog is named Fido, it has fleas.
If a dog has fleas, it scratches.
If a dog scratches, it needs Fly-Away Flea Powder.
My dog is named Fido.
Therefore, <u>My dog needs Fly-Away</u> Flea Powder.

**41–44.** The table below lists four other wordings that are commonly used in geometry for if-then statements. Reword each statement in Exercises 11–14 in each of the four ways below.

| If-then statement | If $a$, then $b$. |
| --- | --- |
| other wordings | **a.** $b$ if $a$. |
| | **b.** $a$ only if $b$. |
| | **c.** $a$ is sufficient for $b$. |
| | **d.** $b$ is necessary for $a$. |

**41. a.** $x^2 = 9$ if $x = 3$.
   **b.** $x = 3$ only if $x^2 = 9$.
   **c.** $x = 3$ is sufficient for $x^2 = 9$.
   **d.** $x^2 = 9$ is necessary for $x = 3$.

**42. a.** $a = 0$ if $a \cdot 5 = 0$.
   **b.** $a \cdot 5 = 0$ only if $a = 0$.
   **c.** $a \cdot 5 = 0$ is sufficient for $a = 0$.
   **d.** $a = 0$ is necessary for $a \cdot 5 = 0$.

**43. a.** $x = 3$ or $x = -3$ if $x^2 = 9$.
   **b.** $x^2 = 9$ only if $x = 3$ or $x = -3$.
   **c.** $x^2 = 9$ is sufficient for $x = 3$ or $x = -3$.
   **d.** $x = 3$ or $x = -3$ is necessary for $x^2 = 9$.

**44. a.** $a = c$ if $a = b$ and $b = c$.
   **b.** $a = b$ and $b = c$ only if $a = c$.
   **c.** $a = b$ and $b = c$ is sufficient for $a = c$.
   **d.** $a = c$ is necessary for $a = b$ and $b = c$.

## ◼ Pick a Category ◼

Choose one of the following categories:

Newspapers      Magazines      Novels      Poetry

In your library find five if-then statements used in your chosen category. Give the source of each statement, listing the name of the author and the name of the newspaper, magazine (and article), novel, or poem.

# 3.2 Proofs

In Chapters 1 and 2, we often used *reasoning* to arrive at a theorem. Actually, we were giving *proofs* of the theorems. A *proof* is just a setting forth of the reasoning that leads from a hypothesis to a conclusion. The proofs in Chapters 1 and 2 were written in paragraph form.

In geometry, we more often use **two-column proofs.** In this method, our reasoning is still the same. But now we write a list of statements and then give a reason for each statement.

The following example illustrates a two-column proof of this statement: If point $R$ is between points $P$ and $T$, then $PR = PT - RT$.

**Suggested Class Time**

| Course | Min. | Reg. | Max. |
|--------|------|------|------|
| Days | 1 | 1 | 1 |

**Example 1:**

Given: Point $R$ is between points $P$ and $T$.

Prove: $PR = PT - RT$

Proof:

| STATEMENTS | REASONS |
|------------|---------|
| 1. $R$ is between $P$ and $T$. | 1. Given |
| 2. $PR + RT = PT$ | 2. Definition of between |
| 3. $PR = PT - RT$ | 3. Subtract $RT$ from both sides. |

In proving an if-then statement, the hypothesis is labeled as *Given*. The conclusion is labeled *Prove*. A figure is drawn for a proof to show the facts given in the hypothesis. (An accurate, neatly drawn figure can be a big help.) The reason listed for each statement is always one of the following:

Given (facts provided in the hypothesis)

A postulate ⎫

A definition ⎬ including those from algebra, as in step 3 above

A previously proved theorem ⎭

**Example 2:**

Given: $B$ is between $A$ and $C$,
  $C$ is between $B$ and $D$,
  $AB = CD$

Prove: $AC = BD$

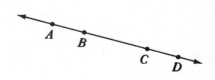

**Proof:**

| STATEMENTS | REASONS |
|---|---|
| 1. $AB = CD$ | 1. Given |
| 2. $AB + BC = BC + CD$ | 2. Add $BC$ to both sides. |
| 3. $B$ is between $A$ and $C$, $C$ is between $B$ and $D$. | 3. Given |
| 4. $AB + BC = AC$, $BC + CD = BD$ | 4. Definition of between |
| 5. $AC = BD$ | 5. Substitute from step 4 into step 2 ($AC$ for $AB + BC$ and $BD$ for $BC + CD$). |

# Exercises 3.2

Ⓐ **1–6.** Complete the following sentences:

**Assignment Guide**
*Oral:* 1–6
*Written:* Min. 7–16
Reg. 7–24
Max. 7–25

1. A <u>Proof</u> is a setting forth of the reasoning that leads from a hypothesis to a conclusion.

2. In proving an if-then statement, the _____ is labeled *Given*, and the _____ is labeled *Prove*. Hypothesis; conclusion

3. In writing a proof, it is helpful to draw a <u>Figure</u>.

4. A two-column proof has one column for _____ and another for _____. Statements; reasons

5. What types of reasons can be used in a two-column proof?
   Given facts, postulates, definitions, previously proved theorems

6. By the definition of between, if $B$ is between $A$ and $C$, then $AB + \underline{\phantom{BC}}^{BC} = AC$.

Ⓑ **7–24.** Give the reasons needed to complete each proof.

**Given:** $B$ is between $A$ and $C$, $AB = AD$, $DB = BC$

**Prove:** $AD + DB = AC$

**Proof:**

| STATEMENTS | REASONS |
|---|---|
| 1. $B$ is between $A$ and $C$. | 1. __**7.**__ Given |
| 2. $AB + BC = AC$ | 2. __**8.**__ Definition of between |
| 3. $AB = AD$, $DB = BC$ | 3. __**9.**__ Given |
| 4. $AD + DB = AC$ | 4. __**10.**__ Substitute from step 3 into step 2. |

Given: $B$ is between $A$ and $C$,
$\quad\quad\ $ $C$ is between $B$ and $D$,
$\quad\quad\ $ $AC = BD$

Prove: $AB = CD$

| Proof:  STATEMENTS | REASONS |
|---|---|
| 1. $AC = BD$ | 1. **11.** Given |
| 2. $AC - BC = BD - BC$ | 2. **12.** Subtract $BC$ from both sides. |
| 3. $B$ is between $A$ and $C$, $C$ is between $B$ and $D$. | 3. **13.** Given |
| 4. $AB + BC = AC$, $\quad BC + CD = BD$ | 4. **14.** Def. of between |
| 5. $AB = AC - BC$, $\quad CD = BD - BC$ | 5. **15.** Subtract $BC$ from both sides. |
| 6. $AB = CD$ | 6. **16.** Substitution (steps 2 and 5) |

Given: $\angle 1$ and $\angle 2$ are vertical angles,
$\quad\quad\ $ $\angle 1$ and $\angle 2$ are supplementary.

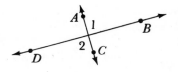

Prove: $\overline{AC} \perp \overline{DB}$

| Proof:  STATEMENTS | REASONS |
|---|---|
| 1. $\angle 1$ and $\angle 2$ are vertical angles. | 1. **17.** Given |
| 2. $m\angle 1 = m\angle 2$ | 2. **18.** Vertical angles are congruent. |
| 3. $\angle 1$ and $\angle 2$ are supplementary. | 3. **19.** Given |
| 4. $m\angle 1 + m\angle 2 = 180$ | 4. **20.** Def. of supplementary angles |
| 5. $m\angle 1 + m\angle 1 = 180$ | 5. **21.** Substitution (steps 2 and 4) |
| 6. $2m\angle 1 = 180$ | 6. **22.** Addition |
| 7. $m\angle 1 = 90$ | 7. **23.** Multiply both sides by $\frac{1}{2}$. |
| 8. $\overline{AC} \perp \overline{DB}$ | 8. **24.** Definition of perpendicular |

25. 1. $Q$ is between $P$ and $R$. (Given)
2. $PQ + QR = PR$ (Def. of between)
3. $PQ = SQ, QR = QT$ (Given)
4. $SQ + QT = PR$ (Substitute from step 3 into step 2.)

© **25.** Give a two-column proof of the following:

Given: $Q$ is between $P$ and $R$,
$\quad\quad\ $ $PQ = SQ, QR = QT$

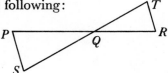

Prove: $SQ + QT = PR$

# What Are Congruent Triangles?

**3.3**

You see examples of *congruent figures* (figures that have the same size and shape) all around you. Objects that are mass-produced on assembly lines are congruent. And congruent figures are used in construction and designs. In this section, we are concerned with congruent triangles like the two triangles below.

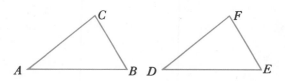

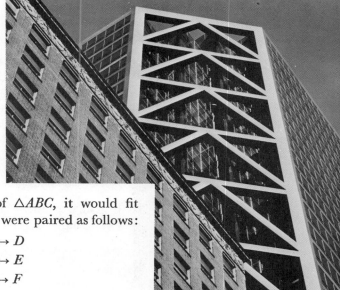

Bill Miller

If $\triangle DEF$ was traced and placed on top of $\triangle ABC$, it would fit exactly. However, it would fit *only* if the vertices were paired as follows:

A paired with D         $A \leftrightarrow D$
B paired with E         $B \leftrightarrow E$
C paired with F         $C \leftrightarrow F$

When the vertices of two triangles are paired in this way, we say there is a one-to-one correspondence between the vertices. A shorter way to write the correspondence above is

$$\triangle ABC \leftrightarrow \triangle DEF$$

There are other correspondences between the vertices of $\triangle ABC$ and $\triangle DEF$. One example is $\triangle ABC \leftrightarrow \triangle EDF$. That is,

$A \leftrightarrow E$       $B \leftrightarrow D$       $C \leftrightarrow F$

In this case, however, the triangles would not fit on top of each other. For example, $\angle A$ and $\angle E$ are not the same size.

Any one-to-one correspondence of two triangles like $\triangle ABC \leftrightarrow \triangle DEF$ leads to six pairs of **corresponding parts.** For example,

$$\triangle ABC \leftrightarrow \triangle DEF$$

| corresponding angles | | corresponding sides |
|---|---|---|
| $\angle A$ and $\angle D$ | $\overline{AB}$ and $\overline{DE}$ | |
| $\angle B$ and $\angle E$ | $\overline{BC}$ and $\overline{EF}$ | |
| $\angle C$ and $\angle F$ | $\overline{AC}$ and $\overline{DF}$ | |

**Congruent triangles** are two triangles that have the six parts of one triangle congruent to the six corresponding parts of the other triangle. For example,

$$\triangle ABC \cong \triangle DEF$$
**means**

| $\angle A \cong \angle D$ | $\overline{AB} \cong \overline{DE}$ |
|---|---|
| $\angle B \cong \angle E$ | $\overline{BC} \cong \overline{EF}$ |
| $\angle C \cong \angle F$ | $\overline{AC} \cong \overline{DF}$ |

◀ Read: "Triangle *ABC* is congruent to triangle *DEF*."

Because congruence of triangles is defined in terms of congruent segments and congruent angles, we can state the following theorems. Each follows from the similar theorems about congruent angles and segments on page 65.

**Congruent Triangles Theorems**

A triangle is congruent to itself.

If $\triangle ABC \cong \triangle DEF$, then $\triangle DEF \cong \angle ABC$. (That is, congruence of two triangles can be stated in either order.)

Two triangles congruent to the same triangle are congruent to each other.

When we draw congruent triangles, we often mark pairs of corresponding parts to show which is congruent to which. For example,

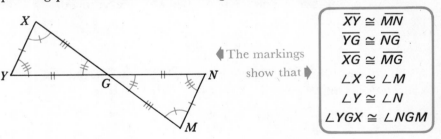

◀ The markings show that ▶

$$\overline{XY} \cong \overline{MN}$$
$$\overline{YG} \cong \overline{NG}$$
$$\overline{XG} \cong \overline{MG}$$
$$\angle X \cong \angle M$$
$$\angle Y \cong \angle N$$
$$\angle YGX \cong \angle NGM$$

# *Exercises 3.3*

**Assignment Guide**
*Oral:* 1–24
*Written:* Min. (day 1) 25–34
          (day 2) 35–37
     Reg.  25–37
     Max.  25–34

Ⓐ **1–6.** For each side or angle, name the corresponding part. $\triangle GHI \cong \triangle JKL$

**1.** $\angle G$    $\angle J$      **2.** $\angle I$    $\angle L$

**3.** $\angle K$    $\angle H$      **4.** $\overline{GI}$    $\overline{JL}$

**5.** $\overline{HI}$    $\overline{KL}$      **6.** $\overline{JK}$    $\overline{GH}$

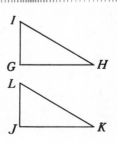

**7–12.** Complete each statement. $\triangle ABC \cong \triangle DBC$

  **7.** $\angle A$ corresponds to $\underline{\angle D}$.

  **8.** $\angle ABC$ corresponds to $\underline{\angle DBC}$.

  **9.** $\angle BCD$ corresponds to $\underline{\angle BCA}$.

  **10.** $\overline{AB}$ corresponds to $\underline{\overline{DB}}$.

  **11.** $\overline{DC}$ corresponds to $\underline{\overline{AC}}$.

  **12.** $\overline{BC}$ corresponds to $\underline{\overline{BC}}$. (That is, $\underline{\overline{BC}}$ corresponds to itself.)

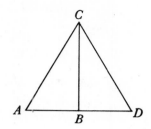

**13–18.** Complete each statement. $\triangle RED \cong \triangle CAP$

  **13.** $\angle R \cong \underline{\angle C}$       **14.** $\angle E \cong \underline{\angle A}$

  **15.** $\angle D \cong \underline{\angle P}$       **16.** $\overline{ED} \cong \underline{\overline{AP}}$

  **17.** $\overline{RE} \cong \underline{\overline{CA}}$       **18.** $\overline{DR} \cong \underline{\overline{PC}}$

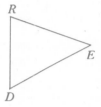
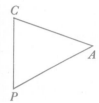

**19–24.** Complete each statement. $\triangle BUM \cong \triangle RAP$

  **19.** $\angle B \cong \underline{\angle R}$       **20.** $\angle M \cong \underline{\angle P}$

  **21.** $\overline{BU} \cong \underline{\overline{RA}}$       **22.** $\overline{UM} \cong \underline{\overline{AP}}$

  **23.** $\underline{\angle U} \cong \angle A$       **24.** $\underline{\overline{BM}} \cong \overline{RP}$

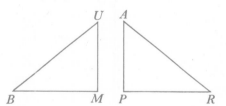

Ⓑ **25–30.** In each exercise, the corresponding congruent parts are marked. Complete each statement.

**25.**

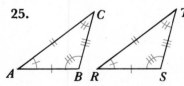

$\triangle ABC \cong \underline{\triangle RST}$

**26.**

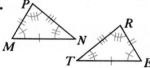

$\triangle PMN \cong \underline{\triangle RET}$

**27.**

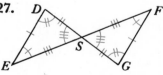

$\triangle SGF \cong \underline{\triangle SDE}$

**28.**

$\triangle ARM \cong \underline{\triangle ATY}$

**29.**

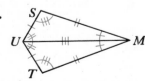

$\triangle SUM \cong \underline{\triangle TUM}$

**30.**

$\triangle HKL \cong \underline{\triangle RLK}$

**31.** List all six congruence statements concerning angles and sides that follow from $\triangle TOP \cong \triangle CAR$. $\overline{TO} \cong \overline{CA}, \overline{OP} \cong \overline{AR}, \overline{TP} \cong \overline{CR},$
$\angle T \cong \angle C, \angle O \cong \angle A, \angle P \cong \angle R$

**32.** List all six congruence statements concerning angles and sides that follow from $\triangle PQR \cong \triangle STV$. $\overline{PQ} \cong \overline{ST}, \overline{QR} \cong \overline{TV}, \overline{PR} \cong \overline{SV},$
$\angle P \cong \angle S, \angle Q \cong \angle T, \angle R \cong \angle V$

**33.** The congruence statement $\triangle PAL \cong \triangle KUH$ can be stated correctly in five other ways. One way is $\triangle LAP \cong \triangle HUK$. Name the other four ways. $\triangle PLA \cong \triangle KHU, \triangle ALP \cong \triangle UHK,$
$\triangle APL \cong \triangle UKH, \triangle LPA \cong \triangle HKU$

**34.** Name the congruence statement $\triangle TOL \cong \triangle NES$ correctly in five other ways. $\triangle LOT \cong \triangle SEN, \triangle TLO \cong \triangle NSE,$
$\triangle OLT \cong \triangle ESN, \triangle OTL \cong \triangle ENS, \triangle LTO \cong \triangle SNE$

© **35–37.** *Activities:* Use strips of cardboard (about 1 centimeter wide) and metal fasteners to make three models of triangles as follows:

**35.** Use three strips, making the distances between the fastening holes 14, 10, and 7 centimeters.

Fasten to form a triangle. ▶

Compare your model with those of your classmates. Are they congruent? Yes

**36.** Use two strips, making the distances between the fastening holes 16 and 12 centimeters. Fasten at one vertex and make the angle between the strips 40°.

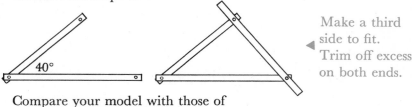

Make a third side to fit. Trim off excess on both ends.

Compare your model with those of your classmates. Are they congruent? Yes

**37.** Use one strip, making the distance between the holes 20 centimeters. Use two other strips of sufficient lengths to meet after the angles are measured as follows:

Fasten here and trim off excess.

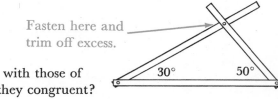

Compare your model with those of your classmates. Are they congruent?
Yes

# Postulates About Congruent Triangles

When two triangles are congruent, there are six pairs of congruent parts. However, you can tell two triangles are congruent without knowing that all six pairs of corresponding parts are congruent. The following postulates indicate conditions that result in congruent triangles.

Suggested Class Time

| Course | Min. | Reg. | Max. |
|--------|------|------|------|
| Days   | 1    | 1    | 1    |

**SSS
Postulate**

> **Side-Side-Side Postulate:** If three sides of one triangle are congruent to the corresponding sides of another triangle, the triangles are congruent.

**Example 1:**

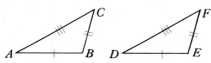

Given: $\overline{AB} \cong \overline{DE}$, $\overline{BC} \cong \overline{EF}$,
$\overline{AC} \cong \overline{DF}$

$\triangle ABC \cong \triangle DEF$ by the
SSS Postulate.

To state the next two postulates, it will be helpful to use the terms **included angle** and **included side**.

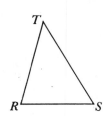

included angles ▶
$\left\{\begin{array}{l}\angle R \text{ is included between } \overline{RT} \text{ and } \overline{RS}. \\ \angle S \text{ is included between } \overline{SR} \text{ and } \overline{ST}. \\ \angle T \text{ is included between } \overline{TR} \text{ and } \overline{TS}.\end{array}\right.$

included sides ▶
$\left\{\begin{array}{l}\overline{RS} \text{ is included between } \angle R \text{ and } \angle S. \\ \overline{ST} \text{ is included between } \angle S \text{ and } \angle T. \\ \overline{RT} \text{ is included between } \angle R \text{ and } \angle T.\end{array}\right.$

**SAS
Postulate**

> **Side-Angle-Side Postulate:** If two sides and the included angle of one triangle are congruent to the corresponding parts of another triangle, the triangles are congruent.

**Example 2:**

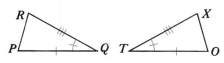

Given: $\overline{PQ} \cong \overline{OT}$, $\overline{QR} \cong \overline{TX}$,
$\angle Q \cong \angle T$

$\triangle PQR \cong \triangle OTX$ by the
SAS Postulate.

**ASA
Postulate**

> **Angle-Side-Angle Postulate:** If two angles and the included side of one triangle are congruent to the corresponding parts of another triangle, the triangles are congruent.

**Example 3:**

Given: $\angle H \cong \angle X$,  $\angle T \cong \angle S$,
$\overline{HT} \cong \overline{XS}$

$\triangle HTA \cong \triangle XSO$ by the ASA Postulate.

Two triangles cannot be proved congruent by **angle-angle-angle** or by **side-side-angle**. The figures below show why.

AAA

SSA

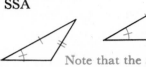

Note that the **angle** is not included between the sides.

# Exercises 3.4

Ⓐ **1–3.** What does each abbreviation stand for?

**Assignment Guide**
*Oral:* 1–6
*Written:* 7–22; Quiz, p. 101
*Constructions:* 23–30

**1. SAS Postulate**
Side-Angle-Side

**2. ASA Postulate**
Angle-Side-Angle

**3. SSS Postulate**
Side-Side-Side

**4–6.** Which postulate lets us conclude that the triangles are congruent?

**4.**

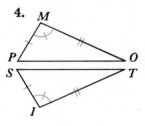

**5.**

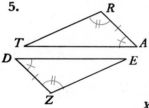

**6.**

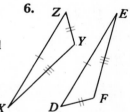

$\triangle MOP \cong \triangle ITS$
SAS Postulate

$\triangle RTA \cong \triangle ZED$
ASA Postulate

$\triangle XYZ \cong \triangle EFD$
SSS Postulate

Ⓑ **7–14.** Are the triangles congruent? If so, write a correct congruence statement like $\triangle GFE \cong \triangle KHE$ and give the correct postulate as SSS, SAS, or ASA. If not, write *not congruent*.

**7.** $\triangle GFE \cong \triangle KHE$; SAS

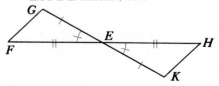

**8.** $\triangle LNM \cong \triangle LTM$; SSS

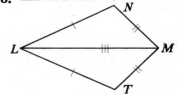

**9.**

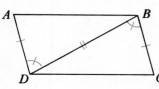

Not congruent

**10.** $\triangle TVW \cong \triangle ROJ$; SAS

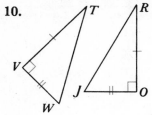

**11.** $\triangle ROF \cong \triangle MOA$; ASA

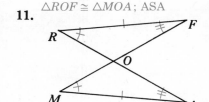

**12.** $\triangle ADB \cong \triangle CBD$; SAS

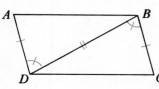

**13.**

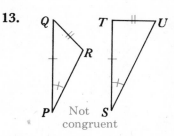

Not congruent

**14.** $\triangle VEA \cong \triangle MLA$; SAS

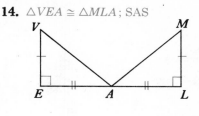

**15.** Which of Exercises 7–14 illustrates that three angles of one triangle can be congruent to the corresponding angles in another triangle without the triangles being congruent?   Ex. 9

**16.** Which of Exercises 7–14 illustrates that two sides  and  an angle *not* included between them can be congruent to the corresponding parts of another triangle without the triangles being congruent?   Ex. 13

**17–20.** Name the postulate you would use to prove $\triangle BCD \cong \triangle EFG$.

**17.** Given: $\overline{BD} \cong \overline{EG}$, $\angle B \cong \angle E$, $\overline{BC} \cong \overline{EF}$   SAS

**18.** Given: $\overline{BD} \cong \overline{EG}$, $\overline{BC} \cong \overline{EF}$, $\overline{CD} \cong \overline{FG}$   SSS

**19.** Given: $\angle B \cong \angle E$, $\angle C \cong \angle F$, $\overline{BC} \cong \overline{EF}$   ASA

**20.** Given: $\overline{BD} \perp \overline{DC}$, $\overline{EG} \perp \overline{FG}$, $\angle C \cong \angle F$, $\overline{CD} \cong \overline{FG}$   ASA

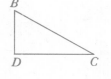

**21–22.** Each pair of triangles below has two pairs of corresponding parts marked congruent. What other information would be needed in order to use the given postulate?

**21.**

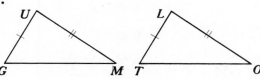

**22.**

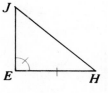

**a.** SAS Postulate        **b.** SSS Postulate
   $\angle U \cong \angle L$         $\overline{GM} \cong \overline{TO}$

**a.** ASA Postulate        **b.** SAS Postulate
   $\angle H \cong \angle D$         $\overline{JE} \cong \overline{SI}$

# construction: triangle, given three sides

| | | |
|---|---|---|
| **1.** Given:<br><br>$a$<br>$b$<br>$c$ | **2.** 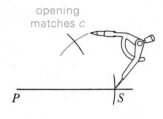<br>opening matches $a$ | **3.** 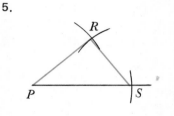<br>opening matches $b$ |
| **4.** opening matches $c$<br>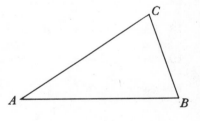 | **5.** <br>R | $\triangle PSR$ is the desired triangle. |

© **23–26.** Draw segments having the given lengths. Then construct a triangle having sides congruent to the segments you drew.

**23.** 5 cm, 6 cm, 8 cm          **24.** 6 cm, 4 cm, 4 cm

**25.** 4.5 cm, 3.6 cm, 5.2 cm          **26.** 5.6 cm, 5.6 cm, 5.6 cm

**27.** Construct a triangle congruent to $\triangle ABC$.

**28.** Which postulate guarantees that the triangle you constructed in Exercise 27 is congruent to $\triangle ABC$?  SSS Postulate

# construction: triangle, given two sides and the included angle

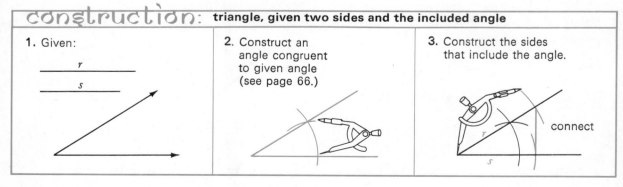

| | | |
|---|---|---|
| **1.** Given:<br><br>$r$<br>$s$ | **2.** Construct an angle congruent to given angle (see page 66.) | **3.** Construct the sides that include the angle.<br><br>connect |

**29–30.** Construct triangles with the given parts. The angle is included between the sides.

**29.**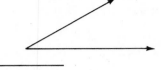

**30.**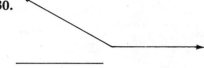

## USING CONGRUENT TRIANGLES

Suppose a carpenter wants to make a pair of congruent triangular braces. The carpenter will cut three pairs of congruent sides and fasten them to form the triangles. Which postulate of Section 3.4 is being used?
SSS Postulate

A surveyor might lay out a pair of congruent triangles as follows: A pair of congruent segments would be measured off. At corresponding endpoints of the segments, pairs of congruent angles would be measured. Which postulate of Section 3.4 is being used?
ASA Postulate

# GEOMETRY AT WORK

1. State the hypothesis and conclusion of the following: If two angles are right angles, they are congruent. H: two angles are right angles
C: they are congruent

2. Change this sentence to if-then form: All collies are dogs.
If an animal is a collie, then it is a dog.

3. Draw an Euler diagram to illustrate the if-then statement in Exercise 2.

4. Name the four types of reasons that can be used in a two-column proof. Given facts, postulates, definitions, previously proved theorems

5. List six statements about congruent angles and sides that follow from $\triangle TED \cong \triangle BIG$. $\overline{TE} \cong \overline{BI}, \overline{ED} \cong \overline{IG}, \overline{TD} \cong \overline{BG},$
$\angle T \cong \angle B, \angle E \cong \angle I, \angle D \cong \angle G$

**6–7.** Which postulate tells you that the triangles are congruent?

**6.** SSS Postulate

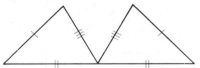

**7.** ASA Postulate

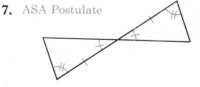

3.

dogs

collies

# 3.5 Proving Triangles Congruent

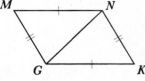

| Suggested Class Time | | | |
|---|---|---|---|
| Course | Min. | Reg. | Max. |
| Days | 1 | 1 | 1 |

With the three postulates from Section 3.4, it is possible to prove many triangles congruent.

**Example 1:**

Given: $\overline{MN} \cong \overline{GK}$,
$\overline{MG} \cong \overline{NK}$

Prove: $\triangle MGN \cong \triangle KNG$

BELVEDERE by Nat Greenwood. Reproduced through the courtesy of Field Newspaper Syndicate.

| Proof: STATEMENTS | REASONS |
|---|---|
| 1. $\overline{MN} \cong \overline{GK}$, $\overline{MG} \cong \overline{NK}$ | 1. Given |
| 2. $\overline{GN} \cong \overline{GN}$ | 2. A segment is congruent to itself. |
| 3. $\triangle MGN \cong \triangle KNG$ | 3. SSS Postulate |

**Example 2:**

Given: $\overline{AB}$ and $\overline{CD}$ bisect each other at $E$.

Prove: $\triangle ADE \cong \triangle BCE$

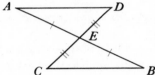

| Proof: STATEMENTS | REASONS |
|---|---|
| 1. $\overline{AB}$ and $\overline{CD}$ bisect each other at $E$. | 1. Given |
| 2. $\overline{AE} \cong \overline{EB}$ and $\overline{CE} \cong \overline{ED}$ | 2. Definition of bisect |
| 3. $\angle AED$ and $\angle BEC$ are vertical angles. | 3. Definition of vertical angles. |
| 4. $\angle AED \cong \angle BEC$ | 4. Vertical angles are congruent. |
| 5. $\triangle ADE \cong \triangle BCE$ | 5. SAS Postulate |

**Example 3:**

Given: $\overline{MP} \perp \overline{PW}$, $\overline{MT} \perp \overline{TR}$,
$M$ is the midpoint of $\overline{PT}$,
$\angle PMW \cong \angle TMR$

Prove: $\triangle MPW \cong \triangle MTR$

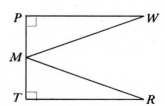

**Proof:**

| STATEMENTS | REASONS |
|---|---|
| 1. $\overline{MP} \perp \overline{PW}$, $\overline{MT} \perp \overline{TR}$ | 1. Given |
| 2. $\angle P$ and $\angle T$ are right angles. | 2. Definition of perpendicular |
| 3. $\angle P \cong \angle T$ | 3. Right angles are congruent. |
| 4. $M$ is the midpoint of $\overline{PT}$. | 4. Given |
| 5. $\overline{PM} \cong \overline{MT}$ | 5. Definition of midpoint |
| 6. $\angle PMW \cong \angle TMR$ | 6. Given |
| 7. $\triangle MPW \cong \triangle MTR$ | 7. ASA Postulate |

# Exercises 3.5

Ⓐ 1. For Example 3, give the numbers of the steps in which we proved the three parts needed before we could use the ASA Postulate.

3, 5, 6

Assignment Guide
*Oral:* 1–6
*Written:* Min. 7–20
Reg. 7–24
Max. 7–33

**2–6.** One more fact is needed to prove $\triangle ABC \cong \triangle DFE$ in each case. Tell what fact is needed in order to use the given postulate.

2. $\overline{AB} \cong \overline{DF}$, $\overline{BC} \cong \overline{FE}$, SSS Postulate
$AC \cong DE$

3. $\overline{BC} \cong \overline{FE}$, $\overline{AC} \cong \overline{DE}$, SAS Postulate
$\angle C \cong \angle E$

4. $\overline{AC} \cong \overline{DE}$, $\angle A \cong \angle D$, ASA Postulate
$\angle C \cong \angle E$

5. $\angle A \cong \angle D$, $\angle B \cong \angle F$, ASA Postulate
$AB \cong DF$

6. $\overline{AB} \perp \overline{BC}$, $\overline{DF} \perp \overline{FE}$, $\overline{AB} \cong \overline{DF}$, SAS Postulate
$BC \cong FE$

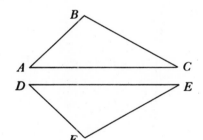

Ⓑ **7–12.** Can the triangles be proved congruent? If so, give the correct postulate as SSS, SAS, or ASA. If not, write *no*.

**7.** SAS

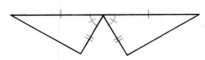

**8.** SSS

**9.** No

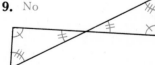

**10.** ASA

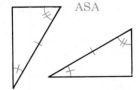

**11.** No

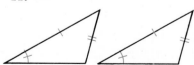

**12.** No

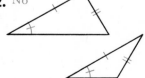

**13–32.** Give the reasons needed to complete each proof.

Given: $E$ is the midpoint of $\overline{DF}$,
$\overline{GD} \cong \overline{HF}$, $\overline{GE} \cong \overline{HE}$

Prove: $\triangle GDE \cong \triangle HFE$

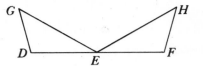

| Proof:    STATEMENTS | REASONS |
|---|---|
| *1.* $E$ is the midpoint of $\overline{DF}$. | *1.* __**13.**__ Given |
| *2.* $\overline{DE} \cong \overline{EF}$ | *2.* __**14.**__ Definition of midpoint |
| *3.* $\overline{GD} \cong \overline{HF}$, $\overline{GE} \cong \overline{HE}$ | *3.* __**15.**__ Given |
| *4.* $\triangle GDE \cong \triangle HFE$ | *4.* __**16.**__ SSS Postulate |

Given: $\angle PMN \cong \angle QMN$,
$\angle PNM \cong \angle QNM$

Prove: $\triangle PMN \cong \triangle QMN$

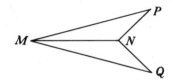

| Proof:    STATEMENTS | REASONS |
|---|---|
| *1.* $\angle PMN \cong \angle QMN$ | *1.* __**17.**__ Given |
| *2.* $\angle PNM \cong \angle QNM$ | *2.* __**18.**__ Given |
| *3.* $\overline{MN} \cong \overline{MN}$ | *3.* __**19.**__ A segment is congruent to itself. |
| *4.* $\triangle PMN \cong \triangle QMN$ | *4.* __**20.**__ ASA Postulate |

Given: $\angle 2 \cong \angle 3$, $\overline{DE} \cong \overline{GH}$,
$\overline{EF} \cong \overline{GF}$

Prove: $\triangle DEF \cong \triangle HGF$

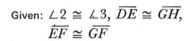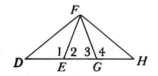

| Proof:    STATEMENTS | REASONS |
|---|---|
| *1.* $\angle 1$ and $\angle 2$ as well as $\angle 3$ and $\angle 4$ are supplementary. | *1.* If noncommon sides of adjacent angles are opposite rays, the angles are supplementary. |
| *2.* $\angle 2 \cong \angle 3$ | *2.* __**21.**__ Given |
| *3.* $\angle 1 \cong \angle 4$ | *3.* __**22.**__ Supplements of congruent angles are congruent. |
| *4.* $\overline{DE} \cong \overline{GH}$, $\overline{EF} \cong \overline{GF}$ | *4.* __**23.**__ Given |
| *5.* $\triangle DEF \cong \triangle HGF$ | *5.* __**24.**__ SAS Postulate |

Given: $EC = DA$, $\overline{RE} \perp \overline{EA}$,
$\overline{BA} \perp \overline{EA}$, $\overline{RE} \cong \overline{AB}$

Prove: $\triangle RED \cong \triangle BAC$

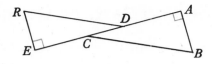

| Proof: STATEMENTS | REASONS |
|---|---|
| 1. $EC = DA$ | 1. **25.** Given |
| 2. $EC + CD = CD + DA$ | 2. **26.** Add $CD$ to both sides. |
| 3. $ED = EC + CD$, $CA = CD + DA$ | 3. Definition of between |
| 4. $ED = CA$ | 4. **27.** Substitution |
| 5. $\overline{ED} \cong \overline{CA}$ | 5. **28.** Def. of congruent segments |
| 6. $\overline{RE} \perp \overline{EA}$, $\overline{BA} \perp \overline{EA}$ | 6. Given |
| 7. $\angle E$ and $\angle A$ are right angles. | 7. **29.** Def. of perpendicular |
| 8. $\angle E \cong \angle A$ | 8. **30.** Right angles are congruent. |
| 9. $\overline{RE} \cong \overline{AB}$ | 9. **31.** Given |
| 10. $\triangle RED \cong \triangle BAC$ | 10. **32.** SAS Postulate |

ⓒ **33–34.** Write a two-column proof for each of the following:

**33.** Given: $\overline{RW} \perp \overline{TS}$, $W$ is the midpoint of $\overline{TS}$.

Prove: $\triangle RWS \cong \triangle RWT$

**34.** Given: $\angle BKE \cong \angle CKE$,
$\angle BER \cong \angle CER$

Prove: $\triangle BKE \cong \triangle CKE$

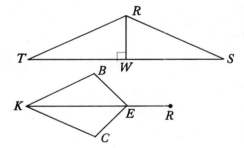

33. 1. $\overline{RW} \perp \overline{TS}$ (Given)
2. $\angle RWT$, $\angle RWS$ are right angles. (Definition of perpendicular)
3. $\angle RWT \cong \angle RWS$ (Right angles are congruent.)
4. $W$ is the midpoint of $\overline{TS}$. (Given)
5. $\overline{WT} \cong \overline{WS}$ (Definition of midpoint)
6. $\overline{WR} \cong \overline{WR}$ (Segment is congruent to itself.)
7. $\triangle RWS \cong \triangle RWT$ (SAS Postulate)

34. 1. $\angle BKE \cong \angle CKE$, $\angle BER \cong \angle CER$ (Given)
2. $\angle BER$, $\angle BEK$ are supplementary, as are $\angle CER$ and $\angle CEK$. (Supplement Post.)
3. $\angle BEK \cong \angle CEK$ (Supplements of congruent angles are congruent.)
4. $\overline{KE} \cong \overline{KE}$ (Segment is congruent to itself.)
5. $\triangle BKE \cong \triangle CKE$ (ASA Postulate)

## USING SAS

An artist, drafter, or geometry student often uses the SAS Postulate without even being aware of it. For example,

given segment

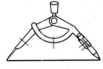

a congruent segment

Note that the legs of the compass need not be congruent to each other.

# GEOMETRY AT WORK

Grant Heilman

## 3.6 Corresponding Parts of Congruent Triangles

Often we can prove that two triangles are congruent by SSS, SAS, or ASA. Then we can use the definition of congruent triangles to prove that other parts of these triangles are also congruent. When we use the definition of congruent triangles in this way, we say

Corresponding parts of congruent triangles are congruent. (Abbreviation: Corres. parts of ≅ △s are ≅.)

**Example 1:**

Given: ∠1 ≅ ∠2,
        ∠3 ≅ ∠4

Prove: $\overline{FH} \cong \overline{KG}$

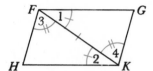

**Proof:**

| STATEMENTS | REASONS |
|---|---|
| 1. ∠1 ≅ ∠2 | 1. Given |
| 2. ∠3 ≅ ∠4 | 2. Given |
| 3. $\overline{FK} \cong \overline{FK}$ | 3. A segment is congruent to itself. |
| 4. △FKH ≅ △KFG | 4. ASA Postulate |
| 5. $\overline{FH} \cong \overline{KG}$ | 5. Corres. parts of ≅ △s are ≅. |

## Suggested Class Time

| Course | Min. | Reg. | Max. |
|---|---|---|---|
| Days | 1 | 1 | 1 |

**Example 2:**

Given: $\overline{AB}$ and $\overline{CD}$ bisect each other at E.

Prove: $\overline{AD} \cong \overline{BC}$

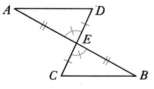

**Proof:**

| STATEMENTS | REASONS |
|---|---|
| 1. $\overline{AB}$ and $\overline{CD}$ bisect at E. | 1. Given |
| 2. $\overline{AE} \cong \overline{EB}$ and $\overline{CE} \cong \overline{ED}$ | 2. Definition of bisect |
| 3. ∠AED and ∠BEC are vertical angles. | 3. Definition of vertical angles |
| 4. ∠AED ≅ ∠BEC | 4. Vertical angles are congruent. |
| 5. △ADE ≅ △BCE | 5. SAS Postulate |
| 6. $\overline{AD} \cong \overline{BC}$ | 6. Corres. parts of ≅ △s are ≅. |

Ⓐ **1–2.** In order to prove $\overline{AB} \cong \overline{CD}$ in each exercise, which two triangles would you first have to prove congruent? By which postulate?

**1.**

$\triangle ADC \cong \triangle CBA$; SAS Postulate

**2.**

$\triangle AEB \cong \triangle DEC$; SAS Postulate

**3.** After you prove the triangles congruent in Exercise 1, what reason would you give for $\overline{AB} \cong \overline{CD}$?   Corres. parts of $\cong$ $\triangle$s are $\cong$.

**4.** After you prove the triangles congruent in Exercise 2, could you say $\angle A \cong \angle CDE$? For what reason?   Yes; *same as Ex. 3*

Ⓑ **5–24.** Supply the missing reasons in each proof.

Given: $\overline{RE} \cong \overline{WT}$, $\overline{ES} \cong \overline{TM}$,
$\quad\quad RM \doteq SW$

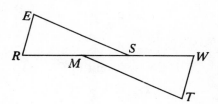

Prove: $\angle E \cong \angle T$

**Proof:**

| STATEMENTS | | REASONS |
|---|---|---|
| 1. $RM = SW$ | 1. **5.** | Given |
| 2. $RM + MS = MS + SW$ | 2. **6.** | Add $MS$ to both sides. |
| 3. $RS = RM + MS$, $MW = MS + SW$ | 3. **7.** | Definition of between |
| 4. $RS = MW$ | 4. **8.** | Substitution (steps 2 and 3) |
| 5. $\overline{RS} \cong \overline{MW}$ | 5. **9.** | Def. of congruent segments |
| 6. $\overline{RE} \cong \overline{WT}$, $\overline{ES} \cong \overline{TM}$ | 6. **10.** | Given |
| 7. $\triangle RES \cong \triangle WTM$ | 7. **11.** | SSS Postulate |
| 8. $\angle E \cong \angle T$ | 8. **12.** | Corres. parts of $\cong$ $\triangle$s are $\cong$. |

**25.**
1. $\overline{AC} \perp \overline{BD}$, $B$ is midpoint of $\overline{AC}$. (Given)
2. $\angle ABD$, $\angle CBD$ are right angles. (Def. of perpendicular)
3. $\angle ABD \cong \angle CBD$ (Right angles are congruent.)
4. $\overline{BD} \cong \overline{BD}$ (Segment is congruent to itself.)
5. $\overline{AB} \cong \overline{CB}$ (Def. of midpoint)
6. $\triangle ABD \cong \triangle CBD$ (SAS Postulate)
7. $\angle A \cong \angle C$ (Corres. parts of $\cong \triangle$s are $\cong$.)

**26.**
1. $G$ is the midpoint of $\overline{EH}$. (Given)
2. $\overline{EG} \cong \overline{HG}$ (Def. of midpoint)
3. $\angle E \cong \angle H$ (Given)
4. $\angle FGE \cong \angle KGH$ (Vertical angles are congruent.)
5. $\triangle FGE \cong \triangle KGH$ (ASA Postulate)
6. $\overline{FG} \cong \overline{KG}$ (Corres. parts of $\cong \triangle$s are $\cong$.)

**27.**
1. $\angle 4 \cong \angle 6$, $\overline{RN} \cong \overline{RQ}$, $\overline{MQ}$ and $\overline{PN}$ intersect at $R$. (Given)
2. $\angle 3$, $\angle 4$ are supplementary, as are $\angle 5$, $\angle 6$. (Supp. Post.)
3. $\angle 3 \cong \angle 5$ (Supplements of congruent angles are congruent.)
4. $\angle 1 \cong \angle 2$ (Vertical angles are congruent.)
5. $\triangle MRN \cong \triangle PRQ$ (ASA Postulate)
6. $\overline{PR} \cong \overline{MR}$ (Corres. parts of $\cong \triangle$s are $\cong$.)

Given: $\angle 1 \cong \angle 2$, $\overline{GC} \perp \overline{CB}$, $\overline{AM} \perp \overline{CB}$, $\overline{HB} \perp \overline{CB}$, $M$ is the midpoint of $\overline{CB}$.

Prove: $\overline{GM} \cong \overline{HM}$

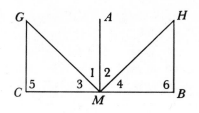

**Proof:**

| STATEMENTS | | REASONS |
|---|---|---|
| 1. $\angle 1 \cong \angle 2$ | 1. | **13.** Given |
| 2. $\overline{AM} \perp \overline{CB}$ | 2. | **14.** Given |
| 3. $\angle M_{13}$ and $\angle M_{24}$ are right angles. | 3. | **15.** Def. of perpendicular |
| 4. $\angle 1$ and $\angle 3$ are complementary, $\angle 2$ and $\angle 4$ are complementary. | 4. | **16.** Def. of complementary angles |
| 5. $\angle 3 \cong \angle 4$    Complements of congruent angles are congruent. | 5. | **17.** *At left* |
| 6. $\overline{GC} \perp \overline{CB}$, $\overline{HB} \perp \overline{CB}$ | 6. | **18.** Given |
| 7. $\angle 5$ and $\angle 6$ are right angles. | 7. | **19.** Def. of perpendicular |
| 8. $\angle 5 \cong \angle 6$ | 8. | **20.** Right angles are congruent. |
| 9. $M$ is the midpoint of $\overline{CB}$. | 9. | **21.** Given |
| 10. $\overline{CM} \cong \overline{MB}$ | 10. | **22.** Def. of midpoint |
| 11. $\triangle GCM \cong \triangle HBM$ | 11. | **23.** ASA Post. (steps 5, 8, and 10) |
| 12. $\overline{GM} \cong \overline{HM}$ | 12. | **24.** Corres. parts of $\cong \triangle$s are $\cong$. |

© **25–28.** Write a two-column proof for each of the following:

**25.** Given: $\overline{AC} \perp \overline{BD}$, $B$ is the midpoint of $\overline{AC}$.

Prove: $\angle A \cong \angle C$

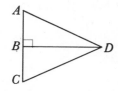

**26.** Given: $G$ is the midpoint of $\overline{EH}$, $\angle E \cong \angle H$

Prove: $\overline{FG} \cong \overline{KG}$

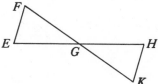

**27.** **Given:** $\angle 4 \cong \angle 6$, $\overline{RN} \cong \overline{RQ}$,
$\overline{MQ}$ and $\overline{PN}$ intersect
at $R$.

**Prove:** $\overline{PR} \cong \overline{MR}$

**HINT:** Prove $\triangle MRN \cong \triangle PRQ$.

**28.** **Given:** $\overline{AB} \cong \overline{CD}$, $\angle 1 \cong \angle 2$,
$\angle 3 \cong \angle 4$, $\overline{AC}$ and $\overline{BD}$
intersect at $E$.

**Prove:** $\overline{AC}$ and $\overline{BD}$ bisect
each other at $E$.

**HINT:** Prove $\overline{AE} \cong \overline{CE}$ and
$\overline{DE} \cong \overline{BE}$ by proving two
triangles congruent.

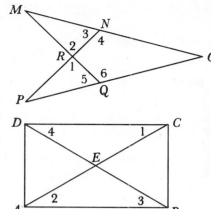

**28.** 1. $\overline{AB} \cong \overline{CD}$, $\angle 1 \cong \angle 2$,
$\angle 3 \cong \angle 4$, $\overline{AC}$ and
$\overline{BD}$ intersect at $E$.
(Given)
2. $\triangle CDE \cong \triangle ABE$
(ASA Postulate)
3. $\overline{AE} \cong \overline{CE}$, $\overline{DE} \cong \overline{BE}$
(Corres. parts of $\cong$
$\triangle$s are $\cong$.)
4. $E$ is the midpoint of
$\overline{AC}$ and $\overline{BD}$. (Def.
of midpoint)
5. $\overline{AC}$ and $\overline{BD}$ bisect
each other at $E$.
(Def. of bisect)

**29.** An observer in a lighthouse tower sights
down at a boat with an instrument called
a clinometer. $\angle SCB$ is measured as $50°$.
Then the observer sights at a $50°$ angle
toward shore until he locates an object at
$A$ that he knows is 120 meters away from $B$.
How far is the boat from $B$? With what
postulate can you justify your answer?

120 m; SAS Post.

Courtesy American Airlines

**30.** The distance between two points $A$ and $B$ can sometimes be found
as follows: Drive a stake at a convenient point $C$. Sight along $\overline{AC}$
and measure off to get $\overline{CE} \cong \overline{AC}$. In the same way, sight along $\overline{BC}$
to get $\overline{BC} \cong \overline{CF}$. Why is $\overline{AB} \cong \overline{EF}$?

Ex. 30

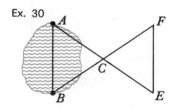

Ex. 31

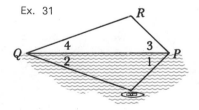

**30.** $\triangle ABC \cong \triangle EFC$ (SAS
Post.), and corres. parts
of $\cong \triangle$s are $\cong$.
**31.** If the ship is at $S$,
$\triangle PRQ \cong \triangle PSQ$ by the
ASA Post. $\overline{PR} \cong \overline{PS}$ because corres. parts of
$\cong \triangle$s are $\cong$.

**31.** An old method that can be used to find the distance from point $P$
to a ship at sea is as follows: Pick a point $Q$. Measure $\angle 1$ and $\angle 2$.
Make $\angle 3 \cong \angle 1$ and $\angle 4 \cong \angle 2$. Why does $\overline{PR}$ give the desired
distance?

# 3.7 More About Perpendiculars

**Perpendicular
Bisector
Theorem**

We can tell if a point is on the perpendicular bisector of a segment as follows:

In a plane,

a. If a point is on the perpendicular bisector of a segment, then the point is equidistant from the endpoints of the segment.

b. If a point is equidistant from the endpoints of a segment, then it is on the perpendicular bisector of the segment.

This theorem is stated in two parts which have the following form:

**Part a:** If $p$, then $q$.

**Part b:** If $q$, then $p$.

Two if-then statements related in this way (where the hypothesis and conclusion are switched) are called **converses**. Each statement is the converse of the other. A true if-then statement does *not* always have a true converse.

*Statement:* If an angle measures 90, then it is a right angle. (True)
*Converse:* If an angle is a right angle, then it measures 90. (True)

*Statement:* If an angle measures more than 90, then it is not a right angle. (True)
*Converse:* If an angle is not a right angle, then it measures more than 90. (False)

Since a converse may be true or false, proving an if-then statement DOES NOT prove its converse. We will prove part **a** of the Perpendicular Bisector Theorem here. The proof of the converse (part **b**) is covered in Exercises 7–14.

**Part a.** First we restate part **a** in terms of a figure where $\overline{AB}$ is any segment and line $\ell$ is its perpendicular bisector.

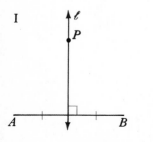

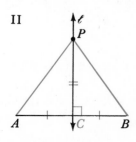

Given: Line $\ell$ is the perpendicular bisector of $\overline{AB}$, $P$ is a point on $\ell$.

Prove: $PA = PB$

[*Plan:* See figure II. Segments $PA$ and $PB$ are corresponding parts of $\triangle PCA$ and $\triangle PCB$. Show that $\triangle PCA \cong \triangle PCB$.]

**Proof:**

| STATEMENTS | REASONS |
|---|---|
| 1. Line $\ell$ intersects $\overline{AB}$ at its midpoint $C$. | 1. Definition of perpendicular bisector |
| 2. $\overline{CA} \cong \overline{CB}$ | 2. Definition of midpoint |
| 3. $\overline{PC} \cong \overline{PC}$ | 3. A segment is congruent to itself. |
| 4. $\angle PCA$ and $\angle PCB$ are right angles. | 4. $\ell$ is the perpendicular bisector of $\overline{AB}$. |
| 5. $\angle PCA \cong \angle PCB$ | 5. Right angles are congruent. |
| 6. $\triangle PCA \cong \triangle PCB$ | 6. SAS Postulate |
| 7. $PA = PB$ | 7. Corres. parts of $\cong$ $\triangle$s are $\cong$. |

NOTE: In the proof above, we picked $P$ not on $\overline{AB}$. So $\triangle PCA$ and $\triangle PCB$ are formed. However, if we pick $P$ on $\overline{AB}$, then $P$ must be the midpoint $C$, and $PA = PB$ by definition of midpoint.

A **corollary** is a theorem that is closely related to and easily proved from another theorem. The next theorem is therefore a corollary. Its proof is covered in Exercises 15–17.

 In a plane, two points that are equidistant from the endpoints of a segment determine the perpendicular bisector of the segment.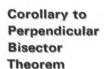

**Corollary to Perpendicular Bisector Theorem**

## Exercises 3.7

**Assignment Guide**
*Oral:* 1–6
*Written:* Min. 7–17
Reg. 7–20
Max. 7–20; 24
*Constructions:* 21–23

Ⓐ **1–4.** Tell whether each if-then statement is true. Then state the converse, and tell if it is true.

**1.** If $\overleftrightarrow{AB} \perp \overleftrightarrow{AC}$, then $m\angle BAC = 90$.

T; If $m\angle BAC = 90$, then $\overleftrightarrow{AB} \perp \overleftrightarrow{AC}$; T

**2.** If $m\angle A$ is less than 90, then $\angle A$ is not a right angle.

T; If $\angle A$ is not a right angle, then $m\angle A$ is less than 90; F

**3.** If the corresponding angles of $\triangle ABC$ and $\triangle DEF$ are congruent, then $\triangle ABC \cong \triangle DEF$.

F; If $\triangle ABC \cong \triangle DEF$, then the corresponding angles of $\triangle ABC$ and $\triangle DEF$ are congruent; T

**4.** If $m\angle A + m\angle B = 90$, then $\angle A$ and $\angle B$ are vertical angles.

F; If $\angle A$ and $\angle B$ are vertical angles, then $m\angle A + m\angle B = 90$; F

**5.** Line $\ell$ is the perpendicular bisector of $\overline{AB}$. Find the values of $x$, $y$, and $z$.

$x = 5, y = 4, z = 9$

Ex. 5

**6.** In the figure below, $EM = 8$, $EN = 8$, $FM = 6$, and $FN = 6$. What can you say about $\overleftrightarrow{EF}$?

$\overleftrightarrow{EF}$ is the perpendicular bisector of $\overline{MN}$

Ex. 6

Ⓑ **7–14.** Give a reason for each statement in the following proof. This is a proof for part **b** of the Perpendicular Bisector Theorem.

**Given:** $P$ is a point not on $\overline{AB}$ and $\overline{PA} \cong \overline{PB}$, $C$ is the midpoint of $\overline{AB}$.

**Prove:** $P$ is on the perpendicular bisector of $\overline{AB}$.

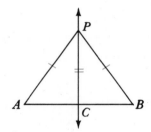

| Proof: STATEMENTS | REASONS |
|---|---|
| 1. $\overline{PC} \cong \overline{PC}$ | 1. **7.** A segment is congruent to itself. |
| 2. $\overline{PA} \cong \overline{PB}$, $C$ is the midpoint of $\overline{AB}$. | 2. **8.** Given |
| 3. $\overline{AC} \cong \overline{CB}$ | 3. **9.** Def. of midpoint |
| 4. $\triangle ACP \cong \triangle BCP$ | 4. **10.** SSS Postulate |
| 5. $\angle ACP \cong \angle BCP$ | 5. **11.** Corres. parts of $\cong$ $\triangle$s are $\cong$. |
| 6. $\angle ACP$ and $\angle BCP$ are supplementary. | 6. Supplement Postulate (p. 56) |
| 7. $\angle ACP$ and $\angle BCP$ are right angles. | 7. **12.** *Answer at left* |
| 8. $\overline{PC} \perp \overline{AB}$ | 8. **13.** Def. of perpendicular |
| 9. $\overleftrightarrow{PC}$ is the perpendicular bisector of $\overline{AB}$. | 9. **14.** Def. of perpendicular bisector |

**12.** If two angles are congruent and supplementary, then they are right angles.

**15–20.** Give a reason for each statement. Exercises 15–17 are a proof of the Corollary to the Perpendicular Bisector Theorem.

Given: $P$ and $Q$ are equidistant from $A$ and $B$.

Prove: $\overleftrightarrow{PQ}$ is the perpendicular bisector of $\overline{AB}$.

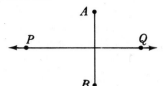

| Proof:    STATEMENTS | REASONS |
|---|---|
| 1. $P$ and $Q$ are equidistant from $A$ and $B$. | 1. **15.** Given |
| 2. $P$ and $Q$ are on the perpendicular bisector of $\overline{AB}$. | 2. **16.** Perpendicular Bisector Thm., part b |
| 3. $\overleftrightarrow{PQ}$ is the perpendicular bisector of $\overline{AB}$. | 3. **17.** Two points determine a line. |

Given: $EG = EK$, $GM = MK$, $H$ is on $\overleftrightarrow{EM}$.

Prove: $GH = KH$

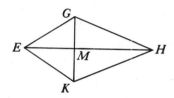

| Proof:    STATEMENTS | REASONS |
|---|---|
| 1. $EG = EK$ and $GM = MK$ | 1. **18.** Given |
| 2. $\overleftrightarrow{EM}$ is the perpendicular bisector of $\overline{GK}$. | 2. **19.** Corollary to Perpendicular Bisector Thm. |
| 3. $GH = HK$ | 3. **20.** Perpendicular Bisector Thm., part a |

**21–22.** Construct the perpendicular bisector of each segment below. Refer to the construction on page 62.

**21.** _____    **22.** _____

© **23.** Which theorem or corollary in this section shows why the construction on page 62 works? Corollary to Perpendicular Bisector Thm.

**24.** Give a two-column proof for the following:

Given: Line $m$ is the perpendicular bisector of $\overline{AB}$, $\overrightarrow{AX}$ intersects $m$ at $C$.

Prove: $AX = CB + CX$

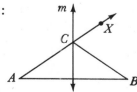

24. 1. $m$ is the perpendicular bisector of $\overline{AB}$, $\overrightarrow{AX}$ intersects $m$ at $C$. (Given)
2. $AC = CB$ (Perpendicular Bisector Thm., part a)
3. $AX = AC + CX$ (Def. of between)
4. $AX = CB + CX$ (Substitution)

# 3.8 Transformations and Congruent Triangles

From Section 2.8, you know that reflections, slides, and turns preserve distance and angle measure. These ideas can help in thinking about congruent triangles.

The following example illustrates the SAS Postulate.

**Example:** Given $\triangle ABC$ and $\triangle DEF$ with $\overline{AB} \cong \overline{DE}$, $\overline{AC} \cong \overline{DF}$, and $\angle BAC \cong \angle EDF$, show that $\triangle ABC$ can be made to coincide with $\triangle DEF$.

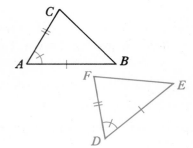

*Case 1:* $\triangle ABC$ and $\triangle DEF$ have the same orientation.

First slide $\triangle ABC$ so that point $A$ falls on point $D$. (See figure below.) Since distance and angle measure are preserved under a slide, $\overline{DC'} \cong \overline{AC}$, $\overline{DB'} \cong \overline{AB}$, and $\angle BAC \cong \angle B'DC'$.

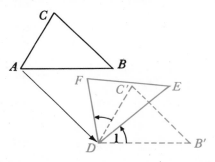

Next turn $\triangle DB'C'$ about $D$ through $\angle 1$. Then $\overline{DB'}$ will coincide with $\overline{DE}$, and $\overline{DC'}$ will coincide with $\overline{DF}$ because angle measure is preserved under a turn. Also $B'$ will coincide with $E$, and $C'$ will coincide with $F$ because distance is preserved under a turn.

As a result, $\triangle ABC$ coincides with $\triangle DEF$.

*Case 2:* $\triangle ABC$ and $\triangle DEF$ have opposite orientation.

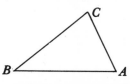

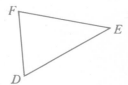

Since $\triangle ABC$ and $\triangle DEF$ have opposite orientation, we can reflect $\triangle ABC$ over any line.

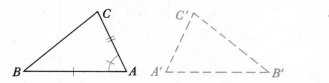

Now $\triangle A'B'C'$ and $\triangle DEF$ have the same orientation. So we can proceed just as we did in Case 1. (We will not repeat the steps here.) As this example shows, two triangles related by SAS are congruent because they can always be made to coincide.

## Exercises 3.8

Ⓐ **1–6.** Tell if a slide, a reflection, or a turn is needed to make the two triangles coincide.

**Assignment Guide**
*Oral:* Max. 1–6
*Written:* Max. 7–20

**1.** Slide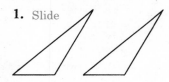

**2.** Reflection

**3.** Turn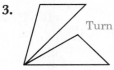

**4.** Turn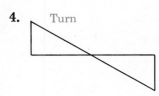

**5.** Slide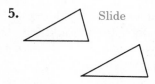

**6.** Reflection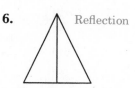

Ⓑ **7–10.** Name two transformations that can be used to make the two triangles coincide in each case. *Typical answers*

**7.** Slide, reflection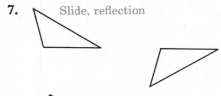

**8.** Slide, turn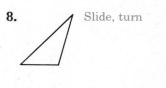

**9.** Reflection, turn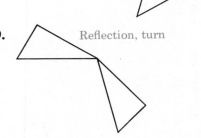

**10.** Slide, turn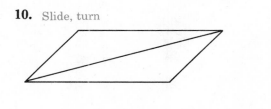

**11–18.** These exercises illustrate how two triangles that are related by SSS can be made to coincide by transformations.

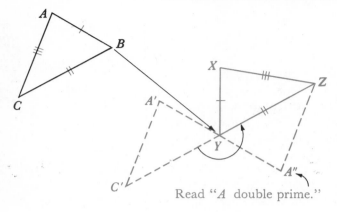

Read "*A* double prime."

**11.** Do $\triangle ABC$ and $\triangle XYZ$ have the same or opposite orientation?
Opposite

**12.** What is the first transformation (shown by the straight arrow)? Which points are made to coincide?
Slide; *B* and *Y*

**13.** What is the second transformation (shown by the curved arrow)? Which segments are made to coincide?
Turn; $\overline{YC'}$ and $\overline{YZ}$

**14.** By both transformations, side $\overline{BC}$ is made to coincide with side _____ $\overline{YZ}$ .

**15.** Compare sides $\overline{A''Y}$ and $\overline{XY}$ as well as sides $\overline{A''Z}$ and $\overline{XZ}$. Is $\overleftrightarrow{YZ}$ the perpendicular bisector of $\overline{A''X}$? Why?
Yes; Corollary to Perp. Bisector Thm., p. 111

**16.** If $\triangle A''YZ$ is reflected over $\overleftrightarrow{YZ}$, what will be the image of $A''$? Why? Will $\triangle A''YZ$ coincide with $\triangle XYZ$?
*X*; $\overleftrightarrow{YZ}$ is perp. bisector of $\overline{A''X}$; yes

**17.** Which three transformations (in order) are used to make $\triangle ABC$ and $\triangle XYZ$ coincide?
Slide, turn, reflection

**18.** If two triangles that are related by SSS have the same orientation, which transformation could be done first before repeating the process above?
Reflection

© **19–20.** Two triangles that are related by ASA can be made to coincide exactly as was done in the example on pages 114–115. Copy, and show with arrows how $\triangle ABC$ can be made to coincide with $\triangle HIJ$.

**19.**

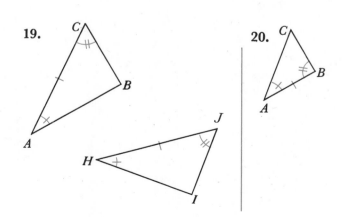

**20.**

# ART AND DESIGN

The art and design occupations include such specialized workers as architects, commercial artists, store-display workers, floral designers, industrial designers, interior designers, landscape architects, and photographers. All these workers are concerned with making products more appealing and useful and with bringing them to the public's attention.

Different art and design careers require different levels of education and training. For example, floral designers learn on the job and may not need a high-school diploma. Architects, on the other hand, need at least five years of college. Regardless of the amount or the kind of training, art and design workers should be creative and be able to communicate ideas through designs and displays. A knowledge of geometry can be a big help.

Look at the famous trademarks and symbols below. For each one, tell at least one use of congruent figures (or parts) or of transformations.

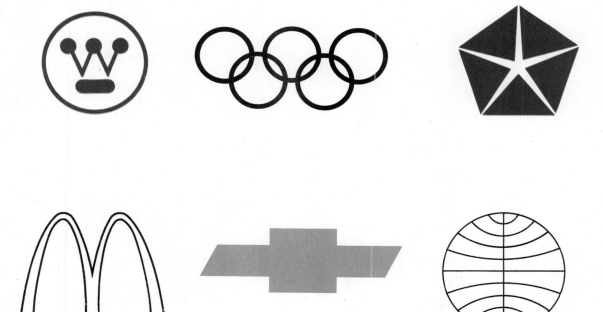

Design a symbol of your own. Let it stand for your school, your town, a club, or a team, or design a new symbol for some famous company or organization.

**Suggested Class Time**

| Course | Min. | Reg. | Max. |
|--------|------|------|------|
| Days   | 1    | 1    | 1    |

**3.1**

**Assignment Guide**
*Written:* Min. 1–24
         Reg. 1–24
         Max. 1–26

1–2. Name the hypothesis and the conclusion of each statement.

1. If $A$, $B$, and $C$ are noncollinear, then $AB + BC > AC$.
   <u>Hypothesis</u>                    <u>Conclusion</u>

2. If $x + y = 5$ and $y = 2$, then $x = 3$.

5.

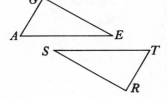

Listerine
garglers

giraffes

3–4. Change each statement to if-then form.

3. All giraffes gargle with Listerine.
   If an animal is a giraffe, it gargles with Listerine.

4. No right angle is an obtuse angle.
   If an angle is a right angle, it is not an obtuse angle.

6.

nonobtuse
angles

right angles

5–6. Draw an Euler diagram for each statement in Exercises 3–4.

**3.2**

7. Which of the following could not be used as a reason in a two-column proof? c

   **a.** Postulate          **b.** Definition          **c.** Instinct

**3.3**

8–12. If $\triangle AEG \cong \triangle TSR$, complete each statement.

8. $\angle A \cong$ <u>$\angle T$</u>          9. $\overline{AE} \cong$ <u>$\overline{TS}$</u>

10. $\overline{RS} \cong$ <u>$\overline{GE}$</u>          11. $\angle T \cong$ <u>$\angle A$</u>

12. In $\triangle AEG$, $\angle A$ is included between <u>$\overline{AG}$</u> and <u>$\overline{AE}$</u>.

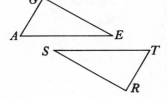

13. List all six congruence statements about angles and sides that follow from $\triangle ARE \cong \triangle YPU$.     $\angle A \cong \angle Y$, $\angle R \cong \angle P$, $\angle E \cong \angle U$, $\overline{AR} \cong \overline{YP}$, $\overline{RE} \cong \overline{PU}$, $\overline{AE} \cong \overline{YU}$

**3.4**

14–16. Which postulate could be used to show that the given triangles are congruent? Like marks are used to show corresponding congruent parts.

14. SAS                15. SSS                16. ASA

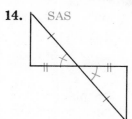          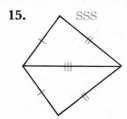          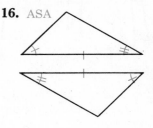

**17–23.** Give a reason for each statement in the following proofs:     **3.5**

Given: $\angle ACD \cong \angle CAB$, $\angle DAC \cong \angle BCA$

Prove: $\triangle ACD \cong \triangle CAB$

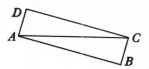

**Proof:** | STATEMENTS | | REASONS |
| --- | --- | --- |
| 1. $\angle ACD \cong \angle CAB$, $\angle DAC \cong \angle BCA$ | 1. | **17.** Given |
| 2. $\overline{AC} \cong \overline{AC}$ | 2. | **18.** Segment is congruent to itself. |
| 3. $\triangle ACD \cong \triangle CAB$ | 3. | **19.** ASA Postulate |

Given: $\overline{WO} \cong \overline{VO}$, $\overline{WT} \cong \overline{VT}$     **3.6**

Prove: $\angle W \cong \angle V$

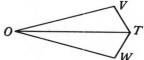

**Proof:** | STATEMENTS | | REASONS |
| --- | --- | --- |
| 1. $\overline{WO} \cong \overline{VO}$, $\overline{WT} \cong \overline{VT}$ | 1. | **20.** Given |
| 2. $\overline{OT} \cong \overline{OT}$ | 2. | **21.** *Same as Ex. 18* |
| 3. $\triangle OWT \cong \triangle OVT$ | 3. | **22.** SSS Post. |
| 4. $\angle W \cong \angle V$ | 4. | **23.** Corres. parts of $\cong$ $\triangle$s are $\cong$. |

**24.** Line $m$ is the perpendicular bisector of $\overline{RS}$. Find the values of $a$ and $b$. $a = 7$, $b = 10$     **3.7**

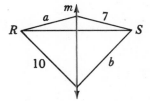

**25–26.** Tell if a slide, a turn, or a reflection is needed to make the two triangles coincide.     **3.8**

**25.**   Reflection

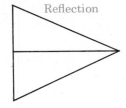

**26.**   Turn

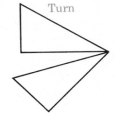

**Assignment Guide**
*Written:* Min. 1–13
Reg. 1–13
Max. 1–15

1. Change the following statement to if-then form: All whole numbers are integers.   *If a number is a whole number, then it is an integer.*

2. Draw an Euler diagram for the statement in Exercise 1.

3. If $\triangle TOH \cong \triangle PIL$, complete each statement.

   **a.** $\angle P \cong$ _$\angle T$_    **b.** $\overline{TH} \cong$ _$\overline{PL}$_    **c.** $\angle I \cong$ _$\angle O$_

**2.**

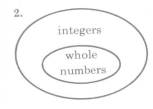

integers
whole
numbers

**4–5.** Which postulate could be used to show that each pair of triangles is congruent? Like marks are used to show corresponding congruent parts.

**4.**  SAS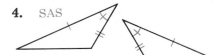

**5.**  ASA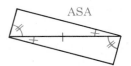

**6–13.** Give a reason for each statement in the following proof:

Given: $B$ is the midpoint of $\overline{AC}$,
$\quad\quad$ $C$ is the midpoint of $\overline{BD}$,
$\quad\quad$ $\angle A \cong \angle D,\ \angle 1 \cong \angle 2$

Prove: $\overline{EB} \cong \overline{FC}$

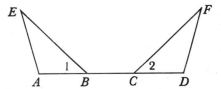

| Proof:  STATEMENTS | REASONS |
|---|---|
| 1. $B$ is the midpoint of $\overline{AC}$. | 1. **6.** Given |
| 2. $\overline{AB} \cong \overline{BC}$ | 2. **7.** Definition of midpoint |
| 3. $C$ is the midpoint of $\overline{BD}$. | 3. **8.** Given |
| 4. $\overline{BC} \cong \overline{CD}$ | 4. **9.** Definition of midpoint |
| 5. $\overline{AB} \cong \overline{CD}$ | 5. **10.** Two segments congruent to the same segment are congruent. |
| 6. $\angle A \cong \angle D,\ \angle 1 \cong \angle 2$ | 6. **11.** Given |
| 7. $\triangle ABE \cong \triangle DCF$ | 7. **12.** ASA Post. |
| 8. $\overline{EB} \cong \overline{FC}$ | 8. **13.** Corres. parts of $\cong \triangle$s are $\cong$. |

**14–15.** Tell if a slide, a reflection, or a turn is needed to make the two triangles coincide.

**14.**  Slide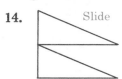

**15.**  Reflection

# ▦ Cumulative Review: Chapters 1–3 ▦

**1–6.** Refer to the figure to complete each sentence.

**Ch. 1**

**1.** A point collinear with $A$ and $B$ is ___$C$___.

**2.** The intersection of $\overleftrightarrow{AB}$ and $\overleftrightarrow{PQ}$ is ___$C$___.

**3.** The ray opposite $\overrightarrow{BA}$ is ___$\overrightarrow{BC}$___.

**4.** The intersection of $\overleftrightarrow{QP}$ and plane $m$ is ___$C$___.

**5.** If the coordinates of $A$ and $B$ are 1 and 5, the ___Length___ of $\overline{AB}$ is $|1 - 5|$.

**6.** If $AB = BC$, then $B$ is the ___Midpoint___ of $\overline{AC}$.

**Assignment Guide**
*Written:* Min. (day 1) 1–20
(day 2) 21–35
Reg. 1–35
Max. 1–35

**7–10.** Match the lettered item to its definition or description.

**7.** reasoning from examples    b

**8.** a statement accepted as true without proof    a

**9.** a statement of a hypothesis and its logical conclusion    c

**10.** reasoning from postulates and definitions    d

**a.** postulate

**b.** inductive reasoning

**c.** theorem

**d.** deductive reasoning

**11–14.** Refer to the figure for Exercises 1–6. Which postulate or theorem leads to the given conclusion?

**11.** Every point on $\overleftrightarrow{AB}$ is in $m$.
Flat Plane Post.

**12.** $\overleftrightarrow{AB}$ and $\overleftrightarrow{PQ}$ determine a plane.
Plane Thm., part b

**13.** There is exactly one point on $\overrightarrow{AB}$ a distance $AB$ from $A$.
Point Plotting Thm.

**14.** There is a point in $m$ not on $\overleftrightarrow{AB}$.
Number-of-Points Postulate

**15.** Is the exterior of a triangle a convex set? Why? No; there are two points of the set that are endpoints of a segment not entirely in the set.

**Ch. 2**

**16.** A plane separates space into two convex sets called _____. Half spaces

**17–20.** $\overleftrightarrow{AC}$ intersects $\overleftrightarrow{BD}$ at $E$.

**17.** Name the vertical angles. $\angle AED$ and $\angle BEC$; $\angle AEB$ and $\angle DEC$

**18.** Name any congruent angles. *Same as Ex. 17*

**19.** Find $m\angle BEC$ with a protractor. 130

**20.** Using Exercise 19, find all the obtuse angles.
$\angle AED$ and $\angle BEC$

**21–22.** Use the figure at the right.

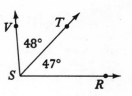

**21.** Is $\overrightarrow{ST}$ the bisector of $\angle RSV$?  No

**22.** Find $m\angle RSV$.  95

**23–25.** $\ell \perp m$ at $P$.

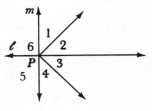

**23.** Name four right angles.
$\angle P_{12}$, $\angle P_{34}$, $\angle 5$, $\angle 6$

**24.** Name the complements of $\angle P_1$ and $\angle P_4$.
$\angle P_2$; $\angle P_3$

**25.** If $\angle 1 \cong \angle 4$, why is $\angle 2 \cong \angle 3$?
Complements of congruent angles are congruent.

**26.** If $m\angle X = 73$, find the measures of the complement of $\angle X$ and the supplement of $\angle X$.  17; 107

**Ch. 3**

**27.** Draw an Euler diagram for the following statement: If a figure is a half plane, then it is a convex set.

27.

**28.** List the six congruence statements about sides and angles that follow from $\triangle ESP \cong \triangle MOT$.
$\angle E \cong \angle M$, $\angle S \cong \angle O$, $\angle P \cong \angle T$,
$\overline{ES} \cong \overline{MO}$, $\overline{SP} \cong \overline{OT}$, $\overline{EP} \cong \overline{MT}$

**29–30.** Which postulate lets us conclude the triangles are congruent?

**29.** ASA

**30.** SAS

**31–34.** Give a reason for each statement in the following proof:

Given: $\overline{AD} \cong \overline{DC}$, $\overline{AB} \cong \overline{BC}$

Prove: $\angle A \cong \angle C$

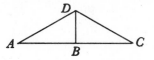

Proof:

| STATEMENTS | REASONS |
|---|---|
| 1. $\overline{AD} \cong \overline{DC}$, $\overline{AB} \cong \overline{BC}$ | 1. **31.** Given |
| 2. $\overline{BD} \cong \overline{BD}$ | 2. **32.** Segment is congruent to itself. |
| 3. $\triangle ABD \cong \triangle CBD$ | 3. **33.** SSS Postulate |
| 4. $\angle A \cong \angle C$ | 4. **34.** Corres. parts of $\cong \triangle$s are $\cong$. |

**35.** In a plane, if points $A$ and $B$ are equidistant from the endpoints of $\overline{CD}$, how is $\overleftrightarrow{AB}$ related to $\overline{CD}$?  $\overleftrightarrow{AB}$ is the perpendicular bisector of $\overline{CD}$.

# PARALLEL LINES IN A PLANE

It may seem obvious that any two lines either meet or do not meet. In geometry, however, their meeting or not meeting has important results, some of which we explore in this chapter. There are actually three ways in which lines in space may be related.

| coplanar intersecting | coplanar nonintersecting | noncoplanar nonintersecting |
|---|---|---|

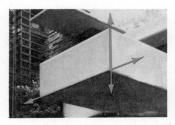 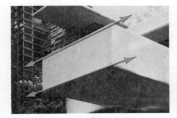 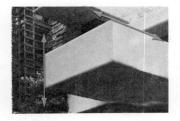

These lines are **parallel.**    These lines are **skew.**

# 4.1  The Parallel Postulate

This model of parallel lines suggests the next theorem.

**Theorem**

Two parallel lines determine a plane.

This theorem concerns two parallel lines, so we draw lines $\ell$ and $k$ to represent *any* two parallel lines. In symbols, $\ell \parallel k$.

Given: $\ell \parallel k$

Prove: Exactly one plane contains both $\ell$ and $k$.

Proof:

• By definition of parallel lines, $\ell$ and $k$ are coplanar, so there is *at least one* plane that contains them both. If there is another plane that contains both $\ell$ and $k$, then $\ell$ and some point $P$ on $k$ are in both planes. (Copying the figure and adding $P$ may help you follow this reasoning.) But, according to the Plane Theorem on page 32, this can't happen. So there is *not more than one* plane that contains both $\ell$ and $k$.

• Since there is *at least one* plane but *not more than one* plane that contains both $\ell$ and $k$, there is *exactly one* plane that contains $\ell$ and $k$.

Look again at this proof.

| | |
|---|---|
| If there is another plane that contains both $\ell$ and $k$, | This assumption is the opposite of what we want to prove. |
| then $\ell$ and some point $P$ on $k$ are in both planes. | It leads to this conclusion. |
| But, according to the Plane Theorem, this can't happen. | The conclusion contradicts a statement already known to be true. |
| So there is not more than one plane that contains $\ell$ and $k$. | So the assumption that led to the conclusion is false. (And its opposite, which we wanted to prove, is true.) |

This kind of reasoning is based on the principle below, which is also used in the proof of the next theorem.

**Principle of Indirect Reasoning**

If assuming statement $p$ is true leads to a contradiction of a true statement, then statement $p$ is false.

In a plane, two lines perpendicular to the same line are parallel. **Theorem**

First, draw line *n*. Then draw *ℓ* and *k* to represent *any* two lines perpendicular to *n*. Finally, restate the theorem in terms of the figure.

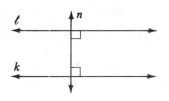

**Given:** Lines *ℓ*, *k*, and *n* are coplanar, *ℓ* ⊥ *n*, *k* ⊥ *n*

**Prove:** *ℓ* ∥ *k*

**Proof:**

| STATEMENTS | REASONS |
|---|---|
| 1. Assume *ℓ* and *k* intersect at *P*. (*It is helpful to draw another figure to show this situation.*) | 1. For an indirect proof, assume the opposite of what is to be proved. |
| 2. Through point *P* there are two lines perpendicular to *ℓ*. | 2. Given that *ℓ* ⊥ *n* and *k* ⊥ *n* |
| 3. But through point *P* there is exactly one line perpendicular to *ℓ*. | 3. In any plane containing a given line and point, there is exactly one line through the point perpendicular to the given line. |
| 4. So *ℓ* and *k* do not intersect (*ℓ* ∥ *k*). | 4. Principle of Indirect Reasoning |

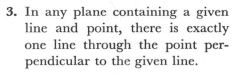

Again suppose there is a line *ℓ* and a point *P* that is not on *ℓ*. We could use the theorem above to prove that there is *at least one* line through *P* parallel to *ℓ* (see Exercises 23–26). But we can't prove that there is *not more than one* such line, so we assume this is the case.

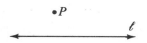

**Parallel Postulate**

If point *P* is not on line *ℓ*, there is exactly one line through *P* parallel to *ℓ*.

---

## Exercises 4.1

**Assignment Guide**
*Oral:* 1–14
*Written:* 15–28
*Constructions:* 29–34

Ⓐ **1–6.** Which of the words listed would best complete each sentence?

**a.** coplanar   **b.** noncoplanar   **c.** intersecting   **d.** nonintersecting

1. Coplanar lines may be ___c___ or ___d___.

2. Nonintersecting lines may be ___a___ or ___b___.

3. Parallel lines are ___a___ and ___d___.

4. Skew lines are ___b___ and ___d___.

5. Intersecting lines are ___a___.

6. Noncoplanar lines are ___d___.

**7–14.** True or False? A plane is determined by:

**7.** two intersecting lines  T

**8.** two skew lines  F

**9.** two parallel lines  T

**10.** a line and a point not on it  T

**11.** a line and a point on it  F

**12.** two points  F

**13.** three collinear points  F

**14.** three noncollinear points  T

ⓑ **15–18.** Match each statement with its restatement in given-prove form.

**15.** In a plane, two lines parallel to a third line are parallel.  b

**a.** Given: $\ell \parallel k$, $t$ intersects $\ell$.
Prove: $t$ intersects $k$.

**16.** In a plane, a line perpendicular to one of two parallel lines is perpendicular to the other.  d

**b.** Given: $t \parallel \ell$, $t \parallel k$
Prove: $\ell \parallel k$

**17.** In a plane, a line that intersects one of two parallel lines intersects the other.  a

**c.** Given: $\ell \parallel k$, $t$ intersects $\ell$, $t$ does not intersect $k$.
Prove: $t$ and $k$ are skew lines.

**18.** A line that intersects only one of two parallel lines is skew to the other.  c

**d.** Given: $\ell \parallel k$, $t \perp \ell$
Prove: $t \perp k$

**19–22.** Suppose an indirect proof is to be used for the exercise listed. Which assumption—a, b, c, or d—would be made as the first step?

**a.** $t$ and $k$ are coplanar.

**b.** $t \parallel k$

**c.** $t$ and $k$ are not perpendicular.

**d.** $\ell$ and $k$ intersect.

**19.** Exercise 15  d   **20.** Exercise 16  c   **21.** Exercise 17  b   **22.** Exercise 18  a

**23–26.** Complete this proof that if $P$ is not on line $\ell$, there is at least one line through $P$ parallel to $\ell$.

Given: **23.** _____  $P$ is not on $\ell$.

Prove: There is a line $k$ through $P$ such that $k \parallel \ell$.

**Proof:**

| STATEMENTS | REASONS |
|---|---|
| *1.* There is a line *n* through *P* such that $n \perp \ell$. | 1. **24.** _____ Perpendicular Line Post., p. 60 |
| 2. There is a line *k* through *P* such that $k \perp n$. | 2. **25.** _____ *Same as Exercise 24* |
| 3. $k \parallel \ell$ | 3. **26.** _____ In a plane, two lines perpendicular to the same line are parallel. |

**27.** Two uprights of a room divider are made parallel using a carpenter's level. Will a solid panel fit flat against both uprights? Why?

Yes; two parallel lines determine a plane.

**28.** Each yard line on a football field is laid out perpendicular to the sidelines. Are the yard lines parallel? Why?

Yes; in a plane, two lines perpendicular to the same line are parallel.

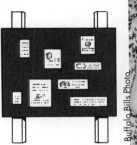
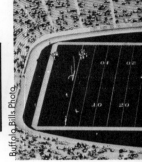

Buffalo Bills Photo

## construction: a line through a given point, parallel to a given line

**1.** Given: Line $\ell$, point *P*

**2.** Construct line *n* through *P* perpendicular to $\ell$.

**3.** Construct line *k* perpendicular to *n* at *P*.

**29–32.** Copy. Then construct a line through *P* parallel to $\overleftrightarrow{AB}$.

**29.**

**30.**

**31.**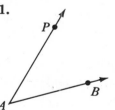

**32.**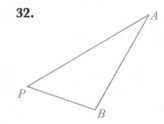

© **33.** In the construction above, what theorem assures that $k \parallel \ell$?

In a plane, two lines perpendicular to the same line are parallel.

**34.** Suppose the instruction for step 2 of the construction read: Construct line *n* so $n \perp \ell$ at any point *Q* on $\ell$. Show how to do step 2. Then write an instruction for step 3 and show how to do it.

Step 3: Construct line *k* through *P* perpendicular to *n*.

## 4.2 Alternate Interior Angles

A **transversal** is a line that intersects two or more coplanar lines at distinct points. The angles formed by two lines and a transversal are named according to position.

interior angles: ∠3, ∠4, ∠5, ∠6
exterior angles: ∠1, ∠2, ∠7, ∠8

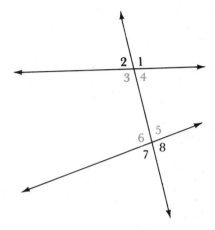

alternate interior angles (2 pairs) { ∠3 and ∠5
{ ∠4 and ∠6

alternate exterior angles (2 pairs) { ∠1 and ∠7
{ ∠2 and ∠8

If one pair of alternate (interior or exterior) angles are congruent, all four such pairs are congruent. For example, let ∠3 ≅ ∠5. Suppose ∠3 and ∠5 have measure 120. Using facts about vertical and supplementary angles, we can find the measures of all eight angles.

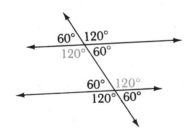

Given     ∠3 ≅ ∠5
We can show     ∠4 ≅ ∠6
∠1 ≅ ∠7
∠2 ≅ ∠8

So theorems involving alternate interior or exterior angles need to be proved for only one pair of angles.

**Alternate Interior Angles Theorem**

When a transversal intersects two lines,

**a.** If alternate interior angles are congruent, the lines are parallel.

**b.** If the lines are parallel, alternate interior angles are congruent.

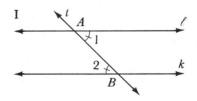

**Part a.** This part of the theorem concerns two lines, a transversal, and congruent alternate interior angles, as in diagram I.

Given: Lines ℓ and k, transversal t, ∠1 ≅ ∠2
Prove: ℓ ∥ k

[*Plan:* Make use of the midpoint $M$ of $\overline{AB}$ and a line $s$ through $M$ perpendicular to $\ell$, as in diagram II.]

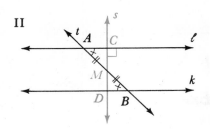

Figures like $M$ and $s$, added to the given figure, are called **auxiliary** figures. The first two reasons below explain why we can use this point and line.

NOTE: Reasons can be shortened by using abbreviations and symbols.

**Proof:**

| STATEMENTS | REASONS |
|---|---|
| 1. Let $M$ be the midpoint of $\overline{AB}$. | 1. A segment has exactly 1 midpoint. |
| 2. Let $\overleftrightarrow{MC}$ be perpendicular to $\ell$. | 2. In a plane, there is exactly 1 line through a pt. $\perp$ to a given line. |
| 3. $\overline{MA} \cong \overline{MB}$ | 3. Definition of midpoint |
| 4. $\angle 1 \cong \angle 2$ | 4. Given |
| 5. $\angle AMC \cong \angle BMD$ | 5. Vertical $\angle$s are $\cong$. |
| 6. $\triangle AMC \cong \triangle BMD$ | 6. ASA Postulate |
| 7. $\angle ACM \cong \angle BDM$ | 7. Corres. parts of $\cong$ $\triangle$s are $\cong$. |
| 8. $m\angle ACM = 90$ | 8. Definition of $\perp$ |
| 9. $m\angle BDM = 90$ | 9. Definition of $\cong$ $\angle$s |
| 10. $\overleftrightarrow{MC} \perp k$ | 10. Definition of $\perp$ |
| 11. $\ell \parallel k$ | 11. In a plane, lines $\perp$ to the same line are $\parallel$. (steps 2 and 10) |

**Part b.** This is the converse of part **a.**

Given: Lines $\ell$ and $k$, transversal $t$, $\ell \parallel k$

Prove: $\angle 1 \cong \angle 2$

[*Plan:* Use auxiliary line $n$ to form congruent alternate interior angles. Show that $n$ is really the same as given line $\ell$.]

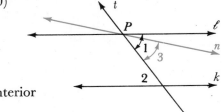

**Proof:**

| STATEMENTS | REASONS |
|---|---|
| 1. Let $n$ go through $P$ so $\angle 3 \cong \angle 2$. | 1. $\angle$ Construction Post. (p. 53) |
| 2. $n \parallel k$ | 2. Part **a,** just proved |
| 3. $\ell \parallel k$ | 3. Given |
| 4. $n$ and $\ell$ are the same line. | 4. Parallel Postulate |
| 5. $\angle 1$ and $\angle 3$ are the same angle. | 5. $\angle$ Construction Post. |
| 6. $\angle 1 \cong \angle 3$ | 6. An $\angle$ is $\cong$ to itself. |
| 7. $\angle 1 \cong \angle 2$ | 7. $\angle$s $\cong$ to the same $\angle$ are $\cong$. (steps 1 and 6) |

# Exercises 4.2 ▐▐▐▐▐▐▐▐▐▐▐▐▐▐▐▐▐▐▐▐▐▐▐▐▐▐▐▐▐▐▐▐▐▐▐▐▐▐▐▐▐▐▐▐

**Assignment Guide**
*Oral:* 1–16
*Written:*
Min. 17–31 odd
Reg. 17–31 odd
Max. 17–31 odd; 40–41
*Constructions:* 33–39

Ⓐ **1–10.** Refer to the figure. Name all angles or pairs of angles of each type.

**1.** exterior
∠s 1, 2, 7, 8

**2.** alternate exterior
∠s 1 and 7, 2 and 8

**3.** interior
∠s 3, 4, 5, 6

**4.** alternate interior
∠s 3 and 5, 4 and 6

**5.** vertical
5. ∠s 1 and 3, 2 and 4, 5 and 7, 6 and 8

**6.** adjacent to ∠1
∠s 2, 4

**7.** supplementary to ∠1
∠s 2, 4

**8.** adjacent to ∠2
∠s 1, 3

**9.** adjacent to ∠5
∠s 6, 8

**10.** supplementary to ∠6
∠s 5, 7

**11–16.** Refer to the figure above.

Meas. of ∠s:

| | 1, 3 | 2, 4 | 5, 7 | 6, 8 |
|---|---|---|---|---|
| 17. | 62 | 118 | 62 | 118 |
| 18. | 53 | 127 | 53 | 127 |
| 19. | 67 | 113 | 67 | 113 |
| 20. | 63 | 117 | 63 | 117 |
| 21. | 68 | 112 | — | — |
| 22. | — | — | 57 | 123 |
| 23. | 75 | 105 | 60 | 120 |
| 24. | 78 | 102 | 83 | 97 |

**11.** If $m\angle 1 = 70$, then $m\angle 3 =$ __70__ .

**12.** If $m\angle 6 = 120$, then $m\angle 8 =$ __120__ .

**13.** If $m\angle 1 = 70$, then
$m\angle 4 = 180 -$ __70__
$=$ __110__ .

**14.** If $m\angle 6 = 120$, then
$m\angle 5 = 180 -$ __120__
$=$ __60__ .

**15.** If $\ell \parallel n$ and $m\angle 3 = 62$, then $m\angle 5 =$ __62__ .

**16.** If $m\angle 4 = 118$ and $m\angle 6 = 118$, then $\ell$ __∥__ $n$.

Ⓑ **17–24.** Refer to the figure above. Use the given information to find the measures of as many angles as possible.

**17.** $m\angle 2 = 118$, $\ell \parallel n$

**18.** $m\angle 7 = 53$, $\ell \parallel n$

**19.** $m\angle 5 = 67$, $\ell \parallel n$

**20.** $m\angle 2 = 117$, $\ell \parallel n$

**21.** $m\angle 4 = 112$

**22.** $m\angle 6 = 123$

**23.** $m\angle 3 = 75$, $m\angle 8 = 120$

**24.** $m\angle 5 = 83$, $m\angle 1 = 78$

**25–30.** Refer to the figure at the left.

**25.** If $\ell \parallel k$, then $\angle 2 \cong$ __∠4__ and $\angle 2 \cong$ __∠6__ .

**26.** If $s \parallel t$, then $\angle 5 \cong$ __∠10__ and $\angle 5 \cong$ __∠12__ .

**27.** If $\angle 2 \cong \angle 7$, then __s__ ∥ __t__ .

**28.** If $\angle 9 \cong \angle 11$, then __ℓ__ ∥ __k__ .

**29.** If $\ell \parallel k$ and $t \parallel s$, which angles are congruent to $\angle 4$?
∠s 2, 6, 7, 9, 11

**30.** If $s \parallel t$ and $k \parallel \ell$, which angles are congruent to $\angle 11$?
∠s 2, 4, 6, 7, 9

**31–32.** A surveyor is laying out a new highway that will intersect state highways 5 and 7 as shown by the map.

**31.** If highways 5 and 7 are parallel, what size acute angle should the new highway make with highway 5? 35°

**32.** If the new highway forms a 140° angle with highway 5, are highways 5 and 7 parallel? No

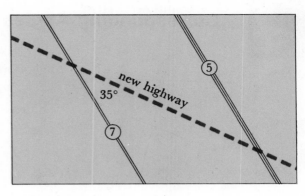

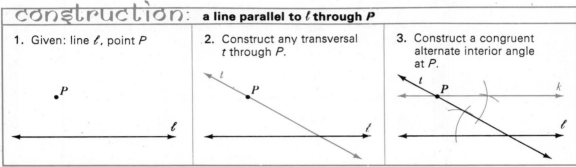

**construction:** **a line parallel to ℓ through P**

| **1.** Given: line ℓ, point P | **2.** Construct any transversal t through P. | **3.** Construct a congruent alternate interior angle at P. |

**33.** Why is k ∥ ℓ in step 3 of the construction above? Alt. int. ∠s are ≅.

**34.** Since t is any transversal through P, what is the only thing you need to consider in constructing t?                    That t intersects ℓ

**35–38.** Copy P, R, n, and s. Then construct the line described.

**35.** through P parallel to n    **36.** through P parallel to s

**37.** through R parallel to s    **38.** through R parallel to n

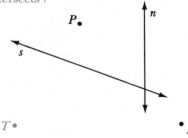

© **39.** Copy T, V, and r. Using only one transversal, construct lines through T and V parallel to r.

**40–41.** Refer to the figure.

**40.** Given: d ∥ c, ∠2 ≅ ∠4
    Prove: d ∥ e

**41.** Given: d ∥ e, ∠1 ≅ ∠3
    Prove: ∠2 ≅ ∠4

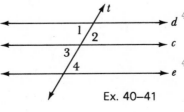

Ex. 40–41

**40.** *Plan:* Use Alt. Int. ∠s Thm., part b, and ∠s ≅ to same ∠ are ≅ to show ∠1 ≅ ∠4.

**41.** *Plan:* Use Alt. Int. ∠s Thm., part b, and ∠s ≅ to same ∠ are ≅ to show ∠3 ≅ ∠4. Use vert. ∠s are ≅ to show ∠3 ≅ ∠2.

# 4.3  Corresponding Angles

| Suggested Class Time | | | |
|---|---|---|---|
| Course | Min. | Reg. | Max. |
| Days | 1 | 1 | 1 |

At the left is shown another way to pair the angles formed by two lines and a transversal.

Suppose ∠3 ≅ ∠5.

∠1 ≅ ∠3, since they are vertical angles.

∠1 ≅ ∠5, since they are congruent to the same angle.

corresponding angles (4 pairs)

∠1 and ∠5    ∠3 and ∠7

∠2 and ∠6    ∠4 and ∠8

So most statements true for alternate interior angles are also true for corresponding angles.

**Corresponding Angles Theorem**

When a transversal intersects two lines,

**a.** If corresponding angles are congruent, the lines are parallel.

**b.** If the lines are parallel, corresponding angles are congruent.

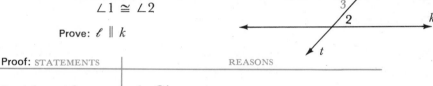

**Part a.**  Given: Lines ℓ and k, transversal t,
∠1 ≅ ∠2

Prove: ℓ ∥ k

**Proof:**

| STATEMENTS | REASONS |
|---|---|
| 1. ∠1 ≅ ∠2 | 1. Given |
| 2. ∠1 ≅ ∠3 | 2. Vertical ∠s are ≅. |
| 3. ∠2 ≅ ∠3 | 3. ∠s ≅ to the same ∠ are ≅. |
| 4. ℓ ∥ k | 4. Alternate Interior ∠s Theorem |

Part **b** of the Corresponding Angles Theorem is the converse of part **a.** It is proved in Exercise 25.

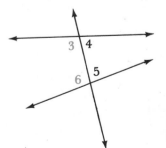

There remains one more way to pair interior angles.

interior angles on the same side of the transversal (2 pairs)    { ∠3 and ∠6
{ ∠4 and ∠5

The next three theorems are corollaries of the Corresponding Angles Theorem. They could just as easily be proved as corollaries of the Alternate Interior Angles Theorem.

> When a transversal intersects two lines,
>
> **a.** If interior angles on the same side of the transversal are supplementary, the lines are parallel.
>
> **b.** If the lines are parallel, interior angles on the same side of the transversal are supplementary.

**Theorem**

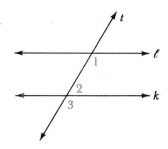

In the figure, $\angle 2$ and $\angle 3$ are supplementary (Supplement Post., p. 56). If $\angle 1$ and $\angle 2$ are also supplementary, then $\angle 1 \cong \angle 3$ (supplements of the same $\angle$). So $\ell \parallel k$, and part **a** is proved.

If $\ell \parallel k$, then $\angle 1 \cong \angle 3$ (corres. $\angle$s). Since $\angle 2$ and $\angle 3$ are supplementary, $m\angle 2 + m\angle 3 = 180$. Substituting, $m\angle 2 + m\angle 1 = 180$. That is, $\angle 1$ and $\angle 2$ are supplementary, and part **b** is proved.

Of course, if $\ell \parallel k$ and $\angle 1$ is a right angle, part **b** of the theorem above tells you that $\angle 2$ is also a right angle. That is, if $\ell \parallel k$ and $t \perp \ell$, then $t \perp k$. This proves the theorem below.

> In a plane, a line perpendicular to one of two parallel lines is perpendicular to the other.

**Theorem**

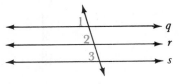

Suppose $q \parallel r$ and $r \parallel s$. Then $\angle 1 \cong \angle 2$ and $\angle 2 \cong \angle 3$. So $\angle 1 \cong \angle 3$ and, as a result, $q \parallel s$. (We can write $q \parallel r \parallel s$.)

> In a plane, two lines parallel to a third line are parallel.

**Theorem**

## Exercises 4.3

(A) **1–4.** Refer to the figure.

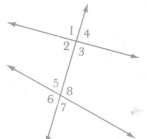

1. $\angle 2$ and __$\angle 8$__ are alternate interior angles.

2. $\angle 2$ and __$\angle 5$__ are interior angles on the same side of the transversal.

3. $\angle 2$ and __$\angle 6$__ are corresponding angles.

4. $\angle 2$ and __$\angle 4$__ are vertical angles.

**Assignment Guide**
*Oral:* 1–6
*Written:*
Min. 7–23 odd;
    Alg. Rev., p. 135
Reg. 7–25 odd; 26;
    Alg. Rev., p. 135
Max. 7–25 odd; 26; 28–30
*Construction:* 27

**5–6.** Refer to the figure.

**5.** Which statements lead to the conclusion that $c \parallel d$?

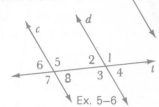

| ∠s | Meas. |
|---|---|
| **7.** 4, 5, 7 | 87 |
| 1, 3, 6, 8 | 93 |
| **8.** 9, 11, 14 | 96 |
| 10, 12, 13, 15 | 84 |
| **9.** 9, 14, 16 | 102 |
| 10, 12, 13, 15 | 78 |
| **10.** 2, 4, 7 | 72 |
| 1, 3, 6, 8 | 108 |

**a.** $\angle 3 \cong \angle 5$    **b.** $m\angle 3 + m\angle 5 = 180$

**c.** $\angle 3 \cong \angle 1$    **d.** $m\angle 3 + m\angle 8 = 180$

**e.** $\angle 3 \cong \angle 7$    **f.** $c \parallel n, d \parallel n$

**6.** If $c \parallel d$, which statements are true?

**a.** $\angle 2 \cong \angle 8$    **b.** $\angle 4 \cong \angle 7$    **c.** If $t \perp d$, then $t \perp c$.

**d.** $\angle 1 \cong \angle 5$    **e.** $\angle 8 \cong \angle 3$    **f.** $m\angle 2 + m\angle 5 = 180$

Ex. 5–6

Ⓑ **7–18.** If $\ell \parallel s$, use the given information to find the measures of as many angles in the figure as possible.

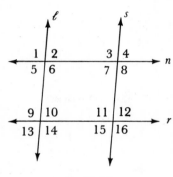

Ex. 7–18

**7.** $m\angle 2 = 87$     **8.** $m\angle 16 = 96$

**9.** $m\angle 11 = 102$     **10.** $m\angle 5 = 72$

**11.** $n \parallel r, m\angle 7 = 72$     **12.** $r \parallel n, m\angle 4 = 83$

**13.** $m\angle 10 = 90$
  $m\angle s$ 9 through 16 is 90

**14.** $s \perp r$
  $m\angle s$ 9 through 16 is 90

**15.** $m\angle 7 + m\angle 11 = 180,$
  $m\angle 13 = 68$

**16.** $m\angle 5 + m\angle 9 = 180,$
  $m\angle 4 = 76$

**17.** $\ell \perp n$
  $m\angle s$ 1 through 8 is 90

**18.** $m\angle 12 = m\angle 16$
  $m\angle s$ 9 through 16 is 90

| | $m\angle s\ 2, 4,$ $5, 7, 10,$ $12, 13, 15$ | $m\angle s\ 1, 3,$ $6, 8, 9,$ $11, 14, 16$ |
|---|---|---|
| **11.** | 72 | 108 |
| **12.** | 83 | 97 |
| **15.** | 68 | 112 |
| **16.** | 76 | 104 |

**19–22.** Use the given information to find the measures of all numbered angles in the figure.

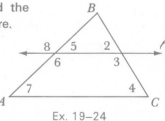

**19.** $\ell \parallel \overleftrightarrow{AC}, m\angle 4 = 60, m\angle 8 = 130$

**20.** $\ell \parallel \overleftrightarrow{AC}, m\angle 2 = 60, m\angle 7 = 50$

**21.** $\angle 2 \cong \angle 4, m\angle 2 = 80, m\angle 7 = 40$

**22.** $m\angle 6 + m\angle 7 = 180, m\angle 3 = 110, m\angle 5 = 60$

Ex. 19–24

Meas. for Ex:

| ∠s | **19.** | **20.** | **21.** | **22.** |
|---|---|---|---|---|
| 2, 4 | 60 | 60 | 80 | 70 |
| 3 | 120 | 120 | 100 | 110 |
| 5, 7 | 50 | 50 | 40 | 60 |
| 6, 8 | 130 | 130 | 140 | 120 |

**23–24.** Refer to the figure for Exercises 19–22.

**23.** If $m\angle 8 = 110$ and $m\angle 7 = 70$, is $\ell \parallel \overleftrightarrow{AC}$?  Yes

**24.** If $m\angle 4 = 85$ and $m\angle 3 = 95$, is $\ell \parallel \overleftrightarrow{AC}$?  Yes

**25–26.** Give a reason for each statement.

**25.** Given: $\ell \parallel k$

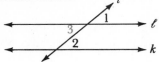

Prove: $\angle 1 \cong \angle 2$

| Proof: STATEMENTS | REASONS |
|---|---|
| *1.* $\angle 2 \cong \angle 3$ | *1.* If lines are $\parallel$, alt. int. $\angle$s are $\cong$. |
| *2.* $\angle 1 \cong \angle 3$ | *2.* Vert. $\angle$s are $\cong$. |
| *3.* $\angle 1 \cong \angle 2$ | *3.* $\angle$s $\cong$ to same $\angle$ are $\cong$. |

**26.** Given: $\angle 1$ and $\angle 2$ are supplementary.

Prove: $r \parallel s$

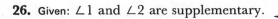

| Proof: STATEMENTS | REASONS |
|---|---|
| *1.* $\angle 1$ and $\angle 2$ are supplementary. | *1.* **Given** |
| *2.* $\angle 2$ and $\angle 3$ are supplementary. | *2.* Supplement Post., p. 56 |
| *3.* $\angle 1 \cong \angle 3$   *3.* Supplements of | *3.* *At left* |
| *4.* $r \parallel s$            same $\angle$ are $\cong$. | *4.* If alt. int. $\angle$s are $\cong$, lines are $\parallel$. |

© **27.** *Construction:* Copy $P$ and $\ell$. Then construct $n$ parallel to $\ell$ through $P$ by using corresponding angles rather than alternate interior angles.

**28–30.** Write a two-column proof of the theorem.     $P_{\bullet}$

**28.** If a transversal intersects two parallel lines, interior angles on the same side of the transversal are supplementary.

**29.** In a plane, a line perpendicular to one of two parallel lines is perpendicular to the other.

**30.** In a plane, two lines parallel to a third line are parallel.

**28.** *See figure at top of p. 133.*
   *Given:* $\ell \parallel k$, transversal $t$
   *Prove:* $\angle 1$ and $\angle 2$ are supplementary.
   *[Plan: See paragraph 2, p. 133.]*

**29.** *See figure at top of p. 133.*
   *Given:* $\ell \parallel k$, $t \perp \ell$
   *Prove:* $t \perp k$
   *[Plan: See paragraph 3, p. 133.]*

**30.** *See figure in middle of p. 133.*
   *Given:* $q \parallel r$, $r \parallel s$, transversal $t$
   *Prove:* $q \parallel s$
   *[Plan: See paragraph 4, p. 133.]*

---

Solve.

**1.** $x = 153 + 21 + 6$    $x = 180$

**2.** $93 + 27 + 60 = y$    $y = 180$

**3.** $125 + 45 + n = 180$    $n = 10$

**4.** $180 = m + 39 + 97$    $m = 44$

**5.** $180 = 67 + p + 88$    $p = 25$

**6.** $x + 124 + 73 = 180$    $x = -17$

**7.** $2a + 58 = 180$    $a = 61$

**8.** $3n = 180$    $n = 60$

*Algebra Review*

**Review this skill:**

● *solving equations*

# PARALLELS IN DRAFTING

In drafting, a T-square may be used to draw parallel lines. The head of the T-square is held tight against the edge of the drawing board as each line is drawn.

Alfa

A. Devaney, Inc.

**1.** What theorem assures that the lines drawn by this method are parallel?

In a plane, two lines ⊥ to the same line are ∥.

Another device used for drawing parallel lines is the triangle. In this method, the T-square is held as described above, and the triangle is held tight against the T-square as each line is drawn.

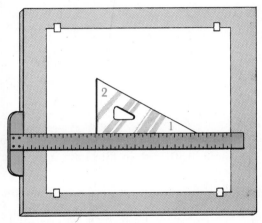

**2.** Which edge of the triangle is used to guide the pencil if the parallel lines are to be perpendicular to the edge of the T-square?    Vertical edge

**3.** Which edge of the triangle is used to guide the pencil if the parallel lines are to make an acute angle the size of ∠1 with the edge of the T-square?    Slanted edge

**4.** How can the triangle be used so that the parallel lines make an acute angle the size of ∠2 with the edge of the T-square?

By placing either of the other two sides of the triangle against the edge of the T-square.

# The Angle Sum Theorem for Triangles

You can cut a triangle from paper, tear it, and arrange the pieces as shown. This suggests the next theorem.

Alfa

 The sum of the measures of the angles of a triangle is 180.

**Angle Sum Theorem for Triangles**

Call the angles at $C$, in the figure at the right, $\angle C_1$, $\angle C_2$, $\angle C_3$, $\angle C_{12}$, and $\angle C_{23}$.

Given: $\triangle ABC$

Prove: $m\angle A + m\angle B + m\angle C_2 = 180$

[*Plan:* Use a line $\ell$ through $C$ to form three angles whose measures add to 180. Make $\ell \parallel \overleftrightarrow{AB}$ so these angles are congruent to the angles of $\triangle ABC$.]

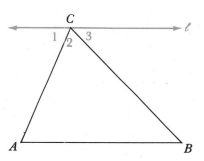

Proof:

| STATEMENTS | REASONS |
| --- | --- |
| **1.** There is a line $\ell$ through $C$ such that $\ell \parallel \overleftrightarrow{AB}$. | **1.** Parallel Postulate |
| **2.** $m\angle A = m\angle C_1$, $m\angle B = m\angle C_3$ | **2.** Alt. Interior $\angle$s Theorem |
| **3.** $\angle C_1$ and $\angle C_{23}$ are supplements. | **3.** Supplement Post. (p. 56) |
| **4.** $m\angle C_1 + m\angle C_{23} = 180$ | **4.** Definition of supplement |
| **5.** $m\angle C_2 + m\angle C_3 = m\angle C_{23}$ | **5.** $\angle$ Addition Post. (p. 53) |
| **6.** $m\angle C_1 + m\angle C_2 + m\angle C_3 = 180$ | **6.** Substitution (steps 4 and 5) |
| **7.** $m\angle A + m\angle B + m\angle C_2 = 180$ | **7.** Substitution (steps 2 and 6) |

The next theorem is a corollary of the Angle Sum Theorem for Triangles. The restatement is below, and the proof is in Exercises 2–6.

 If two angles of one triangle are congruent to two angles of another, the remaining angles of the triangles are congruent.

**Theorem**

Given: $\triangle ABC$, $\triangle DEF$,
$\quad \angle A \cong \angle D$, $\angle B \cong \angle E$

Prove: $\angle C \cong \angle F$

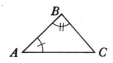 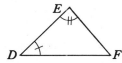

The next three theorems are also corollaries of the Angle Sum Theorem for Triangles.

**Theorem**  If one angle of a triangle is right or obtuse, the other two angles are acute.

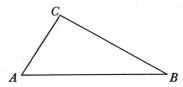

An indirect proof of this theorem is given below in paragraph form.

Given: $\triangle ABC$, $\angle C$ is right or obtuse.

Prove: $\angle A$ and $\angle B$ are acute.

Proof: Suppose $\angle B$ is also right or obtuse. Then the sum of $m\angle B$ and $m\angle C$ is 180 or more, and since $m\angle A + m\angle B + m\angle C = 180$, $m\angle A$ is not greater than 0. But this cannot be so, because the measure of any angle is between 0 and 180. So $\angle B$ is not right or obtuse, and by the same reasoning, $\angle A$ is not right or obtuse. That is, $\angle A$ and $\angle B$ are acute.

A **right triangle** is a triangle with one right angle.

**Theorem**  The acute angles of a right triangle are complementary.

Given: $\triangle ABC$, $m\angle C = 90$          (Refer to the figure above.)

Prove: $m\angle A + m\angle B = 90$

Proof:

| STATEMENTS | REASONS |
|---|---|
| 1. $m\angle A + m\angle B + m\angle C = 180$ | 1. Why? $\angle$ Sum Thm. for $\triangle$s |
| 2. $m\angle C = 90$ | 2. Given |
| 3. $m\angle A + m\angle B + 90 \doteq 180$ | 3. Why? Substitution (steps 1 and 2) |
| 4. $m\angle A + m\angle B = 90$ | 4. Add $-90$ to both sides. |

By extending a side of a triangle, we can form an angle adjacent to an angle of the triangle. The noncommon sides of these adjacent angles are opposite rays, so the angles are supplementary. Terms used to refer to the angles are shown below.

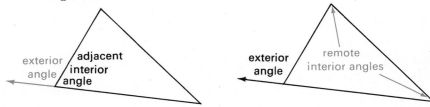

The measure of an exterior angle of a triangle is equal to the sum of the measures of the remote interior angles.

**Exterior Angle Theorem**

Given: $\triangle ABC$, $\angle 2$ is an exterior angle.

Prove: $m\angle 2 = m\angle B + m\angle C$

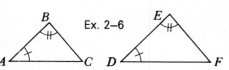

Proof:

| STATEMENTS | REASONS |
|---|---|
| 1. $\angle 1$ and $\angle 2$ are supplementary. | 1. Supplement Post. (p. 56) |
| 2. $m\angle 1 + m\angle 2 = 180$ | 2. Definition of supplementary $\angle$s |
| 3. $m\angle 1 + m\angle B + m\angle C = 180$ | 3. $\angle$ Sum Theorem for $\triangle$s |
| 4. $m\angle 2 = 180 - m\angle 1$, $\quad m\angle B + m\angle C = 180 - m\angle 1$ | 4. Why? *Subtract $m\angle 1$ from both sides of equations in steps 2 and 3.* |
| 5. $m\angle 2 = m\angle B + m\angle C$ | 5. Why? *Substitution* |

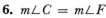 **Exercises 4.4**

Ⓐ **1.** Does the experiment with the paper triangle, on page 137, prove the Angle Sum Theorem for Triangles?

**Assignment Guide**
*Oral:* 1–12
*Written:* 13–23 odd;
    Quiz, p. 140
*Constructions:* 25–36

No (Inductive reasoning is not proof.)

**2–6.** Give a reason for each statement. You may refer to the figure or to preceding steps. (This proves the theorem at the bottom of page 137.)

**2.** $m\angle A + m\angle B + m\angle C = 180$, $m\angle D + m\angle E + m\angle F = 180$
$\angle$ Sum Thm. for $\triangle$s

**3.** $m\angle A + m\angle B + m\angle C = m\angle D + m\angle E + m\angle F$
Substitution

**4.** $m\angle A = m\angle D$, $m\angle B = m\angle E$ Given

**5.** $m\angle D + m\angle E + m\angle C = m\angle D + m\angle E + m\angle F$
Substitution (steps 3 and 4)

**6.** $m\angle C = m\angle F$
Subtract $m\angle D + m\angle E$ from both sides.

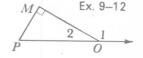

Ex. 2–6

**7–8.** Give the missing reasons in each proof.

**7.** The acute angles of a right triangle are complementary. (p. 138)
*Answer on page 138*

**8.** Exterior Angle Theorem (above) *Answer above*

**9–12.** In the figure, $\overline{MP} \perp \overline{MO}$.

**9.** If $m\angle 2 = 50$, $m\angle 1 = $ ___130___.

**10.** If $m\angle 2 = 30$, $m\angle P = $ ___60___.

**11.** If $\angle P \cong \angle 2$, $m\angle P = $ ___45___.

**12.** If $m\angle P = 40$, $m\angle 1 = $ ___130___.

Ex. 9–12

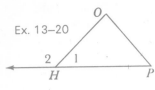

Ex. 13–20

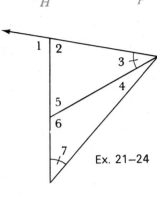

Ex. 21–24

Meas. of ∠s:

| | 1 | 2 | 3, 7 | 4 | 5 | 6 |
|---|---|---|---|---|---|---|
| **21.** | 120 | 60 | 55 | 10 | 65 | 115 |
| **22.** | 100 | 80 | 40 | 20 | 60 | 120 |
| **23.** | 108 | 72 | 40 | 28 | 68 | 112 |
| **24.** | 86 | 94 | 32 | 22 | 54 | 126 |

Ⓑ **13–20.** For each angle in the figure, find the measure if it is not given.

**13.** $m\angle P = 38, m\angle O = 70$
$m\angle 1 = 72, m\angle 2 = 108$

**14.** $m\angle 1 = 46, m\angle P = 38$
$m\angle O = 96, m\angle 2 = 134$

**15.** $m\angle O = 90, m\angle 1 = 55$
$m\angle P = 35, m\angle 2 = 125$

**16.** $m\angle O = 90, m\angle 1 = 63$
$m\angle P = 27, m\angle 2 = 117$

**17.** $\angle O \cong \angle P, m\angle 1 = 36$
$m\angle P = m\angle O = 72, m\angle 2 = 144$

**18.** $\angle P \cong \angle 1, m\angle O = 90$
$m\angle P = m\angle 1 = 45, m\angle 2 = 135$

**19.** $m\angle 2 = 127, m\angle P = 45$
$m\angle O = 82, m\angle 1 = 53$

**20.** $m\angle 2 = 133, m\angle O = 90$
$m\angle P = 43, m\angle 1 = 47$

**21–24.** Use the given information to find the measure of each numbered angle in the figure. $\angle 3 \cong \angle 7$

**21.** $m\angle 2 = 60, m\angle 6 = 115$

**22.** $m\angle 4 = 20, m\angle 6 = 120$

**23.** $m\angle 1 = 108, m\angle 7 = 40$

**24.** $m\angle 3 = 32, m\angle 5 = 54$

Ⓒ **25–26.** *Constructions:* Draw $\overline{MN}$, $\angle A$, and $\angle B$ so that $MN = 5$ cm, $m\angle A = 30$, and $m\angle B = 130$. Then construct the figure described.

**25.** $\triangle POD$ with $\overline{PO} \cong \overline{MN}$, $\angle O \cong \angle A$, and $130°$ exterior angle at $P$

**26.** $\triangle TRS$ with $\overline{TS} \cong \overline{MN}$, $\angle T \cong \angle A$, and $100°$ exterior angle at $S$

---

Quick Quiz

for Sections 4.1 to 4.4

**1–4.** In the figure, identify all angles or pairs of angles of each type.

**1.** exterior
∠s 1, 2, 7, 8

**2.** alternate interior
∠s 3 and 5, 4 and 6

**3.** corresponding
∠s 1 and 5, 2 and 6, 3 and 7, 4 and 8

**4.** interior on same side of transversal
∠s 3 and 6, 4 and 5

**5–8.** In the figure for Exercises 1–4, let $\ell \parallel k$.

**5.** If $m\angle 2 = 55, m\angle 6 = $ _55_.

**6.** If $m\angle 3 = 112, m\angle 5 = $ _112_.

**7.** $m\angle 4 + m\angle 5 = $ _180_.

**8.** If $m\angle 6 = 75, m\angle 3 = $ _105_.

**9–14.** True or False? In the figure for Exercises 1–4, $\ell \parallel k$ when

**9.** $\angle 1 \cong \angle 5$  T

**10.** $\angle 3 \cong \angle 6$  F

**11.** $\angle 6 \cong \angle 4$  T

**12.** $\angle 4 \cong \angle 7$  F

**13.** $m\angle 2 + m\angle 3 = 180$  F

**14.** $m\angle 4 + m\angle 5 = 180$  T

**15.** If point $P$ is not on line $\ell$, there is exactly one line through $P$ parallel to $\ell$.

**16.** The sum of the measures of the angles of a triangle is 180.

**15.** State the Parallel Postulate.

**16.** State the Angle Sum Theorem for Triangles.

# Quadrilaterals: Parallelograms

4.5

*A, B, C,* and *D* are coplanar points (**vertices**), no three of which are collinear. The points are joined by four segments (**sides**) that intersect only at the vertices (two at each vertex). The resulting figure is a **quadrilateral.**

A quadrilateral is named by listing its vertices, starting at any vertex and reading clockwise or counterclockwise. So *ABCD, BCDA, ADCB,* and so forth, name the same figure.

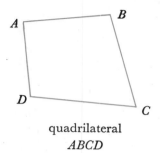

quadrilateral
*ABCD*

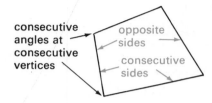

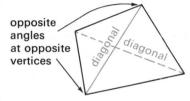

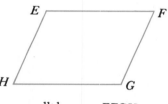

parallelogram *EFGH*
▱*EFGH*

Segments that are contained in parallel lines are also said to be parallel. A quadrilateral with both pairs of opposite sides parallel is a **parallelogram.** The next proof uses both pairs of sides as parallels and uses a diagonal as a transversal.

 The sides and either diagonal of a parallelogram form two congruent triangles.  **Theorem**

Given: ▱*ABCD*, diagonal $\overline{BD}$

Prove: △*ABD* ≅ △*CDB*

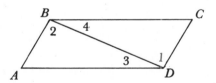

**Proof:**

| STATEMENTS | REASONS |
|---|---|
| 1. $\overleftrightarrow{DC} \parallel \overleftrightarrow{AB}$, $\overleftrightarrow{AD} \parallel \overleftrightarrow{BC}$ | 1. Opp. sides of a ▱ are ∥. |
| 2. ∠1 ≅ ∠2, ∠3 ≅ ∠4 | 2. Alt. Int. ∠s Theorem |
| 3. $\overline{BD} \cong \overline{BD}$ | 3. A segment is ≅ to itself. |
| 4. △*ABD* ≅ △*CDB* | 4. ASA Postulate |

The proof can be repeated using the other diagonal. The next theorem follows directly from the fact that corresponding parts of these congruent triangles are congruent.

**Theorem**  Opposite sides of a parallelogram are congruent.

Opposite angles of a parallelogram are congruent.

The next theorem describes another characteristic of parallelograms.

**Theorem**  The diagonals of a parallelogram bisect each other.

Given: $\square ABCD$, diagonals $\overline{AC}$ and $\overline{BD}$

Prove: $\overline{BP} \cong \overline{PD}$ and $\overline{AP} \cong \overline{PC}$

[*Plan:* Prove $\triangle BPC \cong \triangle DPA$.]

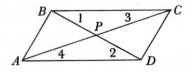

| Proof: STATEMENTS | REASONS |
|---|---|
| 1. $\overline{BC} \cong \overline{AD}$ | 1. Opp. sides of a $\square$ are $\cong$. |
| 2. $\overline{BC} \parallel \overline{AD}$ | 2. Opp. sides of a $\square$ are $\parallel$. |
| 3. Using transversal $\overleftrightarrow{BD}$, $\angle 1 \cong \angle 2$ | 3. Alt. Int. $\angle$s Theorem. |
| Using transversal $\overleftrightarrow{AC}$, $\angle 3 \cong \angle 4$ | |
| 4. $\triangle BPC \cong \triangle DPA$ | 4. ASA Postulate |
| 5. $\overline{BP} \cong \overline{PD}$ and $\overline{AP} \cong \overline{PC}$ | 5. Corres. parts of $\cong \triangle$s are $\cong$. |

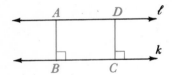

Let $\ell$ and $k$ be any two parallel lines and let $A$ and $D$ be any two points on $\ell$. Then perpendiculars from points $A$ and $D$ to line $k$ are parallel. So $ABCD$ is a parallelogram, and $\overline{AB} \cong \overline{CD}$.

That is, every segment perpendicular to $\ell$ and $k$, with endpoints on $\ell$ and $k$, is congruent to all other such segments. We call the length of these segments the **distance between two parallel lines** $\ell$ and $k$.

**Theorem**  Two parallel lines are everywhere equidistant.

Any side of a parallelogram can be used as a transversal. Then two consecutive angles of the parallelogram are interior angles on the same side of the transversal.

**Theorem**  Consecutive angles of a parallelogram are supplementary.

Ⓐ **1–9.** Choose the best example from the list. Refer to the figure.

**a.** $\overline{PS}$, $\overline{SR}$    **b.** $\overline{PS}$, $\overline{QR}$    **c.** $\angle QRS$, $\angle RSP$

**d.** $\overline{PR}$       **e.** $S$, $Q$     **f.** $P$

**g.** $P$, $S$     **h.** $\overline{SR}$      **i.** $\angle QRS$, $\angle SPQ$

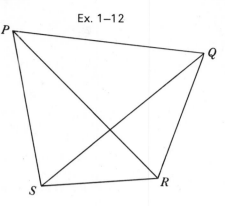

Ex. 1–12

**1.** a vertex   f          **2.** a side   h

**3.** opposite sides    b    **4.** consecutive sides     a

**5.** opposite vertices   e    **6.** consecutive vertices    g

**7.** opposite angles    i    **8.** consecutive angles     c

**9.** a diagonal   d

**10–12.** Refer to the figure above. Name as many transversals as you can for the given lines.

**Assignment Guide**
*Oral:* 1–12
*Written:* Min. 13–39 odd
        Reg. 13–39 odd
        Max. 13–39 odd; 46
*Constructions:* 41–45

**10.** $\overleftrightarrow{PQ}$, $\overleftrightarrow{SR}$       **11.** $\overleftrightarrow{PS}$, $\overleftrightarrow{QR}$       **12.** $\overleftrightarrow{SQ}$, $\overleftrightarrow{PR}$

$\overleftrightarrow{PS}$, $\overleftrightarrow{PR}$, $\overleftrightarrow{QS}$, $\overleftrightarrow{QR}$     $\overleftrightarrow{PQ}$, $\overleftrightarrow{PR}$, $\overleftrightarrow{SQ}$, $\overleftrightarrow{SR}$     $\overleftrightarrow{PQ}$, $\overleftrightarrow{QR}$, $\overleftrightarrow{RS}$, $\overleftrightarrow{PS}$

Ⓑ **13–16.** Refer to the figure below. Identify the two parallel lines and the transversal you would use in each case to show that the angles are interior angles on the same side of the transversal. NOTE: This proves that the consecutive angles of a parallelogram are supplementary.

Ex. 13–16

**13.** $m\angle A + m\angle B = 180$
$\overleftrightarrow{BC} \parallel \overleftrightarrow{AD}$, transversal $\overleftrightarrow{AB}$

**14.** $m\angle B + m\angle C = 180$
$\overleftrightarrow{AB} \parallel \overleftrightarrow{CD}$, transversal $\overleftrightarrow{BC}$

**15.** $m\angle C + m\angle D = 180$
$\overleftrightarrow{BC} \parallel \overleftrightarrow{AD}$, transversal $\overleftrightarrow{CD}$

**16.** $m\angle D + m\angle A = 180$
$\overleftrightarrow{AB} \parallel \overleftrightarrow{CD}$, transversal $\overleftrightarrow{AD}$

**17–30.** Refer to ▱*MNRS* at the right.

**17.** $\triangle MNR \cong$ $\underline{\triangle RSM}$      **18.** $\triangle SRN \cong$ $\underline{\triangle NMS}$

**19.** $\overline{MN} \cong$ $\underline{\overline{RS}}$       **20.** $\overline{NR} \cong$ $\underline{\overline{MS}}$

Ex. 17–30

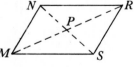

**21.** $\overline{PN} \cong$ $\underline{\overline{PS}}$       **22.** $\overline{MP} \cong$ $\underline{\overline{PR}}$

**23.** $\angle MNR \cong$ $\underline{\angle RSM}$    **24.** $\angle SRN \cong$ $\underline{\angle NMS}$

**25.** If $PM = 3$, then $PR =$ $\underline{\hphantom{0}3\hphantom{0}}$.    **26.** If $RS = 7$, then $\underline{\hphantom{0}MN\hphantom{0}} = 7$.

**27.** If $RN = 10$, then $\underline{\hphantom{0}MS\hphantom{0}} = 10$.    **28.** If $PS = 5$, then $NP =$ $\underline{\hphantom{0}5\hphantom{0}}$.

**29.** If $m\angle PRS = 30$,
then $\underline{\hphantom{000}} = 30$.   $m\angle PMN$

**30.** If $m\angle PNR = 26$,
then $\underline{\hphantom{000}} = 26$.   $m\angle PSM$

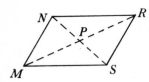

**31–40.** Refer to □*MNRS* at the left.

**31.** If $m\angle SMN = 82$, then $m\underline{\angle NRS} = 82$.

**32.** If $m\angle RPN = 112$, then $m\underline{\angle MPS} = 112$.

**33.** $m\angle RSM + m\angle SMN = \underline{\quad 180 \quad}$

**34.** $m\angle SRN + m\angle MSR = \underline{\quad 180 \quad}$

**35.** If $m\angle RPS = 21$, then $m\underline{\angle MPN} = 21$.

**36.** If $m\angle RSM = 130$, then $m\angle SRN = \underline{\quad 50 \quad}$.

**37.** If $m\angle NRS = 75$, then $m\angle RNM = \underline{\quad 105 \quad}$.

**38.** If $m\angle RSM = 128$, then $m\underline{\angle MNR} = 128$.

**39.** If $m\angle RSN = 35$ and $m\angle RNS = 27$, then $m\angle SRN = \underline{\quad 118 \quad}$.

**40.** If $m\angle SMN = 63$ and $m\angle MSN = 40$, then $m\angle MNS = \underline{\quad 77 \quad}$.

---

**construction: a parallelogram given two consecutive sides and an angle**

| 1. Given: two segments and an angle. | 2. Construct a congruent angle. On the sides of the angle, construct segments congruent to the given segments. | 3. At the endpoints, construct intersecting segments congruent to the opposite segments. |
|---|---|---|
| 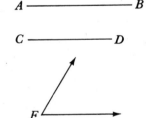 | 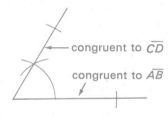 congruent to $\overline{CD}$  congruent to $\overline{AB}$ | 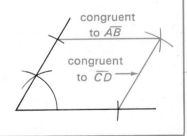 congruent to $\overline{AB}$  congruent to $\overline{CD}$ |

---

**46.** *Given:* $\ell \parallel k$, $A$ and $D$ on $\ell$, $\overline{AB} \perp k$ at $B$, $\overline{CD} \perp k$ at $C$
*Prove:* $AB = CD$
*Proof:*
1. $\ell \parallel k$, $\overline{AB} \perp k$, $\overline{DC} \perp k$ (Given)
2. $\overline{AB} \parallel \overline{DC}$ (In a plane, 2 lines $\perp$ to same line are $\parallel$.)
3. $ABCD$ is a □. (Def. of □)
4. $AB = CD$ (Opp. sides of □ are $\cong$.)

**41–44.** Draw segments and an angle with the given measures. Then construct a parallelogram with consecutive sides and an angle congruent to the figures you drew.

**41.** 3 cm, 5 cm, 30°

**42.** 4 cm, 6 cm, 70°

**43.** 35 mm, 52 mm, 130°

**44.** 47 mm, 63 mm, 140°

© **45.** *Construction:* Draw segments 3, 4, and 5 cm long. Then construct □*TAPS* with $PA = 5$ cm, $PS = 3$ cm, and $SA = 4$ cm.

**46.** Write a two-column proof that parallel lines are everywhere equidistant. HINT: Restate the *given* and *prove* in terms of the second figure on page 142.

# PICTURING PARALLELS

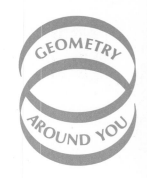

Most of the parallel lines in this chapter have been drawn as if we were looking down on the plane which contains the parallel lines. But in everyday experience, we seldom see models of parallels from this point of view. In these pictures, you know which lines are parallel in the situation shown, even though they are not parallel on the plane of the page.

H. Armstrong Roberts

Photo Research International

Herb Slodounik

# More About Quadrilaterals

## 4.6

| If a quadrilateral is a parallelogram, the opposite sides of the quadrilateral are congruent. | If the opposite sides of a quadrilateral are congruent, the quadrilateral is a parallelogram. |
|---|---|

The two statements above are converses. In fact, the statement on the left says simply that *opposite sides of a parallelogram are congruent.* This was proved in Section 4.5. But can the converse also be proved? Here is one way to look for an answer to that question.

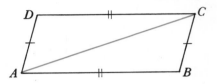

**1** Draw quadrilateral *ABCD*.

**2** Remembering how useful the diagonal was in earlier proofs, add a diagonal to the figure.

**3** Notice that the diagonal forms two congruent triangles, so there are three pairs of congruent angles.

**4** To prove *ABCD* is a parallelogram, prove opposite sides parallel.

**5** The opposite sides are parallel if alternate interior (or corresponding) angles are congruent.

**6** Are any congruent angles in the triangles (step 3 above) alternate interior angles?

22. *(Continued from p. 147)*
    4. $\triangle PNT \cong \triangle SNR$,
       $\triangle PNR \cong \triangle SNT$
       (SAS Post.)
    5. $\overline{PT} \cong \overline{SR}$, $\overline{PR} \cong \overline{ST}$
       (Corres. parts of $\cong$
       $\triangle$s are $\cong$.)
    6. *PRST* is a $\square$. (Opp.
       sides are $\cong$.)

Once the plan for the proof is decided on, writing the proof itself is not hard. Part **a** of the following theorem is proved in Exercises 17–20. Parts **b** and **c** are the subjects of Exercises 21 and 22.

**Theorem**

If any one of the following conditions is met, a quadrilateral is a parallelogram.

  **a.** Opposite sides are congruent.

  **b.** Two sides are parallel and congruent.

  **c.** The diagonals bisect each other.

## Exercises 4.6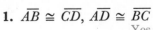

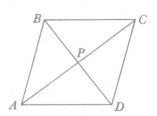

Ⓐ **1–8.** Under the given conditions, is *ABCD* a parallelogram?

1. $\overline{AB} \cong \overline{CD}$, $\overline{AD} \cong \overline{BC}$
   Yes
2. $\overline{AB} \cong \overline{CD}$, $\overline{BC} \parallel \overline{AD}$
   No
3. $\overline{AB} \cong \overline{CD}$, $\overline{AB} \parallel \overline{CD}$
   Yes
4. $\overline{BP} \cong \overline{PD}$, $\overline{AP} \cong \overline{PC}$
   Yes
5. $\overline{AB} \parallel \overline{CD}$, $\overline{AD} \parallel \overline{BC}$
   Yes
6. $\overline{AB} \cong \overline{BC}$, $\overline{AD} \cong \overline{DC}$
   No

**7.** $m\angle DAB + m\angle ABC = 180,$    **8.** $m\angle DAB + m\angle ABC = 180,$
$m\angle BCD + m\angle CDA = 180$ No    $m\angle ABC + m\angle BCD = 180$   Yes

Ⓑ **9–14.** Refer to the figure for Exercises 1–8. Why is $ABCD$ a parallelogram under the given conditions?     *a, b, c in ans. refers to thm. on page 146.*

**9.** $AP = 2, PC = 2,$    **10.** $AB = 5, BC = 5,$    **11.** $AD = 3, BC = 3,$
    $BP = 1.5, PD = 1.5$   c     $CD = 5, DA = 5$   a      $\angle DAC \cong \angle ACB$   b

**12.** $\angle BCA \cong \angle CAD,$    **13.** $AB = 7, CD = 7,$    **14.** $BP = 3, PC = 3,$
    $\angle DCA \cong \angle CAB$      $BC = 5, AD = 5$   a      $PD = 3, PA = 3$   c
    Opp. sides are ∥.

**15–16.** State the converse and tell whether it seems to be true.

**15.** If two angles are consecutive angles of a parallelogram, then they are supplementary. F

**16.** If a figure is a parallelogram, it is a quadrilateral. F

**17–20.** Refer to the figure for Exercises 1–8. Complete the proof.

**Given:** $\overline{AD} \cong \overline{BC}, \overline{AB} \cong \overline{DC}$

**Prove:** $ABCD$ is a parallelogram.

**Proof:**

| STATEMENTS | REASONS |
|---|---|
| *1.* Let $\overline{AC}$ be a diagonal of $ABCD$. | **1.** Definition of diagonal |
| *2.* $\overline{AC} \cong \overline{AC}$ | **2.** __17.__ Seg. is ≅ to itself. |
| *3.* $\overline{AD} \cong \overline{BC}, \overline{AB} \cong \overline{DC}$ | **3.** Given |
| *4.* $\triangle ADC \cong \triangle CBA$ | **4.** __18.__ SSS Post. |
| *5.* $\angle CAD \cong \angle ACB, \angle ACD \cong \angle CAB$ | **5.** __19.__ *Answer below* |
| *6.* $\overline{AD} \parallel \overline{BC}, \overline{AB} \parallel \overline{DC}$ | **6.** __20.__ If alt. int. ∠s are ≅, lines are ∥. |
| *7.* $ABCD$ is a parallelogram. | **7.** Definition of ▱ |

19. Corres. parts of ≅ △s are ≅.

Ⓒ **21–22.** Write a two-column proof.

**21.** **Given:** $\overline{KN} \cong \overline{ML}, \overline{KN} \parallel \overline{ML}$
    **Prove:** $KLMN$ is a parallelogram.
    [*Plan:* Prove either $\overline{KL} \cong \overline{MN}$ or $\overline{KL} \parallel \overline{MN}$.]

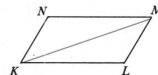

**22.** **Given:** $\overline{PS}$ and $\overline{RT}$ bisect each other.
    **Prove:** $PRST$ is a parallelogram.
    [*Plan:* Use congruent triangles and the definition of ▱ or part **a** or part **b** of the theorem on page 146.]

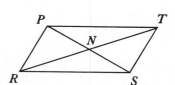

**21.** *1.* $\overline{KN} \cong \overline{ML},$
    $\overline{KN} \parallel \overline{ML}$ (Given)
*2.* Let $\overline{KM}$ be a diagonal of $KLMN$ (Def. of diagonal)
*3.* $\angle NKM \cong \angle LMK$ (If lines are ∥, alt. int. ∠s are ≅.)
*4.* $\overline{KM} \cong \overline{KM}$ (Seg. is ≅ to itself.)
*5.* $\triangle KMN \cong \triangle MKL$ (SAS Post.)
*6.* $\overline{KL} \cong \overline{MN}$ (Corres. parts of ≅ △s are ≅.)
*7.* $KLMN$ is a ▱. (Opp. sides are ≅; steps 1 and 6)

**22.** *1.* $\overline{PS}$ and $\overline{RT}$ bisect each other. (Given)
*2.* $\overline{PN} \cong \overline{SN}, \overline{RN} \cong \overline{TN}$ (Def. of bisect)
*3.* $\angle PNT \cong \angle SNR,$
    $\angle PNR \cong \angle SNT$ (Vert. ∠s are ≅.)

*(Continued on p. 146)*

## 4.7 The Triangle Midline Theorem

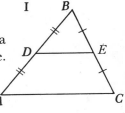

The segment joining the midpoints of two sides of a triangle (called a **midline**) is parallel to the third side.

**Suggested Class Time**

| Course | Min. | Reg. | Max. |
|--------|------|------|------|
| Days   | 1    | 1    | 1    |

Given: $\triangle ABC$, $\overline{AD} \cong \overline{DB}$, $\overline{CE} \cong \overline{EB}$

Prove: $\overline{DE} \parallel \overline{AC}$

Form a quadrilateral and two (congruent) triangles.

$\overleftrightarrow{DF}$ is a transversal of $\overline{AB}$ and $\overline{FC}$.

Proof:

| STATEMENTS | REASONS |
|------------|---------|
| 1. Let $F$ be on $\overrightarrow{DE}$, $\overline{EF} \cong \overline{DE}$. | 1. Point Plotting Thm. (p. 27) |
| 2. Join $F$ and $C$. | 2. 2 pts. determine a line. |
| 3. $\overline{CE} \cong \overline{EB}$ | 3. Given |
| 4. $\angle BED \cong \angle CEF$ | 4. Vertical $\angle$s are $\cong$. |
| 5. $\triangle BED \cong \triangle CEF$ | 5. SAS Postulate |
| 6. $\angle F \cong \angle BDE$, $\overline{FC} \cong \overline{DB}$ | 6. Corres. parts of $\cong \triangle$s are $\cong$. |
| 7. $\overline{AB} \parallel \overline{FC}$, so $\overline{AD} \parallel \overline{FC}$ | 7. Alt. Interior $\angle$s Thm. |
| 8. $\overline{AD} \cong \overline{DB}$ | 8. Given |
| 9. $\overline{AD} \cong \overline{FC}$ | 9. Segs. $\cong$ to same seg. are $\cong$. |
| 10. $ADFC$ is a $\square$. | 10. 2 sides are $\parallel$ and $\cong$. |
| 11. $\overline{DF} \parallel \overline{AC}$, so $\overline{DE} \parallel \overline{AC}$ | 11. Opp. sides of a $\square$ are $\parallel$. |

A midline of a triangle is half as long as the third side.

Given: $\triangle ABC$, $AD = DB$, $CE = EB$     (See figures I and II above.)

Prove: $DE = \frac{1}{2}AC$

Proof:

| STATEMENTS | REASONS |
|------------|---------|
| 1. Form $\square ADFC$, with $EF = DE$. | 1. Steps 1–10 above |
| 2. $DE + EF = DF$ | 2. Definition of between |
| 3. $DE + DE = DF$, so $2DE = DF$ | 3. Substitution and addition |
| 4. $DE = \frac{1}{2}DF$ | 4. Mult. both sides by $\frac{1}{2}$ |
| 5. $DF = AC$ | 5. Opp. sides of a $\square$ are $\cong$. |
| 6. $DE = \frac{1}{2}AC$ | 6. Substitution |

The two properties just proved are usually combined in one theorem.

Gene Kuechmann

**Triangle Midline Theorem**

The segment joining the midpoints of two sides of a triangle is parallel to the third side and half as long.

Ⓐ **1–7.** Refer to the figure.

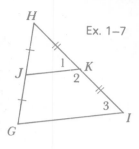

Ex. 1–7

**1.** $\overline{JK} \parallel$ ___GI___

**2.** If $GI = 6$, $JK =$ ___3___ .

**3.** If $JK = 12$, $GI =$ ___24___ .

**4.** If $m\angle 1 = 42$, $m\angle 3 =$ ___42___ .

**5.** $m\angle 2 + m\angle 3 =$ ___180___

**6.** $\overline{JK}$ is called a ___Midline___ of $\triangle GHI$.

**7.** If $B$ is the midpoint of $\overline{GI}$, name another midline of $\triangle GHI$.

$\overline{BJ}$ (or $\overline{BK}$)

**8.** How many midlines does any triangle have? 3

**Assignment Guide**
*Oral:* 1–8
*Written:* Min. 9–18
Reg. 9–18
Max. 9–26

Ⓑ **9–18.** In the figure, $M$ and $N$ are the midpoints of $\overline{PT}$ and $\overline{RT}$.

**9.** If $m\angle 4 = 48$, then $m\angle 2 =$ ___48___ .

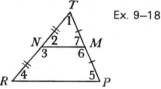

Ex. 9–18

**10.** If $m\angle 6 = 96$, then $m\angle 5 =$ ___84___ .

**11.** If $PR = 12$, then $MN =$ ___6___ .

**12.** If $m\angle 7 = 83$, then $m\angle 5 =$ ___83___ .

**13.** If $m\angle 3 = 120$ and $m\angle 7 = 72$, then $m\angle 1 =$ ___48___ .

**14.** If $MN = 7\frac{1}{2}$, then $PR =$ ___15___ .

**15.** If $\overline{TR} \cong \overline{TP}$ and $TN = 4$, then $MP =$ ___4___ .

**16.** If $\overline{TN} \cong \overline{NM}$ and $TN = 4$, then $RP =$ ___8___ .

**17.** If $\overline{MN} \cong \overline{TN}$ and $RP = 16$, then $TN =$ ___8___ .

**18.** If $\overline{MP} \cong \overline{NR}$ and $MP = 5$, then $TN =$ ___5___ .

Ⓒ **19–26.** Let $ABCD$ be any quadrilateral, and let $E$, $F$, $G$, and $H$ be midpoints of its sides. $\overline{AC}$ is a diagonal.

**21.** In a plane, 2 lines $\parallel$ to the same line are $\parallel$.

**19.** Why is $\overline{EF} \parallel \overline{AC}$?
△ Midline Thm.

**20.** Why is $\overline{GH} \parallel \overline{AC}$? △ Midline Thm.

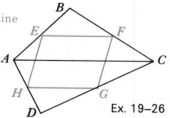

Ex. 19–26

**21.** Why is $\overline{EF} \parallel \overline{GH}$?

**22.** $EF = \frac{1}{2}$ ___AC___

**23.** $GH = \frac{1}{2}$ ___AC___

**24.** Why is $\overline{EF} \cong \overline{GH}$?
Both have measure $\frac{1}{2}AC$.

**25.** Since $\overline{EF} \cong \overline{GH}$ and $\overline{EF} \parallel \overline{GH}$, $EFGH$ is a ___▱___ .

**26.** If the midpoints of the sides of any quadrilateral are joined, the segments joining them form a ___▱___ . NOTE: This is called Varignon's Theorem, after a French mathematician.

# 4.8 Special Parallelograms

**Suggested Class Time**

| Course | Min. | Reg. | Max. |
|--------|------|------|------|
| Days   | 1    | 1    | 1    |

rectangle

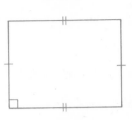

parallelogram with
a right angle

rhombus

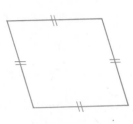

parallelogram with
all sides congruent

square

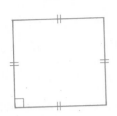

rhombus with a right
angle or rectangle with
all sides congruent

Since a rectangle is a parallelogram, its consecutive angles are supplementary. But an angle supplementary to a right angle is also a right angle, so consecutive sides of a rectangle are perpendicular. That is,

**Theorem**       A rectangle has four right angles.

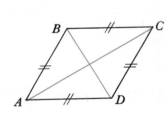

In rhombus $ABCD$, $\overline{AB} \cong \overline{BC}$ and $\overline{AD} \cong \overline{DC}$. That is, $B$ and $D$ are each equidistant from the endpoints of $\overline{AC}$. But in a plane, two points equidistant from the endpoints of a segment determine its perpendicular bisector, so $\overleftrightarrow{BD}$ is the perpendicular bisector of $\overline{AC}$. And, by the same reasoning, $\overleftrightarrow{AC}$ is the perpendicular bisector of $\overline{BD}$.

**Theorem**       The diagonals of a rhombus are perpendicular and bisect each other.

**Theorem**       If the diagonals of a parallelogram are perpendicular, the parallelogram is a rhombus.

Given: $\square MNOP$, $\overline{PN} \perp \overline{MO}$

Prove: $\square MNOP$ is a rhombus.

[*Plan*: Prove $\overline{MN} \cong \overline{NO} \cong \overline{OP} \cong \overline{PM}$ by proving $\triangle MNQ \cong \triangle ONQ \cong \triangle OPQ \cong \triangle MPQ$.]
(Exercise 29 calls for the completed proof.)

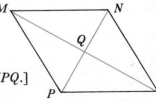

This chart shows how special parallelograms are related. Think of the properties of each figure as carried along to those below it on the chart.

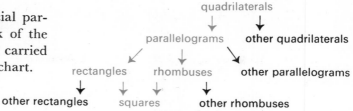

Ⓐ **1–10.** True or False?

**1.** Every quadrilateral is a parallelogram. F

**2.** Every parallelogram is a rhombus. F

**3.** Every square is a rhombus. T

**4.** Every square is a rectangle. T

**5.** No parallelogram is a square. F

**6.** Every square is a parallelogram. T

**7.** The diagonals of a rhombus are perpendicular and bisect each other. T

**8.** The diagonals of a rectangle are perpendicular. F

**9.** The opposite angles of a rhombus are congruent. T

**10.** If the diagonals of a quadrilateral bisect each other and are perpendicular, the quadrilateral is a rhombus. T

**Assignment Guide**
*Oral:* 1–10
*Written:* Min. 11–26
　　　Reg. 11–26
　　　Max. 11–26; 29–30
*Constructions:* 27–28

Ⓑ **11–22.** *COLD* is a rectangle, *SUIT* is a rhombus, and *WHEN* is a square.

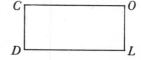
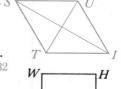

**11.** $\overline{IS} \perp \underline{\ \overline{UT}\ }$

**12.** $\overline{UT}$ bisects $\underline{\ \overline{SI}\ }$.

**13.** If $m\angle ITS = 130$, find $m\angle TSU$. 50

**14.** If $LO = 4$, $CD = \underline{\ \ 4\ \ }$.

**15.** If $CO = 12$, $LD = \underline{\ \ 12\ \ }$.

**16.** If $NE = 4$, $WN = \underline{\ \ 4\ \ }$.

**17.** Find $m\angle D$. 90

**18.** If $m\angle TSU = 48$, find $m\angle SUI$. 132

**19.** If $WH = 7$, $HE = \underline{\ \ 7\ \ }$.

**20.** If $ST = 12$, $US = \underline{\ \ 12\ \ }$.

**21.** If $US = 6$, $IT = \underline{\ \ 6\ \ }$.

**22.** Find $m\angle N$. 90

**23–26.** Why is the conclusion true?

**23.** *PINK* is a parallelogram, $\overline{PI} \cong \overline{IN}$
*Conclusion*: *PINK* is a rhombus.
　　We can prove all sides are ≅.

**24.** *BONE* is a parallelogram, $\overline{BN} \perp \overline{OE}$
*Conclusion*: *BONE* is a rhombus.
　Parallelogram with ⊥ diagonals is a rhombus.

**25.** *SONG* is a rhombus, $m\angle G = 90$
*Conclusion*: $m\angle S = 90$
　We can prove *SONG* is a rectangle.

**26.** *ROAM* is a rhombus.
*Conclusion*: $\overline{AR} \perp \overline{OM}$
　Diagonals of a rhombus are ⊥.

**30.**
1. Rhombus $PDQT$
   (Given)
2. $\overline{PD} \cong \overline{QD}$, $\overline{PT} \cong \overline{QT}$
   (Def. of rhombus)
3. $\overline{DT} \cong \overline{DT}$ (Seg. is $\cong$ to
   itself.)
4. $\triangle PDT \cong \triangle QDT$
   (SSS Post.)
5. $\angle 1 \cong \angle 2$, $\angle 3 \cong$
   $\angle 4$ (Corres. parts of $\cong$
   $\triangle$s are $\cong$.)

**27–28.** *Constructions:* Draw $\overline{MN}$, $\overline{PD}$, and $\angle A$ so that $MN = 4$ cm, $PD = 3$ cm, and $m\angle A = 50$. Then construct the figure described.

**27.** rhombus $RHOS$ with $\angle R \cong \angle A$ and $\overline{RH} \cong \overline{MN}$

**28.** rectangle $RECT$ with $\overline{RE} \cong \overline{MN}$ and $\overline{EC} \cong \overline{PD}$

© **29–30.** Write a two-column proof.

**29.** If the diagonals of a parallelogram are perpendicular, the parallelogram is a rhombus.
*See plan for proof at bottom of p. 150.*

**30.** The diagonals of a rhombus bisect the angles.
Given: Rhombus $PDQT$, diagonal $\overline{DT}$
Prove: $\angle 1 \cong \angle 2$, $\angle 3 \cong \angle 4$

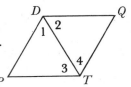

# KITES AND ARROWS

Did you know that kites and arrows are geometric figures?

A kite and an arrow both have two pairs of consecutive sides congruent, and no side is common to both pairs. But the diagonals of a kite intersect, while the diagonals of an arrow do not.

Here are some questions to explore.

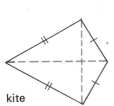

kite

● What is a kite with four congruent sides called? Rhombus

● Can an arrow have four congruent sides? No

● Are any angles congruent in a kite? In an arrow?
Yes, at least 1 pair; yes, exactly 1 pair

● How are the lines containing the diagonals of a kite or an arrow related? They are perpendicular.

arrow

The kite is so named because it is shaped like the simplest form of the flying toy called a kite.

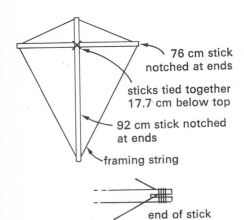

76 cm stick notched at ends

sticks tied together 17.7 cm below top

92 cm stick notched at ends

framing string

end of stick

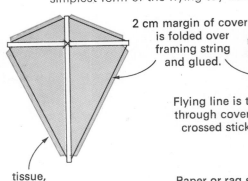

2 cm margin of cover is folded over framing string and glued.

Flying line is tied through cover to crossed sticks.

tissue, newspaper, or polyethylene cover

Paper or rag strips add weight to tail.

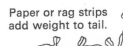

# Transversals and Parallel Lines

**4.9**

The edge of the ruler in the photograph represents a transversal of the parallel lines marked on the board. The parallel lines **intercept** segments on the transversal.

**Suggested Class Time**

| Course | Min. | Reg. | Max. |
|--------|------|------|------|
| Days   | 1    | 1    | 1    |

If three parallel lines intercept congruent segments on transversal $t$, they intercept congruent segments on every transversal parallel to $t$.

Given: $\ell \parallel k \parallel n, s \parallel t, \overline{AB} \cong \overline{BC}$

Prove: $\overline{DE} \cong \overline{EF}$

**Proof:**

| STATEMENTS | REASONS |
|------------|---------|
| 1. $ABED$, $BCFE$ are parallelograms. | 1. Definition of $\square$ |
| 2. $\overline{AB} \cong \overline{DE}, \overline{BC} \cong \overline{EF}$ | 2. Opp. sides of a $\square$ are $\cong$. |
| 3. $\overline{AB} \cong \overline{BC}$ | 3. Given |
| 4. $\overline{DE} \cong \overline{BC}$ | 4. Segs. $\cong$ to the same seg. are $\cong$. |
| 5. $\overline{DE} \cong \overline{EF}$ | 5. Segs. $\cong$ to the same seg. are $\cong$. |

We can now prove this more general statement:

If three parallel lines intercept congruent segments on transversal $t$, they intercept congruent segments on all other transversals.

Given: $\ell \parallel k \parallel n$, transversals $r$ and $t$,
$\overline{AB} \cong \overline{BC}$

Prove: $\overline{DE} \cong \overline{EF}$

**Proof:**

| STATEMENTS | REASONS |
|------------|---------|
| 1. There is a line $s$ through $E$, so that $s \parallel t$. | 1. Parallel Postulate (p. 125) |
| 2. $\ell \parallel k \parallel n, \overline{AB} \cong \overline{BC}$ | 2. Given |
| 3. $\overline{GE} \cong \overline{EH}$ | 3. Steps 1 and 2 and proof above |
| 4. $\angle DEG \cong \angle FEH$ | 4. Vertical $\angle$s are $\cong$. |
| 5. $\angle DGE \cong \angle FHE$ | 5. Alt. Interior $\angle$s Theorem |
| 6. $\triangle DGE \cong \triangle FHE$ | 6. ASA Postulate |
| 7. $\overline{DE} \cong \overline{EF}$ | 7. Corres. parts of $\cong$ $\triangle$s are $\cong$. |

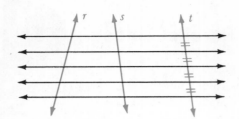

Suppose there are more than three parallel lines. By using the same reasoning as before, over and over again, we can prove that all of the intercepted segments on $s$ (or on $r$) are congruent to one another.

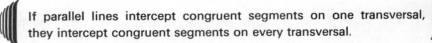

**Intercepted Segment Theorem** — If parallel lines intercept congruent segments on one transversal, they intercept congruent segments on every transversal.

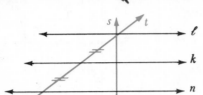

Suppose parallel lines $\ell$, $k$, and $n$ intercept congruent segments on transversal $t$. By the Intercepted Segment Theorem, the intercepted segments on $s$ are also congruent. Since $s$, $t$, and $n$ form a triangle,

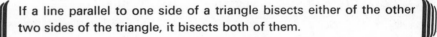

**Theorem** — If a line parallel to one side of a triangle bisects either of the other two sides of the triangle, it bisects both of them.

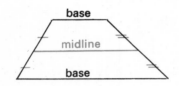

A **trapezoid** is a quadrilateral with exactly *one* pair of parallel sides. The parallel sides are the **bases** of the trapezoid. The **midline** (or **median**) of a trapezoid joins the midpoints of the nonparallel sides (called **legs**).

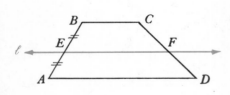

In trapezoid $ABCD$, $E$ is the midpoint of $\overline{AB}$, and $\ell$ goes through $E$ parallel to $\overleftrightarrow{AD}$ and $\overleftrightarrow{BC}$. Since $\ell$, $\overleftrightarrow{AD}$, and $\overleftrightarrow{BC}$ intercept congruent segments on $\overline{AB}$, they intercept congruent segments on $\overline{CD}$. So $F$ is the midpoint of $\overline{CD}$, and $\overline{EF}$ is the midline of trapezoid $ABCD$. There is exactly one midline and exactly one parallel through $E$, so part **a** of the next theorem is proved.

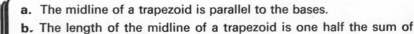
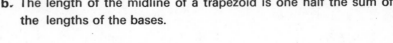

**Trapezoid Midline Theorem** —
a. The midline of a trapezoid is parallel to the bases.
b. The length of the midline of a trapezoid is one half the sum of the lengths of the bases.

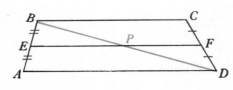

**Part b.**
Given: Trapezoid $ABCD$, midline $\overline{EF}$
Prove: $EF = \frac{1}{2}(AD + BC)$
[*Plan:* Draw diagonal $\overline{BD}$ and apply the Triangle Midline Theorem, p. 148, to $\triangle ABD$ and $\triangle BCD$.]

Ⓐ **1–10.** In the given figure, lines *a*, *b*, *c*, and *d* are parallel.

**Assignment Guide**
*Oral:* 1–10
*Written:* Min. 11–22
        Reg. 11–22
        Max. 11–22; 29–30
*Constructions:* 23–28

**1.** We can write $a \parallel b \parallel c \parallel d$ to indicate ‾‾That each line is ∥‾‾ to the other 3

**2.** The transversals of the parallel lines are ‾‾$k$‾‾ and ‾‾$n$‾‾.

**3.** On *k*, lines *a* and *b* intercept ‾‾$\overline{ST}$‾‾.

Ex. 1–10

**4.** On *n*, lines *b* and *c* intercept ‾‾$\overline{NP}$‾‾.

**5.** If $\overline{ST} \cong \overline{TV}$, name congruent segments on *n*. $\overline{SN}$ and $\overline{NP}$

**6.** If *b* bisects $\overline{SP}$, it also bisects ‾‾$\overline{SV}$‾‾.

**7.** Figure *TNPV* is a ‾‾Trapezoid‾‾.

**8.** If *V* and *P* are midpoints of $\overline{TW}$ and $\overline{NR}$, then $\overline{VP}$ is the ‾‾Midline‾‾ of *TNRW*.

**9.** If $\overline{TN}$ is the midline of $\triangle SVP$, then $TN = \frac{1}{2}$‾‾$VP$‾‾.

**10.** If $\overline{VP}$ joins the midpoints of $\overline{TW}$ and $\overline{NR}$, then $VP = \frac{1}{2}$(‾‾‾‾). $TN + WR$

Ⓑ **11–20.** In the given figure, $\ell \parallel k \parallel n \parallel p$ and $\overline{DE} \cong \overline{EF} \cong \overline{FG}$.

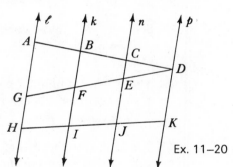

Ex. 11–20

**11.** If $AB = 4$, then $BC =$ ‾‾4‾‾.

**12.** If $CD = 7$, then $AB =$ ‾‾7‾‾.

**13.** If $BF = 6$, then $CE =$ ‾‾3‾‾.

**14.** If $CE = 4$, then $BF =$ ‾‾8‾‾.

**15.** If $AG = 6$ and $CE = 2$, then $BF =$ ‾‾4‾‾.

**16.** If $DK = 8$ and $IF = 4$, then $EJ =$ ‾‾6‾‾.

**17.** If $IF = 6$, $EJ + GH =$ ‾‾12‾‾.

**18.** If $EJ = 12$, $DK + IF =$ ‾‾24‾‾.

**19.** If $DK = 8$ and $EJ = 6$, then $IF =$ ‾‾4‾‾.

**20.** If $IF = 4$ and $EJ = 10$, then $DK =$ ‾‾16‾‾.

**21–22.** The photograph on page 153 shows how a carpenter can use a ruler to mark a board off into five strips of equal width. How should the position of the ruler be changed to mark the board off into

**21.** six strips of equal width?

**22.** four strips of equal width?

21. So sides of board are at 0 and 12 (Use marks at 2, 4, 6, 8, and 10.)

22. So sides of board are at 0 and 12 (Use marks at 3, 6, and 9.)

| 1. Given: any segment $\overline{AB}$ | 2. Construct $\overrightarrow{AP}$. Mark off 3 congruent segments on $AP$ starting at $A$. | 3. Join $B$ and $E$. Construct parallels to $\overline{BE}$ through $C$ and $D$. |
|---|---|---|
| | 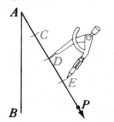 | 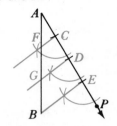 |

**30.** *Sketch of Proof:* Diagonal $\overline{BD}$ separates trapezoid $ABCD$ into 2 △s. Since $\overline{EF}$ is the midline of $ABCD$, $\overline{EF} \parallel \overline{AD}$ and $\overline{EF} \parallel \overline{BC}$. $\overline{BP} \cong \overline{PD}$ (If a line $\parallel$ to 1 side of △ bisects 1 of its other 2 sides, it bisects both), and $\overline{EP}$ and $\overline{PF}$ are midlines of △s $ABD$ and $BCD$. By the △ Midline Thm., $EP = \frac{1}{2}AD$ and $PF = \frac{1}{2}BC$. Since $EF = EP + PF$, $EF = \frac{1}{2}(AD + BC)$.

**23–26.** Refer to the construction above.

**23.** Why is $\overleftrightarrow{FC} \parallel \overleftrightarrow{GD} \parallel \overleftrightarrow{BE}$?
 Corres. ∠s are ≅.

**24.** Why is $\overline{AF} \cong \overline{FG} \cong \overline{GB}$?
 Intercepted Seg. Thm.

**25.** To separate $\overline{AB}$ into 4 congruent segments, what would you do in step 2?
 Mark off 4 ≅ segments on $\overrightarrow{AP}$.

**26.** How would you separate $\overline{AB}$ into 5 congruent segments?
 Mark off 5 ≅ segments on $\overrightarrow{AP}$ in step 2.

**27–28.** Draw $\overline{MN}$ 10 cm long. Use the method above to do each exercise.

**27.** Separate $\overline{MN}$ into 3 congruent segments.

**28.** Separate $\overline{MN}$ into 5 congruent segments.

**29.** Cut a strip of unlined paper 6.5 by 27.5 cm. Then use the edge of a sheet of ruled paper to mark off seven strips of equal width each 27.5 cm long. HINT: See Exercises 21–22.

**30.** Prove that the length of the midline of a trapezoid is one half the sum of the lengths of the bases (see p. 154).

**31.** Shows the set of rectangles is in the set of ▱s

**32.** Shows part of the set of ▱s is the set of rhombuses

**33.** Shows no part of the set of trapezoids is in the set of rectangles

**34.** Shows the set of squares is in the set of rectangles

**35.** Shows part of the set of rectangles is part of the set of rhombuses

**36.** Shows no part of the set of ▱s is in the set of trapezoids

**31–36.** How does this Euler diagram illustrate each statement?

**31.** Every rectangle is a parallelogram.

**32.** Some parallelograms are rhombuses.

**33.** No trapezoid is a rectangle.

**34.** Every square is a rectangle.

**35.** Some rectangles are rhombuses.

**36.** No parallelogram is a trapezoid.

quadrilaterals

trapezoids

parallelograms

rectangles

squares

rhombuses

In the Andes mountains of southeastern Peru lie the ruins of the fortress-city Machu Picchu. This city and others nearby were built by the Incas, natives of the region, probably about five hundred years ago.

One of the surprising things about Machu Picchu is the way trapezoids were used in buildings—including trapezoid-shaped doors and windows.

Photos by David Mangurian

# 4.10  Transformations: Slides

A slide can be described by using an arrow to show how far each point slides (the **magnitude** of the slide) and in what **direction**.

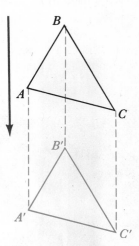

To draw the slide image of $\triangle ABC$:

1. From each vertex, draw a ray with the same direction as the arrow.

2. On each ray, measure off a segment with the same length as the arrow. (The points so located are $A'$, $B'$, and $C'$, the images of $A$, $B$, and $C$.)

3. Join $A'$, $B'$, and $C'$. ($\triangle A'B'C'$ is the slide image of $\triangle ABC$.)

Since a slide preserves length, $\overline{AB} \cong \overline{A'B'}$. And since each point slides as far as each other point, $\overline{AA'} \cong \overline{BB'}$. Thus, quadrilateral $ABB'A'$ has opposite sides congruent, so it is a parallelogram.

The same reasoning would show that $BCC'B'$ and $ACC'A'$ are also parallelograms, so we can come to the following conclusions:

> A line is parallel to its slide image (if they don't coincide). Segments joining points and their slide images are parallel.

You can see from the figure that the next statement is also justified.

> Slides preserve orientation.

If you were to draw two parallel lines on a piece of paper and slide, flip, or turn the paper, you would probably decide that all three of these transformations preserve parallelism.

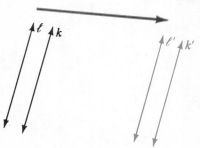

Consider the case in which $\ell$ and $k$ are parallel and $\ell'$ and $k'$ are slide images of $\ell$ and $k$. Since a line is parallel to its slide image, $\ell \parallel \ell'$ and $k \parallel k'$.

But $\ell \parallel k$, and a line parallel to one of two parallel lines is also parallel to the other. So $\ell' \parallel k$ and, finally, $\ell' \parallel k'$.

> Slides preserve parallelism.

Ⓐ **1.** An arrow can show the _____ and the _____ of a slide.
   *Magnitude; direction*

**2.** When would a line and its slide image coincide?
   *When the line is ∥ to the direction of the slide*

**Assignment Guide**
*Oral:* Max. 1–8
*Written:* Max. 9–13 odd; 15–22

**3–8.** True or False?

**3.** Slides preserve length.  T

**4.** Slides reverse orientation.  F

**5.** Slides preserve parallelism.  T

**6.** Slides change angle measure.  F

**7.** A line is perpendicular to its slide image.

**8.** Slides preserve collinearity.  T

Ⓑ **9–12.** The arrow in the figure describes a slide. Copy the figure listed and draw the slide image.

**9.** △*MOE*

**10.** △*ONA*

**11.** trapezoid *NAME*

**12.** □*LAME*

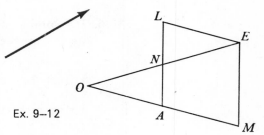

Ex. 9–12

**13–14.** Copy △*ABC* and point *P*. Then draw the slide image of △*ABC*. HINT: First draw an arrow from the given vertex to *P*.

**13.** *P* is the image of *B*.

**14.** *P* is the image of *C*.

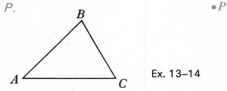

•*P*

Ex. 13–14

**15–18.** Copy ℓ and *t*. Then draw the slide images of ℓ and *t* if *P′* is the image of *P*.

**15.** Is ℓ ∥ ℓ′? Why?
   *Yes; a line is ∥ to its slide image.*

**16.** Are any angles at *P* and *P′* congruent? Why?
   *Yes; slides preserve ∠ measure.*

**17.** What theorem about corresponding angles does this suggest?
   *Corres. ∠s Thm., p. 132*

**18.** What theorem about alternate interior angles does this suggest?
   *Alt. Int. ∠s Thm., p. 128*

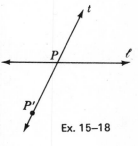

Ex. 15–18

Ⓒ **19–22.** Copy △*ABC* and point *P* used for Exercises 13–14.

**19.** Draw a line ℓ through *P*. Draw line *k* so *k* ∥ ℓ and the distance between ℓ and *k* is 8 cm.

**20.** Reflect △*ABC* over ℓ. Label the image △*A′B′C′*.

**21.** Reflect △*A′B′C′* over *k*. Label the image △*A″B″C″*.

**22.** How do △*ABC* and △*A″B″C″* appear to be related?

**22.** △*A″B″C″* is the slide image of △*ABC*. (Slide has magnitude *AA″* and direction of *AA″*.)

# ■ Chapter 4 Review ■

**4.1**

**1–4.** Correctly complete the sentence in as many ways as possible using

**a.** coplanar          **b.** noncoplanar          **c.** nonintersecting

**1.** Two parallel lines are ____a, c____.          **2.** Two skew lines are ____b, c____.

**3.** Two intersecting lines are ____a____.          **4.** In a plane, two lines perpendicular to a line $\ell$ are ____c____.

**5.** Point $P$ is not on line $k$. Can two lines through $P$ both be parallel to $k$? Why?  No; Parallel Post.

**6.** If assuming statement $p$ is true leads to a contradiction of a true statement, then _____. $p$ is false

**4.2**

**7–20.** Refer to the figure below.

**7.** Using $\ell$, $k$, and transversal $r$, name a pair of alternate interior angles.  ∠1 and ∠5

**8.** If ∠1 ≅ ____∠5____, then $\ell \parallel k$.          **9.** If $\ell \parallel k$, then ∠10 ≅ ____∠9____.

**4.3**

**10.** ∠5 and ____∠3____ are corresponding angles.

**11.** If $m∠4 + m$ ____∠5____ $= 180$, then $\ell \parallel k$.

**12.** If $\ell \parallel k$, then $m∠9 + m$ ____∠8____ $= 180$.

**13.** If $\ell \parallel k$ and $m∠9 = 90$, then $m∠8 =$ ____90____.

**14.** If $\ell \parallel k$ and $t \perp \ell$, then $t \perp$ ____k____.

**15.** If ∠3 ≅ ____∠5____, then $\ell \parallel k$.          **16.** If $\ell \parallel k$, ∠6 ≅ ____∠4____.

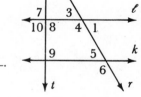

**4.4**

**17.** $m∠2 + m∠5 + m∠9 =$ ____180____          **18.** $m∠7 = m∠3 + m$ ____∠2____

**19.** If ∠9 is obtuse, ∠2 and ∠5 are ____Acute____.

**20.** If $m∠9 = 90$, then $m∠5 + m∠2 =$ ____90____.

**4.5**

**21–28.** Which are always true for ▱ABCD?  HINT: Draw a diagram.

**21.** $\overline{AB} \cong \overline{CD}$  T          **22.** △ABC ≅ △ADC  F

**23.** ∠A ≅ ∠B  F          **24.** ∠D ≅ ∠B  T

**25.** $\overline{AC} \perp \overline{BD}$   F
**26.** $\overline{AC}$ bisects $\overline{BD}$.   T

**27.** $m\angle B + m\angle C = 180$   T
**28.** $\overline{BD}$ and $\overline{AC}$ bisect each other.   T

**29–32.** Which conditions make quadrilateral *MNOP* a parallelogram?   **4.6**

**29.** $\overline{MN} \cong \overline{NO}$, $\overline{NO} \cong \overline{OP}$   No
**30.** $\overline{NO} \parallel \overline{PM}$, $\overline{NO} \cong \overline{PM}$   Yes

**31.** $\overline{MO}$ bisects $\overline{NP}$.   Yes
**32.** $MN = OP$, $NO = PM$   Yes

**33–35.** In the figure, *E* is the midpoint of $\overline{AB}$.   **4.7**

**33.** If $AC = 8$, $ED = $ ___4___ .
**34.** $\angle 3 \cong$ ___$\angle 1$___

**35.** $m\angle 2 + m\angle 3 = $ ___180___

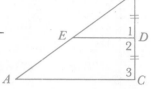

**36–40.** Give another name for each figure.   **4.8**

**36.** In $\square MNPR$, $\overline{MN} \perp \overline{NP}$.
Rectangle
**37.** In $\square MNPR$, $\overline{MN} \cong \overline{NP}$.
Rhombus

**38.** In rectangle *TREW*, $\overline{TR} \cong \overline{TW}$.
Square
**39.** In $\square GRAM$, $\overline{GA} \perp \overline{RM}$.
Rhombus

**40.** In rhombus *RHOM*, $m\angle M = 90$.
Square

**41.** In the figure above, let $\overline{ED} \parallel \overline{AC}$. Why does $AE = EB$?   If a line $\parallel$   **4.9**
to 1 side of a $\triangle$ bisects either of the other 2 sides, it bisects both of them.

**42–44.** In the figure, $n \parallel \ell$ and $\overrightarrow{AD}$ and $\overleftrightarrow{BC}$ intersect.

**42.** If $k \parallel n$ and $\overline{FC} \cong \overline{FB}$, then $\overline{AE} \cong$ ___$ED$___ .

**43.** *ABCD* is a __Trapezoid__

**44.** If $AE = ED$ and $BF = FC$, then $\overline{AB} \parallel \overline{DC} \parallel$ ___$EF$___
and $FE = \frac{1}{2}$_____ . $(AB + DC)$

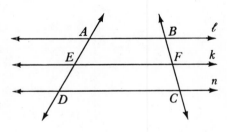

**45–49.** $\triangle P'D'T'$ is the slide image of $\triangle PDT$.   **4.10**

**45.** The slide has _____ $PP'$ and the same _____ as $\overrightarrow{PP'}$.   Magnitude; direction

**46.** $\overline{PD} \parallel$ ___$P'D'$___
**47.** $\overline{DD'} \parallel$ ___$PP'$___ $\parallel$ ___$TT'$___

**48.** $\triangle PDT$ and $\triangle P'D'T'$ have (the same, opposite) orientation.

**49.** Segments joining the vertices of a triangle and their slide images (are, are not) parallel.

1. Coplanar nonintersecting lines are (<u>parallel</u>, skew).

2. The first step in (inductive, <u>indirect</u>) reasoning is to assume the opposite of what is to be proved.

**3–16.** In the figure, $\ell \parallel r$.

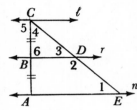

3. $\angle 5$ and $\angle 6$ are (corresponding, <u>alternate interior</u>) angles.

4. In quadrilateral $ABDE$, $\overline{AB}$ is a (diagonal, <u>side</u>).

5. If $\overline{CD} \cong \overline{DE}$, $\overline{BD}$ is the (median, <u>midline</u>) of $\triangle ACE$.

6. If $r \parallel n$, $ABDE$ is a (parallelogram, <u>trapezoid</u>).

**Assignment Guide**
*Written:* Min. 1–24
   Reg. 1–24
   Max. 1–25

7. If $m\angle 5 = 87$,
$m \underline{\quad \angle 6 \quad} = 87$.

8. If $m\angle C_{45} = 130$,
$m \underline{\quad \angle 3 \quad} = 50$.

9. If $m\angle 1 = 55$ and
$m \underline{\quad \angle 3 \quad} = 55$, $r \parallel n$.

10. If $n \perp \overline{CA}$ and $m\angle 6 = 90$,
$r \underline{\quad \parallel \quad} n$.

11. If $m\angle 2 = 140$ and
$m\angle 4 = 50$, $m\angle 6 = \underline{\quad 90 \quad}$.

12. If $m\angle 1 = 50$ and
$m \underline{\quad \angle 2 \quad} = 130$, $r \parallel n$.

13. If $r \parallel n$ and $DE = 6$,
$\underline{\quad CD \quad} = 6$.

14. If $m\angle 6 = 90$,
$m\angle 3 + m\angle 4 = \underline{\quad 90 \quad}$.

15. If $r \parallel n$ and $BD = 4$,
$AE = \underline{\quad 8 \quad}$.

16. If $CD = 3$ and $\underline{\quad DE \quad} = 3$,
$r \parallel n$.

**17–24.** Complete the statement in as many ways as possible using

 **a.** parallelogram  **b.** rhombus  **c.** rectangle  **d.** square

17. If $ABCD$ is a $\underline{\text{a, b, c, d}}$,
$\triangle ABC \cong \triangle CDA$.

18. If $\overline{AB} \parallel \overline{CD}$ and $\overline{AB} \cong \overline{CD}$,
$ABCD$ is a $\underline{\quad \text{a} \quad}$.

19. If $ABCD$ is a $\underline{\quad \text{b, d} \quad}$,
$\overline{AB} \cong \overline{BC}$.

20. If $ABCD$ is a $\underline{\quad \text{c, d} \quad}$,
$\angle A \cong \angle B$.

21. In $\square ABCD$, if $\overline{AB} \perp \overline{CB}$,
$ABCD$ is a $\underline{\quad \text{c} \quad}$.

22. If $\overline{AC}$ and $\overline{BD}$ bisect each
other, $ABCD$ is a $\underline{\quad \text{a} \quad}$.

23. If $ABCD$ is a $\underline{\text{a, b, c, d}}$,
$m\angle A + m\angle B = 180$.

24. If $\overline{AC}$ and $\overline{BD}$ bisect and
$\overline{AC} \perp \overline{BD}$, $ABCD$ is a $\underline{\quad \text{b} \quad}$.

25. Slides (<u>do</u>, do not) preserve parallelism.

YIELD

NARROW BRIDGE

# POLYGONS

**5**

Different types of traffic signs have different shapes. But the outline of each sign is roughly a *polygon*.

You have already worked with two important kinds of polygons — triangles and quadrilaterals. In this chapter, we introduce other kinds of polygons and continue the study of triangles and quadrilaterals.

ONE
WAY
→

STOP

# 5.1 What Are Polygons?

Suggested Class Time

| Course | Min. | Reg. | Max. |
|--------|------|------|------|
| Days   | 1    | 1    | 1    |

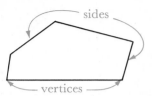

sides

vertices

A **polygon** is a figure formed by joining three or more coplanar segments (called *sides*) at their endpoints (called *vertices*). The sides intersect at the vertices only, with each side intersecting exactly one other side at each vertex. Also, two sides with a common vertex are *not* collinear.

Polygons

Not Polygons

Sides $\overline{AB}$ and $\overline{EF}$ do not intersect another side at each of their endpoints.

Side $\overline{DE}$ does not intersect sides $\overline{AC}$ and $\overline{FG}$ at their endpoints.

Side $\overline{AC}$ intersects more than one side at vertex $C$.

Sides $\overline{CD}$ and $\overline{CB}$ are collinear. (Though $ABCD$ is not a four-sided polygon, $ABD$ is a three-sided one.)

| Notice | Comments |
|--------|----------|
| polygon $ABCDEF$ or polygon $CBAFED$ | Name a polygon by naming its vertices in order. |
| The *diagonals* that can be drawn from vertex $A$ are $\overline{AC}$, $\overline{AD}$, and $\overline{AE}$. | **Diagonals** are segments with nonconsecutive vertices as endpoints. |
| The *interior* of this polygon is a *convex* set. | A polygon separates the plane into two parts, its **interior** and its **exterior**. |
| $ABCDEF$ is a *convex polygon*. | A polygon is **convex** when its interior is a convex set. |

Every triangle is a convex polygon, but polygons with more than three sides may or may not be convex.

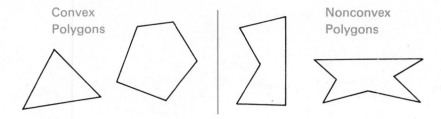

Convex Polygons    Nonconvex Polygons

Types of Polygons

| Name | Number of sides | Figures |
|------|-----------------|---------|
| triangle | 3 | |
| quadrilateral | 4 | |
| pentagon | 5 | |
| hexagon | 6 | |
| heptagon | 7 | |
| octagon | 8 | |
| nonagon | 9 | |
| decagon | 10 | |
| 12-gon | 12 | |
| 28-gon | 28 | |
| $n$-gon | $n$ | |

triangle    quadrilateral    pentagon    hexagon

heptagon    octagon    decagon    12-gon

Any polygon may be called an $n$-gon (where $n$ is the number of sides). Common names for some polygons are listed above.

## Exercises 5.1

Ⓐ 1–2. Complete each statement with the best words possible.

1. A polygon is a figure formed by joining three or more _____ segments (called _____) at their endpoints (called _____).

   Coplanar; sides; vertices

2. The sides intersect at the _____ only. Each side intersects exactly _____ other side(s) at each vertex.

   Vertices; one

Assignment Guide
*Oral:* 1–6
*Written:* Min. 7–26
          Reg. 7–26
          Max. 7–29

3–5. Is the given figure a polygon?

3. No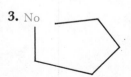

4. 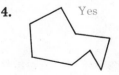 Yes

5. 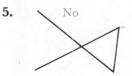 No

**6.** When is a polygon convex?
*When its interior is a convex set*

**7–10.** Use the polygon at the right.

**7.** Name its sides.
*CI, IN, NE, EM, MA, AC*   

**8.** Name its vertices.
*C, I, N, E, M, A*

**9.** Is polygon *AMECIN* a name for this polygon? Why?
*No; vertices not named in order.*

**10.** Name the diagonals that can be drawn from vertex *E*. *EI, EC, EA*

**11–18.** How many sides does each polygon have?

**11.** pentagon  *5*     **12.** hexagon  *6*     **13.** heptagon  *7*     **14.** octagon  *8*

**15.** nonagon  *9*     **16.** decagon  *10*     **17.** 36-gon  *36*     **18.** *n*-gon  *n*

**19–22.** Draw each type of polygon.

**19.** convex pentagon     **20.** convex decagon

**21.** nonconvex hexagon     **22.** nonconvex heptagon

**23–26.** For each convex polygon, draw all possible diagonals.

**23.** quadrilateral  *There are 2.*     **24.** pentagon  *There are 5.*

**25.** hexagon  *There are 9.*     **26.** heptagon  *There are 14.*

**28.** Clockwise from upper left: pentagon, triangle, quadrilateral, octagon, quadrilateral

**29.** Left: chiefly quadrilaterals, but also triangles and other polygons; Right: pentagon

**27.** Without drawing, find how many diagonals are in these convex polygons: an octagon, a nonagon, and a 12-gon. HINT: Make a table of your answers for Exercises 23–26.
*Octagon: 20; nonagon: 27; 12-gon: 54*

**28.** Identify the polygon that is the shape of each traffic sign on page 163.

**29.** Identify the polygons in each photo.

Rohn Engh/Van Cleve Photography

Van Cleve/Van Cleve Photography

The **perimeter** of a polygon is the sum of the lengths of its sides. To find the perimeter $P$ of polygon $ABCDE$, we add the lengths of the sides.

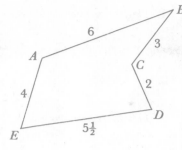

$$P = AB + BC + CD + DE + EA$$
$$P = 6 + 3 + 2 + 5\tfrac{1}{2} + 4 = 20\tfrac{1}{2}$$

**Suggested Class Time**

| Course | Min. | Reg. | Max. |
|--------|------|------|------|
| Days   | 1    | 1    | 1    |

The perimeter $P$ of $ABCDE$ is $20\tfrac{1}{2}$.

Consider $\square JKMN$ with $JK = MN$ and $KM = NJ$. For one pair of sides $JK = MN = b_1$, and for the other pair of sides $KM = NJ = b_2$.

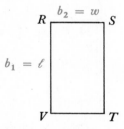

$$P = JK + KM + MN + NJ$$
$$P = b_1 + b_2 + b_1 + b_2$$
$$P = 2b_1 + 2b_2$$
$$\boxed{P = 2(b_1 + b_2)}$$

Use the formula above to find the perimeter of any parallelogram.

Rectangle $RSTV$ is also a parallelogram. Suppose that $b_1$ is the length of $RSTV$ and $b_2$ is the width. To find the perimeter of a rectangle, we use this formula:

$$P = 2(b_1 + b_2)$$

Substituting $b_1 = \ell$ and $b_2 = w$   $\boxed{P = 2(\ell + w)}$

A **regular polygon** is a convex polygon that is *equiangular* (all angles congruent) and *equilateral* (all sides congruent).

| square | rectangle | rhombus |
|--------|-----------|---------|

 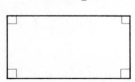 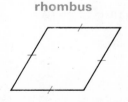

regular polygon      equiangular polygon      equilateral polygon

Consider any regular polygon with $n$ sides. Each side has the same length $s$. To find the perimeter, multiply the length of one side by the number of sides.

$$\boxed{P = ns}$$

# Exercises 5.2

**Assignment Guide**
*Oral:* 1–6
*Written:*
Min. 7–16; 19–22
Reg. 7–24
Max. 7–13 odd; 15–28
*Constructions:* 29–30

Ⓐ **1.** Define *perimeter* of a polygon. *See page 167.*

**2–4.** Identify each variable in the following formulas:

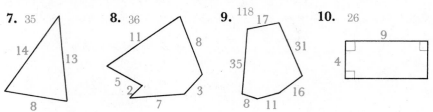

perimeter of □
**2.** $P = 2(b_1 + b_2)$

perimeter of rectangle
**3.** $P = 2(\ell + w)$

lengths of consec. sides

perimeter of reg. polygon
**4.** $P = ns$
no. of sides
length of a side

**5.** Define *regular polygon.*
See page 167.

**6.** Define *equilateral polygon.*
See page 167.

Ⓑ **7–10.** Find the perimeter of each of the following:

**7.** 35  14  13  8

**8.** 36  11  8  5  2  7  3

**9.** 118  17  31  35  16  8  11

**10.** 26  9  4

**11–14.** Find the perimeter of each parallelogram with sides of the given lengths.

**11.** 12 cm, 6 cm    36 cm

**12.** 8 m, 7.3 m    30.6 m

**13.** 2.1 km, 3 km   10.2 km

**14.** 13 km, 8 km    42 km

**15–18.** Use the given information to find the perimeter of each rectangle.

**15.** $\ell = 18$ m, $w = 2$ m

**16.** $\ell = 5.2$ cm, $w = 7.9$ cm   26.2 cm

**17.** $\ell = x$, $w = 4x$

**18.** $\ell = 5$, $w = 7 + 2y$    $24 + 4y$

**19–20.** Measure the sides and angles of each figure. Is it a regular polygon? Why or why not?

**19.**

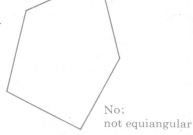

No;
not equiangular

**20.**

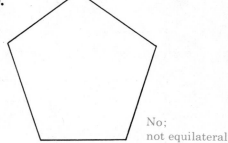

No;
not equilateral

**21–24.** Use the given information to find the perimeter of each regular polygon ($s =$ length of a side).

**21.** hexagon, $s = 4$ cm    24 cm

**22.** decagon, $s = 2.6$ m    26 m

**23.** pentagon, $s = 7 + 8x$
                    35 + 40x

**24.** nonagon, $s = 4w$    $36w$

ⓒ **25.** How many meters of fencing are needed for this tennis-court area?    85.4 m

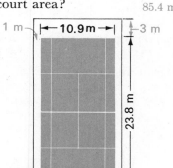

**26.** What is the perimeter of the Mescalero Apache Indian Reservation in Arizona, shown below?    192 km

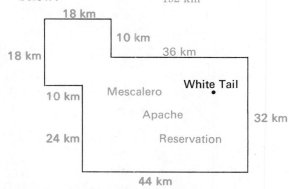

**27.** Find the perimeter of a rhombus with sides of the given length.

    **a.** 5 m    20 m     **b.** 12 cm    48 cm     **c.** $r$    $4r$

**28.** Using your answer to Exercise 27, state a formula for the perimeter of a rhombus.    $P = 4s$, where $s$ is the length of each side

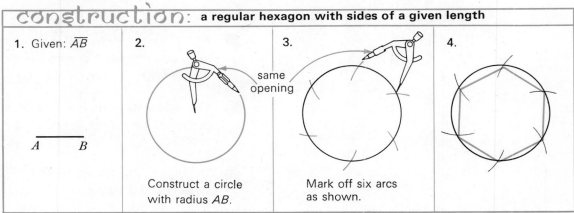

**construction:** **a regular hexagon with sides of a given length**

**1.** Given: $\overline{AB}$

$\overline{A \qquad B}$

**2.**

same opening

Construct a circle with radius $AB$.

**3.**

Mark off six arcs as shown.

**4.**

**29–30.** Construct a regular hexagon with sides of the given length.

**29.** _____

**30.** _____

# 5.3　Angles of Convex Polygons

**Suggested Class Time**

| Course | Min. | Reg. | Max. |
|--------|------|------|------|
| Days | 2 | 1 | 1 |

For any convex polygon, each pair of consecutive sides determines an **angle** of the polygon. These angles are also called **interior angles**.

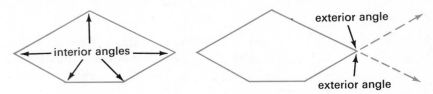

By extending the sides of a convex polygon, two **exterior angles** are determined at each vertex. Each of these two exterior angles is adjacent and supplementary to the interior angle at that vertex.

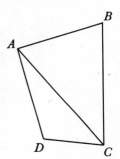

We can find the sum of the measures of the angles of any convex quadrilateral as follows. Either diagonal and the sides form two triangles.

The sum of the measures of the angles in each triangle is 180.

So the sum of the measures of the angles of the convex quadrilateral is $180 \cdot 2$ or 360.

Using a similar procedure, you can find the sum of the measures of the interior angles of any convex polygon. (For convenience, in the rest of this section we'll shorten *sum of the measures of the angles* to *sum of the angles*.)

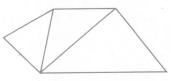

5 sides, 3 triangles

6 sides, 4 triangles

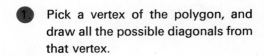

1. Pick a vertex of the polygon, and draw all the possible diagonals from that vertex.

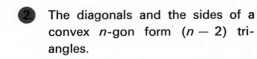

2. The diagonals and the sides of a convex *n*-gon form $(n - 2)$ triangles.

3. The sum of the angles in each triangle is 180. Therefore,

| sum of interior angles of a convex polygon with *n* sides | $= 180 \cdot (n - 2)$ |
|---|---|

Remember that $(n - 2)$ is the number of triangles.

Once you know the sum of the interior angles of a convex polygon, you can find the sum of the exterior angles, *one* at each vertex. The sum of the interior angle and one exterior angle at each vertex is 180. So the sum of the interior angles and exterior angles (one at each vertex) of a polygon is 180 times the number of vertices (or sides). We find the sum of the exterior angles as follows:

**1.** In any polygon with $n$ sides, ▶ $$\text{sum of interior angles} + \text{sum of exterior angles} = 180n$$

**2.** By subtracting, ▶ $$\text{sum of exterior angles} = 180n - \text{sum of interior angles}$$

**3.** The sum of the interior angles equals $180(n - 2)$. ▶ $$= 180n - 180(n - 2)$$

**4.** Simplifying, we have ▶ $$= 180n - 180n - (-360)$$
$$= 360$$

In a regular polygon, all the interior angles are congruent. The exterior angles are also congruent, since supplements of congruent angles are congruent. Therefore, for regular polygons, we can write formulas for finding the measure of *each* interior or exterior angle.

$$\text{Measure of each interior angle of a regular } n\text{-gon} = \frac{180(n - 2)}{n}$$ ← sum of all interior angles / number of congruent angles

$$\text{Measure of each exterior angle of a regular } n\text{-gon} = \frac{360}{n}$$ ← sum of all exterior angles / number of congruent angles

## Exercises 5.3

Ⓐ **1–2.** Answer questions **a–d** for each polygon.

**1.**

**2.**

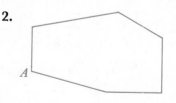

**Assignment Guide**
*Oral:* 1–2
*Written:* Min. (day 1) 3–22
(day 2) 23–40
Reg. 3–39 odd
Max. 3–39 odd
*Constructions:* 41–42

**a.** How many diagonals can be drawn from point $A$?  1; 3

**b.** How many triangles are formed?  2; 4

**c.** What is the sum of the interior angles?  360; 720

**d.** What is the sum of the exterior angles, one at each vertex?  360; 360

Ⓑ 3–16. Copy and complete the table.

| | Convex polygon | Number of sides | Number of triangles | Sum of interior angles | Sum of exterior angles |
|---|---|---|---|---|---|
| 3. | triangle | 3 | 1 | 180 | 360 |
| 4. | Quadrilateral | 4 | 2 | 360 | 360 |
| 5. | pentagon | 5 | 3 | 540 | 360 |
| 6. | Hexagon | 6 | 4 | 720 | 360 |
| 7. | Heptagon | 7 | 5 | 900 | 360 |
| 8. | Octagon | 8 | 6 | 1080 | 360 |
| 9. | nonagon | 9 | 7 | 1260 | 360 |
| 10. | 10-gon | 10 | 8 | 1440 | 360 |
| 11. | 12-gon | 12 | 10 | 1800 | 360 |
| 12. | 17-gon | 17 | 15 | 2700 | 360 |
| 13. | 20-gon | 20 | 18 | 3240 | 360 |
| 14. | 22-gon | 22 | 20 | 3600 | 360 |
| 15. | 36-gon | 36 | 34 | 6120 | 360 |
| 16. | 52-gon | 52 | 50 | 9000 | 360 |

17–18. Four of the angle measures in a convex pentagon are given. Find the measure of the fifth angle.

**17.** 70, 120, 80, 92   178

**18.** 150, 148, 93, 76   73

19–20. Five of the angle measures in a convex hexagon are given. Find the measure of the sixth angle.

**19.** 150, 148, 137, 81, 76   128

**20.** 43, 78, 148, 160, 151   140

21–22. For these polygons, measure the angles. Find the sum of (a) the interior angles and (b) the exterior angles, one at each vertex.

**21.**

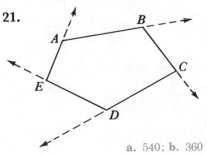

a. 540; b. 360

**22.**

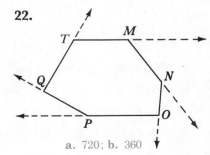

a. 720; b. 360

**23–36.** Copy and complete the table.

| | Regular polygon | Number of sides | Measure of each interior angle | Measure of each exterior angle |
|---|---|---|---|---|
| **23.** | Triangle | 3 | 60 | 120 |
| **24.** | Quadrilateral or square | 4 | 90 | 90 |
| **25.** | pentagon | 5 | 108 | 72 |
| **26.** | hexagon | 6 | 120 | 60 |
| **27.** | Heptagon | 7 | $128\frac{4}{7}$ | $51\frac{3}{7}$ |
| **28.** | Octagon | 8 | 135 | 45 |
| **29.** | nonagon | 9 | 140 | 40 |
| **30.** | Decagon or 10-gon | 10 | 144 | 36 |
| **31.** | 50-gon | 50 | 172.8 | 7.2 |
| **32.** | 100-gon | 100 | 176.4 | 3.6 |
| **33.** | 12-gon | 12 | 150 | 30 |
| **34.** | 30-gon | 30 | 168 | 12 |
| **35.** | 18-gon | 18 | 160 | 20 |
| **36.** | 45-gon | 45 | 172 | 8 |

**37–40.** Draw each regular polygon. HINT: Use a protractor to draw interior angles of the proper measure.

**37.** pentagon: side 6 cm      **38.** hexagon: side 4 cm

**39.** octagon: side 45 mm     **40.** pentagon: side 5 cm

© **41.** *Construct:* a regular quadrilateral with a side of length 2 cm

**42.** *Construct:* a regular octagon with a side of length 2 cm

HINT:

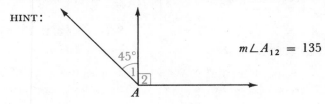

$m\angle A_{12} = 135$

# 5.4 Congruent Polygons

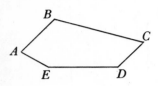

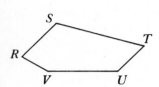

**Congruent polygons** are two polygons that have all parts (sides and angles) of one polygon congruent to the corresponding parts of the other. As with congruent triangles, there is a one-to-one correspondence between the vertices of congruent polygons.

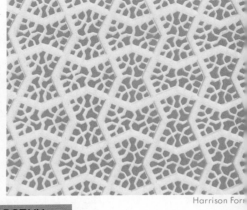

Harrison Forr

| $ABCDE \cong RSTUV$ | |
|---|---|
| $\angle A$ and $\angle R$ | $\overline{AB}$ and $\overline{RS}$ |
| $\angle B$ and $\angle S$ | $\overline{BC}$ and $\overline{ST}$ |
| $\angle C$ and $\angle T$ | $\overline{CD}$ and $\overline{TU}$ |
| $\angle D$ and $\angle U$ | $\overline{DE}$ and $\overline{UV}$ |
| $\angle E$ and $\angle V$ | $\overline{AE}$ and $\overline{RV}$ |

corresponding angles → ← corresponding sides

For certain special polygons we can tell whether they are congruent without knowing that all corresponding parts are congruent.

**SAS Theorem for Parallelograms**

**Side-Angle-Side Theorem for Parallelograms:** If two consecutive sides and the angle they determine of one parallelogram are congruent to the corresponding parts of another parallelogram, then the parallelograms are congruent.

Given: $\overline{AD} \cong \overline{WZ}$, $\overline{DC} \cong \overline{ZY}$, $\angle D \cong \angle Z$

Prove: $\Box ABCD \cong \Box WXYZ$

[*Plan:* Use properties of parallelograms and parallel lines to show that all corresponding sides and angles are congruent.]

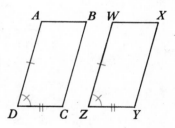

Proof:

| STATEMENTS | REASONS |
|---|---|
| 1. $\overline{AD} \cong \overline{WZ}$, $\overline{DC} \cong \overline{ZY}$, $\angle D \cong \angle Z$ | 1. Given |
| 2. $\overline{AD} \cong \overline{BC}$, $\overline{DC} \cong \overline{AB}$, $\overline{WZ} \cong \overline{XY}$, $\overline{ZY} \cong \overline{WX}$ | 2. Opposite sides of a $\Box$ are $\cong$. |
| 3. $\overline{BC} \cong \overline{WZ}$, $\overline{AB} \cong \overline{ZY}$, $\overline{BC} \cong \overline{XY}$, $\overline{AB} \cong \overline{WX}$ | 3. Segments $\cong$ to the same segment are $\cong$. |
| 4. $\angle A$ and $\angle D$ are supplementary, $\angle W$ and $\angle Z$ are supplementary. | 4. Consecutive $\angle$s of a $\Box$ are supplementary. |

**5.** $\angle A \cong \angle W$

**6.** $\angle D \cong \angle B, \angle A \cong \angle C,$
$\angle Z \cong \angle X, \angle W \cong \angle Y$

**7.** $\angle B \cong \angle Z, \angle C \cong \angle W$
$\angle B \cong \angle X, \angle C \cong \angle Y$

**8.** $\square ABCD \cong \square WXYZ$

**5.** Two angles supp. to $\cong \angle$s are $\cong$.

**6.** Opp. $\angle$s of a $\square$ are $\cong$.

**7.** $\angle$s $\cong$ to the same angle are $\cong$.

**8.** Definition of congruent polygons

# Exercises 5.4

Ⓐ **1.** Define *congruent polygons.*  *See page 174.*

**2–3.** Name the corresponding parts of the congruent polygons.

**2.**

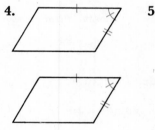

$\angle A, \angle B; \underline{\angle C}, \angle R; \underline{\angle G}, \angle E; \underline{\angle F}, \angle S;$
$\overline{AC}, \overline{BR}; \overline{CG}, \overline{RE}; \overline{GF}, \overline{ES}; \overline{FA}, \overline{SB}$

**3.**

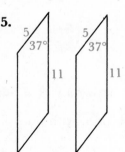

**Assignment Guide**
*Oral:* 1–6
*Written:*
Min. 7–15; Quiz, p. 176
Reg. 7–16; Quiz, p. 176
Max. 7–18; Quiz, p. 176

**3.** $\angle M, \angle H; \angle P, \angle N;$
$\angle Q, \angle O; \angle D, \angle T;$
$\angle K, \angle S; \angle J, \angle W;$
$\overline{MP}, \overline{HN}; \overline{PQ}, \overline{NO};$
$\overline{QD}, \overline{OT}; \overline{DK}, \overline{TS};$
$\overline{KJ}, \overline{SW}; \overline{JM}, \overline{WH}$

**4–6.** Corresponding congruent parts are marked. Is each pair of parallelograms congruent? Why?

**4–6.** Yes; SAS Thm. for $\square$s

**4.**    **5.**    **6.**

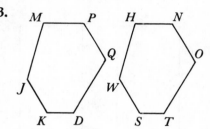

Ⓑ **7–14.** *RELYZA* $\cong$ *MOSNPD,* find:

**7.** *MO*  3    **8.** *LE*  8    **9.** *RA*  4

**10.** *YZ*  4    **11.** $m\angle O$  150    **12.** $m\angle A$  165

**13.** $m\angle Y$  45    **14.** $m\angle Z$  165

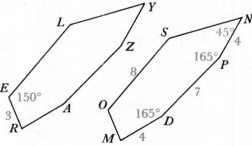

**15.** 1. ▱*ABCD*, ▱*EFGH*,
∠*A* ≅ ∠*E*, $\overline{BC} \cong \overline{FG}$
(Given)
2. $\overline{BC} \cong \overline{AD}$, $\overline{FG} \cong \overline{EH}$
(Opp. sides of ▱
are ≅.)
3. $\overline{AD} \cong \overline{FG}$ (Segs. ≅
to same seg. are ≅.)
4. $\overline{AD} \cong \overline{EH}$ (Same as
step 3)
5. $\overline{AB} \cong \overline{EF}$ (Given)
6. ▱*ABCD* ≅ ▱*EFGH*
(SAS Thm. for ▱s)

**16.** 1–4. Steps 1–4, Ex. 15
5. $\overline{EF} \cong \overline{DC}$ (Given)
6. $\overline{DC} \cong \overline{AB}$ (Opp.
sides of ▱ are ≅.)
7. $\overline{AB} \cong \overline{EF}$ (Segs. ≅
to same seg. are ≅.)
8. ▱*ABCD* ≅ ▱*EFGH*
(SAS Thm. for ▱s)

**17.** SAS Thm. for ▱s (All ∠s
are ≅ rt. ∠s.)

**18.** SAS Thm. for ▱s (All
other sides are ≅.)

**15.** Given: ▱*ABCD*, ▱*EFGH*,
∠*A* ≅ ∠*E*, $\overline{AB} \cong \overline{EF}$, $\overline{BC} \cong \overline{FG}$

Prove: ▱*ABCD* ≅ ▱*EFGH*

**16.** Given: ▱*ABCD*, ▱*EFGH*,
$\overline{BC} \cong \overline{FG}$, $\overline{EF} \cong \overline{DC}$, ∠*A* ≅ ∠*E*

Prove: ▱*ABCD* ≅ ▱*EFGH*

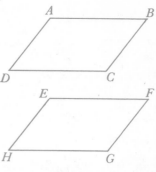

© **17.** Rectangles *MEZO* and *BDAF*
have two pairs of corresponding consecutive sides congruent.
Why is *MEZO* ≅ *BDAF*?

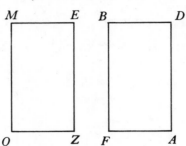

**18.** Rhombuses *RHOM* and *BUSI*
have one pair of corresponding sides and angles congruent.
Why is *RHOM* ≅ *BUSI*?

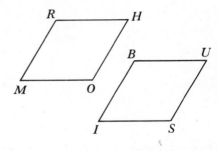

**1–3.** Define these terms.

**1.** *polygon*
See page 164.

**2.** *convex polygon*
See page 164.

**3.** *equilateral polygon*
See page 167.

**4–9.** Find the following:

**4.** perimeter of a regular hexagon with a side of length 3  18

**5.** perimeter of a parallelogram with sides of lengths 5 and 7  24

**6.** sum of the interior angles of a convex hexagon  720

**7.** sum of the exterior angles, one at each vertex, of a convex heptagon
360

**8.** measure of each interior angle of a regular octagon  135

**9.** measure of each exterior angle of a regular 12-gon  30

**10.** When are any two regular hexagons congruent polygons?
When a side of one is ≅ to a side of the other

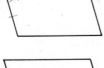
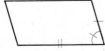

**11.** Are the parallelograms at the left congruent? Why?
Yes; SAS Thm. for ▱s

# PRACTICAL POLYGONS

The congruent polygons shown here are used in industry, buildings, and designs.

Authenticated News International

Marimekko

Courtesy Burroughs Wellcome Company

## 5.5 AAS Theorem

We now return to the study of congruent triangles that was begun in Chapter 3.

In any triangle, each side is **opposite** one of the angles.

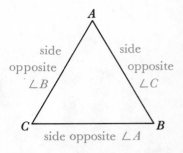

side opposite ∠B    side opposite ∠C

side opposite ∠A

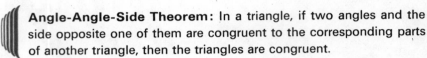

**AAS Theorem**

> **Angle-Angle-Side Theorem:** In a triangle, if two angles and the side opposite one of them are congruent to the corresponding parts of another triangle, then the triangles are congruent.

Given: $\overline{AB} \cong \overline{DE}$, $\angle C \cong \angle F$, $\angle A \cong \angle D$

Prove: $\triangle ABC \cong \triangle DEF$

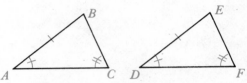

Proof:

| STATEMENTS | REASONS |
|-----------|---------|
| 1. $\angle C \cong \angle F$, $\angle A \cong \angle D$ | 1. Given |
| 2. $\angle B \cong \angle E$ | 2. If two angles of a △ are ≅ to two ∠s of another △, the remaining ∠s are ≅. |
| 3. $\overline{AB} \cong \overline{DE}$ | 3. Given |
| 4. $\triangle ABC \cong \triangle DEF$ | 4. ASA Postulate |

## Exercises 5.5

(A) **1–4.** Corresponding congruent parts are marked. Tell which postulate (from Chapter 3) or theorem (AAS) can be used to prove the triangles congruent.

**1.**     **2.**     **3.**     **4.**

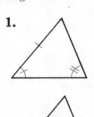

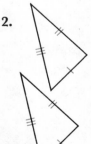

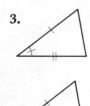

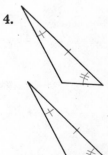

AAS Thm.     SSS Post.     SAS Post.     ASA Post.

**(B)** **5–10.** Using the given information, which postulate or theorem can be used to prove $\triangle NAR \cong \triangle NAI$? Remember $\overline{AN} \cong \overline{AN}$.

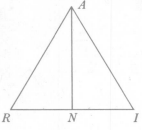

**5.** $\angle RNA$, $\angle INA$ right angles, $\angle R \cong \angle I$        AAS Thm.

**6.** $\angle RNA \cong \angle INA$, $\overrightarrow{AN}$ the bisector of $\angle RAI$        ASA Post.

**7.** $\angle RNA \cong \angle INA$, $\overline{NR} \cong \overline{NI}$        SAS Post.

**8.** $\overline{RA} \cong \overline{IA}$, $\overline{RN} \cong \overline{IN}$        SSS Post.

**9.** $\angle R \cong \angle I$, $\overrightarrow{AN}$ the bisector of $\angle RAI$        AAS Thm.

**10.** $\overline{AR} \cong \overline{AI}$, $m\angle RAN = m\angle IAN$        SAS Post.

**11–20.** Give a reason for each statement.

Given: $\overline{AE}$ bisects $\overline{ST}$ at $K$. $\angle E \cong \angle A$

Prove: $\triangle SKE \cong \triangle TKA$

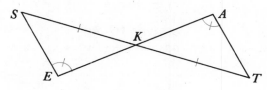

**Proof:**

| STATEMENTS | | REASONS |
|---|---|---|
| 1. $\overline{AE}$ bisects $\overline{ST}$ at $K$. | 1. | **11.** Given |
| 2. $\overline{SK} \cong \overline{KT}$ | 2. | **12.** Definition of bisector |
| 3. $\angle SKE \cong \angle TKA$ | 3. | **13.** Vertical $\angle$s are $\cong$. |
| 4. $\angle E \cong \angle A$ | 4. | **14.** Given |
| 5. $\triangle SKE \cong \triangle TKA$ | 5. | **15.** AAS Theorem |

Given: $\overline{BU} \cong \overline{TU}$, $\angle BRU \cong \angle TEU$, $\overline{BE}$ and $\overline{TR}$ intersect at $U$.

Prove: $\overline{UR} \cong \overline{UE}$

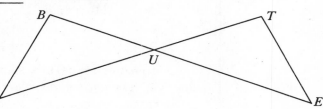

**Proof:**

| STATEMENTS | | REASONS |
|---|---|---|
| 1. $\overline{BU} \cong \overline{TU}$ | 1. | **16.** Given |
| 2. $\angle BRU \cong \angle TEU$ | 2. | **17.** Given |
| 3. $\angle BUR \cong \angle TUE$ | 3. | **18.** Vertical $\angle$s are $\cong$. |
| 4. $\triangle BUR \cong \triangle TUE$ | 4. | **19.** AAS Theorem |
| 5. $\overline{UR} \cong \overline{UE}$ | 5. | **20.** Corres. parts of $\cong \triangle$s are $\cong$. |

**21.**
1. $\angle DIM \cong \angle EIM$
   $\angle D \cong \angle E$ (Given)
2. $\overline{IM} \cong \overline{IM}$ (Seg. is $\cong$ to itself.)
3. $\triangle DIM \cong \triangle EIM$ (AAS Thm.)
4. $\overline{DM} \cong \overline{EM}$ (Corres. parts of $\cong \triangle$s are $\cong$.)

**(C)** **21.** Given: $\angle D \cong \angle E$, $\angle DIM \cong \angle EIM$

Prove: $\overline{DM} \cong \overline{EM}$

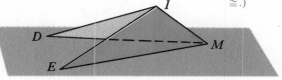

# 5.6 Isosceles Triangles and Trapezoids

**Suggested Class Time**

| Course | Min. | Reg. | Max. |
|--------|------|------|------|
| Days   | 1    | 1    | 1    |

Some triangles are given special names because of their sides or angles.

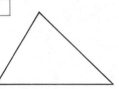 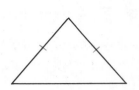 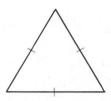

| Triangles named according to their sides | **scalene triangle:** no congruent sides | **isosceles triangle:** at least two congruent sides | **equilateral triangle:** three congruent sides |
|---|---|---|---|

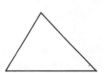  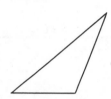 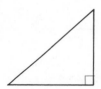 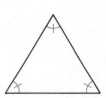

| Triangles named according to their angles | **acute triangle:** three acute angles | **obtuse triangle:** exactly one obtuse angle | **right triangle:** exactly one right angle | **equiangular triangle:** three congruent angles |
|---|---|---|---|---|

An **isosceles trapezoid** is a trapezoid whose nonparallel sides are congruent. The parts of isosceles triangles and isosceles trapezoids have similar names.

Isosceles triangle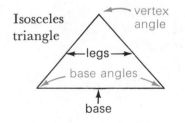

Isosceles trapezoid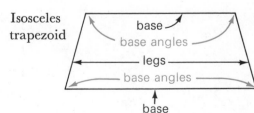

**Isosceles Triangle Theorem**

**a.** If two sides of a triangle are congruent, the angles opposite those sides are congruent.

**b.** If two angles of a triangle are congruent, the sides opposite those angles are congruent.

Part **a** of this theorem is often stated as follows: *Base angles of an isosceles triangle are congruent.* The proof of part **a** follows. Part **b** (the converse of part **a**) is proved in Exercises 31–36.

Given: $\overline{AC} \cong \overline{BC}$

Prove: $\angle A \cong \angle B$

[*Plan:* Use the bisector of $\angle ACB$ as an auxiliary ray. Prove $\triangle ACM \cong \triangle BCM$.]

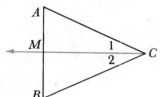

Proof:

| STATEMENTS | REASONS |
|---|---|
| 1. Let $\overrightarrow{CM}$ be the bisector of $\angle ACB$. | 1. Every angle has a bisector. |
| 2. $\angle 1 \cong \angle 2$ | 2. Definition of angle bisector |
| 3. $\overline{AC} \cong \overline{BC}$ | 3. Given |
| 4. $\overline{MC} \cong \overline{MC}$ | 4. A segment is $\cong$ to itself. |
| 5. $\triangle ACM \cong \triangle BCM$ | 5. SAS Postulate |
| 6. $\angle A \cong \angle B$ | 6. Corres. parts of $\cong$ $\triangle$s are $\cong$. |

The next theorem is a corollary of the Isosceles Triangle Theorem.

**a.** If a triangle is equilateral, it is equiangular.

**b.** If a triangle is equiangular, it is equilateral.

**Equilateral Triangle Theorem**

**Part a.**

Given: $\overline{RS} \cong \overline{TS} \cong \overline{TR}$

Prove: $\angle T \cong \angle R \cong \angle S$

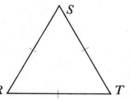

Proof:

| STATEMENTS | REASONS |
|---|---|
| 1. $\overline{RS} \cong \overline{TS}$, $\overline{TS} \cong \overline{TR}$ | 1. Given |
| 2. $\angle T \cong \angle R$, $\angle R \cong \angle S$ | 2. Isosceles Triangle Theorem |
| 3. $\angle T \cong \angle R \cong \angle S$ | 3. $\angle$s $\cong$ to the same $\angle$ are $\cong$. |

Part **b**, above, is proved in Exercises 37–38.

**a.** If the nonparallel sides of a trapezoid are congruent, both pairs of base angles are congruent.

**b.** If either pair of base angles of a trapezoid are congruent, the nonparallel sides are congruent.

**Isosceles Trapezoid Theorem**

The proof of part **a** follows. Part **b** is proved in Exercises 39–48.

Given: Trapezoid $ABCD$ with $\overline{AB} \parallel \overline{DC}$,
    $\overline{AD} \cong \overline{BC}$

Prove: $\angle D \cong \angle C$, $\angle DAB \cong \angle B$

[*Plan:* Let $\overline{AE}$ be parallel to $\overline{BC}$. Show that $\triangle DAE$ is isosceles.]

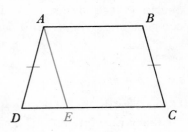

Proof:

| STATEMENTS | REASONS |
|---|---|
| 1. Let $\overline{AE}$ be parallel to $\overline{BC}$. | 1. Parallel Postulate (p. 125) |
| 2. $\overline{AB} \parallel \overline{DC}$ | 2. Given |
| 3. $ABCE$ is a parallelogram. | 3. Definition of parallelogram |
| 4. $\overline{BC} \cong \overline{AE}$ | 4. Opposite sides of a $\square$ are $\cong$. |
| 5. $\overline{AD} \cong \overline{BC}$ | 5. Given |
| 6. $\overline{AD} \cong \overline{AE}$ | 6. Segments $\cong$ to the same seg. are $\cong$. |
| 7. $\angle D \cong \angle AED$ | 7. Isosceles Triangle Theorem |
| 8. $\angle AED \cong \angle C$ | 8. Since $\overleftrightarrow{BC} \parallel \overleftrightarrow{AE}$, corres. $\angle$s are $\cong$. ($\overleftrightarrow{CD}$ is a transversal of $\overleftrightarrow{BC}$ and $\overleftrightarrow{AE}$.) |
| 9. $\angle D \cong \angle C$ | 9. $\angle$s $\cong$ to same $\angle$ are $\cong$. |
| 10. $\angle DAB$ and $\angle D$ are supplementary, $\angle B$ and $\angle C$ are supplementary. | 10. Since $\overleftrightarrow{AB} \parallel \overleftrightarrow{DC}$, interior $\angle$s on same side of transversal are supp. |
| 11. $\angle DAB \cong \angle B$ | 11. Supplements of $\cong$ $\angle$s are $\cong$. |

# Exercises 5.6

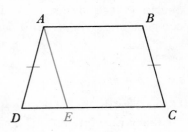 (assignment guide)

Assignment Guide
*Oral:* 1–16
*Written:* Min. 17–30
       Reg. 17–27; 31–38
       Max. 17–27; 31–48

(A) **1–8.** Describe each of the following special polygons:   1–8. *See page 180.*

1. equilateral triangle

2. equiangular triangle

3. scalene triangle

4. right triangle

5. obtuse triangle

6. isosceles triangle

7. acute triangle

8. isosceles trapezoid

**9–10.** Use the figure.

**9.** For isosceles △*DAE*, name the

    **a.** legs  $\overline{DA}, \overline{EA}$  **b.** base angles  $\angle D, \angle AED$

    **c.** base  $\overline{DE}$  **d.** vertex angle  $\angle DAE$

**10.** For isosceles trapezoid *ABCD* name the

    **a.** legs  $\overline{AD}, \overline{BC}$  **b.** bases  $\overline{AB}, \overline{DC}$

    **c.** base angles (both pairs)
    $\angle DAB$ and $\angle B$, $\angle D$ and $\angle C$

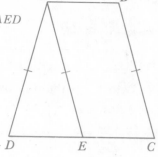

**11–16.** Using △*HES* and the given information, name any other segments or angles that will be congruent.

**11.** $\overline{HE} \cong \overline{HS}$  $\angle S, \angle E$      **12.** $\overline{HS} \cong \overline{ES}$  $\angle H, \angle E$

**13.** $\overline{HS} \cong \overline{SE} \cong \overline{EH}$      **14.** $\angle H \cong \angle S$  $\overline{HE}, \overline{SE}$
    $\angle H, \angle S, \angle E$

**15.** $\angle H \cong \angle E$      **16.** $\angle H \cong \angle E \cong \angle S$
    $\overline{HS}, \overline{ES}$                   $\overline{HS}, \overline{SE}, \overline{EH}$

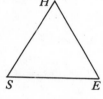

Ⓑ **17–24.** Draw these triangles if possible. If it is impossible to draw the triangle, write *impossible* on your paper.

**17.** isosceles right triangle      **18.** right scalene triangle

**19.** obtuse equilateral triangle      **20.** obtuse isosceles triangle
                   Impossible
**21.** right equilateral triangle      **22.** obtuse scalene triangle
                   Impossible
**23.** acute scalene triangle      **24.** acute isosceles triangle

**25–30.** *ODEC* is an isosceles trapezoid. Use the given information to find the measures of as many segments and angles as possible.

**25.** △*COG* is isosceles. $CO = GO = 12$, $m\angle COG = 50$

**26.** △*OGC* is equiangular. $OC = 4$

**27.** △*GOC* is equilateral. $OC = 8$, *ODEG* is a rhombus.

**28.** △*COG* is isosceles. $OC = CG = 3$, $m\angle CGO = 70$

**29.** △*COG* is isosceles. $OC = CG = 5$, $m\angle CGO = 74$

**30.** △*OGC* is isosceles. $OC = CG = 20$, $m\angle OGC = 52$

**25.** $DE = 12$;
$m\angle C = m\angle OGC =$
$m\angle E = m\angle DOG = 65$;
$m\angle OGE = m\angle D =$
$m\angle DOC = 115$

**26.** $OG = CG = DE = 4$;
$m\angle C = m\angle COG =$
$m\angle OGC = m\angle E =$
$m\angle DOG = 60$;
$m\angle OGE = m\angle D =$
$m\angle DOC = 120$

**27.** $CG = OG = OC =$
$GE = ED = DO = 8$;
$CE = 16$; *same angle measures as Ex. 26*

**28.** $DE = 3$; $m\angle OGE = 110$;
$m\angle COG = m\angle DOG =$
$70$;
$m\angle C = m\angle E = 40$;
$m\angle DOC = m\angle D = 140$

**29.** $DE = 5$; $m\angle OGE = 106$;
$m\angle COG = m\angle DOG =$
$74$;
$m\angle C = m\angle E = 32$;
$m\angle DOC = m\angle D = 148$

**30.** $DE = 20$; $m\angle OGE = 128$;
$m\angle COG = m\angle DOG =$
$52$;
$m\angle C = m\angle E = 76$;
$m\angle DOC = m\angle D = 104$

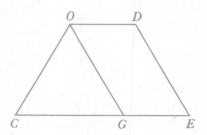

**31–48.** Give a reason for each statement.

Given: $\angle A \cong \angle B$

Prove: $\overline{AC} \cong \overline{BC}$

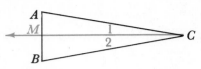

Proof:

| STATEMENTS | REASONS |
|---|---|
| 1. Let $\overrightarrow{CM}$ be the bisector of $\angle ACB$. | 1. **31.** Every $\angle$ has a bisector. |
| 2. $\angle 1 \cong \angle 2$ | 2. **32.** Def. of $\angle$ bisector |
| 3. $\angle A \cong \angle B$ | 3. **33.** Given |
| 4. $\overline{CM} \cong \overline{CM}$ | 4. **34.** Seg. is $\cong$ to itself. |
| 5. $\triangle ACM \cong \triangle BCM$ | 5. **35.** AAS Thm. |
| 6. $\overline{AC} \cong \overline{BC}$ | 6. **36.** Corres. parts of $\cong$ $\triangle$s are $\cong$. |

Given: $\angle T \cong \angle R \cong \angle S$

Prove: $\overline{RS} \cong \overline{TS} \cong \overline{TR}$

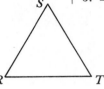

Proof:

| STATEMENTS | REASONS |
|---|---|
| 1. $\angle T \cong \angle R, \angle R \cong \angle S$ | 1. Given |
| 2. $\overline{RS} \cong \overline{TS}, \overline{TS} \cong \overline{TR}$ | 2. **37.** If 2 $\angle$s of $\triangle$ are $\cong$, sides opp. are $\cong$. |
| 3. $\overline{RS} \cong \overline{TS} \cong \overline{TR}$ | 3. **38.** Segs. $\cong$ to same seg. are $\cong$. |

© Given: Trapezoid $ABCD$ with $\overline{AB} \parallel \overline{DC}$, $\angle DAB \cong \angle B$

Prove: $\overline{AD} \cong \overline{BC}$

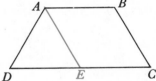

39. Given

40. Int. $\angle$s on same side of transversal are supp.

41. Supps. of $\cong$ $\angle$s are $\cong$.

42. Parallel Post.

43. Definition of $\square$

44. Opp. sides of $\square$ are $\cong$.

45. If lines are $\parallel$, corres. $\angle$s are $\cong$.

46. $\angle$s $\cong$ to same $\angle$ are $\cong$. (steps 3 and 7)

47. If 2 $\angle$s of $\triangle$ are $\cong$, sides opp. are $\cong$.

48. Segs. $\cong$ to same seg. are $\cong$. (steps 6 and 9)

Proof:

| STATEMENTS | REASONS |
|---|---|
| 1. $\overline{AB} \parallel \overline{DC}, \angle DAB \cong \angle B$ | 1. **39.** |
| 2. $\angle C$ and $\angle B$, $\angle D$ and $\angle DAB$ are supp. | 2. **40.** |
| 3. $\angle C \cong \angle D$ | 3. **41.** |
| 4. Let $\overline{AE}$ be parallel to $\overline{BC}$. | 4. **42.** |
| 5. $ABCE$ is a parallelogram. | 5. **43.** |
| 6. $\overline{AE} \cong \overline{BC}$ | 6. **44.** |
| 7. $\angle AED \cong \angle C$ | 7. **45.** |
| 8. $\angle AED \cong \angle D$ | 8. **46.** |
| 9. $\overline{AD} \cong \overline{AE}$ | 9. **47.** |
| 10. $\overline{AD} \cong \overline{BC}$ | 10. **48.** |

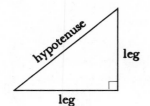

# Congruent Right Triangles

**5.7**

In a right triangle, the side opposite the right angle is called the **hypotenuse**. The sides opposite the acute angles are called **legs**.

**Suggested Class Time**

| Course | Min. | Reg. | Max. |
|--------|------|------|------|
| Days | 1 | 1 | 1 |

**Hypotenuse–Acute-Angle Theorem:** If the hypotenuse and an acute angle of one right triangle are congruent to the corresponding parts of another right triangle, then the triangles are congruent.

**HA Theorem**

Given: $\overline{AC} \cong \overline{XZ}$, $\angle C \cong \angle Z$, $\angle B$ and $\angle Y$ are right angles.

Prove: $\triangle ABC \cong \triangle XYZ$

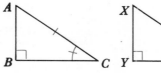

Proof: 

| STATEMENTS | REASONS |
|------------|---------|
| 1. $\overline{AC} \cong \overline{XZ}$, $\angle C \cong \angle Z$ | 1. Given |
| 2. $\angle B$ and $\angle Y$ are right angles. | 2. Given |
| 3. $\angle B \cong \angle Y$ | 3. Any two right $\angle$s are $\cong$. |
| 4. $\triangle ABC \cong \triangle XYZ$ | 4. AAS Theorem |

**Leg–Acute-Angle Theorem:** If a leg and an acute angle of one right triangle are congruent to the corresponding parts of another right triangle, then the triangles are congruent.

**LA Theorem**

*Case 1:* The given leg is opposite the given acute angle.

Given: $\angle A \cong \angle D$, $\overline{BC} \cong \overline{EF}$, $\angle B$ and $\angle E$ are right angles.

Prove: $\triangle ABC \cong \triangle DEF$

Proof: 

| STATEMENTS | REASONS |
|------------|---------|
| 1. $\angle A \cong \angle D$, $\overline{BC} \cong \overline{EF}$ | 1. Given |
| 2. $\angle B$ and $\angle E$ are right angles. | 2. Given |
| 3. $\angle B \cong \angle E$ | 3. Any two right $\angle$s are $\cong$. |
| 4. $\triangle ABC \cong \triangle DEF$ | 4. AAS Theorem |

*Case 2:* The given leg is *not* opposite the given acute angle.
Case 2 is proved in Exercises 13–15.

Other theorems for proving right triangles congruent are the Leg-Leg Theorem and the Hypotenuse-Leg Theorem.

**LL Theorem**

**Leg-Leg Theorem:** If two legs of one right triangle are congruent to the corresponding parts of another right triangle, then the triangles are congruent.

Given: $\overline{AB} \cong \overline{DE}$, $\overline{BC} \cong \overline{EF}$, $\angle B$ and $\angle E$ are right angles.

Prove: $\triangle ABC \cong \triangle DEF$

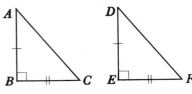

Proof:

| STATEMENTS | REASONS |
|---|---|
| 1. $\overline{AB} \cong \overline{DE}$, $\overline{BC} \cong \overline{EF}$ | 1. Given |
| 2. $\angle B$ and $\angle E$ are right angles. | 2. Given |
| 3. $\angle B \cong \angle E$ | 3. Any two right $\angle$s are $\cong$. |
| 4. $\triangle ABC \cong \triangle DEF$ | 4. SAS Postulate |

**HL Theorem**

**Hypotenuse-Leg Theorem:** If the hypotenuse and a leg of one right triangle are congruent to the corresponding parts of another right triangle, then the triangles are congruent.

Given: $\overline{AB} \cong \overline{DE}$, $\overline{BC} \cong \overline{EF}$, $\angle A$ and $\angle EDF$ are right angles.

Prove: $\triangle ABC \cong \triangle DEF$

[*Plan:* Use auxiliary segment $DG$ on the ray opposite $\overrightarrow{DF}$ and congruent to $\overline{AC}$. Then prove $\triangle DEG \cong \triangle ABC$. Next prove $\triangle DEG \cong \triangle DEF$.]

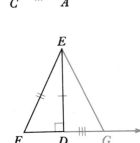

Proof:

| STATEMENTS | REASONS |
|---|---|
| 1. Draw the ray opposite ray $DF$ and choose point $G$ so $\overline{DG} \cong \overline{AC}$. | 1. Point Plotting Theorem (p. 27) |
| 2. $\overline{AB} \cong \overline{DE}$, $\angle A$ and $\angle EDF$ are right $\angle$s. | 2. Given |
| 3. $\overleftrightarrow{DE} \perp \overleftrightarrow{FG}$ at $D$ | 3. Definition of $\perp$ lines |
| 4. $\angle EDG$ is a right angle. | 4. $\perp$ lines form 4 right angles. |
| 5. $\triangle DEG$, $\triangle DEF$, $\triangle ABC$ are right $\triangle$s. | 5. Definition of a right $\triangle$ |

**6.** $\triangle ABC \cong \triangle DEG$

**7.** $\overline{BC} \cong \overline{EG}$

**8.** $\overline{BC} \cong \overline{EF}$

**9.** $\overline{EG} \cong \overline{EF}$

**10.** $\angle G \cong \angle F$

**11.** $\triangle DEG \cong \triangle DEF$

**12.** $\triangle ABC \cong \triangle DEF$

**6.** LL Theorem

**7.** Corres. parts of $\cong$ $\triangle$s are $\cong$.

**8.** Given

**9.** Segments $\cong$ to the same segment are $\cong$.

**10.** Isosceles Triangle Theorem

**11.** HA Theorem

**12.** $\triangle$s $\cong$ to the same $\triangle$ are $\cong$.

**Assignment Guide**
*Oral:* 1–6
*Written:* Min. 7–20
Reg. 7–21
Max. 7–21; 23

# Exercises 5.7

Ⓐ **1–6.** Corresponding congruent parts and right angles are indicated. What theorem from this section can be used to prove the triangles congruent?

**1.** HA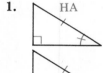

**2.** LA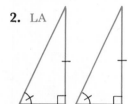

**3.** LA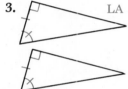

**4.** LL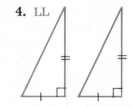

**5.** HL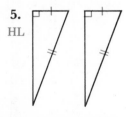

**6.**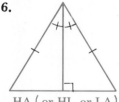
HA ( or HL or LA )

Ⓑ **7–12.** With the given information, what theorem from this section can be used to prove $\triangle NAS \cong \triangle NAT$? Remember $\overline{AN} \cong \overline{AN}$.

**7.** $\angle 3$ and $\angle 4$ are right $\angle$s, $\angle 1 \cong \angle 2$  LA

**8.** $\angle 3$ and $\angle 4$ are right $\angle$s, $\angle S \cong \angle T$  LA

**9.** $\angle 3$ and $\angle 4$ are right $\angle$s, $\overline{SA} \cong \overline{TA}$  HL

**10.** $m\angle 3 = 90$, $m\angle 4 = 90$, $\angle S \cong \angle T$, $\overline{AS} \cong \overline{AT}$
LA ( or HA or HL )

**11.** $\overleftrightarrow{AN}$ the perpendicular bisector of $\overline{ST}$
LL

**12.** $\overline{AN} \perp \overline{ST}$, $AS = AT$  HL

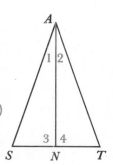

Question 9.

How do you find a hypotenuse?

Look for tracks around the water hole!

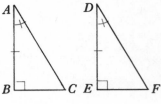

21. *1.* ∠1, ∠2 are rt. ∠s.
(Given)
*2.* △RSQ, △TSQ are rt.
△s. (Def. of rt. △)
*3.* RS = 5, ST = 5
(Given)
*4.* $\overline{RS} \cong \overline{ST}$ (Def. of ≅
segs.)
*5.* $\overline{SQ} \cong \overline{SQ}$ (Seg. is
≅ to itself.)
*6.* △RSQ ≅ △TSQ
(LL Thm.)

22. *1.* ∠C, ∠S are rt. ∠s.
(Given)
*2.* △MCU, △ISU are rt.
△s. (Def. of rt. △)
*3.* $\overline{MC} \cong \overline{IS}$ (Given)
*4.* ∠MUC ≅ ∠IUS
(Vert. ∠s are ≅.)
*5.* △MCU ≅ △ISU
(LA Thm.)

23. *Plan:* Prove △BCA ≅
△BCD by the LL Thm.
Then $\overline{AB}$ and $\overline{DB}$ are
≅ corres. parts.

24. *Plan:* Show $\overline{DE} \cong \overline{CE}$
and $\overline{AE} \cong \overline{BE}$. Then
△EAD ≅ △EBC by the
HL Thm.

**13–20.** Give a reason for each statement.

**Given:** $\angle A \cong \angle D$, $\overline{AB} \cong \overline{DE}$,
∠B and ∠E are right ∠s.

**Prove:** △ABC ≅ △DEF

**Proof:**

| STATEMENTS | | REASONS |
|---|---|---|
| *1.* $\angle A \cong \angle D$, $\overline{AB} \cong \overline{DE}$ | *1.* __13.__ | Given |
| *2.* ∠B and ∠E are right ∠s. | *2.* __14.__ | Given |
| *3.* ∠B ≅ ∠E | *3.* __15.__ | Rt. ∠s are ≅. |
| *4.* △ABC ≅ △DEF | *4.* ASA Post. | |

**Given:** $\overleftrightarrow{GC}$ the ⊥ bisector of $\overline{DE}$,
$\overline{GE} \cong \overline{CD}$

**Prove:** △GFE ≅ △CFD

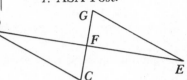

**Proof:**

| STATEMENTS | | REASONS |
|---|---|---|
| *1.* $\overleftrightarrow{GC}$ the ⊥ bisector of $\overline{DE}$, $\overline{GE} \cong \overline{CD}$ | *1.* __16.__ | Given |
| *2.* $\overline{DF} \cong \overline{EF}$ | *2.* __17.__ | Def. of bisector |
| *3.* ∠CFD and ∠GFE are right ∠s. | *3.* __18.__ | Def. of ⊥ |
| *4.* △CFD and △GFE are right △s. | *4.* __19.__ | Def. of rt. △ |
| *5.* △GFE ≅ △CFD | *5.* __20.__ | HL Thm. |

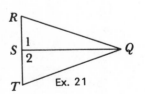

Ex. 21

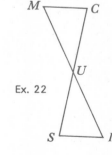

Ex. 22

21. **Given:** ∠1 and ∠2 are right ∠s,
RS = 5, ST = 5

**Prove:** △RSQ ≅ △TSQ

22. **Given:** ∠C and ∠S are right ∠s,
$\overline{MC} \cong \overline{IS}$

**Prove:** △MCU ≅ △ISU

© 23. **Given:** $\overline{AC} \cong \overline{DC}$,
∠BCA and ∠BCD are right ∠s.

**Prove:** $\overline{AB} \cong \overline{DB}$

24. **Given:** Rectangle ABCD, ∠1 ≅ ∠2,
E the midpoint of $\overline{AB}$

**Prove:** △EAD ≅ △EBC

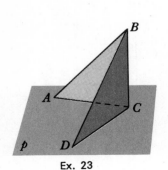

Ex. 23

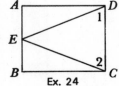

Ex. 24

# Triangle Congruence Summarized

5.8

### TRIANGLES CAN BE PROVED CONGRUENT BY

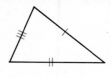 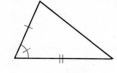 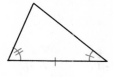 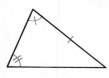

 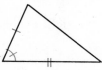 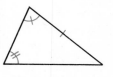

Side-Side-Side     Side-Angle-Side     Angle-Side-Angle     Angle-Angle-Side

### RIGHT TRIANGLES CAN BE PROVED CONGRUENT BY

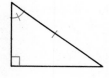 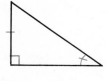 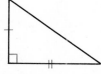 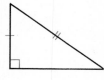

Hypotenuse–Acute-Angle    Leg–Acute-Angle    Leg-Leg    Hypotenuse-Leg

Triangles **cannot** be proved congruent by

Side-Side-Angle       Angle-Angle-Angle

## *Exercises 5.8*

Ⓐ **1–4.** Corresponding congruent parts are marked. What theorem or postulate lets you state that the triangles are congruent?

**1.**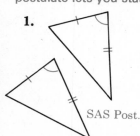

SAS Post.

**2.**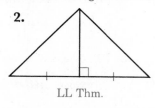

LL Thm.

**3.**

LA Thm.

**4.**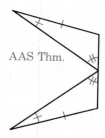

AAS Thm.

**Assignment Guide 5.8**
*Oral:* 1–10
*Written:* Min. 11–13 odd
      Reg. 11–13
      Max. 11–17 odd

**11.** *1.* $\overline{HP} \cong \overline{MK}$, $\angle P \cong \angle K$
    (Given)
  *2.* $\angle PJH \cong \angle KJM$
    (Vert. $\angle$s are $\cong$.)
  *3.* $\triangle PJH \cong \triangle KJM$
    (AAS Thm.)

**12.** *1.* $J$ is midpt. of $\overline{KP}$
    and $\overline{HM}$. (Given)
  *2.* $\overline{PJ} \cong \overline{KJ}$, $\overline{JH} \cong \overline{JM}$
    (Def. of midpt.)
  *3.* $\angle PJH \cong \angle KJM$
    (Vert. $\angle$s are $\cong$.)
  *4.* $\triangle PJH \cong \triangle KJM$
    (SAS Post.)

**13.** *1.* $\overline{PR} \cong \overline{PR}$ (Seg. is
    $\cong$ to itself.)
  *2.* $\overleftrightarrow{PS}$ the $\perp$ bis. of
    $\overline{AT}$ (Given)
  *3.* $\overline{AR} \cong \overline{TR}$ (Def. of
    bisector)
  *4.* $\angle PRA$, $\angle PRT$ rt.
    $\angle$s. (Def. of $\perp$)
  *5.* $\triangle PRA$, $\triangle PRT$ rt.
    $\triangle$s. (Def. of rt. $\triangle$)
  *6.* $\triangle PRA \cong \triangle PRT$
    (LL Thm.)

**14.** *1.* $\overline{PA} \cong \overline{PT}$ (Given)
  *2.* $\overline{PR} \cong \overline{PR}$ (Seg. is
    $\cong$ to itself.)
  *3.* $m\angle PRT = 90$,
    $m\angle PRA = 90$ (Given)
  *4.* $\triangle PRA$, $\triangle PRT$ rt.
    $\triangle$s. (Def. of rt. $\triangle$)
  *5.* $\triangle PRA \cong \triangle PRT$
    (HL Thm.)
  *6.* $\overline{AR} \cong \overline{TR}$ (Corres.
    parts of $\cong$ $\triangle$s are $\cong$.)

*15–18. Answers on page 195*

**5–10.** Using the given information, what theorem or postulate can be used to prove $\triangle ABC \cong \triangle ADC$?

**5.** $\overline{AB} \cong \overline{AD}$, $\overline{BC} \cong \overline{DC}$   SSS Post.

**6.** $\angle B$ and $\angle D$ are right angles, $AB = AD$
                        HL Thm.

**7.** $\overrightarrow{CA}$ bisects $\angle C$, $\overrightarrow{AC}$ bisects $\angle A$.   ASA Post.

**8.** $\overrightarrow{AC}$ bisects $\angle A$, $\overline{AD} \cong \overline{AB}$   SAS Post.

**9.** $\overline{BC} \cong \overline{DC}$, $\angle B$ and $\angle D$ are right angles.   HL Thm.

**10.** $\overrightarrow{CA}$ bisects $\angle C$, $\overline{BC} \cong \overline{DC}$   SAS Post.

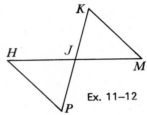

Ex. 11–12

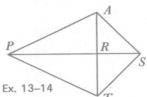

Ex. 13–14

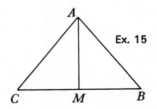

Ex. 15

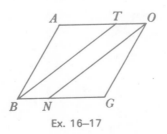

Ex. 16–17

Ⓑ **11.** Given: $\overline{HP} \cong \overline{MK}$, $\angle P \cong \angle K$
    Prove: $\triangle PJH \cong \triangle KJM$

**12.** Given: Point $J$ the midpoint
    of $\overline{KP}$ and $\overline{HM}$
    Prove: $\triangle PJH \cong \triangle KJM$

**13.** Given: $\overleftrightarrow{PS}$ the $\perp$ bisector of $\overline{AT}$
    Prove: $\triangle PRA \cong \triangle PRT$

**14.** Given: $m\angle PRT = 90$, $\overline{PA} \cong \overline{PT}$,
    $m\angle PRA = 90$
    Prove: $\overline{AR} \cong \overline{TR}$

Ⓒ **15.** Given: $\overleftrightarrow{AM}$ the $\perp$ bisector of $\overline{BC}$
    Prove: $\triangle ABC$ isosceles

**16.** Given: $\square BTON$, $\angle ABT \cong \angle GON$
    Prove: $\triangle ABT \cong \triangle GON$

**17.** Given: Rhombus $AOGB$, $\overline{BT} \parallel \overline{NO}$
    Prove: $\triangle ATB \cong \triangle GNO$

**18.** Given: Regular hexagon $ABCDEF$
    Prove: $ACDF$ is a rectangle.

# Overlapping Triangles

5.9

If you look closely, you will see a vase and the silhouette of two faces.

**Suggested Class Time**

| Course | Min. | Reg. | Max. |
| --- | --- | --- | --- |
| Days | 1 | 1 | 1 |

I.

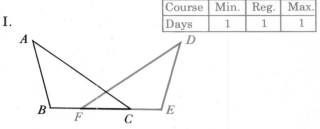

By looking closely at figure I, you will see two congruent triangles that overlap. **Overlapping triangles** are triangles whose interiors have points in common.

If we redraw the figure so that the triangles no longer overlap, it is easier to see which parts correspond. See figure II.

II.

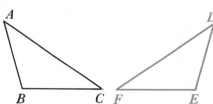

$$\overline{AB} \cong \overline{DE} \qquad \angle A \cong \angle D$$
$$\overline{BC} \cong \overline{EF} \qquad \angle B \cong \angle E$$
$$\overline{CA} \cong \overline{FD} \qquad \angle C \cong \angle F$$

If we draw in the diagonals of an isosceles trapezoid, overlapping triangles $ADC$ and $BCD$ are formed. See figure III. These triangles can be used in proving the next theorem. Part **a** is proved in Exercises 13–17.

III.

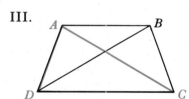

**a.** If a trapezoid is isosceles, its diagonals are congruent.
**b.** If a trapezoid has congruent diagonals, it is isosceles.

**Theorem**

---

## Exercises 5.9

**Assignment Guide**
*Oral:* 1–6
*Written:* Min. 7–22
            Reg. 7–24
            Max. 7–25

Ⓐ **1–8.** Tell **(a)** if the triangles overlap or not and **(b)** if they appear to be congruent.

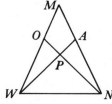

**1.** $\triangle MAW$, $\triangle MON$
  **a.** Yes   **b.** Yes

**2.** $\triangle MAW$, $\triangle NAW$
  **a.** No   **b.** No

**3.** $\triangle POW$, $\triangle PAN$
  **a.** No   **b.** Yes

**4.** $\triangle MEI$, $\triangle OEV$
  **a.** No   **b.** Yes

**5.** $\triangle VEI$, $\triangle VEO$
  **a.** No   **b.** No

**6.** $\triangle MIV$, $\triangle OVI$
  **a.** Yes   **b.** Yes

**Proof:**

| STATEMENTS | REASONS |
|---|---|
| 1. $HGDC$ a rectangle, $\overline{CF} \cong \overline{DA}$ | 1. __**18.**__ Given |
| 2. $\overline{CH} \cong \overline{DG}$ | 2. __**19.**__ Opp. sides of $\square$ are $\cong$. |
| 3. $\angle CHF$ and $\angle DGA$ are right $\angle$s. | 3. __**20.**__ $\square$ has 4 rt. $\angle$s. |
| 4. $\triangle ADG$ and $\triangle FCH$ are right $\triangle$s. | 4. __**21.**__ Def. of rt. $\triangle$ |
| 5. $\triangle ADG \cong \triangle FCH$ | 5. __**22.**__ HL Thm. |

**23.** Given: $\overline{GE} \cong \overline{GA}$, $\angle RGA \cong \angle TGE$

Prove: $\triangle RGA \cong \triangle TGE$

Ex. 23–24

**24.** Given: $\angle R \cong \angle T$, $\overline{RA} \cong \overline{TE}$

Prove: $\triangle RGA \cong \triangle TGE$

© **25.** Given: $\overline{SC} \cong \overline{EC}$, $\overline{NC} \cong \overline{DC}$, $\angle 1 \cong \angle 2$

Prove: $\overline{SU} \cong \overline{EA}$

Ex. 25–26

**26.** Given: $\angle U$ and $\angle A$ are right $\angle$s, $\overline{SU} \cong \overline{EA}$, $\angle 1 \cong \angle 2$

Prove: $\overline{NC} \cong \overline{DC}$

**27.** Prove part **b** of the theorem on page 191. [*Plan:* In the figure for Exercises 13–17, draw $\overline{AF} \perp \overline{DC}$ at $F$ and $\overline{BE} \perp \overline{DC}$ at $E$. Prove $\triangle AFC \cong \triangle BED$. Then prove $\triangle ADC \cong \triangle BCD$.]

**27.** *Given:* Trapezoid $ABCD$, $\overline{AC} \cong \overline{BD}$
*Prove:* $\overline{AD} \cong \overline{BC}$
*Proof:*
1. Let $\overline{AF} \perp \overline{DC}$ at $F$. Let $\overline{BE} \perp \overline{DC}$ at $E$. (In a plane, there is 1 line through a pt. $\perp$ to a given line.)
2. $\angle AFE$, $\angle BEF$ rt. $\angle$s (Def. of $\perp$)
3. $\triangle AFC$, $\triangle BED$ rt. $\triangle$s (Def. of rt. $\triangle$s)
4. $\overline{AF} \cong \overline{BE}$ ($\parallel$ lines are equidistant.)
5. $\overline{AC} \cong \overline{BD}$ (Given)
6. $\triangle AFC \cong \triangle BED$ (HL Thm.)
7. $\angle ACE \cong \angle BDF$ (Corres. parts of $\cong$ $\triangle$s are $\cong$.)
8. $\overline{DC} \cong \overline{DC}$ (Seg. is $\cong$ to itself.)
9. $\triangle ACD \cong \triangle BDC$ (SAS Post.)
10. $\overline{AD} \cong \overline{BC}$ (Corres. parts of $\cong$ $\triangle$s are $\cong$.)

## TRIANGLES IN BUILDINGS

Carpenters build supports in the shape of triangles for roofs of buildings. The photo shows one way of building the framework for a roof. Pick out where the carpenter used isosceles triangles and right triangles.

The framework is built in the shape of triangles because triangles are rigid figures. Triangular supports change shape only when a side breaks. Quadrilateral supports can change shape when boards become loose at their joints.

GEOMETRY AT WORK

# 5.10 Transformations: Line Symmetry

**Suggested Class Time**

| Course | Min. | Reg. | Max. |
|--------|------|------|------|
| Days | 1 | 1 | 1 |

Alfa

If a figure can be folded into two "congruent halves" (same size and shape) so that one half coincides with the other half, the figure has line, or reflection, symmetry. A figure that has **line symmetry** can be reflected over a line so that the original figure is its own image. The reflecting line is called a symmetry line of the figure.

These figures have line symmetry. They are called line symmetric figures. Notice that a figure may be line symmetric to more than one line.

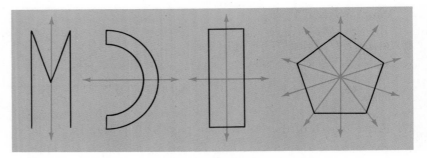

These figures do not have line symmetry.

**Assignment Guide**
*Oral:* 1–4
*Written:* Min. 5–21 odd
Reg. 5–26
Max. 5–31

Some polygons have line symmetry, while others do not. Are regular polygons line symmetric? Exercises 5–16 will help you answer that question.

## Exercises 5.10

(A) **1.** What is a line symmetric figure? *See above.*

**2–4.** Name the symmetry lines, if any, for each figure.

**2.** $\ell$

**3.** None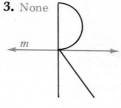

**4.** $c$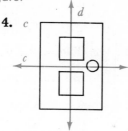

Answers for page 190

Ⓑ **5–16.** Copy each figure. Draw all symmetry lines.

*5–16.* No. of symmetry lines is given.

**5.**

**6.**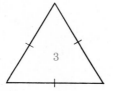

**7.**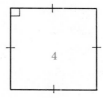

**8.**

**9.**

**10.**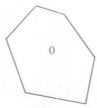

**11.**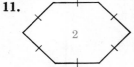

**12.**

**13.**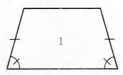

**14.**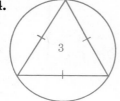

**15.**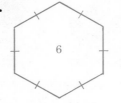

**16.**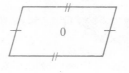

**15.** 1. $\overrightarrow{AM}$ is the ⊥ bis. of $\overline{BC}$. (Given)
   2. $\overline{AC} \cong \overline{AB}$ (Pt. on ⊥ bis. of seg. is equidist. from endpts.)
   3. $\triangle ABC$ is isosceles. (Def. of isos. $\triangle$)

**16.** 1. ▱ $BTON$ (Given)
   2. $\overline{BT} \cong \overline{ON}$ (Opp. sides of a ▱ are ≅.)
   3. $\overleftrightarrow{BT} \parallel \overleftrightarrow{ON}$, $\overleftrightarrow{BN} \parallel \overleftrightarrow{TO}$ (Def. of ▱)
   4. $\angle ATB \cong \angle TBN$ (If lines are ∥, alt. int. $\angle$s are ≅.)
   5. $\angle TBN \cong \angle GNO$ (If lines are ∥, corres. $\angle$s are ≅.)
   6. $\angle ATB \cong \angle GNO$ ($\angle$s ≅ to same $\angle$ are ≅.)
   7. $\angle ABT \cong \angle GON$ (Given)
   8. $\triangle ABT \cong \triangle GON$ (ASA Post.)

**17.** *Plan:* Prove that since $AOGB$ is a rhombus, $\angle A \cong \angle G$ and $\overline{AB} \cong \overline{GO}$. Prove $\angle ATB \cong \angle GNO$ as in steps 4–6, Ex. 16. So the $\triangle$s are ≅ by the AAS Thm.

**18.** *Plan:* Prove $\triangle ABC \cong \triangle FED$ by the SAS Post. Then opp. sides of $ACDF$ are ≅, so it is a ▱. Use the $\angle$ Add. Post. and the def. of regular polygon to prove that consecutive $\angle$s of $ACDF$ are ≅. Prove they are also supplementary so they are right $\angle$s and $ACDF$ is a rectangle.

**17–22.** True or False? Draw a figure to explain your answer.

**17.** The symmetry line of an isosceles triangle bisects the vertex angle.  T

**18.** The diagonal of a rectangle is on a symmetry line for the rectangle.  F

**19.** The bisector of an angle is on a symmetry line for the angle.  T

**20.** A line has exactly one symmetry line.  F

**21.** A symmetry line of an equilateral triangle bisects a side.  T

**22.** The perpendicular bisector of a segment is a symmetry line for the segment.  T

**23–28.** How many symmetry lines does each polygon have?  HINT: Your answers to Exercises 5–16 will be helpful.

**23.** isosceles triangle    1

**24.** equilateral triangle  3

**25.** square            4

**26.** regular octagon    8

ⓒ **27.** regular 20-gon    20

**28.** regular $n$-gon    $n$

**29–30.** Many designs used in floor tiles, fabrics, and rugs are line symmetric. Is each design line symmetric?

**29.**
Yes

**30.**
Yes

**31.** Some words are line symmetric. WOW and DID are examples. Where are the symmetry lines? Name two more words that have a symmetry line.    WOW    DID

# ■ Chapter 5 Review ■

| Suggested Class Time | | | |
|---|---|---|---|
| Course | Min. | Reg. | Max. |
| Days | 1 | 1 | 1 |

**1.** Define *polygon*. *See page 164.*   **2.** Define *convex polygon*. *See page 164.*          **5.1**

**3–5.** Use the figure at the right.

**3.** Use the letters in the figure to give two names for the polygon.
*Typical answer: ABCDE, EDCBA*

**4.** What type of convex polygon is this?
Pentagon

**5.** Find the perimeter. 34.2

**6.** Find the perimeter of a regular hexagon with side of length 3.   18

**7.** Find the perimeter of a rectangle if $\ell = 4$ and $w = 7\frac{1}{2}$.   23

**8.** Find the sum of the exterior angles, one at each vertex, of a 300-gon. 360   **5.3**

**9.** Find the sum of the interior angles of a 42-gon.   7200

**10.** Find the measure of each interior angle of a regular 22-gon.   $163\frac{7}{11}$

**11.** Find the measure of each exterior angle of a regular 30-gon.   12

**12–15.** *ABCD* ≅ *EFGH*, *ABCD* a parallelogram, find:          **5.4**

**12.** *AB*   9      **13.** *GF* 6

**14.** $m\angle H$  37     **15.** $m\angle E$
143

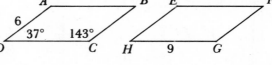

**16.** Is $\triangle RST \cong \triangle WXY$ by the AAS Theorem? Why?          **5.5**
No; corres. ∠s are not ≅.

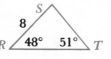

**17–20.** Identify each triangle with the most specific name possible.          **5.6**

**17.**

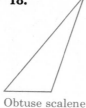

Right scalene

**18.**

Obtuse scalene

**19.**

Equilateral

**20.**

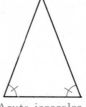

Acute isosceles

**Assignment Guide**
*Written:* Min. 1–20; 24–33
Reg. 1–33
Max. 1–33

**21.**
1. $\angle T \cong \angle S$ (Given)
2. $\overline{AT} \cong \overline{AS}$ (If 2 $\angle$s of $\triangle$ are $\cong$, sides opp. are $\cong$.)

**5.7**

**5.8**

**5.9**

**22.**
1. $\overline{RI} \perp \overline{RE}, \overline{RI} \perp \overline{WI}$ (Given)
2. $\angle R, \angle I$ are rt. $\angle$s (Def. of $\perp$)
3. $\triangle REV, \triangle IWV$ are rt. $\triangle$s. (Def. of rt. $\triangle$)
4. $\overline{EV} \cong \overline{WV}$ (Given)
5. $\angle RVE \cong \angle IVW$ (Vert. $\angle$s are $\cong$.)
6. $\triangle REV \cong \triangle IWV$ (HA Thm.)

**23.**
1. $\overline{RV} \cong \overline{VI}$ (Given)
2. $\angle RVE \cong \angle IVW$ (Vert. $\angle$s are $\cong$.)
3. $\angle R, \angle I$ are rt. $\angle$s. (Given)
4. $\triangle VER, \triangle VWI$ are rt. $\triangle$s. (Def. of rt. $\triangle$)
5. $\triangle VER \cong \triangle VWI$ (LA Thm.)

**5.10**

---

**21.** Given: $\angle T \cong \angle S$

Prove: $\overline{AT} \cong \overline{AS}$

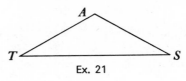

Ex. 21

**22.** Given: $\overline{RI} \perp \overline{RE}, \overline{RI} \perp \overline{WI}, \overline{EV} \cong \overline{WV}$

Prove: $\triangle REV \cong \triangle IWV$

**23.** Given: $\angle R$ and $\angle I$ are right $\angle$s, $\overline{RV} \cong \overline{VI}$

Prove: $\triangle VER \cong \triangle VWI$

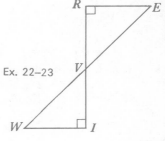

Ex. 22–23

**24.** Name 8 postulates or theorems used to prove triangles congruent. Postulates: SSS, SAS, ASA; theorems: AAS, HA, LA, LL, HL

**25.** Name the corresponding parts of the overlapping triangles, $\triangle RTS \cong \triangle WTU$.
$\overline{RT} \cong \overline{WT}, \overline{RS} \cong \overline{WU}, \overline{ST} \cong \overline{UT},$
$\angle R \cong \angle W, \angle S \cong \angle U, \angle RTS \cong \angle WTU$

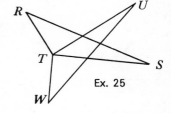

Ex. 25

**26–30.** Give a reason for each statement.

Given: $\overline{AX} \cong \overline{CX}, \overline{CB} \cong \overline{AD}$

Prove: $\triangle ACB \cong \triangle CAD$

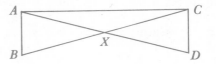

**Proof:**

| STATEMENTS | REASONS |
|---|---|
| 1. $\overline{AX} \cong \overline{CX}$ | 1. **26.** Given |
| 2. $\angle XCA \cong \angle XAC$ | 2. **27.** If 2 sides of $\triangle$ are $\cong$, $\angle$s opp. are $\cong$. |
| 3. $\overline{AC} \cong \overline{AC}$ | 3. **28.** Seg. is $\cong$ to itself. |
| 4. $\overline{CB} \cong \overline{AD}$ | 4. **29.** Given |
| 5. $\triangle ACB \cong \triangle CAD$ | 5. **30.** SAS Post. |

**31–33.** Is the red line a symmetry line for the figure?

**31.** Yes

**32.** No
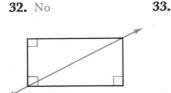

**33.** Yes
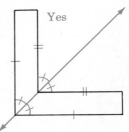

1. Define *congruent polygons*.  *See page 174.*

2. Define *regular polygon*.  *See page 167.*

3. Draw a nonconvex polygon.  *See page 165.*

4. Why is the figure at right not a polygon?

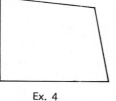

Ex. 4

5. Can a scalene triangle have an obtuse angle?  Yes

6. Is an equiangular triangle always isosceles?  Yes

**Assignment Guide**
*Written:* Min. 1–11; 14
Reg. 1–14
Max. 1–14

4. Two sides do not intersect another side at both endpoints.

7. For a convex 20-gon find the sum of (**a**) the interior angles and (**b**) the exterior angles, one at each vertex.  **a.** 3240; **b.** 360

8. For a regular 36-gon find the measure of each (**a**) interior angle and (**b**) exterior angle.  **a.** 170; **b.** 10

9. Find the perimeter of a parallelogram with sides of lengths 5 and 3.2.  16.4

**10–11.** State a reason for each conclusion.

10. *Given:* $\square ABCD$, $\square FEHG$, $\overline{EH} \cong \overline{BC}$, $\overline{EF} \cong \overline{AB}$, $\angle B \cong \angle E$   SAS Thm. for $\square$s

   *Conclusion:* $ABCD \cong FEHG$

11. *Given:* $\angle E \cong \angle B$, $\angle EFH \cong \angle BAC$, $\overline{AC} \cong \overline{HF}$

   *Conclusion:* $\triangle EFH \cong \triangle BAC$   AAS Thm.

Ex. 10–12

12. Given: $ABCD$ a rhombus

   Prove: $\triangle ADC$ isosceles

13. Given: $\overline{MZ} \cong \overline{NZ}$, $\overline{MQ} \cong \overline{NP}$

   Prove: $\triangle MQN \cong \triangle NPM$

14. Draw a square and all of its symmetry lines.

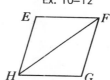

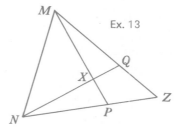

Ex. 13

12. 1. $ABCD$ is a rhombus. (Given)
   2. $\overline{AD} \cong \overline{DC}$ (Def. of rhombus)
   3. $\triangle ADC$ is isosceles. (Def. of isos. $\triangle$)

13. 1. $\overline{MZ} \cong \overline{NZ}$, $\overline{MQ} \cong \overline{NP}$ (Given)
   2. $\angle QMN \cong \angle PNM$ (If 2 sides of $\triangle$ are $\cong$, $\angle$s opp. are $\cong$.)
   3. $\overline{MN} \cong \overline{MN}$ (Seg. is $\cong$ to itself.)
   4. $\triangle MQN \cong \triangle NPM$ (SAS Post.)

14. The 4 symmetry lines contain the diagonals and the $\perp$ bisectors of the sides.

# MINI-CHAPTER: REPEATING DESIGNS

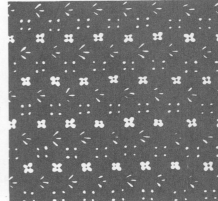
Marimekk

Courtesy Armstrong Resilient Flooring

The floor tiles cover the floor with a repeating design.

The wallpaper covers the wall with a repeating design.

Consider the floor or wall as part of a plane. The entire plane can be covered with the repeating design of wallpaper, floor tile, or polygons, as shown below. Covering a plane with a repeating design is called **tessellating** the plane.

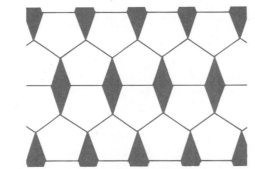

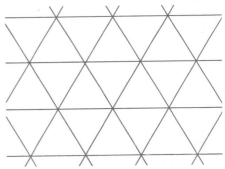

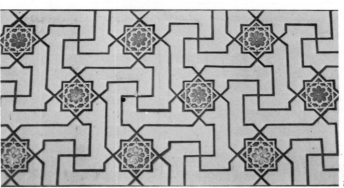
Photri

About 700 years ago, repeating designs were used to decorate the Alhambra, a palace in Spain. Moorish artists used tiles to make their designs. A Moorish design is pictured at the left.

These designs influenced a modern Dutch artist, M. C. Escher. He saw the possibility of covering a surface with a repeating design of animals or people. Here are some examples of Escher's work.

Notice that each of these designs, if repeated, will cover a plane. Escher constructed his designs from regular polygons. In the first figure he used an equilateral triangle, in the second a square, and in the third a regular hexagon.

You can make designs that tessellate the plane from both regular and nonregular polygons.

**Example 1:**

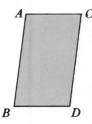 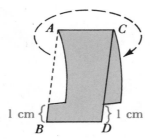 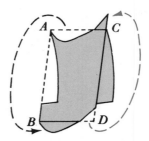

Since parallelograms will tessellate the plane, we can use them to make a repeating design.

Cut a pattern from side $\overline{AB}$ and slide it to side $\overline{DC}$ or vice versa.

Cut a pattern from side $\overline{AC}$ and slide it to side $\overline{BD}$ or vice versa. Or as in this case, do both.

The last shape above can usually be made to look like something interesting by adding some lines and shading. In this case, we can make it look like a sailboat.

Then the sailboat pattern can be used to make a repeating design. Trace the outline of the pattern, slide it, trace again, and so on. Then add the necessary lines and shading.

Notice that we can slide any figure onto any other figure in the design.

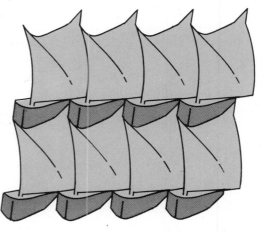

**Example 2:**

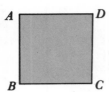 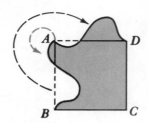 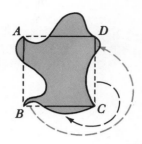

To make a figure that will tessellate the plane from square *ABCD*, pair sides $\overline{AB}$ and $\overline{AD}$ with common vertex *A*, and sides $\overline{CB}$ and $\overline{CD}$ with common vertex *C*.

Cut a shape from side $\overline{AD}$. Turn it onto side $\overline{AB}$ or vice versa. Place the shape so that it is the same distance from *A*.

Cut a shape from side $\overline{CD}$. Turn it onto side $\overline{CB}$ or vice versa. Place the shape so that it is the same distance from *C*.

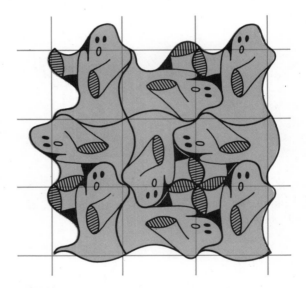

At certain points in this design, one figure can be turned onto another. For example, the four figures in the upper left can be turned to coincide with one another.

**Example 3:**

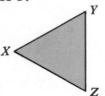

Using equilateral triangle *XYZ*, we can make one of Escher's figures that tessellate a plane.

Cut a shape from side $\overline{XY}$, flip it over, and add it to side $\overline{XZ}$ so that any point on the shape will be the same distance from point $X$ as it was from point $Y$.

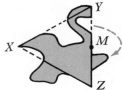

Construct $M$, the midpoint of $\overline{YZ}$.

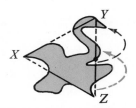

Cut a shape from $\overline{YM}$, flip it, and add it to $\overline{MZ}$ so that a point is the same distance from $M$ as it was from $Y$.

Cut a shape from $\overline{MZ}$, flip it, and add it to $\overline{YM}$ so that a point is the same distance from $Y$ as it was from $M$.

Notice that we can slide any white or gray swan onto any swan of the same color. We can also reflect and then slide any white or gray swan onto any swan of the other color.

M. C. Escher, Escher Foundation, Haags Gemeentemuseum, The Hague

Now try to tessellate the plane. First use polygons in a repeating pattern. Then draw your own repeating design. Use any method shown in the three examples.

© United Features Syndicate, Inc., 1968

# 6 MORE ABOUT PROOFS

Reasoning is very important in writing proofs. But reasoning is used in other places besides geometry. Even Charlie Brown uses reasoning to decide that he cannot talk to the little red-haired girl.

Now that you have worked with proofs, we can take a more detailed look at the ideas involved.

# True and False If-Then Statements

We use if-then statements frequently in everyday life, as well as in mathematics. Obviously, not every if-then statement is true.

```
   ┌──── hypothesis ────┐  ┌──── conclusion ────┐
If you have a white beard, your name is Santa Claus.
```

A. Devaney, Inc.       Authenticated News International

The sentence is true for the man on the left, but not for the man on the right. In Uncle Sam's case, the hypothesis is true (he has a white beard), but the conclusion is false. Since a case exists for which the hypothesis is true and the conclusion is false, we say the if-then statement is false.

> An if-then statement is false if an example can be found for which the hypothesis is true and the conclusion is false.

Such an example is called a **counterexample.** Only one counterexample is needed to prove that an if-then statement is false. (The statement might be true in some cases, but it must be true in *all* cases before we say it is true.)

**Example 1:** Find a counterexample to show that the following if-then statement is false:

If $x^2 = 16$, then $x = 4$.

*Counterexample:* $x = -4$ (The hypothesis $x^2 = 16$ is true, but the conclusion $x = 4$ is false.)

To show that an if-then statement is true, we usually prove it as a theorem. First, however, we have to accept some if-then statements as being true without proof. These are our postulates.

We can't prove theorems without having some postulates. If we try to do that, our reasoning will take us in circles. This is similar to circular definitions. If we try to define terms without first accepting some undefined terms, our definitions would circle back to the term we are trying to define.

**Example 2:** What if-then statement is proved by the following two-column proof?

Given: $4x = 20$

Prove: $x = 5$

| Proof: STATEMENTS | REASONS |
|---|---|
| 1. $\quad 4x = 20$ | 1. Given |
| 2. $\quad \frac{1}{4}(4x) = \frac{1}{4}(20)$ | 2. Multiplication Property of $=$ |
| 3. $\quad \frac{1}{4}(4x) = 5$ | 3. Substitution of 5 for $\frac{1}{4}(20)$ |
| 4. $(\frac{1}{4} \cdot 4)x = 5$ | 4. Associative Property of Mult. |
| 5. $\quad 1x = 5$ | 5. Inverse Prop. of Mult. |
| 6. $\quad x = 5$ | 6. Identity Prop. of Mult. |

This proves If $4x = 20$, then $x = 5$.

In Example 2, you might be tempted to say that we have proved $x = 5$. You would be wrong! We proved *If* $4x = 20$, *then* $x = 5$. In any proof we are proving that an if-then statement is true.

> An if-then statement is **true** if when the hypothesis is true, the conclusion is true.

When we prove a general if-then statement (such as the Angle-Angle-Side Theorem on page 178), we usually restate it in given-prove form. We draw a figure and introduce appropriate labels. Remember that every theorem can be restated in if-then form, even if it is not stated that way to begin with.

## Exercises 6.1 ▮▮▮▮▮▮▮▮▮▮▮▮▮▮▮▮▮▮▮▮▮▮▮▮▮▮▮▮▮▮▮▮▮▮▮▮▮▮▮▮▮▮▮▮▮▮

**Assignment Guide**
*Oral:* 1–4
*Written:*
Min. (day 1) 5–23 odd
(day 2) 6–24 even
Reg. 5–23 odd
Max. 5–33 odd

Ⓐ 1. An if-then statement is false when the hypothesis is true and the conclusion is (true, <u>false</u>).

2. An example that makes the hypothesis true and the conclusion false in an if-then statement is called a _____.     Counterexample

**3.** An if-then statement is true if whenever the hypothesis is true, the conclusion is (<u>true</u>, false).

**4.** When we use a two-column proof to prove an if-then statement, we label the (<u>hypothesis</u>, conclusion) as *Given*.

Ⓑ **5–16.** Find a counterexample to show that each if-then statement is false. Use the real numbers as the replacement set in Exercises 9–12.

TA means *typical answer*.

**5.** If a man lives in Kansas City, he lives in Kansas.
TA: man living in Kansas City, Missouri

**6.** If a woman lives in Missouri, she lives in St. Louis.
TA: woman living in Kansas City, Mo.

**7.** If an animal can fly, it is a bird.
TA: a bat

**8.** If an animal is a bird, it can fly.
TA: a penguin

**9.** If $x^2 = 25$, then $x = -5$.
$x = 5$

**10.** If $x > 3$, then $x = 4$ or $x > 4$.
TA: $x = 3\frac{1}{2}$

**11.** If $ab = 0$, then $a = 0$.
TA: $a = 5,\ b = 0$

**12.** If $x$ is nonnegative, then $x > 0$.
$x = 0$

Authenticated News International

**13.** If two angles are complementary, the angles are not congruent.
$\angle A$ and $\angle B$ where $m\angle A = m\angle B = 45$

**14.** If two angles are supplementary, one is acute and the other is obtuse.
$\angle C$ and $\angle D$ where $m\angle C = m\angle D = 90$

**15.** If two angles have the same vertex, the angles are adjacent.
TA: any 2 vertical $\angle$s

**16.** If three angles of one triangle are congruent to the corresponding angles of another triangle, the triangles are congruent.
TA: any 2 equilateral $\triangle$s whose corres. sides are not $\cong$

**17–20.** Restate each theorem in if-then form.

**17.** Vertical angles are congruent.    If 2 $\angle$s are vertical $\angle$s, the $\angle$s are $\cong$.

**18.** Alternate interior angles formed by a transversal and two parallel lines are congruent.    If 2 $\angle$s are alt. int. $\angle$s formed by a transversal and 2 ∥ lines, the $\angle$s are $\cong$.

**19.** In a plane, two lines that are perpendicular to the same line are parallel.    In a plane, if 2 lines are ⊥ to the same line, the lines are ∥.

**20.** The diagonals of a rectangle are congruent.
If segments are diagonals of the same □, the segments are $\cong$.

**21–24.** Which theorem in Exercises 17–20 is restated in given-prove form in each exercise below? (You do *not* need to prove the theorem.)

**21.** Given: Coplanar lines $a$, $b$, and $c$; $a \perp c$; $b \perp c$

Prove: $a \parallel b$     Exercise 19

**22.** Given: Intersecting lines $a$ and $b$

Prove: $\angle 1 \cong \angle 2$    Exercise 17

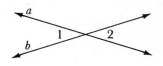

**23.** Given: $c \parallel d$, transversal $t$

Prove: $\angle 1 \cong \angle 2$   Exercise 18

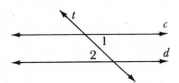

**24.** Given: Rectangle $ABCD$ with diagonals $\overline{AC}$ and $\overline{BD}$

Prove: $\overline{AC} \cong \overline{BD}$   Exercise 20

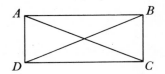

© **25–28.** Refer to Exercises 25–28 on pages 108 and 109. Write the if-then statement that is proved in each exercise.

**25.** If $\overline{AC} \perp \overline{BD}$ and $B$ is the midpt. of $\overline{AC}$, then $\angle A \cong \angle C$.

**26.** If $G$ is the midpt. of $\overline{EH}$ and $\angle E \cong \angle H$, then $\overline{FG} \cong \overline{KG}$.

**27.** If $\angle 4 \cong \angle 6$, $\overline{RN} \cong \overline{RQ}$, and $\overline{MQ}$ and $\overline{PN}$ intersect at $R$, then $\overline{PR} \cong \overline{MR}$.

**28.** If $\overline{AB} \cong \overline{CD}$, $\angle 1 \cong \angle 2$, $\angle 3 \cong \angle 4$, and $\overline{AC}$ and $\overline{BD}$ intersect at $E$, then $\overline{AC}$ and $\overline{BD}$ bisect each other at $E$.

**29–34.** The if-then statement *If X, then Y* can be expressed in other ways such as the following:

| | |
|---|---|
| *Y* if *X*. | *X* is sufficient for *Y*. |
| *X* only if *Y*. | *Y* is necessary for *X*. |
| *X* implies *Y*. | *Y* follows from *X*. |

Express each statement below in if-then form.

**29.** Fudge is good only if it has walnuts in it.
    If fudge is good, then it has walnuts in it.

**30.** Today is Monday implies tomorrow is Tuesday.
    If today is Monday, then tomorrow is Tuesday.

**31.** Two angles are supplementary if the sum of their measures is 180.
    If the sum of the measures of 2 $\angle$s is 180, the $\angle$s are supplementary.

**32.** Two lines being in the same plane is necessary for the lines to be parallel or intersecting.
    If 2 lines are $\parallel$ or intersecting, the lines are in the same plane.

**33.** $x = 4$ follows from $2x - 1 = 7$.
    If $2x - 1 = 7$, then $x = 4$.

**34.** $x^2 = 16$ is sufficient for $x = 4$ or $x = -4$.
    If $x^2 = 16$, then $x = 4$ or $x = -4$.

# If-and-Only-If Statements

If an animal is a giraffe, it has a long neck.

If an animal has a long neck, it is a giraffe.

H. Armstrong Roberts

Grant Heilman

Recall that two if-then statements related as above (the hypothesis and the conclusion are interchanged) are **converses.** An if-then statement can be true while its converse is false.

**Suggested Class Time**

| Course | Min. | Reg. | Max. |
|--------|------|------|------|
| Days   | 2    | 2    | 1    |

In some cases, however, both the if-then statement and its converse are true. In that case, the two sentences can be replaced by one true sentence that employs **if and only if**.

| If an angle is acute, its measure is less than 90. | These two true statements can be replaced by one true statement. | If its measure is less than 90, an angle is acute. |

An angle is acute *if and only if* its measure is less than 90.

In general,

both true
- If $X$, then $Y$.
- If $Y$, then $X$.

is equivalent to

$X$ if and only if $Y$.

**Example:** Replace the following true statements with one true statement:

If $a + c = b + c$, then $a = b$.
If $a = b$, then $a + c = b + c$.

$a + c = b + c$ if and only if $a = b$.

Sometimes theorems are stated in *if-and-only-if* form. If so, the proof consists of two parts. Consider the following theorem:

A point is on the bisector of an angle if and only if the point is *equidistant* from the sides of the angle.

NOTE: We take *equidistant* to mean the point is in the interior of the angle and the perpendicular segments from the point to both sides are congruent.

The two statements to be proved are

**a.** If a point is on the bisector of an angle, it is equidistant from the sides of the angle.

**b.** If a point is equidistant from the sides of an angle, it is on the bisector of the angle.

**Part a.**

Given: Point $P$ is on the bisector of $\angle ABC$.

Prove: $\overline{PM} \cong \overline{PN}$

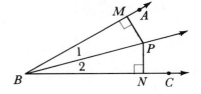

Proof:

| STATEMENTS | REASONS |
|---|---|
| **1.** $\angle 1 \cong \angle 2$ | **1.** Definition of angle bisector |
| **2.** $\overline{PM} \perp \overline{MB}$, $\overline{PN} \perp \overline{NB}$ | **2.** Perp. Line Post. (p. 60) |
| **3.** $\angle BMP$ and $\angle BNP$ are rt. $\angle$s. | **3.** Definition of perpendicular |
| **4.** $\triangle BMP$ and $\triangle BNP$ are rt. $\triangle$s. | **4.** Definition of right triangle |
| **5.** $\overline{BP} \cong \overline{BP}$ | **5.** A segment is $\cong$ to itself. |
| **6.** $\triangle BMP \cong \triangle BNP$ | **6.** HA Theorem |
| **7.** $\overline{PM} \cong \overline{PN}$ | **7.** Corres. parts of $\cong$ $\triangle$s are $\cong$. |

The proof of part **b** is left as an exercise.

# *Exercises 6.2* ||||||||||||||||||||||||||||||||||||||||||||||||||||||||||||||||||||||||||||||||||

**Assignment Guide**
*Oral:* 1–4
*Written:*
Min. (day 1) 5–23 odd
(day 2) 6–24 even
Reg. (day 1) 5–31 odd
(day 2) 6–32 even
Max. 5–31 odd; 33–39

Ⓐ **1.** When you interchange the hypothesis and the conclusion of an if-then statement, the resulting sentence is called the <u>Converse</u>.

**2.** When an if-then statement and its converse are both true, we can restate them as one true _____ statement.   If-and-only-if

3. True or False? If an if-then statement is true, its converse is also true.    F

4. What is the converse of *If* $3x = 9$, *then* $x = 3$?

   If $x = 3$, then $3x = 9$.

Ⓑ 5–16. Write *true* or *false* for each statement. Then write the converse of each statement and tell if it is true or false.

5. If a family lives in Hawaii, the family lives on an island.

   T; If a family lives on an island, it lives in Hawaii; F

6. If a flower has thorns, it is a rose.

   F; If a flower is a rose, it has thorns; T

7. If a car is a foreign car, it is a Fiat.

   F; If a car is a Fiat, it is a foreign car; T

8. If a cat's name is Morris, it is finicky.

   F; If a cat is finicky, its name is Morris; F

9. If $a^2 > 0$, then $a > 0$.

   F; If $a > 0$, then $a^2 > 0$; T

10. If $x^2 = 64$, then $x = 8$.

   F; If $x = 8$, then $x^2 = 64$; T

11. If two angles are vertical angles, the angles are congruent.

   T; If 2 ∠s are ≅, they are vert. ∠s; F

12. If two triangles are congruent, the corresponding sides and angles are congruent.

   T; If the corres. sides and ∠s of 2 △s are ≅, the △s are ≅; T

13. If two lines are parallel, the alternate interior angles formed by the two lines and a transversal are congruent.    T; If the alt. int.

   ∠s formed by 2 lines and a transversal are ≅, the lines are ∥; T

14. If two angles are congruent, the angles are right angles.

   F; If 2 ∠s are rt. ∠s, the ∠s are ≅; T

15. If $x$ is an integer, $x$ is a real number.

   T; If $x$ is a real number, $x$ is an integer; F

16. If $a^2 - b^2 = 0$, then $a = b$.

   F; If $a = b$, then $a^2 - b^2 = 0$; T

17–20. Rewrite each pair of statements by using *if and only if.*

17. If $a = b$, then $a - b = 0$.
    If $a - b = 0$, then $a = b$.    $a = b$ if and only if $a - b = 0$.

18. If $\triangle ABC$ is equilateral, then $\triangle ABC$ is equiangular.
    If $\triangle ABC$ is equiangular, then $\triangle ABC$ is equilateral.

    $\triangle ABC$ is equilateral if and only if it is equiangular.

19. If an angle is a right angle, then its measure is 90.
    If its measure is 90, then an angle is a right angle.

    An ∠ is a rt. ∠ if and only if its measure is 90.

*Answer for page 213*

33. 1. $\overline{PM} \perp \overline{MB}$, $\overline{PN} \perp \overline{NB}$ (Given)
    2. ∠ $BMP$ and ∠ $BNP$ are rt. ∠s. (Def. of ⊥)
    3. △$BMP$ and △$BNP$ are rt. △s. (Def. of rt. △)
    4. $\overline{BP} \cong \overline{BP}$ (Seg. is ≅ to itself.)
    5. $\overline{PM} \cong \overline{PN}$ (Given)
    6. △$BMP \cong$ △$BNP$ (HL Thm.)
    7. ∠ $1 \cong$ ∠ $2$ (Corres. parts of ≅ △s are ≅.)
    8. $\overrightarrow{BP}$ is the bis. of ∠ $ABC$. (Def. of ∠ bis.)
    9. $P$ is on the bis. of ∠ $ABC$. (Step 8 and def. of ray)

**20.** If the nonparallel sides of a trapezoid are congruent, both pairs of base angles are congruent.

If both pairs of base angles of a trapezoid are congruent, the nonparallel sides are congruent. The nonparallel sides of a trapezoid are ≅ if and only if both pairs of base ∠s are ≅.

**21–24.** Rewrite each theorem in if-and-only-if form.

**21.** Perpendicular Bisector Theorem (p. 110)

**22.** Alternate Interior Angles Theorem (p. 128)

**23.** Corresponding Angles Theorem (p. 132)

**24.** Isosceles Triangle Theorem (p. 180) Two sides of a △ are ≅ if and only if the ∠s opp. those sides are ≅.

**25–28.** Determine if statements *X* and *Y* can be connected by *if and only if* to form a true statement. If not possible, write *no*. If possible, write the statement.

X         Y

**25.** Two angles are adjacent.    Two angles share a vertex.    No

**26.** $a - c = b - c$        $a = b$
$a - c = b - c$ if and only if $a = b$.

**27.** The sum of the measures of    Two angles are complementary.
two angles is 90. The sum of the measures of 2 ∠s is 90 if and only if the ∠s are complementary.

**28.** Two lines are perpendicular.    The lines form a right angle.
Two lines are ⊥ if and only if the lines form a rt. ∠.

**29–32.** Write the two if-then statements that can be formed from each if-and-only-if statement.

**29.** $\dfrac{x^2 - y^2}{x - y} = x + y$ if and only if $x \neq y$.

**30.** An if-then statement is false if and only if the hypothesis is **true** and the conclusion is **false**.

**31.** An angle is an obtuse angle if and only if its measure is greater than 90.

**32.** Two lines in the same plane are parallel if and only if the lines do not intersect. In a plane, if 2 lines are ∥, the lines do not intersect.<br>In a plane, if two lines do not intersect, the lines are ∥.

---

**21.** In a plane, a pt. is on the ⊥ bis. of a seg. if and only if it is equidistant from the endpts. of the seg.

**22.** When a transversal intersects 2 lines, alt. int. ∠s are ≅ if and only if the lines are ∥.

**23.** When a transversal intersects 2 lines, corres. ∠s are ≅ if and only if the lines are ∥.

**29.** If $\dfrac{x^2 - y^2}{x - y} = x + y$, then $x \neq y$.
If $x \neq y$, then $\dfrac{x^2 - y^2}{x - y} = x + y$.

**30.** If an if-then statement is false, the hypothesis is true and the conclusion is false.
If the hypothesis is true and the conclusion is false, an if-then statement is false.

**31.** If an ∠ is obtuse, its measure is > 90.
If its measure is > 90, an ∠ is obtuse.

© **33.** Prove part **b** of the Angle Bisector Theorem, using the restatement and the figure below.

Given: $\overline{PM} \perp \overline{MB}$, $\overline{PN} \perp \overline{NB}$,
$\overline{PM} \cong \overline{PN}$

Prove: Point $P$ is on the bisector of $\angle ABC$.

[*Plan:* Prove $\triangle BMP \cong \triangle BNP$ by the HL Theorem.] *Answer on page 211*

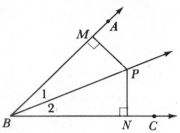

**34–37.** Every if-then statement has two other related statements besides the converse. These are called the **inverse** and the **contra-positive**.

*Given statement:* If $X$, then $Y$.

*Inverse:* If not $X$, then not $Y$.

*Contrapositive:* If not $Y$, then not $X$.

Write the inverse and the contrapositive of each statement in Exercises 11–14. Then write *true* or *false* for each.

**38.** When an if-then statement is true, is its inverse necessarily true?
No

**39.** When an if-then statement is true, does its contrapositive seem to be true? Yes

**40.** True or False? For a given if-then statement, the contrapositive of the converse is the inverse. T

**41.** True or False? For a given if-then statement, the converse of the inverse is the contrapositive. T

**42.** Some other ways of stating $X$ if and only if $Y$ are as follows:

$X$ is necessary and sufficient for $Y$.

$Y$ is necessary and sufficient for $X$.

If $X$, then $Y$, and conversely.

If $Y$, then $X$, and conversely.

Rewrite the statement in Exercise 31 in each form above.

**34.** If 2 $\angle$ s are not vert. $\angle$ s, the $\angle$ s are not $\cong$ ; F
If 2 $\angle$ s are not $\cong$, the $\angle$ s are not vert. $\angle$ s; T

**35.** If 2 $\triangle$ s are not $\cong$, the corres. sides and $\angle$ s are not $\cong$ ; T
If corres. sides and $\angle$ s are not $\cong$, 2 $\triangle$ s are not $\cong$ ; T

**36.** If 2 lines are not $\parallel$, the alt. int. $\angle$ s formed by 2 lines and a transversal are not $\cong$ ; T
If the alt. int. $\angle$ s formed by 2 lines and a transversal are not $\cong$, the lines are not $\parallel$ ; T

**37.** If 2 $\angle$ s are not $\cong$, the $\angle$ s are not rt. $\angle$ s; T
If 2 $\angle$ s are not rt. $\angle$ s, the $\angle$ s are not $\cong$ ; F

**42.** An $\angle$ being obtuse is necessary and suffi-cient for its meas. to be > 90.
Its meas. being > 90 is necessary and suffi-cient for an $\angle$ to be obtuse.
If an $\angle$ is obtuse, then its meas. is > 90, and conversely.
If an $\angle$ has a meas. > 90, then it is ob-tuse, and conversely.

# 6.3 Good Definitions

A good definition should be stated in such a way that it is reversible. For example, the definition

A *regular polygon* is an equilateral and equiangular convex polygon

can be reversed as

An equilateral and equiangular convex polygon is a *regular polygon*.

Definitions should be reversible, because in geometry we consider all definitions to be equivalent to if-and-only-if statements, which are reversible.

$X$ if and only if $Y$     means the same as    $Y$ if and only if $X$.

We often state definitions in if-and-only-if form to make sure that they are reversible. For example,

A polygon is a *regular polygon* if and only if it is an equilateral and equiangular convex polygon.

## Exercises 6.3

**Assignment Guide**
*Oral:* 1–10
*Written:*
Min. (day 1) 11–23 odd
     (day 2) 12–24 even
Reg. (day 1) 11–27 odd
     (day 2) 12–28 even
Max. 11–27 odd; 29–30

Ⓐ 1. In geometry, all definitions are equivalent to ———— statements, which are reversible.   If-and-only-if

2. $X$ if and only if $Y$ means the same as ($X$ and $Y$, $Y$ if $X$, <u>$Y$ if and only if $X$</u>).

3–10. Are the following definitions reversible?

3. A cow is an animal with four legs.   No

4. A banjo is a stringed musical instrument.   No

5. The midpoint of a segment is the point that is between the endpoints and equidistant from them.   Yes

6. A triangle is a 3-sided polygon.   Yes

7. A rectangle is a 4-sided polygon.   No

8. Alabama is a southern state.   No

**9.** A right angle is an angle whose measure is 90.     Yes

**10.** Adjacent angles are two angles with a common side.   No

Ⓑ **11–18.** Complete each definition.

**11.** Points are collinear if and only if _____. (p. 14)
They are on the same line.

**12.** A figure is a segment $DE$ if and only if _____. (p. 15)
It contains $D$, $E$, and all points between $D$ and $E$.

**13.** Two rays are opposite rays if and only if _____. (p. 15)
They are distinct, collinear rays with a common endpt.

**14.** A statement is a postulate if and only if _____. (p. 11)
It is accepted as true without proof.

**15.** A ray $AZ$ is the bisector of $\angle BAC$ if and only if _____. (p. 56)
$Z$ is in the interior of $\angle BAC$, and $m\angle BAZ = m\angle CAZ$.

**16.** Two angles are supplementary if and only if _____. (p. 56)
Their measures have the sum of 180.

**17.** In a plane, a line is the perpendicular bisector of a segment if and only if _____. (p. 61)   It is $\perp$ to the seg. at its midpt.

**18.** Angles are congruent angles if and only if _____. (p. 64)
They have the same measure.

**19–28.** Restate the definition of each term in if-and-only-if form.

**19.** coplanar points (p. 14)       **20.** angle (p. 48)

**21.** acute angle (p. 60)          **22.** complementary angles (p. 60)

**23.** perpendicular lines (p. 60)   **24.** congruent triangles (p. 94)

**25.** isosceles triangle (p. 180)   **26.** obtuse triangle (p. 180)

**27.** transversal (p. 128)         **28.** right triangle (p. 180)

**19.** Pts. are coplanar if and only if they are all in the same plane.

**20.** A figure is an $\angle$ if and only if it is formed by 2 noncollinear rays with the same endpt.

**21.** An $\angle$ is acute if and only if its measure is $< 90$.

**22.** Two $\angle$s are complementary if and only if their measures have the sum of 90.

**23.** Lines are $\perp$ if and only if they meet to form a 90°, or rt., $\angle$.

**24.** Two $\triangle$s are $\cong$ if and only if the 6 parts of 1 $\triangle$ are $\cong$ to the 6 corres. parts of the other $\triangle$.

**25.** A $\triangle$ is isos. if and only if it has at least 2 $\cong$ sides.

**26.** A $\triangle$ is obtuse if and only if it has exactly 1 obtuse $\angle$.

**27.** A line is a transversal if and only if it intersects 2 or more coplanar lines at distinct pts.

**28.** A $\triangle$ is a rt. $\triangle$ if and only if it has exactly 1 rt. $\angle$.

Ⓒ **29–30.** Write *yes* or *no* to tell if the "definition" can be used as a reason for the given conclusion.

*Definition:* If the measure of an angle is less than 90, it is acute.

**29.** *Given:* $m\angle A < 90$

*Conclusion:* $\angle A$ is acute.  Yes

**30.** *Given:* $\angle A$ is acute.

*Conclusion:* $m\angle A < 90$  No

# 6.4 Patterns of Reasoning

**Suggested Class Time**

| Course | Min. | Reg. | Max. |
|--------|------|------|------|
| Days   | 1    | 1    | 1    |

If a car is a Cadillac, it is an American car.

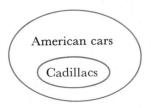

Courtesy General Motors Corporation

Look at the Euler diagram and consider each argument below.

| | | |
|---|---|---|
| TRUE | A Seville is a Cadillac.<br>So a Seville is an American car. | A Toyota is not an American car.<br>So a Toyota is not a Cadillac. |
| FALSE | A Volare is an American car.<br>So a Volare is a Cadillac. | A Corvette is not a Cadillac.<br>So a Corvette is not an American car. |

Each argument above is based on the original if-then statement and one other statement. If we let $X$ stand for the hypothesis and $Y$ for the conclusion, the patterns of reasoning can be shown as follows:

| | **Affirming the Hypothesis** | | **Denying the Conclusion** |
|---|---|---|---|
| VALID<br>ARGUMENTS | If $X$, then $Y$.<br>$X$.<br>So $Y$. | ◀When these▶<br>◀are true,▶<br>◀this is true.▶ | If $X$, then $Y$.<br>Not $Y$.<br>So not $X$. |

| | **Affirming the Conclusion** | | **Denying the Hypothesis** |
|---|---|---|---|
| FAULTY<br>ARGUMENTS | If $X$, then $Y$.<br>$Y$.<br>So $X$. | ◀When these▶<br>◀are true,▶<br>◀this might▶<br>be false. | If $X$, then $Y$.<br>Not $X$.<br>So not $Y$. |

**Examples:** Decide if each argument is valid or faulty. Then name the pattern of reasoning that is illustrated.

1. If two angles are vertical angles, the angles are congruent.
   $\angle A$ and $\angle B$ are vertical angles.
   So $\angle A$ and $\angle B$ are congruent.

   The argument is valid. It illustrates Affirming the Hypothesis.

**2.** If a cat eats Tasty Tuna Cat Food, it will be healthy and happy.
Minerva does not eat Tasty Tuna Cat Food.
So Minerva will not be healthy and happy.

   The argument is faulty. It illustrates Denying the Hypothesis.

**3.** If a woman wears Blinky-Winky Eyelashes, she will be beautiful.
Ms. Hollywood Starr is beautiful.
So Ms. Hollywood Starr wears Blinky-Winky Eyelashes.

   The argument is faulty. It illustrates Affirming the Conclusion.

   Most advertisers are too clever to make their advertising as clearly false as in Examples 2 and 3. Nevertheless, some of them hope you will use faulty reasoning when you see their advertisements. Suppose you see an advertisement like the following:

USE **SLICKO** HAIR CREAM

**Assignment Guide**
*Oral:* 1–6
*Written:*
Min. 7–10; 11–19 odd;
   Quiz, p. 219
Reg. 7–10; 11–21 odd;
   Quiz, p. 219
Max. 7–10; 11–25 odd;
   Quiz, p. 219

   The advertiser hopes you will use the following faulty pattern of reasoning (Denying the Hypothesis):

   If a man uses Slicko Hair Cream, he will attract beautiful women.
The man on the right doesn't use Slicko.
So the man on the right will not attract beautiful women.

## Exercises 6.4

Ⓐ **1.** Which patterns of reasoning below are valid?   a, c

   **a.** Affirming the Hypothesis     **b.** Denying the Hypothesis

   **c.** Denying the Conclusion     **d.** Affirming the Conclusion

**2.** Which patterns of reasoning in Exercise 1 are faulty?  b, d

**3–6.** Which pattern of reasoning in Exercise 1 is illustrated?

**3.** If $X$, then $Y$.
Not $X$.
So not $Y$.  b

**4.** If $X$, then $Y$.
Not $Y$.
So not $X$.  c

**5.** If $X$, then $Y$.
$X$.
So $Y$.  a

**6.** If $X$, then $Y$.
$Y$.
So $X$.  d

Ⓑ **7–10.** Write *valid* or *faulty* for each argument. Then name the pattern of reasoning that is used.

Courtesy Qantas Airways Limited

**7.** If a person lives in Quebec, he or she lives in Canada.
Pierre lives in Quebec.
So Pierre lives in Canada.
Valid; affirming the hypothesis

**8.** If today is Friday, tomorrow is Saturday.
Tomorrow is not Saturday.
So today is not Friday.
Valid; denying the conclusion

**9.** If you are from Australia, you have seen a koala.
Ann is not from Australia.
So Ann has not seen a koala.
Faulty; denying the hypothesis

**10.** If it rains in Spain, it falls mainly on the plain.
The rain is falling mainly on the plain.
So it is raining in Spain.
Faulty; affirming the conclusion

**11–22.** Make a valid conclusion from each pair of statements if possible. If not possible, write *no conclusion possible*.

**11.** If $x = \sqrt{2}$, then $x^2 = 2$.
$x^2 \neq 2$
$x \neq \sqrt{2}$

**12.** If a number is rational, the number is real.
$\frac{2}{3}$ is rational.
$\frac{2}{3}$ is real.

**13.** If a person lives in Boise, he or she lives in Idaho.
Connie lives in Idaho.
No conclusion possible

**14.** If you live in Puerto Rico, you live on an island.
Juan doesn't live on an island.
Juan does not live in Puerto Rico.

**15.** If two angles are congruent, their measures are equal.
$\angle A \cong \angle B$
$m\angle A = m\angle B$

**16.** If an angle is acute, its measure is less than 90.
$m\angle A$ is less than 90.
No conclusion possible

**17.** In $\triangle ABC$ if $\overline{AC} \cong \overline{AB}$, then $\angle B \cong \angle C$.
$\overline{AC}$ is not $\cong$ to $\overline{AB}$.
No conclusion possible

**18.** If $\triangle ABC \cong \triangle DEF$, then $\angle A \cong \angle D$.
$\angle A$ is not $\cong$ to $\angle D$.
$\triangle ABC$ is not $\cong$ to $\triangle DEF$.

**19.** If alternate interior angles
1 and 2 are congruent, lines
$\ell$ and $k$ are parallel.
$\ell$ and $k$ are not parallel.
Alt. int. ∠s 1 and 2 are not ≅.

**20.** If lines $r$ and $s$ are parallel,
corresponding angles 3 and 4
are congruent.
$r$ and $s$ are not parallel.
No conclusion possible

**21.** No pigs can fly.
Porky is a pig.
Porky cannot fly.

**22.** All fish can swim.
Flipper cannot swim.
Flipper is not a fish.

© **23–25.** The following pairs of statements come from a book called
*Symbolic Logic* by Lewis Carroll. Carroll is better known as the author of
*Alice in Wonderland*, but he was also a mathematician. See if you can
draw a conclusion from each pair of statements. You may find it helpful
to change the statements to if-then form.

**23.** All well-fed canaries sing loud.
No canary is melancholy if it sings loud.
Well-fed canaries are not melancholy.

**24.** All my sisters have colds.
No one can sing who has a cold.
My sisters cannot sing.

**25.** No lobsters are unreasonable.
No reasonable creatures expect impossibilities.
Lobsters do not expect impossibilities.

**1–2.** Find a counterexample to show that each statement is false.

**1.** If $x^2$ is positive, then $x$ is positive.
Any negative number

**2.** If an angle is acute, its measure is less than 45.
Any ∠ $A$ where $45 \leq m\angle A < 90$

**3–4.** Write the converse of each statement in Exercises 1–2. Then tell
if the converse is true or false.

**3.** If $x$ is positive, then $x^2$ is positive; T

**4.** If its measure is < 45, an ∠ is acute; T

**5.** Can statements $A$ and $B$ be connected by *if and only if* to form
a true statement? (Assume $c \neq 0$).  Yes

$A$: If $a = b$, then $ac = bc$.    $B$: If $ac = bc$, then $a = b$.

**6.** Restate the following definition in if-and-only-if form:
An obtuse angle is an angle whose measure is greater than 90.
An ∠ is obtuse if and only if its measure is > 90.

**7.** Is the pattern
of reasoning at
the right valid?  Yes

If $X$, then $Y$.
Not $Y$.
So not $X$.

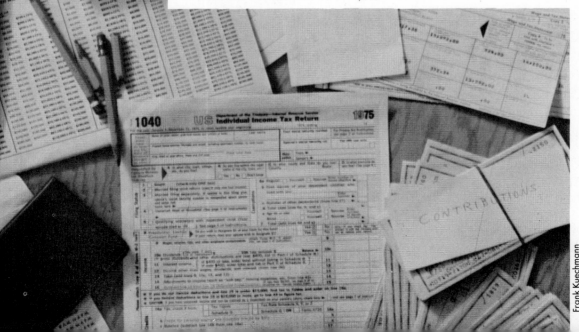

# OFFICE OCCUPATIONS

Office workers do a wide range of jobs. Many clerical employees work with objects and often do detailed and repetitive tasks. On the other hand, most professional office employees work with ideas. To do their jobs, they need good judgment and the ability to use valid reasoning.

Office workers might deal with any of the following topics. See if you can use reasoning to answer each question.

1. *Labor Contract: Employees who have earned 1–4 days of paid vacation may request an additional number of days without pay for a total of no more than 5 days. Employees who have earned 6–9 days of paid vacation may request an additional number of days without pay for a total of no more than 10 days.*
   An employee has earned 3 days of paid vacation. How many days of total vacation can he or she take? How many of these days will be unpaid?   5; 2

2. *Insurance Policy: If a total of $200 of eligible expenses is incurred collectively by the covered members of a family during the calendar year, the deductible requirement will be waived for all covered members of the family for the rest of the year.*
   A certain family has had $457 in eligible expenses during the calendar year till now. If further expenses are incurred, will the deductible have to be paid again?   No

3. *Income Tax: If interest is $400 or less, do not complete this part. But enter amount of interest received on Form 1040, line 11.*
   A person received $178 in interest. What amount should be entered on Form 1040, line 11?   $178

Frank Kuechmann

Most of the proofs in this book have been *direct proofs*. Another type of proof is the **indirect proof.** Theorems that are difficult to prove with a direct proof can sometimes be proved easily with an indirect proof.

**Suggested Class Time**

| Course | Min. | Reg. | Max. |
|--------|------|------|------|
| Days   | 1    | 1    | 1    |

Let's talk about an example of indirect proof from everyday life. This type of indirect argument is heard often on TV detective shows.

**Example 1:**

Defending attorney: If my clients had committed the crime, they had to be at the scene of the crime. According to witnesses, the crime occurred at 3:10 A.M. We have a witness who saw the defendants at an all-night diner at 3:20 A.M. The diner is 17 miles from the scene of the crime. Therefore, my clients are not guilty.

A brief outline of the attorney's indirect argument is as follows:

*1.* The clients are either guilty or not guilty.

*2.* To prove they are *not* guilty, I will assume they are guilty and show that this leads to a contradiction of a known fact.

*3.* When I assume they are guilty, this means they had to be at the scene of the crime. But we have a witness who saw them at another place at about the time the crime was committed.

*4.* Therefore, my clients are not guilty.

This same type of argument can be used in proving a mathematical theorem by an indirect proof:

*1.* Assume the opposite of the fact you want to prove.

*2.* Show that this leads to a contradiction of a known fact.

*3.* So you know that your original assumption is false and that the fact you want to prove must be true.

H. Armstrong Roberts

We have already used indirect proofs earlier, and we introduced the Principle of Indirect Reasoning at that time.

If assuming statement $p$ is true leads to a contradiction of a true statement, then statement $p$ is false.

Notice how the Principle of Indirect Reasoning is used in the following proof. (NOTE: $\not\cong$ means "is not congruent to.")

**Example 2:**

Given: $\angle 1 \not\cong \angle 2$

Prove: $p$ is not parallel to $n$.

Proof:

| STATEMENTS | REASONS |
|---|---|
| 1. Assume $p \parallel n$. | 1. Assumption for indirect proof |
| 2. $\angle 1 \cong \angle 2$ | 2. If a transversal intersects two $\parallel$ lines, the alternate interior $\angle$s are $\cong$. |
| 3. But, $\angle 1 \not\cong \angle 2$. | 3. Given |
| 4. Therefore, $p$ is not parallel to $n$. | 4. Principle of Indirect Reasoning |

Assignment Guide
*Oral:* 1–10
*Written:*
Min. 11–24; Alg. Rev.,
   p. 224, odd
Reg. 11–24; Alg. Rev.,
   p. 224, odd
Max. 11–24; 25–29 odd

Notice how step 3 denies the conclusion in step 2. So in step 4 we can conclude the opposite of the hypothesis in step 1.

The proofs of the next two theorems will be left as exercises. Restatements are given in Exercises 28 and 29.

**Theorem** In a plane, if two lines intersect and there is a line perpendicular to each of them, the perpendiculars to the intersecting lines also intersect.

**Theorem** In a plane, if two lines intersect and there is a line parallel to each of them, the parallels to the intersecting lines also intersect.

# Exercises 6.5

1. In an indirect proof, you assume the $\underline{\text{Opposite}}$ of the fact you want to prove.

2. Then you show that this leads to a $\underline{\text{Contradiction}}$ of a known fact.

**3–10.** Give the opposite of each statement.

**3.** $m\angle A = m\angle B$
   $m\angle A \neq m\angle B$

**4.** $\angle C \cong \angle D$
   $\angle C \not\cong \angle D$

**5.** $\ell \perp k$
   $\ell$ is not $\perp$ to $k$.

**6.** $y = 4$
   $y \neq 4$

**7.** $n$ is odd.
   $n$ is not odd.

**8.** $x^2 \neq 2$
   $x^2 = 2$

**9.** $\overline{AB} \not\cong \overline{CD}$   $\overline{AB} \cong \overline{CD}$   **10.** $\ell$ is not parallel to $p$.   $\ell \parallel p$

Ⓑ **11–24.** Give the missing reasons.

Given: $\overline{AC} \not\cong \overline{BC}$

Prove: $\angle A \not\cong \angle B$

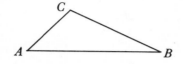

**Proof:**

| STATEMENTS | REASONS |
|---|---|
| *1.* Assume $\angle A \cong \angle B$. | *1.* **11.** Assump. for ind. prf. |
| *2.* Then $\overline{AC} \cong \overline{BC}$   **12.** $\angle$s opp. $\cong$ sides of $\triangle$ are $\cong$. | *2.* **12.** *At left* |
| *3.* But, $\overline{AC} \not\cong \overline{BC}$ | *3.* **13.** Given |
| *4.* Therefore, $\angle A \not\cong \angle B$. | *4.* **14.** Prin. of Ind. Reas. |

Given: $\overline{DF} \not\cong \overline{EF}$, $\overline{FG} \perp \overline{DE}$

Prove: $G$ is not the midpoint of $\overline{DE}$.

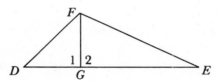

**Proof:**

| STATEMENTS | REASONS |
|---|---|
| *1.* Assume $G$ is the midpoint of $\overline{DE}$. | *1.* **15.** Assump. for ind. prf. |
| *2.* Then $\overline{DG} \cong \overline{GE}$. | *2.* **16.** Def. of midpt. |
| *3.* $\overline{FG} \perp \overline{DE}$ | *3.* **17.** Given |
| *4.* $\angle 1$ and $\angle 2$ are right angles. | *4.* **18.** Def. of $\perp$ |
| *5.* $\triangle DGF$ and $\triangle EGF$ are right $\triangle$s. | *5.* **19.** Def. of rt. $\triangle$ |
| *6.* $\overline{FG} \cong \overline{FG}$ | *6.* **20.** Seg. is $\cong$ to itself. |
| *7.* $\triangle DGF \cong \triangle EGF$ | *7.* **21.** LL Thm. |
| *8.* $\overline{DF} \cong \overline{EF}$   **22.** Corres. parts of $\cong$ $\triangle$s are $\cong$. | *8.* **22.** *At left* |
| *9.* But, $\overline{DF} \not\cong \overline{EF}$. | *9.* **23.** Given |
| *10.* Therefore, $G$ is not the midpoint of $\overline{DE}$. | *10.* **24.** Prin. of Ind. Reas. |

*Answers for page 224*

**27.** *1.* Assume $\overrightarrow{AP}$ is bis. of $\angle CAB$. (Assump. for ind. prf.)
*2.* $\angle CAP \cong \angle BAP$ (Def. of $\angle$ bis.)
*3.* $\overline{AC} \cong \overline{AB}$ (Given)
*4.* $\overline{AP} \cong \overline{AP}$ (Seg. is $\cong$ to itself.)
*5.* $\triangle CAP \cong \triangle BAP$ (SAS Post.)
*6.* $\overline{CP} \cong \overline{BP}$ (Corres. parts of $\cong$ $\triangle$s are $\cong$.)
*7.* But, $\overline{CP} \not\cong \overline{BP}$. (Given)
*8.* So, $\overrightarrow{AP}$ is not bis. of $\angle CAB$. (Prin. of Ind. Reas.)

**28.** *1.* Assume $c \parallel d$. (Assump. for ind. prf.)
*2.* $c \perp a$ (Given)
*3.* $a \perp d$ (In a plane, line $\perp$ to one of 2 $\parallel$ lines is $\perp$ to the other.)
*4.* $d \perp b$ (Given)
*5.* $a \parallel b$ (In a plane, 2 lines $\perp$ to same line are $\parallel$.)
*6.* But, $a$ and $b$ intersect. (Given)
*7.* So, $c$ intersects $d$. (Prin. of Ind. Reas.)

**29.** *Sketch of Proof:* Assume $r \parallel s$. Given $r \parallel p$, so $p \parallel s$, and given $s \parallel n$, so $p \parallel n$ (In a plane, 2 lines $\parallel$ to same line are $\parallel$). But, $p$ and $n$ intersect (Given), so $r$ intersects $s$ (Prin. of Ind. Reas.).

© **25–29.** Give an indirect proof of each of the following:

**25.** *1.* Assume $b \parallel a$. (Assump. for ind. prf.)

*2.* $a \parallel c$ (Given)

*3.* $b \parallel c$ (In a plane, 2 lines $\parallel$ to same line are $\parallel$.)

*4.* $\angle 2 \cong \angle 3$ (If lines are $\parallel$, corres. $\angle$s are $\cong$.)

*5.* But, $\angle 2 \not\cong \angle 3$. (Given)

*6.* So, $b$ is not $\parallel$ to $a$. (Prin. of Ind. Reas.)

**26.** *1.* Assume $\ell \parallel k$. (Assump. for ind. prf.)

*2.* $m\angle 2 + m\angle 3 = 180$ (If lines are $\parallel$, int. $\angle$s on same side of trans. are supp.)

*3.* But, $m\angle 2 + m\angle 3 \neq 180$. (Given)

*4.* So, $\ell$ is not $\parallel$ to $k$. (Prin. of Ind. Reas.)

*27–29. Answers on p. 223*

**25.** Given: $a \parallel c$, $\angle 2 \not\cong \angle 3$

Prove: $b$ is not parallel to $a$.

**Ex. 26**

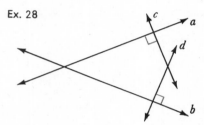

**27.** Given: $\overline{AC} \cong \overline{AB}$, $\overline{CP} \not\cong \overline{PB}$

Prove: $\overrightarrow{AP}$ is not the bisector of $\angle CAB$.

**Ex. 28**

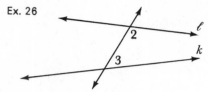

**29.** Given: $p$ and $n$ are intersecting lines, $r \parallel p$, $s \parallel n$

Prove: $r$ intersects $s$.

**Ex. 25**

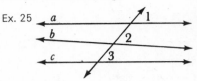

**26.** Given: $m\angle 2 + m\angle 3 \neq 180$

Prove: $\ell$ is not parallel to $k$.

**Ex. 27**

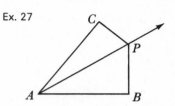

**28.** Given: $a$ and $b$ are intersecting lines, $c \perp a$, $d \perp b$

Prove: $c$ intersects $d$.

HINT: Assume $c \parallel d$.

**Ex. 29**

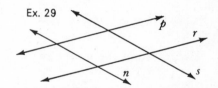

---

# *Algebra Review*

**Review these skills:**

- using $<$, $=$, and $>$

- solving inequalities

**1–9.** Which symbol, $<$, $=$, or $>$, should replace each ▨ ?

**1.** $0 \cdot 5$ ▨ $5$    $<$

**2.** $2^3$ ▨ $8$    $=$

**3.** $|-3|$ ▨ $0$    $>$

**4.** $\frac{3}{4}$ ▨ $\frac{5}{6}$    $<$

**5.** $\frac{1}{8}$ ▨ $0.125$    $=$

**6.** $10^3$ ▨ $999$    $>$

**7–18.** Solve.

**7.** $x + 2 < 3$    $x < 1$

**8.** $y - 7 > 10$    $y > 17$

**9.** $7y < 49$    $y < 7$

**10.** $4a > 36$    $a > 9$

**11.** $\frac{x}{2} > 8$    $x > 16$

**12.** $\frac{b}{5} < 2$    $b < 10$

**13.** $3r > 2$    $r > \frac{2}{3}$

**14.** $5x - 2 < 23$    $x < 5$

**15.** $6x + 3 > 15$    $x > 2$

**16.** $\frac{a}{3} + 2 < 1$    $a < -3$

**17.** $-x < 2$    $x > -2$

**18.** $-3y > 15$    $y < -5$

# Is There Only One Proof?

**6.6**

There is usually more than one way to prove the same theorem. In this section, we consider some different proofs for theorems proved earlier. First, we introduce two new terms.

A **median** of a triangle is a segment from a vertex to the midpoint of the opposite side.

An **altitude** of a triangle is a segment from a vertex perpendicular to the line containing the opposite side.

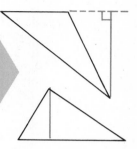

Every triangle has three medians and three altitudes, and every triangle has three bisectors of its angles. Also, in the plane of a given triangle there are three perpendicular bisectors of the sides.

In Section 5.6 we proved both parts of the Isosceles Triangle Theorem (p. 180) by using the bisector of the vertex angle as an auxiliary figure. Now we give another proof of part **a,** using the median to the base. (In Exercises 9–13, another proof of part **b** is given, using the altitude to the base.)

Given: $\overline{AC} \cong \overline{BC}$

Prove: $\angle A \cong \angle B$

[*Plan:* Use the median to side $\overline{AB}$ as an auxiliary segment. Prove $\triangle ACM \cong \triangle BCM$ by SSS.]

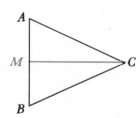

**Proof:**

| STATEMENTS | REASONS |
|---|---|
| 1. Let $M$ be the midpoint of $\overline{AB}$. | 1. Every segment has exactly one midpoint. |
| 2. $\overline{CM}$ is a median. | 2. Definition of a median. |
| 3. $\overline{CM} \cong \overline{CM}$ | 3. A segment is $\cong$ to itself. |
| 4. $\overline{MA} \cong \overline{MB}$ | 4. Definition of midpoint |
| 5. $\overline{AC} \cong \overline{BC}$ | 5. Given |
| 6. $\triangle ACM \cong \triangle BCM$ | 6. SSS Postulate |
| 7. $\angle A \cong \angle B$ | 7. Corres. parts of $\cong$ $\triangle$s are $\cong$. |

In using an auxiliary figure, we must be careful not to put too many conditions on it. Otherwise, we might "prove" something absurd. For example, we could "prove" *any triangle is isosceles* as follows:

Given: $\triangle ABC$

Prove: $\overline{AB} \cong \overline{AC}$

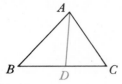

Proof:

| STATEMENTS | REASONS |
|---|---|
| 1. Let $\overline{AD}$ be the median and the altitude from $A$ to $\overline{BC}$. | 1. Every triangle has a median and an altitude from each vertex. |
| 2. $\overline{BD} \cong \overline{DC}$ | 2. Definition of median |
| 3. $\overline{AD} \perp \overline{BC}$ | 3. Definition of altitude |
| 4. $\angle ADB$ and $\angle ADC$ are rt. $\angle$s. | 4. Definition of perpendicular |
| 5. $\triangle ADB$ and $\triangle ADC$ are rt. $\triangle$s. | 5. Definition of rt. $\triangle$ |
| 6. $\overline{AD} \cong \overline{AD}$ | 6. A segment is $\cong$ to itself. |
| 7. $\triangle ADB \cong \triangle ADC$ | 7. LL Theorem |
| 8. $\overline{AB} \cong \overline{AC}$ | 8. Corres. parts of $\cong$ $\triangle$s are $\cong$. |

The error above is that we stated $\overline{AD}$ can be *both* a median and an altitude. This can be true only if $\triangle ABC$ is isosceles.

## Exercises 6.6
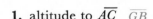

**Assignment Guide**
*Oral:* 1–8
*Written:* Min. 9–22
    Reg. 9–24
    Max. 9–25
*Constructions:* 26–29

(A) **1–5.** Refer to $\triangle ABC$ and $\triangle SET$ to name the following:

1. altitude to $\overline{AC}$    $\overline{GB}$

2. altitude to $\overleftrightarrow{AB}$    $\overline{CD}$

3. altitude to $\overline{ET}$    $\overline{SE}$

4. median to $\overline{ET}$    $\overline{SQ}$

5. altitude to $\overline{SE}$    $\overline{TE}$

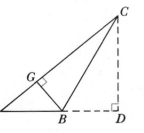
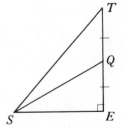

**6–8.** Can an auxiliary figure meet the conditions described? Refer to the figure at left.

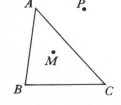

6. $\overline{BD}$ is the median to $\overline{AC}$.   Yes

7. $\overleftrightarrow{BP}$ is the $\perp$ bis. of $\overline{AC}$.   No

8. $\overline{AM}$ is the altitude from $A$ to $\overline{BC}$.   No

Ⓑ **9–22.** Give the missing reasons.

Given: $\angle A \cong \angle B$

Prove: $\overline{AC} \cong \overline{BC}$

[*Plan:* Use the altitude to side $\overline{AB}$ as an auxiliary segment. Prove $\triangle ACM \cong \triangle BCM$ by LA.]

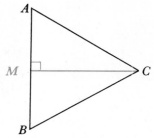

**Proof:**

| STATEMENTS | REASONS |
|---|---|
| *1.* Let $\overline{CM}$ be $\perp$ to $\overline{AB}$. | *1.* Perp. Line Post. (p. 60) |
| *2.* $\angle CMB$ and $\angle CMA$ are right $\angle$s. | *2.* Def. of perpendicular |
| *3.* $\triangle ACM$ and $\triangle BCM$ are right $\triangle$s. | *3.* __**9.**__ Def. of rt. $\triangle$ |
| *4.* $\angle A \cong \angle B$ | *4.* __**10.**__ Given |
| *5.* $\overline{MC} \cong \overline{MC}$ | *5.* __**11.**__ Seg. is $\cong$ to itself. |
| *6.* $\triangle ACM \cong \triangle BCM$ | *6.* __**12.**__ LA Thm. |
| *7.* $\overline{AC} \cong \overline{BC}$ | *7.* __**13.**__ Corres. parts of $\cong$ $\triangle$s are $\cong$. |

Given: Trapezoid $ABCD$ with $\overline{AB} \parallel \overline{DC}$, $\overline{AD} \cong \overline{BC}$

Prove: $\angle D \cong \angle C$, $\angle DAB \cong \angle CBA$

[*Plan:* Let $\overline{AE}$ and $\overline{BF}$ be $\perp$ to $\overline{DC}$. Show $\triangle AED \cong \triangle BFC$ by HL.]

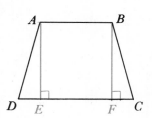

NOTE: This is another proof of part **a** of the Isosceles Trapezoid Theorem, page 181.

**Proof:**

| STATEMENTS | REASONS |
|---|---|
| *1.* Let $\overline{AE} \perp \overline{DC}$ and $\overline{BF} \perp \overline{DC}$. | *1.* __**14.**__ $\perp$ Line Post. (p. 60) |
| *2.* $\angle AED$ and $\angle BFC$ are rt. $\angle$s. | *2.* __**15.**__ Def. of $\perp$ |
| *3.* $\triangle AED$ and $\triangle BFC$ are rt. $\triangle$s. | *3.* __**16.**__ Def. of rt. $\triangle$ |
| *4.* $\overline{AD} \cong \overline{BC}$, $\overline{AB} \parallel \overline{DC}$ | *4.* __**17.**__ Given |
| *5.* $\overline{AE} \cong \overline{BF}$ | *5.* __**18.**__ $\parallel$ lines are everywhere equidistant. |
| *6.* $\triangle AED \cong \triangle BFC$ | *6.* __**19.**__ HL Thm. |
| *7.* $\angle D \cong \angle C$ | *7.* __**20.**__ Corres. parts of $\cong$ $\triangle$s are $\cong$. |
| *8.* $\angle DAB$ and $\angle D$ are supp., as are $\angle CBA$ and $\angle C$. | *8.* __**21.**__ If lines are $\parallel$, int. $\angle$s on same side of trans. are supp. |
| *9.* $\angle DAB \cong \angle CBA$ | *9.* __**22.**__ Supplements of $\cong$ $\angle$s are $\cong$. |

23–24. *Answers on p. 230*

25. *Sketch of Proof:* Given $\overline{AB} \parallel \overline{DC}$. Let $AE \perp$ $\overline{DC}$, $BF \perp \overline{DC}$ ($\perp$ Line Post., p. 60). So $\triangle ADE$ and $\triangle BCF$ are rt. $\triangle$s and $AE \cong BF$ ($\parallel$ lines are equidistant). $\angle DAB$ and $\angle ADE$ are supp., and $\angle CBA$ and $\angle BCF$ are supp. (If lines are $\parallel$, int. $\angle$s on same side of trans. are supp.). Since $\angle DAB \cong$ $\angle CBA$ (Given), $\angle ADE$ $\cong \angle BCF$ (Supplements of $\cong \angle$s are $\cong$) and $\triangle ADE \cong \triangle BCF$ (LA Thm.). So, $\overline{AD} \cong \overline{BC}$.

**23–24.** Use the plan given to write a proof.

**Given:** $\triangle ABC$ with $\overline{AB} \cong \overline{AC}$,
$\overline{CM}$ is the median to $\overline{AB}$,
$\overline{BL}$ is the median to $\overline{AC}$.

**Prove:** $\overline{CM} \cong \overline{BL}$

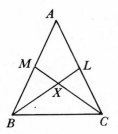

**23.** [*Plan:* Show $\triangle BCL \cong \triangle CBM$.]

**24.** [*Plan:* Show $\triangle BLA \cong \triangle CMA$.]

© **25.** **Given:** Trapezoid $ABCD$ with $\overline{AB} \parallel \overline{DC}$,
$\angle DAB \cong \angle CBA$

**Prove:** $\overline{AD} \cong \overline{BC}$

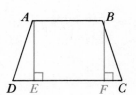

[*Plan:* Show $\triangle ADE \cong \triangle BCF$ by LA.]

**NOTE:** This is another proof of part **b** of the Isosceles Trapezoid Theorem, page 181.

---

## construction: median and altitude of a triangle

| Median | | Altitude Case I | Altitude Case II |
|---|---|---|---|
| 1. Given: $\triangle ABC$ | 2. | Given: $\triangle ABC$ | Given: $\triangle ABC$ |
| Construct the perpendicular bisector of $\overline{AC}$. | $X$ is the midpoint of $\overline{AC}$. $\overline{BX}$ is the median to side $\overline{AC}$. | Construct a segment from point $B$ perpendicular to segment $AC$. | If necessary, extend $\overline{AC}$ and construct a segment from point $B$ perpendicular to $\overleftrightarrow{AC}$. |

**26–29.** Use $\triangle DEF$ shown at the left.

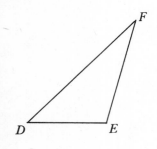

**26.** Copy $\triangle DEF$ and construct its medians.

**27.** Copy $\triangle DEF$ and construct its altitudes.

**28.** Copy $\triangle DEF$ and construct the perpendicular bisectors of its sides.

**29.** Copy $\triangle DEF$ and construct the bisectors of its angles.

# Some Concurrence Theorems

We can prove that the perpendicular bisectors of the sides of a triangle intersect at the same point. We say the perpendicular bisectors are *concurrent*. Two or more lines are **concurrent** if and only if there is a single point at which they all intersect.

| Suggested Class Time | | | |
|---|---|---|---|
| Course | Min. | Reg. | Max. |
| Days | 1 | 1 | 1 |

We can also prove that the lines containing the altitudes of a triangle are concurrent, as are the angle bisectors and the medians.

 The perpendicular bisectors of the sides of a triangle are concurrent at a point that is equidistant from the vertices of the triangle.

**Perpendicular Bisector Concurrence Theorem**

Given: $\triangle ABC$ with $\ell_1$, $\ell_2$, and $\ell_3$ the $\perp$ bisectors of $\overline{AB}$, $\overline{AC}$, and $\overline{CB}$

Prove: $\ell_1$, $\ell_2$, and $\ell_3$ are concurrent at $P$, and $P$ is equidistant from $A$, $B$, and $C$.

[*Plan:* Let $P$ be the pt. where two of the $\perp$ bis. intersect. Show that the pt. is equidistant from the endpts. of the third side and is therefore on its $\perp$ bis.]

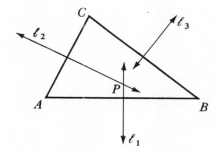

**Proof:**

| STATEMENTS | REASONS |
|---|---|
| 1. Let $P$ be the point where $\ell_1$ and $\ell_2$ intersect. | 1. Perpendiculars to intersecting lines also intersect. |
| 2. $PA = PB$, $PA = PC$ | 2. A pt. on the $\perp$ bis. of a seg. is equidistant from the endpts. ($P$ is on $\ell_1$ and on $\ell_2$.) |
| 3. $PB = PC$ | 3. Substitution |
| 4. $P$ is on the perpendicular bisector of $\overline{BC}$. ($P$ is on $\ell_3$.) | 4. A pt. equidistant from the endpts. of a seg. is on the $\perp$ bis. ($PB = PC$) |
| 5. $\ell_1$, $\ell_2$, and $\ell_3$ are concurrent at $P$. | 5. $P$ is on $\ell_1$, $\ell_2$, and $\ell_3$. |
| 6. $P$ is equidistant from $A$, $B$, and $C$. | 6. $PA = PB = PC$ |

## Altitude Concurrence Theorem

> The lines containing the altitudes of a triangle are concurrent.

**Given:** $\triangle ABC$, $\ell_1$ contains the altitude from $B$ to $\overline{AC}$, $\ell_2$ contains the altitude from $C$ to $\overline{AB}$, $\ell_3$ contains the altitude from $A$ to $\overline{BC}$.

**Prove:** $\ell_1$, $\ell_2$, and $\ell_3$ are concurrent.

[*Plan:* Form $\triangle DEF$ by drawing a line through each vertex of $\triangle ABC$ and parallel to the opposite side. Show that the lines containing the altitudes of $\triangle ABC$ are the $\perp$ bisectors of the sides of $\triangle DEF$.]

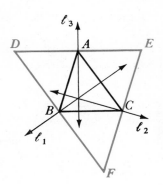

**Proof:**

| STATEMENTS | REASONS |
|---|---|
| 1. Through each vertex of $\triangle ABC$, there is a line $\parallel$ to the opp. side. | 1. Parallel Postulate |
| 2. These three lines determine a triangle, $\triangle DEF$. | 2. Parallels to intersecting lines also intersect. |
| 3. $ACBD$ is a parallelogram. $ACFB$ is a parallelogram. | 3. The opposite sides are parallel. |
| 4. $AC = DB$, $AC = BF$ | 4. Opp. sides of a $\square$ are $\cong$. |
| 5. $DB = BF$ | 5. Substitution |
| 6. $\ell_1 \perp DF$ | 6. In a plane, a line $\perp$ to one of two parallel lines is $\perp$ to the other. |
| 7. $\ell_1$ is the $\perp$ bis. of $\overline{DF}$. | 7. $DB = BF$, $\ell_1 \perp \overline{DF}$ |
| 8. Likewise, $\ell_2$ and $\ell_3$ are the $\perp$ bis. of $\overline{FE}$ and $\overline{DE}$. | 8. Reasoning similar to steps 3–7 |
| 9. The $\perp$ bis. of the sides of $\triangle DEF$ are concurrent. | 9. Perpendicular Bisector Concurrence Theorem |
| 10. The lines containing the altitudes of $\triangle ABC$ are concurrent. | 10. The lines containing the alt. of $\triangle ABC$ are the $\perp$ bis. of the sides of $\triangle DEF$. |

---

*Answers for page 228*

23. *1.* $\overline{CM}$, $\overline{BL}$ are medians to $\overline{AB}$, $\overline{AC}$. (Given)

*2.* M bisects $\overline{AB}$, L bisects $\overline{AC}$. (Defs. of median and midpt.)

*3.* $BM = \frac{1}{2}AB$, $CL = \frac{1}{2}AC$ (Def. of bisect)

*4.* $\overline{AB} \cong \overline{AC}$, so $AB = AC$ (Given)

*5.* $\frac{1}{2}AB = \frac{1}{2}AC$ (Mult. both sides by $\frac{1}{2}$.)

*6.* $BM = CL$, so $\overline{BM} \cong \overline{CL}$ (Subst.)

*7.* $\angle ABC \cong \angle ACB$ (In $\triangle$, $\angle$s opp. $\cong$ sides are $\cong$.)

*8.* $\overline{BC} \cong \overline{BC}$ (Seg. is $\cong$ to itself.)

*9.* $\triangle BCL \cong \triangle CBM$ (SAS Post.)

*10.* $\overline{CM} \cong \overline{BL}$ (Corres. parts of $\cong \triangle$s are $\cong$.)

24. *1.* $\overline{CM}$, $\overline{BL}$ are medians to $\overline{AB}$, $\overline{AC}$. (Given)

*2.* M bisects $\overline{AB}$, L bisects $\overline{AC}$. (Defs. of median and midpt.)

*3.* $AM = \frac{1}{2}AB$, $AL = \frac{1}{2}AC$ (Def. of bisect)

*4.* $\overline{AB} \cong \overline{AC}$, so $AB = AC$ (Given)

*5.* $\frac{1}{2}AB = \frac{1}{2}AC$ (Mult. both sides by $\frac{1}{2}$.)

*6.* $AM = AL$, so $\overline{AM} \cong \overline{AL}$ (Subst.)

*7.* $\angle A \cong \angle A$ ($\angle$ is $\cong$ to itself.)

*8.* $\triangle BLA \cong \triangle CMA$ (SAS Post.)

*9.* $\overline{CM} \cong \overline{BL}$ (Corres. parts of $\cong \triangle$s are $\cong$.)

The proofs of the next two theorems are covered in the exercises.

 The bisectors of the angles of a triangle are concurrent.

 **Angle Bisector Concurrence Theorem**

 The medians of a triangle are concurrent. The point of concurrence is two thirds the distance from each vertex to the midpoint of the opposite side.

 **Median Concurrence Theorem**

▌▌▌▌▌▌▌▌▌▌▌▌▌▌▌▌▌▌▌▌▌▌▌▌▌▌▌▌▌▌▌▌▌▌▌▌▌▌▌▌▌▌▌▌▌▌▌▌▌▌▌ *Exercises 6.7*

Ⓐ **1–4.** Which concurrence theorem is illustrated by each figure?

**1.** Median

**2.** ⊥ Bis.

**3.** ∠ Bis.

**4.** Altitude

**5.** In △ABC above, AE = 6. Find AG.   4

**6.** In △ABC above, DG = 3. Find GC.   6

**Assignment Guide**
*Oral:* 1–6
*Written:* Min. 7–20
           Reg.  7–20
           Max. 7–21

Ⓑ **7–20.** Give the missing reasons.

Given: △ABC with angle bisectors $b_1$, $b_2$, and $b_3$; $b_1$ and $b_2$ intersect at P.

Prove: $b_1$, $b_2$, and $b_3$ are concurrent.

[*Plan:* Show that P is equidistant from the sides of ∠C and is therefore on the bisector of ∠C.]

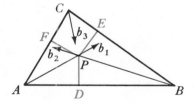

**Proof:**

| STATEMENTS | | REASONS |
|---|---|---|
| 1. $b_1$ and $b_2$ intersect at P. | 1. | Given |
| 2. Let $\overline{PD}$, $\overline{PE}$, and $\overline{PF}$ be the perpendiculars from P to $\overline{AB}$, $\overline{BC}$, and $\overline{AC}$. | 2. **7.** | ⊥ Line Post. (p. 60) |
| 3. $PF = PD$, $PD = PE$ | 3. **8.** | ∠ Bis. Thm. (p. 210) |
| 4. $PF = PE$ | 4. **9.** | Substitution |
| 5. P is on the bisector of ∠C. | 5. **10.** | ∠ Bis. Thm. (p. 210) |
| 6. $b_1$, $b_2$, and $b_3$ are concurrent. | 6. **11.** | Def. of concurrent |

Given: $\triangle ABC$, medians $\overline{BE}$ and $\overline{CF}$ intersect at $P$, $\overrightarrow{AP}$ intersects $\overline{BC}$ at $D$.

Prove: The medians of $\triangle ABC$ are concurrent.

[*Plan:* Draw a ray from $A$ through $P$ and extend it to $G$ so that $AP = PG$. Show $BPCG$ is a parallelogram.]

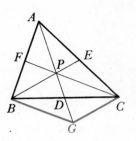

| Proof: STATEMENTS | REASONS |
|---|---|
| 1. Medians $\overline{BE}$ and $\overline{CF}$ intersect at $P$, $\overrightarrow{AP}$ intersects $\overline{BC}$ at $D$. | 1. Given |
| 2. Let $G$ be the point of $\overrightarrow{AP}$ beyond $P$ from $A$, such that $AP = PG$. | 2. __12.__ There is exactly 1 pt. on $\overrightarrow{AP}$ whose distance from $A$ is a given pos. no. |
| 3. $P$ is the midpoint of $\overline{AG}$. | 3. __13.__ Def. of midpt. |
| 4. Draw $\overline{BG}$ and $\overline{CG}$. | 4. __14.__ Two pts. determine a line. |
| 5. $F$ is the midpoint of $\overline{AB}$, $E$ is the midpoint of $\overline{AC}$. | 5. __15.__ Def. of median |
| 6. $\overleftrightarrow{FP} \parallel \overline{BG}$ | 16. Seg. joining midpts. of 2 sides of $\triangle$ is $\parallel$ to third 6. __16.__ side. |
| 7. Likewise, $\overleftrightarrow{PE} \parallel \overline{GC}$. | 7. __17.__ Same reasoning as steps 1–6 |
| 8. $BPCG$ is a parallelogram. | 8. __18.__ Def. of $\square$ |
| 9. $D$ is the midpoint of $\overline{BC}$. | 9. __19.__ Diags. of $\square$ bisect each other. |
| 10. $\overline{AD}$ is a median to $\overline{BC}$. | 10. __20.__ Def. of median |
| 11. The medians $\overline{CF}$, $\overline{BE}$, and $\overline{AD}$ are concurrent. | 11. $P$ is on $\overline{CF}$, $\overline{BE}$, and $\overline{AD}$. |

21. *Sketch of Proof:* Ex. 12–15 show that $\overleftrightarrow{PE}$ is a midline of $\triangle AGC$. So $PE = \frac{1}{2}GC$ (Seg. joining midpts. of 2 sides of $\triangle$ is half as long as third side). Ex. 18 shows $BPCG$ is a $\square$, so $BP = GC$ (Opp sides of $\square$ are $\cong$). $BP + PE = BE$ (Def. of between), and by substitution, $BP + \frac{1}{2}GC = BE$ and $BP + \frac{1}{2}BP = BE$. By Distrib. Prop., $\frac{3}{2}BP = BE$, and by multiplying both sides by $\frac{2}{3}$, $BP = \frac{2}{3}BE$. Similar proofs can be given for the other two medians.

Ⓒ 21. Prove that the medians of a triangle are concurrent at a point that is two thirds the distance from each vertex to the midpoint of the opposite side. (Use the figure for Exercises 12–20 and prove $BP = \frac{2}{3}BE$. HINT: $PE = \frac{1}{2}GC$)

22. *Activity:* The point of concurrence of the medians of a triangle is called the **centroid** (center of mass). Draw a triangle on cardboard or stiff paper and carefully construct the medians to find their point of intersection. Then cut out the triangle and suspend it with string from its centroid. Suspend another triangle by an interior point that is not the centroid. What happens in each case?

First $\triangle$ hangs "flat" (is horizontal). Second one "tilts."

# Transformations and Proofs

We have used transformations in earlier chapters to explore various properties of figures. In this section, we show how transformations can also be used in proofs. First, we would have to accept some postulates about transformations. For example, let's accept these postulates.

**Suggested Class Time**

| Course | Min. | Reg. | Max. |
|--------|------|------|------|
| Days   | 0    | 0    | 1    |

*Postulate*: Reflections preserve collinearity.

*Postulate*: Reflections preserve distance.

Then we can prove

*Theorem*: Reflections preserve betweenness.

Given: $A'$, $B'$, and $C'$ are the reflection images of $A$, $B$, and $C$ over line $\ell$; $B$ is between $A$ and $C$.

Prove: $B'$ is between $A'$ and $C'$.

**Proof:**

| STATEMENTS | REASONS |
|------------|---------|
| 1. $B$ is between $A$ and $C$. | 1. Given |
| 2. $A$, $B$, and $C$ are collinear, $AB + BC = AC$. | 2. Definition of between |
| 3. $A'$, $B'$, and $C'$ are collinear. | 3. Reflections preserve collinearity. |
| 4. $A'B' = AB$, $B'C' = BC$, $A'C' = AC$ | 4. Reflections preserve distance. |
| 5. $A'B' + B'C' = AB + B'C'$ | 5. Add $B'C'$ to both sides of $A'B' = AB$. |
| 6. $A'B' + B'C' = AB + BC$ $= AC$ $= A'C'$ | 6. Substitution (from steps 2 and 4, $BC$ for $B'C'$, $AC$ for $AB + BC$, and $A'C'$ for $AC$) |
| 7. $B'$ is between $A'$ and $C'$. | 7. Definition of between |

# Exercises 6.8

Ⓐ 1. Transformations (<u>can</u>, cannot) be used in proofs.

2. We postulated that reflections preserve _____ and _____ to prove that reflections preserve betweenness.  Collinearity; distance

**Assignment Guide**
*Oral:* Max. 1–4
*Written:* Max. 5–13

**3.** In going from step 5 to step 6 in the proof on page 233, we first substituted ___*BC*___ for $B'C'$.

**4.** Then we substituted $AC$ for _____, then _____ for $AC$.

$AB + BC$; $A'C'$

Ⓑ **5–12.** Give the missing reasons.

*Theorem:* Reflections preserve angle measure.

Given: $X'$, $Y'$, and $Z'$ are the reflection images of $X$, $Y$, and $Z$ over line $\ell$.

Prove: $m\angle X' = m\angle X$

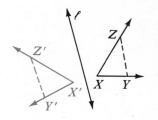

Proof:

| STATEMENTS | | REASONS |
|---|---|---|
| *1.* Draw $\overline{Y'Z'}$ and $\overline{YZ}$. | *5.* Reflections preserve distance. | *1.* Two points determine a line. |
| *2.* $X'Y' = XY$, $X'Z' = XZ$, $Y'Z' = YZ$ | | *2.* __**5.**__ *At left* |
| *3.* $\overline{X'Y'} \cong \overline{XY}$, $\overline{X'Z'} \cong \overline{XZ}$, $\overline{Y'Z'} \cong \overline{YZ}$ | | *3.* __**6.**__ Def. of $\cong$ segs. |
| *4.* $\triangle X'Y'Z' \cong \triangle XYZ$ | | *4.* __**7.**__ SSS Post. |
| *5.* $\angle X' \cong \angle X$ | *8.* Corres. parts of $\cong \triangle$s are $\cong$. | *5.* __**8.**__ *At left* |
| *6.* $m\angle X' = m\angle X$ | | *6.* __**9.**__ Def. of $\cong \angle$s |

*Theorem:* A triangle and its reflection image are congruent.

Given: $\triangle D'E'F'$ is the reflection image of $\triangle DEF$ over line $\ell$.

Prove: $\triangle D'E'F' \cong \triangle DEF$

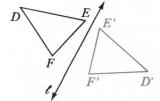

Proof:

| STATEMENTS | | REASONS |
|---|---|---|
| *1.* $D'E' = DE$, $E'F' = EF$, $F'D' = FD$ | | *1.* __**10.**__ *At left* |
| *2.* $\overline{D'E'} \cong \overline{DE}$, $\overline{E'F'} \cong \overline{EF}$, $\overline{F'D'} \cong \overline{FD}$ | | *2.* __**11.**__ Def. of $\cong$ segs. |
| *3.* $\triangle D'E'F' \cong \triangle DEF$ | *10.* Reflections preserve distance. | *3.* __**12.**__ SSS Post. |

**13.** *1.* $r'$ and $n'$ are the reflection images of $r$ and $n$, $r \parallel n$. (Given)

*2.* Draw $k \perp r$ at any pt. on $r$. ($\perp$ Line Post., p. 60)

*3.* $k \perp n$ (In a plane, line $\perp$ to 1 of 2 $\parallel$ lines is $\perp$ to the other.)

*4.* Draw $k'$, the reflection image of $k$. (Reflect any 2 pts. of $k$ over $\ell$.)

*5.* $k' \perp r'$, $k' \perp n'$ (Reflections preserve $\angle$ measure.)

*6.* $r' \parallel n'$ (In a plane, lines $\perp$ to same line are $\parallel$.)

Ⓒ **13.** Prove this theorem: Reflections preserve parallelism.

Given: $r'$ and $n'$ are the reflection images of $r$ and $n$ over $\ell$, $r \parallel n$

Prove: $r' \parallel n'$

[*Plan:* Use an auxiliary line $k$ perpendicular to $r$.]

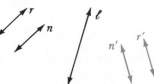

## ■ Chapter 6 Review ■

**Suggested Class Time**

| Course | Min. | Reg. | Max. |
|--------|------|------|------|
| Days   | 1    | 1    | 1    |

1. An if-then statement is false when the hypothesis is true and the conclusion is ___F___.

**6.1**

**Assignment Guide**
*Written:* Min. 1–17; 20–23
Reg. 1–23
Max. 1–24

2–3. Find a counterexample to show that each statement is false.

2. If the product of two numbers is positive, the numbers are positive.
   Any two negative numbers

3. If two angles are supplementary, the angles are not congruent.
   Two 90° $\angle$ s

4–5. Write *true* or *false* for each statement. Then write the converse and tell if it is true or false.

**6.2**

4. If a triangle has two congruent sides, it has two congruent angles.
   T; If a $\triangle$ has 2 $\cong$ $\angle$ s, it has 2 $\cong$ sides; T

5. If a number is a rational number, it is a real number.
   T; If a number is a real number, it is a rational number; F

6. What two true if-then statements can be formed from the following?
   $x^2 = 36$ if and only if $x = 6$ or $x = -6$.
   If $x^2 = 36$, then $x = 6$ or $x = -6$.   If $x = 6$ or $x = -6$, then $x^2 = 36$.

7. Can statements $X$ and $Y$ be connected by *if and only if* to form a true statement?   Yes

   $X$: Two lines are parallel.
   $Y$: The two lines form congruent alternate interior angles with a transversal.

8. Restate the following definition in if-and-only-if form:

**6.3**

   A median of a triangle is a segment from a vertex to the midpoint of the opposite side.   A seg. is a median of a $\triangle$ if and only if it is a seg. from a vertex to the midpt. of the opp. side.

9–10. Write *valid* or *faulty* for each argument. Then name the pattern of reasoning that is used.

**6.4**

9. If a dog eats Briskies, the dog will not be hungry.
   Spot is not hungry.
   So Spot eats Briskies.   Faulty; affirming the conclusion

10. If two angles are vertical angles, the angles are congruent.
    $\angle A$ and $\angle B$ are not congruent.
    So $\angle A$ and $\angle B$ are not vertical angles.   Valid; denying the conclusion

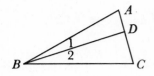

**6.5**

**18.** 1. $\overline{TL}$ and $\overline{ER}$ are altitudes to $\overline{GE}$ and $\overline{GT}$. (Given)
2. $\angle TLE$ and $\angle ERT$ are rt. $\angle$s. (Def. of alt.)
3. $\triangle ETL$ and $\triangle TER$ are rt. $\triangle$s. (Def. of rt. $\triangle$)
4. $\overline{TG} \cong \overline{EG}$ (Given)
5. $\angle TEG \cong \angle ETG$ (In $\triangle$, $\angle$s opp. $\cong$ sides are $\cong$.)
6. $\overline{TE} \cong \overline{TE}$ (Seg. is $\cong$ to itself.)
7. $\triangle ETL \cong \triangle TER$ (HA Thm.)

**6.6**

8. $\overline{ER} \cong \overline{TL}$ (Corres. parts of $\cong$ $\triangle$s are $\cong$.)

**19.** 1. $\overline{TL}$ and $\overline{ER}$ are altitudes to $\overline{GE}$ and $\overline{GT}$. (Given)
2. $\angle TLG$ and $\angle ERG$ are rt. $\angle$s. (Def. of alt.)

**6.7**

3. $\triangle TLG$ and $\triangle ERG$ are rt. $\triangle$s. (Def. of rt. $\triangle$)
4. $\overline{TG} \cong \overline{EG}$ (Given)
5. $\angle G \cong \angle G$ ($\angle$ is $\cong$ to itself.)
6. $\triangle TLG \cong \triangle ERG$ (HA Thm.)
7. $\overline{ER} \cong \overline{TL}$ (Corres. parts of $\cong$ $\triangle$s are $\cong$.)

**6.8**

**11–17.** Give a reason for each step in this indirect proof.

Given: $\triangle ABC$ with $\overline{AB} \cong \overline{BC}$, $\angle 1 \not\cong \angle 2$

Prove: $\overline{AD} \not\cong \overline{DC}$

Proof:

| STATEMENTS | | REASONS |
|---|---|---|
| 1. Assume $\overline{AD} \cong \overline{DC}$. | 1. | **11.** Assump. for ind. prf. |
| 2. $\overline{AB} \cong \overline{BC}$ | 2. | **12.** Given |
| 3. $\overline{BD} \cong \overline{BD}$ | 3. | **13.** Seg. is $\cong$ to itself. |
| 4. $\triangle ADB \cong \triangle CDB$ | 4. | **14.** SSS Post. |
| 5. $\angle 1 \cong \angle 2$ | 5. | **15.** Corres. parts of $\cong$ $\triangle$s are $\cong$. |
| 6. But, $\angle 1 \not\cong \angle 2$. | 6. | **16.** Given |
| 7. So, $\overline{AD} \not\cong \overline{DC}$. | 7. | **17.** Prin. of Ind. Reas. |

**18–19.** Use the plan given to write a proof.

Given: $\triangle TEG$ with $\overline{TG} \cong \overline{EG}$.
$\overline{TL}$ is the altitude from $T$ to $\overline{GE}$,
$\overline{ER}$ is the altitude from $E$ to $\overline{GT}$.

Prove: $\overline{ER} \cong \overline{TL}$

**18.** [*Plan*: Show $\triangle ETL \cong \triangle TER$.]

**19.** [*Plan*: Show $\triangle TLG \cong \triangle ERG$.]

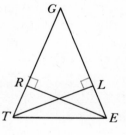

**20.** Two or more lines are _____ if and only if there is a single point at which they all intersect.    Concurrent

**21–22.** Which concurrence theorem is illustrated by each diagram?

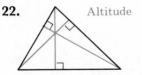

**21.**    Median    **22.**    Altitude

**23.** In $\triangle ABC$ above, how long is $AD$ if $AE = 9$?    6

**24.** What postulates did we assume in order to prove that reflections preserve betweenness?
Reflections preserve collinearity. Reflections preserve distance.

**1–2.** Find a counterexample to show that each statement is false.

**1.** If $x \geq 0$, then $-x < 0$.
$x = 0$

**2.** If two angles have a common side, the angles are adjacent.
*Typical answer:* $\angle DEF$ and $\angle DEG$ where $F$ is in the int. of $\angle DEG$

**Assignment Guide**
*Written:* Min. 1–13
          Reg. 1–13
          Max. 1–14

**3–4.** Write *true* or *false* for each statement. Then write the converse and tell if it is true or false.

**3.** If you live in Florida, the weather is usually warm.
T; If the weather is usually warm, you live in Florida; F

**4.** If a triangle has three congruent angles, it has three congruent sides.
T; If a $\triangle$ has 3 $\cong$ sides, it has 3 $\cong$ $\angle$s; T

**5.** What two true statements can be made from the following?

$$x = 2 \text{ if and only if } x^3 = 8.$$

If $x = 2$, then $x^3 = 8$. If $x^3 = 8$, then $x = 2$.

**6.** Restate the following definition in if-and-only-if form:

An altitude of a triangle is a segment from a vertex perpendicular to the line containing the opposite side.

**6.** A seg. is an alt. of a $\triangle$ if and only if it is a seg. from a vertex $\perp$ to the line containing the opp. side.

**7–8.** Write *valid* or *faulty* for each argument. Then name the pattern of reasoning that is used.

**7.** If $M$ is the midpoint of $\overline{AB}$, then $AM = MB$.
$AM = MB$
So $M$ is the midpoint of $\overline{AB}$.

Faulty; affirming the conclusion

**8.** If a horse wins the Derby, it can run fast.
Lightning cannot run fast.
So Lightning cannot win the Derby.

Valid; denying the conclusion

**9–12.** Give a reason for each step in this indirect proof.

Given: $c$ is not parallel to $d$.

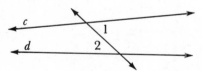

Prove: $\angle 1 \not\cong \angle 2$

**Proof:**

| STATEMENTS | | REASONS |
|---|---|---|
| *1.* Assume $\angle 1 \cong \angle 2$. | *1.* | **9.** Assump. for ind. prf. |
| *2.* Then $c \parallel d$. | *2.* | **10.** If alt. int. $\angle$s are $\cong$, the lines are $\parallel$. |
| *3.* But, $c$ is not parallel to $d$. | *3.* | **11.** Given |
| *4.* So, $\angle 1 \not\cong \angle 2$. | *4.* | **12.** Prin. of Ind. Reas. |

**13.** Draw a sketch to illustrate the Altitude Concurrence Theorem.

**14.** True or False? Proofs about transformations are based on postulates.  T

© King Features Syndicate, Inc., 1975.

# 7

# GEOMETRIC INEQUALITIES

In geometry, as in life, it can be just as important to notice how things differ as it is to notice how they are alike. In this chapter we apply the ideas of *smaller than*, *larger than*, *less than*, and *greater than* to geometric figures.

# Properties of Inequality

7.1

The meanings of *is less than* and *is greater than* were given on page 7 by using the number line. But these terms can also be defined without using the number line. Let $a$ and $b$ stand for any real numbers.

### Suggested Class Time

| Course | Min. | Reg. | Max. |
|---|---|---|---|
| Days | 2 | 2 | 1 |

$a > b$ if and only if $a = b + c$ for some positive number $c$.

$a < b$ if and only if $a + c = b$ for some positive number $c$.

> Two numbers are unequal if and only if there is a positive number that can be added to one number to get the other number.

**Example 1:**

**a.** $5 > 3$, since $5 = 3 + 2$.    positive

**b.** $6\frac{1}{2} < 7$, since $6\frac{1}{2} + \frac{1}{2} = 7$.    positive

**c.** If $x + 4 = 6$, $x < 6$.

**d.** $-3 + n = 2$ for $n = 5$, so $-3 < 2$.

Three order properties of real numbers are also listed on page 7.

| Let $a$, $b$, and $c$ stand for any real numbers. | Examples: |
|---|---|
| $a < b$, $a = b$, or $a > b$ ◀ Exactly one of these is true. | • $3 < 2$, $3 = 2$, or $3 > 2$<br>• $\frac{1}{2} < 0.5$, $\frac{1}{2} = 0.5$, or $\frac{1}{2} > 0.5$ |
| If $a < b$ and $b < c$, then $a < c$. | $2 < 5$ and $5 < 6$, so $2 < 6$ |
| If $a < b$, then $b > a$. | $4 < 7$, so $7 > 4$ |

The properties below are used to simplify (or *solve*) statements of inequality. Though stated here for $>$, they are also true for $<$.

|  | $a > b$ | ◀ Given an inequality, you can: |
|---|---|---|
| **Addition Property** | $a + c > b + c$ | ◀ add the same number to both sides |
| **Subtraction Property** | $a - c > b - c$ | ◀ subtract the same number from **both sides** |
| **Multiplication Property** | If $c > 0$, $ac > bc$. | ◀ multiply both sides by the same **positive** number |
| **Division Property** | If $c > 0$, $\frac{a}{c} > \frac{b}{c}$. | ◀ divide both sides by the same **positive** number |

**Example 2:**

**a.**
$$x - 3 > 4$$
$$x - 3 + 3 > 4 + 3$$
$$x > 7$$

**b.**
$$n + 2 > 5$$
$$n + 2 - 2 > 5 - 2$$
$$n > 3$$

**c.**
$$\tfrac{1}{2}r < 5$$
$$2 \cdot \tfrac{1}{2}r < 2 \cdot 5$$
$$r < 10$$

Because $a < b$, $a = b$, or $a > b$ for any real numbers $a$ and $b$, a statement that one or more of these is *not* true tells us which possibilities may be true. For example,

This statement ▼ is equivalent to this statement. ▼

| a is not less than b. | a is greater than or equal to b. |
|---|---|
| a is not greater than or equal to b. | a is less than b. |
| a is not equal to b. | a is less than or greater than b. |

# Exercises 7.1

**Assignment Guide**
*Oral:* 1–8
*Written:*
Min. (day 1) 9–39 odd
     (day 2) 10–40 even
Reg. (day 1) 9–43 odd
     (day 2) 10–44 even
Max. 9–51 odd

Ⓐ **1–6.** Which symbol, $>$ or $<$, should replace the ▨?

**1.** If $n + 2 = 5$, $n$ ▨ 5. $<$      **2.** If $0 = s + 3$, $s$ ▨ 0. $<$

**3.** Since $-2 + 4 = 2$, $-2$ ▨ 2. $<$    **4.** Since $\frac{5}{8} = \frac{1}{4} + \frac{3}{8}$, $\frac{1}{4}$ ▨ $\frac{5}{8}$. $<$

**5.** If $a - 8 > 7$, then $a$ ▨ 15. $>$    **6.** If $14 < \frac{1}{2}d$, then 28 ▨ $d$. $<$

**7.** If $x$ is not greater than 12, then $x$ is $\underline{\text{Less than}}$12 or $x$ is $\underline{\text{Equal to}}$12.

**8.** If $n$ is greater than or equal to 3, then $n$ is not $\underline{\text{Less than}}$3.

Ⓑ **9–16.** Use the definitions of $>$ and $<$ to state four inequalities for each equation. (*Example:* $7 = 3 + 4$:   $7 > 3$, $3 < 7$, $7 > 4$, $4 < 7$)

**9.** $12 = 9 + 3$      **10.** $5 + 10 = 15$      **11.** $50 + 130 = 180$

**12.** $90 = 30 + 60$      **13.** $23 = x + 7$      **14.** $19 = y + 6$

**15.** $5 + 9 = n$      **16.** $6 + 13 = c$

**17–20.** Use the definitions of $>$ and $<$ to state an equation for each inequality.

**17.** $14 > 3$      **18.** $28 > 5$      **19.** $60 < 90$      **20.** $45 < 75$
$14 = 3 + 11$     $28 = 5 + 23$     $60 + 30 = 90$     $45 + 30 = 75$

**21–28.** Write an equivalent statement.

**21.** $m$ is greater than 12.
    $m$ is not less than or equal to 12.
**22.** 4 is less than $r$.
    4 is not greater than or equal to $r$.
**23.** $n$ is not less than 3.
    $n$ is greater than or equal to 3.
**24.** $x$ is not equal to 15.
    $x$ is less than or greater than 15.
**25.** $t$ is not greater than 9.
    $t$ is less than or equal to 9.
**26.** $a$ is equal to 4.
    $a$ is not less than or greater than 4.

**9.** $9 < 12$, $12 > 9$,
  $3 < 12$, $12 > 3$
**10.** $5 < 15$, $15 > 5$,
  $10 < 15$, $15 > 10$
**11.** $50 < 180$, $180 > 50$,
  $130 < 180$, $180 > 130$
**12.** $30 < 90$, $90 > 30$,
  $60 < 90$, $90 > 60$
**13.** $x < 23$, $23 > x$,
  $7 < 23$, $23 > 7$
**14.** $y < 19$, $19 > y$,
  $6 < 19$, $19 > 6$
**15.** $5 < n$, $n > 5$,
  $9 < n$, $n > 9$
**16.** $6 < c$, $c > 6$,
  $13 < c$, $c > 13$

**27.** 5 is less than or equal to $s$.

     5 is not greater than $s$.

**28.** $v$ is not less than or equal to 23.    $v$ is greater than 23.

**29–44.** Solve.

**29.** $n + 4 > 9$
     $n > 5$

**30.** $d + 7 < 16$
     $d < 9$

**31.** $s - 5 < 6$
     $s < 11$

**32.** $m - 3 > 15$
     $m > 18$

**33.** $4x < 20$
     $x < 5$

**34.** $7n > 28$
     $n > 4$

**35.** $m - 8 > 2$
     $m > 10$

**36.** $r - 15 < 4$
     $r < 19$

**37.** $\dfrac{t}{3} < 5$
     $t < 15$

**38.** $\dfrac{r}{4} > 6$
     $r > 24$

**39.** $3 > \frac{1}{2}p$
     $p < 6$

**40.** $10 < \frac{1}{7}y$
     $y > 70$

**41.** $\frac{1}{5}p < -2$
     $p < -10$

**42.** $\frac{1}{3}n > -5$
     $n > -15$

**43.** $\frac{2}{5}x < 6$
     $x < 15$

**44.** $\frac{3}{4}n > 9$
     $n > 12$

Ⓒ **45.** $\frac{3}{5}x + 2 < 14$
     $x < 20$

**46.** $\frac{5}{6}n - 2 > 8$
     $n > 12$

**47.** $-5 < \frac{4}{7}r$
     $r > -\frac{35}{4}$

**48.** $\frac{7}{8}t - 2 > 3$
     $t > \frac{40}{7}$

**49–52.** Give an example of each property of inequality listed.

**49.** If $a > b$ and $c < 0$, then $ac < bc$.
     $4 > 3,\ -1 < 0,\ 4(-1) < 3(-1)$ or $-4 < -3$

**50.** If $a > b$ and $c = 0$, then $ac = bc$.
     $4 > 3,\ 0 = 0,\ 4(0) = 3(0)$ or $0 = 0$

**51.** If $a > b$, then $c - a < c - b$.
     $4 > 3,\ 5 - 4 < 5 - 3$ or $1 < 2$

**52.** If $a > b$ and $c > d$, then $a + c > b + d$.
     $4 > 3,\ 5 > 2,\ 4 + 5 > 3 + 2$ or $9 > 5$

## ⚬⚬⚬⚬⚬⚬⚬⚬ Putting It Another Way ⚬⚬⚬⚬⚬⚬⚬⚬

The three sentences on each line below all say the same thing. Using the numbers and segments as clues, can you rewrite the sentences in English?

$A \bullet\!\!-\!\!-\!\!-\!\!-\!\!-\!\!-\!\!-\!\!-\!\!-\!\!\bullet B$

$C \bullet\!\!-\!\!-\!\!-\!\!-\!\!-\!\!-\!\!\bullet D$

| Swahili | Spanish | Swedish |
|---|---|---|
| 15 ni sawa na $9 + 6$. | 15 es igual a $9 + 6$. | 15 är den samma $9 + 6$. <br>    15 equals $9 + 6$. |
| 9 si sawa na 7. | 9 no es igual a 7. | 9 är inte den samma 7. <br>    9 is not equal to 7. |
| 9 ni kubwa kuliko 7. | 9 es mayor que 7. | 9 är mera än 7. <br>    9 is greater than 7. |
| 7 ni dogo kuliko 9. | 7 es menor que 9. | 7 är mindre än 9. <br>    7 is less than 9. |
| $\overline{AB}$ ni refu kuliko $\overline{CD}$. | $\overline{AB}$ es más largo que $\overline{CD}$. | $\overline{AB}$ är längare än $\overline{CD}$. <br>    $\overline{AB}$ is longer than $\overline{CD}$. |
| $\overline{CD}$ ni fupi kuliko $\overline{AB}$. | $\overline{CD}$ es más corto que $\overline{AB}$. | $\overline{CD}$ är kortare än $\overline{AB}$. <br>    $\overline{CD}$ is shorter than $\overline{AB}$. |

# 7.2 Comparing Geometric Figures

**Suggested Class Time**

| Course | Min. | Reg. | Max. |
|--------|------|------|------|
| Days   | 2    | 1    | 1    |

Since lengths of segments are real numbers, segments can be compared. That is, one segment can be described as *shorter than*, *congruent to*, or *longer than* another. Measures of angles are also real numbers, so angles can be compared. The chart below summarizes how equal measures and congruent figures, and unequal measures and non-congruent figures, are related.

| Measures | Figures |
|----------|---------|
| $AB = CD$ | $\overline{AB} \cong \overline{CD}$ |
| $AB < CD$ | $\overline{AB}$ is shorter than $\overline{CD}$. |
| $AB > CD$ | $\overline{AB}$ is longer than $\overline{CD}$. |

| Measures | Figures |
|----------|---------|
| $m\angle A = m\angle B$ | $\angle A \cong \angle B$ |
| $m\angle A < m\angle B$ | $\angle A$ is smaller than $\angle B$. |
| $m\angle A > m\angle B$ | $\angle A$ is larger than $\angle B$. |

When $B$ is between $A$ and $C$, $AC = AB + BC$. Because both $AB$ and $BC$ are positive numbers, this one equation leads to four inequalities by using the definitions of $>$ and $<$ on page 239.

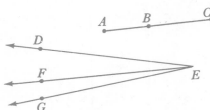

$$AC = AB + BC \left[ \begin{array}{cc} AC > AB & AB < AC \\ AC > BC & BC < AC \end{array} \right.$$

The Angle Addition Postulate also results in four inequalities.

$$m\angle DEG = m\angle DEF + m\angle FEG \left[ \begin{array}{cc} m\angle DEG > m\angle DEF & m\angle DEF < m\angle DEG \\ m\angle DEG > m\angle FEG & m\angle FEG < m\angle DEG \end{array} \right.$$

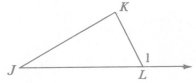

The definitions of $<$ and $>$ can also be used to prove an inequality theorem for exterior angles. The Exterior Angle Theorem tells us that $m\angle 1 = m\angle J + m\angle K$. So we can write four inequalities.

$$m\angle 1 = m\angle J + m\angle K \left[ \begin{array}{cc} m\angle 1 > m\angle J & m\angle J < m\angle 1 \\ m\angle 1 > m\angle K & m\angle K < m\angle 1 \end{array} \right.$$

Then this theorem follows.

**Exterior Angle Inequality Theorem**

An exterior angle of a triangle is larger than either remote interior angle.

Ⓐ 1. If $MN < PD$, then $\overline{MN}$ _____ $\overline{PD}$. Is shorter than

2. If $m\angle R > m\angle S$, then $\angle R$ _____ $\angle S$. Is larger than

3. Since $GH < MN$, $GH = MN$, or $GH > MN$, it follows that $\overline{GH}$ _____ $\overline{MN}$, $\overline{GH}$ _____ $\overline{MN}$, or $\overline{GH}$ _____ $\overline{MN}$.
Is shorter than; ≅ ; is longer than

4. How many inequalities does the equation $RS + 3 = RT$ lead to?
4

5–22. Refer to the figures to decide which symbol, $<$, $=$, or $>$, should replace the ▨.

5. $GS$ ▨ $GK$ $<$      6. $m\angle 1$ ▨ $m\angle RPT$ $<$

7. $m\angle D$ ▨ $m\angle 3$ $<$      8. $KS + SG$ ▨ $KG$ $=$

Ⓑ 9. $GS + EF$ ▨ $GK + EF$ $<$      10. $EF + GK$ ▨ $EF + SK$ $>$

11. $GK - EF$ ▨ $GS - EF$ $>$      12. $GK - SK$ ▨ $GS - SK$ $>$

13. $GK - SK$ ▨ $GS$ $=$      14. $GK - GS$ ▨ $SK$ $=$

15. $m\angle 2 + m\angle A$ ▨ $m\angle RPT + m\angle A$ $<$

16. $m\angle RPT - m\angle 1$ ▨ $m\angle 2 - m\angle 1$ $>$

17. $3m\angle RPT$ ▨ $3m\angle 2$ $>$      18. $\frac{1}{2}m\angle 1$ ▨ $\frac{1}{2}m\angle RPT$ $<$

19. $m\angle 3 + m\angle 4$ ▨ $180$ $=$      20. $m\angle N + m\angle D$ ▨ $m\angle 3$ $=$

21. If $\overline{MN} \perp \overline{ND}$, $m\angle D$ ▨ $90$. $<$      22. If $m\angle N = 90$, $m\angle 3$ ▨ $90$. $>$

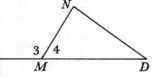

Assignment Guide
*Oral:* 1–8
*Written:*
Min. (day 1) 9–22
    (day 2) 23–24; Alg.
    Rev., p. 244, odd
Reg. 9–23 odd; Alg. Rev.,
    p. 244, odd
Max. 9–25 odd; 27–32

23–24. What theorem, along with the definition of $<$, leads to the statement?

23. In $\triangle ABC$, $m\angle A + m\angle B < 180$.      $\angle$ Sum Thm. for $\triangle$s (p. 137)

24. If $\overline{DE}$ is a midline of $\triangle MNP$ and $\overline{DE} \parallel \overline{MN}$, then $DE < MN$.
$\triangle$ Midline Thm. (p. 148)

Ⓒ 25–26. Prove the theorem.

25. If $N$ and $P$ are between $R$ and $S$, then $NP < RS$.
*Answer on page 244*

26. If $A$ and $B$ are in the interior of $\angle DEF$, then $m\angle AEB < m\angle DEF$.
*Answer on page 245*

*Answer for page 243*

**25.** *Given:* $N$, $P$ between $R$, $S$; $N$ between $R$, $P$ (or $N$ between $P$, $S$)

*Prove:* $NP < RS$

*Proof:*

1. $N$, $P$ between $R$, $S$; $N$ between $R$, $P$ (Given)
2. $NP + PS = NS$, $RN + NS = RS$ (Def. of between)
3. $NP < NS$, $NS < RS$ (Def. of $<$)
4. $NP < RS$ (If $a < b$ and $b < c$, then $a < c$.)

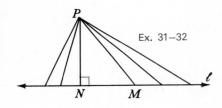
Ex. 31–32

**27–32.** A conclusion that has not been proved is a **conjecture**. Though not every conjecture is true, theorems usually begin as conjectures. You may want to work with models or drawings to make the conjectures asked for in these exercises.

**27.** $AB + BC = AC$ if and only if $B$ is between $A$ and $C$ on $\overline{AC}$. Where is $B$ if $AB + BC > AC$? Can $AB + BC < AC$?

Anywhere in the plane except between $A$ and $C$; no

**28.** What conjectures can you make from these situations?

**a.** $m\angle AIB + m\angle BIC > m\angle AIC$    **b.** $m\angle AIB + m\angle BIC < m\angle AIC$

$C$ is in the interior of $\angle AIB$.    Is not possible

**29.** Two sides of a triangle are congruent if and only if the angles opposite those sides are congruent. In $\triangle DEF$, $EF > DE$. What conjecture can you make about the angles opposite $\overline{EF}$ and $\overline{DE}$?

$\angle$ opp. $\overline{EF}$ is larger than $\angle$ opp. $\overline{DE}$.

**30.** In $\triangle DEF$, $m\angle F \lneqq m\angle E$. What conjecture can you make about the sides opposite $\angle F$ and $\angle E$?

Side opp. $\angle F$ is shorter than side opp. $\angle E$.

**31.** What conjecture can you make about the shortest segment from $P$ to $\ell$ in the figure?    It is $\perp$ to $\ell$.

**32.** In $\triangle MNP$, $\angle N$ is a right angle. What conjectures can you make comparing the sides of $\triangle MNP$?

$\overline{MP}$ is the longest side.

---

## *Algebra Review*

**Review these skills:**

- *multiplying monomials*
- *multiplying a monomial and a binomial*
- *multiplying binomials*

**Find each product.**

**1.** $3 \cdot 6n$    $18n$

**2.** $\frac{1}{2} \cdot 4x$    $2x$

**3.** $\frac{2}{3} \cdot 5r$    $\frac{10}{3}r$ or $\frac{10r}{3}$

**4.** $-8 \cdot 3c$    $-24c$

**5.** $-7(-9f)$    $63f$

**6.** $6(-5h)$    $-30h$

**7.** $(4p)^2$    $16p^2$

**8.** $(\frac{1}{2}h)^2$    $\frac{1}{4}h^2$ or $\frac{h^2}{4}$

**9.** $(\frac{3}{5}t)^2$    $\frac{9}{25}t^2$ or $\frac{9t^2}{25}$

**10.** $(-\frac{2}{3}v)^2$    $\frac{4}{9}v^2$ or $\frac{4v^2}{9}$

**11.** $6(s + 4)$    $6s + 24$

**12.** $(a + 9)b$    $ab + 9b$

**13.** $\frac{1}{3}(3q + 1)$    $q + \frac{1}{3}$

**14.** $-2(p + \frac{3}{4})$    $-2p - \frac{3}{2}$

**15.** $-9(d - \frac{2}{3})$    $-9d + 6$

**16.** $(r + 5)(r + 2)$    $r^2 + 7r + 10$

**17.** $(n + \frac{2}{3})(3n + 6)$    $3n^2 + 8n + 4$

**18.** $(b - 4)(b - 2)$    $b^2 - 6b + 8$

**19.** $(d + 3)(d - 3)$    $d^2 - 9$

**20.** $(x + 3)^2$    $x^2 + 6x + 9$

**21.** $(m - 5)^2$    $m^2 - 10m + 25$

**22.** $(s - \frac{1}{2})(s + \frac{1}{2})$    $s^2 - \frac{1}{4}$

**23.** $(2y + 1)^2$    $4y^2 + 4y + 1$

**24.** $(3n - \frac{1}{2})^2$    $9n^2 - 3n + \frac{1}{4}$

# GEOMETRIC GEOGRAPHY

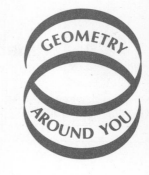

Have you ever heard of Equality, Illinois, or Converse, Louisiana? There are many place-names that are made up partly or entirely of terms used in mathematics. Some that involve geometry terms are listed here. Identify the terms from the descriptions and figures in 1–14, below. Then decode each place-name by replacing the number with the corresponding term.

Sources: *Hammond New Contemporary World Atlas* and *National Geographic Atlas of the World*

1. in a drawing, represents a point
2. postulate, or axiom
3. joins opposite vertices of a square
4. rectangular rhombus
5. geometric figure with no dimensions
6. part of a circle

7. [ray figure]
8. [parallelogram figure]
9. [angle figure]
10. [circle figure]
11. [line figure]
12. [triangle figure]
13. [triangle with marked sides figure]
14. [point with dashed circle figure]

Newtown __4__, Pa.
    Square

State __11__, Miss.
    Line

__9__ Inlet, Minn.
    Angle

__1__ Lake, Alaska
    Dot

__4__ Butte, Mont.
    Square

Rocky __5__, Wyo.
    point

__10__ Pines, Minn.
    Circle

Central __4__, N.Y.
    Square

__6__ Dome Peak, Nev.
    Arc

__5__ Washington, Fla.
    Point

Social __10__, Ga.
    Circle

Central __5__, Oreg.
    Point

Crest __11__, Kans.
    line

Dead Horse __5__, Utah
    Point

__7__ River, Alaska
    Ray

__6__ola, Ind.
    Arc

Dela __8__, Va.
    plane

__7__, N.Dak.
    Ray

__3__, Iowa
    Diagonal

__12__ Idaho
    Triangle

__13__ Ga.
    Kite

__10__, Mont.
    Circle

__2__, Ill.
    Assumption

Ex __11__, Iowa
    line

Two __1__, Mont.
    dot

__5__s, W.Va.
    Point

__6__o, Idaho
    Arc

__14__, Mo.
    Center

__7__ City, Ga.
    Ray

La __14__, Ky.
    Center

__7__ __14__, Mich.
    Ray Center

Rich __4__, N.C.
    Square

Brook __11__, Mass.
    line

Peri __1__, Ariz.
    dot

__10__ Back, Tex.
    Circle

__11__boro, Md.
    Line

__4__ Lake, Maine
    Square

__14__ __5__, La.
    Center Point

__10__ville, Ohio
    Circle

__6__ata, Calif.
    Arc

__14__ __11__, Mich.
    Center Line

__11__ville, Ala.
    Line

__14__ Hill, Ark.
    Center

__14__dale, R.I.
    Center

Shady __5__, Okla.
    Point

Answer for page 243

26. *Given:* $A$, $B$ in int. of $\angle DEF$; $A$ in int. of $\angle DEB$ (or $B$ in int. of $\angle DEA$)
*Prove:* $m\angle AEB < m\angle DEF$
*Proof:*
1. $A$, $B$ in int. of $\angle DEF$; $A$ in int. of $\angle DEB$ (Given)
2. $m\angle AEB + m\angle BEF = m\angle AEF$, $m\angle DEA + m\angle AEF = m\angle DEF$ ($\angle$ Add. Post., p. 53)
3. $m\angle AEB < m\angle AEF$, $m\angle AEF < m\angle DEF$ (Def. of $<$)
4. $m\angle AEB < m\angle DEF$ (If $a < b$ and $b < c$, then $a < c$.)

# Inequalities in a Triangle

On a trail over the top of a hill, you expect the climb up the long side of the hill to be easier than the climb up the short side. This illustrates a theorem relating sides and angles of a triangle.

**Suggested Class Time**

| Course | Min. | Reg. | Max. |
|--------|------|------|------|
| Days   | 2    | 1    | 1    |

Simmerman/Van Cleve Photograp

First, we prove this statement:

If two sides of a triangle are not congruent, the angle opposite the longer side is larger than the angle opposite the shorter side.

Given: $\triangle DEF$, $EF > DE$

Prove: $m\angle 3 > m\angle 1$

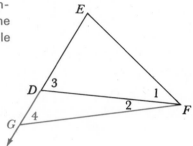

**Proof:**

| STATEMENTS | REASONS |
|------------|---------|
| 1. Let $G$ be on $\overrightarrow{ED}$ and $EG = EF$. | 1. Point Plotting Theorem (p. 27) |
| 2. $m\angle 4 = m\angle EFG$ | 2. Base $\angle$s of an isos. $\triangle$ are $\cong$. |
| 3. $m\angle 3 > m\angle 4$ | 3. Exterior $\angle$ Inequality Thm. (p. 242) |
| 4. $m\angle 3 > m\angle EFG$ | 4. Substitution |
| 5. $EF > DE$ | 5. Given |
| 6. $EG > DE$ | 6. Substitution (steps 1 and 5) |
| 7. $m\angle EFG = m\angle 1 + m\angle 2$ | 7. $\angle$ Addition Post. (p. 53) |
| 8. $m\angle EFG > m\angle 1$ | 8. Definition of $>$ |
| 9. $m\angle 3 > m\angle 1$ | 9. If $a > b$ and $b > c$, then $a > c$. (steps 4 and 8) |

An indirect proof is used for the converse of the statement above.

If two angles of a triangle are not congruent, the side opposite the larger angle is longer than the side opposite the smaller angle.

Given: $\triangle DEF$, $m\angle 3 > m\angle 1$

Prove: $EF > DE$

(See the figure on page 246.)

Proof:

| STATEMENTS | REASONS |
|---|---|
| 1. Assume $EF$ is not greater than $DE$. | 1. For an indirect proof, assume the opposite of what is to be proved. |
| 2. $EF < DE$ or $EF = DE$. | 2. $a < b$, $a = b$, or $a > b$. |
| 3. $m\angle 3 < m\angle 1$ or $m\angle 3 = m\angle 1$. | 3. Larger $\angle$ is opp. longer side of $\triangle$, or base $\angle$s of an isos. $\triangle$ are $\cong$. |
| 4. But, $m\angle 3 > m\angle 1$. | 4. Given |
| 5. So, $EF > DE$. | 5. Principle of Indirect Reasoning |

Since the two statements just proved are converses, we can combine them in one theorem by using *if and only if*.

 In any triangle, one angle is larger than another if and only if the side opposite the first angle is longer than the side opposite the second angle.  **Theorem**

I

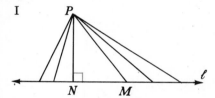

II

Which segment from $P$ to $\ell$ seems to be the shortest?

Which side of the right triangle appears to be the longest?

The answers to these two questions give us the theorems below. The proofs appear in Exercises 27–32.

 The shortest segment from a point to a line is the segment perpendicular to the line.  **Theorem**

 The hypotenuse of a right triangle is longer than either leg.  **Theorem**

The first of these two theorems leads us to define **the distance from a point to a line** as the length of the perpendicular segment from the point to the line.

# Exercises 7.3

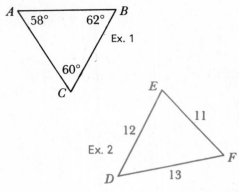

Ex. 1

Ex. 2

**Assignment Guide**

*Oral:* 1–8

*Written:*

Min. (day 1) 9–25 odd; 27–30
  (day 2) 10–26 even;
  31–32

Reg. 9–25 odd; 26–32

Max. 9–25 odd; 26–33

(A) **1.** Which side of $\triangle ABC$ is the longest? The shortest?
$\overline{AC}$; $\overline{BC}$

**2.** Which angle of $\triangle DEF$ is the largest? The smallest? $\angle E$; $\angle D$

**3.** In a triangle, the $\underline{\text{Largest}}$ angle is always opposite the longest side.

**4.** You must show that assuming $a < b$ or $a = b$ leads to a contradiction of a true statement to prove that $\underline{a > b}$ by an indirect proof.

**5.** Assuming that $c$ is less than or equal to $d$ is equivalent to assuming that $c$ _____ $d$.
Is not greater than

**6.** Neither leg of a right triangle can be longer than _____.
The hypotenuse

**7.** The distance from point $P$ to line $\ell$ is the length of _____.
The $\perp$ seg. from $P$ to $\ell$

**8.** If $\overrightarrow{RD}$ is the shortest segment from $R$ to $\overleftrightarrow{DB}$, then $\overleftrightarrow{RD}$ $\underline{\perp}$ $\overleftrightarrow{DB}$.

(B) **9–18.** Which symbol, $<$, $=$, or $>$, should replace the ▨?

**9.** If $m\angle G = 70$ and $m\angle J = 40$, $GH$ ▨ $HJ$. $<$

**10.** If $m\angle H = 85$ and $m\angle G = 60$, $HJ$ ▨ $JG$. $<$

**11.** If $m\angle H = 80$ and $m\angle J = 45$, $HJ$ ▨ $HG$. $>$

**12.** If $m\angle J = 40$ and $m\angle G = 60$, $HJ$ ▨ $GJ$. $<$

**13.** If $m\angle H = 90$, $GJ$ ▨ $GH$. $>$　**14.** If $\overline{HG} \perp \overline{HJ}$, $GJ$ ▨ $HJ$. $>$

**15.** If $GH = 3$ and $HJ = 5$, $>$　**16.** If $GJ = 7$ and $HJ = 6$, $>$
$m\angle G$ ▨ $m\angle J$.　　　$m\angle H$ ▨ $m\angle G$.

**17.** If $\angle H$ is obtuse, $HG$ ▨ $GJ$. $<$　**18.** If $\angle H$ is obtuse, $HJ$ ▨ $GJ$. $<$

Ex. 9–18

**19–24.** Refer to the figure to find each distance.

**19.** from $A$ to $L$　4　**20.** from $N$ to $E$　1.8　Ex. 19–24

**21.** from $L$ to $\overleftrightarrow{AN}$　4　**22.** from $N$ to $\overleftrightarrow{LA}$　3

**23.** from $A$ to $\overleftrightarrow{LN}$　**24.** from $L$ to $N$
2.4　　　　5.0

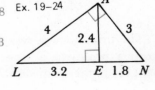

**25.** What is the longest segment in the figure? $\overline{DC}$

**26.** What is the shortest segment in the figure? $\overline{AB}$

*B*
*A* 59°
58° *C*
59°
*D*

**27–30.** Copy figure I on page 247. Then copy and complete this proof that the shortest segment from a point to a line is the segment perpendicular to the line.

Given: $\overline{PN} \perp \ell$, M is any point on $\ell$ other than N.

Prove: $PN < PM$

Proof:

| STATEMENTS | REASONS |
|---|---|
| 1. $m\angle PNM = 90$ | 1. Given that $\overline{PN} \perp \ell$ |
| 2. $\triangle PNM$ is a right triangle. | 2. __27.__ Def. of rt. $\triangle$ |
| 3. $m\angle NMP < 90$ | 3. __28.__ If 1 $\angle$ of $\triangle$ is rt. or obtuse, other 2 $\angle$s are acute. |
| 4. $m\angle NMP < m\angle PNM$ | 4. __29.__ Subst. (Steps 1 and 3) |
| 5. $PN < PM$ | 5. __30.__ In a $\triangle$, side opp. larger $\angle$ is longer. |

**31–32.** Copy figure II on page 247. Then copy and complete this proof that the hypotenuse of a right triangle is longer than either leg.

Given: $\angle N$ is the right angle in $\triangle MNP$.

Prove: $PN < PM$, $MN < PM$

Proof:

| STATEMENTS | REASONS |
|---|---|
| 1. $\overline{PN} \perp \overleftrightarrow{MN}$, $\overline{MN} \perp \overleftrightarrow{PN}$ | 1. __31.__ Def. of $\perp$ |
| 2. $PN < PM$, $MN < PM$ | 2. __32.__ Shortest seg. from a pt. to a line is seg. $\perp$ to line. |

© **33.** Prove that in an acute or an obtuse triangle, an altitude to any side is shorter than either of the other two sides.

Given: $\triangle CAT$, altitude $\overline{AF}$

Prove: $AF < AC$, $AF < AT$

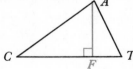

**34.** Prove that in a right triangle, an altitude to any side is not longer than either of the other two sides. HINT: Consider two cases—the altitude to the hypotenuse and an altitude to either leg.

**33.** 1. Alt. $\overline{AF}$ (Given)
2. $\overline{AF} \perp \overleftrightarrow{CT}$ (Def. of alt.)
3. $AF < AC$, $AF < AT$ (Shortest seg. from a pt. to a line is seg. $\perp$ to line.)

**34.** *Given:* $\angle B$ is rt. $\angle$ in $\triangle ABC$; altitudes $\overline{BD}$ to $\overline{AC}$, $\overline{CB}$ to $\overline{AB}$, $\overline{AB}$ to $\overline{BC}$
*Prove:* $\overline{BD}$ is not longer than $\overline{AB}$ or $\overline{BC}$; $\overline{CB}$ is not longer than $\overline{CB}$ or $\overline{AC}$; $\overline{AB}$ is not longer than $\overline{AB}$ or $\overline{AC}$.
*Proof:*
1. Altitudes $\overline{BD}$, $\overline{CB}$, $\overline{AB}$ (Given)
2. $\overline{BD} \perp \overline{AC}$, $\overline{CB} \perp \overline{AB}$, $\overline{AB} \perp \overline{BC}$ (Def. of alt.)
3. $BD < AB$, $BD < BC$, $CB < AC$, $AB < AC$ (Shortest seg. from a pt. to a line is seg. $\perp$ to line.)
4. $CB = CB$, $AB = AB$ (Seg. is $\cong$ to itself.)
5. $\overline{BD}$ is not longer than $\overline{AB}$ or $\overline{BC}$; $\overline{CB}$ is not longer than $\overline{CB}$ or $\overline{AC}$; $\overline{AB}$ is not longer than $\overline{AB}$ or $\overline{AC}$. (Equivalent statements to those in steps 3 and 4)

# 7.4 The Triangle Inequality

Bees are said to fly back to the hive in a straight line after they have gathered a load of nectar. So a straight, direct route is often called a *beeline*. In fact, we can prove that such a beeline is the shortest route to the hive from the last flower visited by the bee.

First, we compare the distance from the flower ($F$) to the hive ($H$) with the distance from the flower to a second point ($S$) and then to the hive.

Larsen/Van Cleve Photography

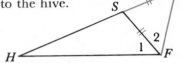

Given: $\triangle FSH$

Prove: $FS + SH > FH$

Proof:

| STATEMENTS | REASONS |
| --- | --- |
| 1. Let $P$ be on $\overrightarrow{HS}$, $S$ be between $H$ and $P$, and $PS = FS$. | 1. Point Plotting Theorem (p. 27) |
| 2. $m\angle P = m\angle 2$ | 2. Base $\angle$s of an isos. $\triangle$ are $\cong$. |
| 3. $m\angle HFP = m\angle 1 + m\angle 2$ | 3. $\angle$ Addition Post. (p. 53) |
| 4. $m\angle HFP > m\angle 2$ | 4. Definition of $>$ |
| 5. $m\angle HFP > m\angle P$ | 5. Substitution (steps 2 and 4) |
| 6. In $\triangle FPH$, $PH > FH$. | 6. Longer side of $\triangle$ is opp. larger $\angle$. |
| 7. $PH = PS + SH$ | 7. Def. of between (step 1) |
| 8. $PH = FS + SH$ | 8. Substitution (steps 1 and 7) |
| 9. $FS + SH > FH$ | 9. Substitution (steps 6 and 8) |

What we have just proved can be stated in terms of any triangle.

**Triangle Inequality Theorem**

**The sum of the lengths of any two sides of a triangle is greater than the length of the third side.**

According to this theorem, if any two sides of a triangle are laid end to end, the resulting segment must be longer than the third side of the triangle. Consider a triangle whose sides have lengths 5, 7, and $x$.

30. *Given:* Square $ABCD$, diagonal $\overline{AC}$
*Prove:* $AC < 2AB$
*Sketch of Proof:* By $\triangle$ Inequality Thm., $AB + BC > AC$. $AB = BC$ (Def. of square), so $AB + AB > AC$, or $AC < 2AB$.

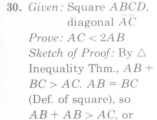

5      7

$5 + 7 > x$, so
**sum** of the two ▶    $12 > x$
known lengths      ↳ $x$ is between 12 and 2. ↵

5      $x$

$5 + x > 7$, so
     $x > 2$    ◀ **difference** of the
             two known lengths

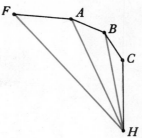

Suppose the bee doesn't make a beeline from the flower at $F$ to the hive at $H$. The bee might take the path formed by the line segments from $F$ to $A$ to $B$ to $C$ to $H$ (call this path $F$-$A$-$B$-$C$-$H$). The length of this path is $FA + AB + BC + CH$. But, since $FB < FA + AB$ by the Triangle Inequality, $F$-$B$-$C$-$H$ is shorter. Similar reasoning shows that $F$-$C$-$H$ is shorter than $F$-$B$-$C$-$H$ and, finally, that $F$-$H$ is shorter than $F$-$C$-$H$. Since the length of $F$-$H$ is $FH$, we have this theorem.

**The shortest path between two points is the segment joining them.** **Theorem**

## Exercises 7.4

**Assignment Guide**
*Oral:* 1–4
*Written:*
Min. 5–23 odd; 25–28
Reg. 5–23 odd; 25–28
Max. 5–23 odd; 25–30

Ⓐ **1.** Can a triangle have sides 3, 5, and 9 units long?  No

**2.** Can a triangle have sides 3, 5, and 6 units long?  Yes

**3.** If $\triangle MNP$ has sides 3, 7, and $x$ units long, then $x < $ ___10___.

**4.** If $\triangle MNP$ has sides 3, 7, and $x$ units long, then $x > $ ___4___.

Ⓑ **5–16.** Can the given numbers be the lengths of the sides of a triangle?

**5.** 8, 7, 10  Yes  **6.** 6, 9, 4  Yes  **7.** 9, 4, 5  No  **8.** 6, 12, 5  No

**9.** 7, 7, 9  Yes  **10.** 7, 15, 8  No  **11.** 4, 10, 6  No  **12.** 5, 5, 2  Yes

**13.** 4, 6, $2\frac{1}{2}$  Yes  **14.** 7, 4, $2\frac{1}{2}$  No  **15.** 8, $4\frac{2}{3}$, 3  No  **16.** $3\frac{1}{3}$, 5, 3  Yes

**29.** *Sketch of Proof:* Draw $\overline{RT}$. By $\triangle$ Inequality Thm., $RS + ST > RT$. $RS + ST + TU > RT + TU$ (If $a > b$, then $a + c > b + c$). $RT + TU > RU$ ($\triangle$ Inequality Thm.), so $RS + ST + TU > RU$ (If $a > b$ and $b > c$, then $a > c$).

**17–24.** $\triangle ABC$ has sides of the given lengths. $x$ is between what numbers?

**17.** 10, 13, $x$  3, 23  **18.** 11, 15, $x$  4, 26  **19.** 11, 5, $x$  6, 16  **20.** 3, 12, $x$  9, 15

**21.** $2\frac{1}{2}$, 5, $x$  $2\frac{1}{2}$, $7\frac{1}{2}$  **22.** 4, $5\frac{1}{2}$, $x$  $1\frac{1}{2}$, $9\frac{1}{2}$  **23.** $7\frac{1}{2}$, $9\frac{1}{2}$, $x$  2, 17  **24.** $3\frac{1}{2}$, $6\frac{1}{2}$, $x$  3, 10

**25–28.** Refer to the given segments. Can a triangle be formed using the three listed? If the answer is *yes*, construct the triangle.

**25.** a, b, c  No  **26.** b, c, d  Yes    **a.** _____    **b.** _____

**27.** a, c, d  Yes  **28.** a, b, d  No    **c.** _____    **d.** _____

Ⓒ **29–30.** Use the Triangle Inequality Theorem to prove that

**29.** $RS + ST + TU > RU$ in the figure.

**30.** A diagonal of a square is less than twice as long as a side.

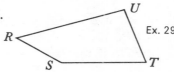

Ex. 29

# 7.5

## Noncongruent Triangles

Frank Kuechmann

Suppose a pendulum hangs in a triangular frame, as shown in the photograph. When the weight is on the perpendicular bisector of the base of the frame, it is equidistant from the endpoints of the base. But when the weight swings to one side, its distance from either endpoint is related to the angles at the vertex of the frame.

The proof of the next theorem does not depend on the fact that the weight (point $P$) is in the interior of $\angle ACB$.

**Given:** $\overline{AC} \cong \overline{BC}$, $P$ is any point for which $m\angle PCA < m\angle PCB$.

**Prove:** $PA < PB$

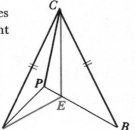

**Proof:**

| STATEMENTS | REASONS |
|------------|---------|
| 1. Let $\overrightarrow{CE}$ bisect $\angle ACB$ and intersect $\overrightarrow{PB}$ at $E$. | 1. Every $\angle$ has exactly 1 bisector. |
| 2. $\angle ACE \cong \angle BCE$ | 2. Definition of $\angle$ bisector |
| 3. $\overline{AC} \cong \overline{BC}$ | 3. Given |
| 4. $\overline{CE} \cong \overline{CE}$ | 4. A segment is $\cong$ to itself. |
| 5. $\triangle ACE \cong \triangle BCE$ | 5. SAS Postulate |
| 6. $EA = EB$ | 6. Corres. parts of $\cong \triangle$s are $\cong$. |
| 7. $PA < PE + EA$ | 7. $\triangle$ Inequality Theorem |
| 8. $PA < PE + EB$ | 8. Substitution (steps 6 and 7) |
| 9. $PE + EB = PB$ | 9. Definition of between |
| 10. $PA < PB$ | 10. Substitution (steps 8 and 9) |

This theorem is stated below in symbols rather than in words.

**Pendulum Theorem**

If $\overline{AC} \cong \overline{BC}$ and $P$ is any point for which $m\angle PCA < m\angle PCB$, then $P$ is closer to $A$ than to $B$; that is, $PA < PB$.

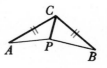

A derrick (named after a seventeenth-century English hangman) is used to lift and move heavy loads.

Notice that the mast, boom, and boom lines form a triangle. When the length of the boom lines is changed, the angle formed by the mast and the boom also changes. The relationship between this angle and the length of the lines is expressed by the next theorem.

Courtesy Port of New Orleans

If two noncongruent triangles have two sides of one congruent to two sides of the other,

**a.** The triangle with the smaller included angle has the shorter third side.

**b.** The triangle with the shorter third side has the smaller included angle.

**Hangman Theorem**

Part **a** is proved here, while part **b,** the converse, is proved in Exercises 31–38.

Given: $\overline{AC} \cong \overline{DF}$, $\overline{AB} \cong \overline{DE}$, $m\angle D < m\angle 1$

Prove: $EF < BC$

[*Plan:* On one of the congruent sides of $\triangle ABC$, construct a triangle congruent to $\triangle DEF$. Prove the third side of this triangle is shorter than the third side of $\triangle ABC$.]

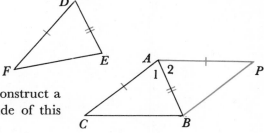

**Proof:**

| STATEMENTS | REASONS |
|---|---|
| 1. Let $m\angle 2 = m\angle D$, so $\angle 2 \cong \angle D$. | 1. $\angle$ Construction Post. (p. 53) |
| 2. Let $AP = DF$, so $\overline{AP} \cong \overline{DF}$. | 2. Point Plotting Theorem (p. 27) |
| 3. $\overline{AB} \cong \overline{DE}$ | 3. Given |
| 4. $\triangle ABP \cong \triangle DEF$ | 4. SAS Postulate |
| 5. $\overline{AC} \cong \overline{DF}$, so $AC = DF$. | 5. Given |
| 6. $AC = AP$ | 6. Substitution (steps 2 and 5) |
| 7. $m\angle D < m\angle 1$ | 7. Given |
| 8. $m\angle 2 < m\angle 1$ | 8. Substitution (steps 1 and 7) |
| 9. $BP < BC$ | 9. Pendulum Theorem (steps 6 and 8) |
| 10. $BP = EF$ | 10. Corres. parts of $\cong \triangle$s are $\cong$. (step 4) |
| 11. $EF < BC$ | 11. Substitution (steps 9 and 10) |

## Exercises 7.5

**Assignment Guide**
*Oral:* 1–6
*Written:*
Min. (day 1) 7–23 odd
(day 2) 8–24 even;
39–40
Reg. (day 1) 7–23 odd
(day 2) 25–30; 39–40
Max. 7–23 odd; 25–38

Ⓐ **1–24.** Refer to the figures. Which symbol, <, =, or >, should replace the ▨ ?

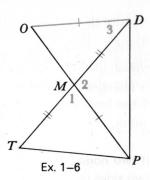

Ex. 1–6

1. *MD* ▨ *MT*   =   2. *MP* ▨ *MP*   =

3. If $PT < PD$, then $m\angle 1$ ▨ $m\angle 2$.   <

4. If $m\angle 1 < m\angle 2$, then $PT$ ▨ $PD$.   <

5. $m\angle 2$ ▨ $m\angle 3$   >   6. *MO* ▨ *PD*   <

Ⓑ  **7.** If $m\angle R = 30$ and $m\angle N = 40$, *LE* ▨ *FS*.   >

**8.** If $m\angle N = 50$ and $m\angle R = 40$, *FS* ▨ *LE*.   <

**9.** If $EL = 5$ and $FS = 4$, $m\angle N$ ▨ $m\angle R$.   >

**10.** If $SF = 8$ and $LE = 9$, $m\angle N$ ▨ $m\angle R$.   >

**11.** If $LE = 10$ and $FS = 10$, $m\angle N$ ▨ $m\angle R$.   =

**12.** If $m\angle R = 35$ and $m\angle N = 35$, *LE* ▨ *FS*.   =

Ex. 7–16

**13.** If $FS < LE$, then $m\angle R$ ▨ $m\angle N$.   <

**14.** If $EL < FS$, then $m\angle N$ ▨ $m\angle R$.   <

**15.** If $m\angle N > m\angle R$, then *LE* ▨ *FS*.   >

**16.** If $m\angle R > m\angle N$, then *EL* ▨ *FS*.   <

**17.** If $AB = 5$ and $BC = 7$, then $m\angle 1$ ▨ $m\angle 2$.   <

**18.** If $BC = 9$ and $AB = 12$, then $m\angle 1$ ▨ $m\angle 2$.   >

**19.** If $AB = 5$ and $BC = 7$, then $m\angle C$ ▨ $m\angle A$.   <

**20.** If $BC = 9$ and $AB = 12$, then $m\angle C$ ▨ $m\angle A$.   >

**21.** If $m\angle 1 = 95$, then *AB* ▨ *BC*.   >

**22.** If $m\angle 1 = 75$, then *BC* ▨ *AB*.   >

**23.** If $m\angle 1 = 75$, $m\angle C$ ▨ $m\angle A$.   <

**24.** If $m\angle 1 = 95$, $m\angle A$ ▨ $m\angle C$.   <

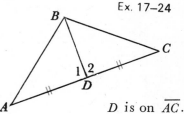

Ex. 17–24

*D* is on $\overline{AC}$.

**25–30.** Suppose two noncongruent triangles have two sides of one congruent to two sides of the other.

**25.** Can one angle of one triangle be congruent to one angle of the other triangle?  Yes

**26.** Can two angles of one triangle be congruent to two angles of the other triangle?  No

**27.** Can the third sides be congruent?  No

**28.** Can the triangles be isosceles?  Yes

**29.** Can the triangles be right triangles?  Yes

**30.** Can the triangles be equilateral?  No

© **31–38.** Complete this proof of part **b** of the Hangman Theorem.

Given: $\triangle ABC$ and $\triangle DEF$ are not congruent,
$\overline{AB} \cong \overline{DE}$, $\overline{BC} \cong \overline{EF}$, $DF < AC$

Prove: $m\angle E < m\angle B$

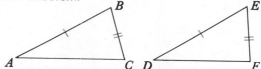

**Proof:**

| STATEMENTS | REASONS |
|---|---|
| 1. Assume $m\angle E$ is not less than $m\angle B$. | 1. **31.**  Assump. for ind. prf. |
| 2. First, assume $m\angle E = m\angle B$. | 2. $a < b$, $a = b$, or $a > b$. |
| 3. $\overline{AB} \cong \overline{DE}$, $\overline{BC} \cong \overline{EF}$ | 3. **32.**  Given |
| 4. $\triangle ABC \cong \triangle DEF$ | 4. **33.**  SAS Post. |
| 5. But, $\triangle ABC$, $\triangle DEF$ are not congruent. | 5. **34.**  Given |
| 6. So, $m\angle E \neq m\angle B$. | 6. **35.**  Prin. of Ind. Reas. |
| 7. Now assume $m\angle E > m\angle B$. | 7. $a < b$, $a = b$, or $a > b$. |
| 8. $DF > AC$ | 8. **36.**  Hangman Thm., part a |
| 9. But, $DF < AC$. | 9. **37.**  Given |
| 10. So, $m\angle E$ is not greater than $m\angle B$. | 10. **38.**  Prin. of Ind. Reas. |
| 11. Thus, $m\angle E < m\angle B$. | 11. $a < b$, $a = b$, or $a > b$. (steps 6 and 10) |

**39.** Why does the second compass mark off the longer segment?

Hangman Thm., part a

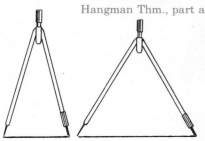

**40.** Why does the first roof have a larger angle at the top?

Hangman Thm., part b

Courtesy American Airlines

# THE SHORTEST PATH FROM HERE TO THERE

GEOMETRY AROUND YOU

Grant Heilman

Photri

Courtesy Nevada State Highway Dept.

# Transformations: Shortest Paths

**7.6**

Suppose that on a flat surface a ball starts rolling from point $B$. It bounces off wall $s$ at $P$ and stops rolling at point $E$. At first, the ball is rolling toward $E'$, the reflection image of $E$ over $s$. But after it hits the wall, its path is the reflection over $s$ of the path it would take if it could go through the wall.

I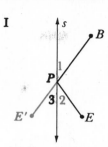

We can prove two things about the path of this ball.

1. It leaves the wall at the same angle at which it approaches the wall ($\angle 1 \cong \angle 2$).

2. It is the shortest path from $B$ to $s$ to $E$.

It is easy to show that $\angle 1 \cong \angle 2$ (see figure I).

| | |
|---|---|
| Since reflections preserve angle measure, | $\angle 2 \cong \angle 3$ |
| But $\angle 1$ and $\angle 3$ are vertical angles, so | $\angle 1 \cong \angle 3$ |
| Since $\angle 1$ and $\angle 2$ are both congruent to $\angle 3$, | $\angle 1 \cong \angle 2$ |

Now consider any other path from $B$ to $s$ to $E$. In figure II this path touches $s$ at $R$.

| | |
|---|---|
| By the Triangle Inequality, | $BR + RE' > BE'$ |
| By the definition of between, | $BE' = BP + PE'$ |
| Substituting, | $BR + RE' > BP + PE'$ |
| Since reflections preserve distance, | $RE = RE'$ and $PE = PE'$ |
| Substituting again, | $BR + RE > BP + PE$ |

II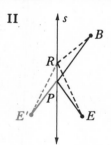

So the shortest path from $B$ to $s$ to $E$ touches the wall where $\overline{BE'}$ intersects $s$.

In a game of pool, you might want the ball to bounce off two sides of the table before stopping at $E$. In that case, first reflect $E$ over either side of the table to get $E'$, and then reflect $E'$ over the other side of the table to get $E''$. Aim at $E''$ as shown in figure III.

III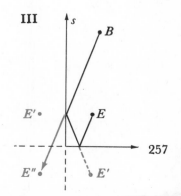

Camerique

257

# Exercises 7.6

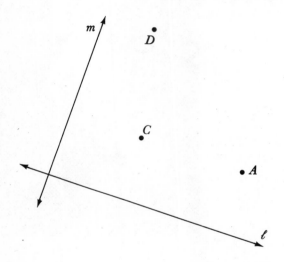

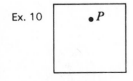

Ⓐ 1. To roll a ball along the shortest path from point $B$ to wall $s$ to point $E$, at what imaginary point should you aim?
          $E'$ (the reflection image of $E$ over $s$)

2. A ball is rolled in a path perpendicular to a wall. Describe its path after it hits the wall.    Along same line as it rolled to the wall

3. If a rolling ball must touch two walls before stopping, how many images must be found?  2

4. If a rolling ball must touch $n$ walls before stopping, how many images do you think must be found?  $n$

Ⓑ 5–8. Copy the figure.

5. Draw the shortest path from $A$ to $\ell$ to $D$. Then draw the shortest path from $D$ to $\ell$ to $A$. Are the paths different?    No

6. Draw the shortest path from $C$ to $\ell$ to $A$. Then draw the shortest path from $A$ to $\ell$ to $C$. Are the paths different?    No

7. Draw the shortest path from $A$ to $D$ touching $\ell$ and $m$ at distinct points.

8. Draw the shortest path from $C$ to $A$ touching $m$ and $\ell$ at distinct points.

Ⓒ 9–10. Light and sound waves bounce off surfaces in the same way a ball does. Use this fact to answer these questions.

9. Light enters a camera at $S$ and is reflected from surfaces at $b$, $c$, and $d$ (in that order) before reaching the view-finder where the photographer sees it. Copy the figure and draw the path of the light.

10. Copy the figure and draw the path of a sound wave that bounces off each side of the room exactly once before it returns to the speaker at $P$.

11. The congruent angles made by the wall and the ball's path are known as the **angle of incidence** and the **angle of reflection**. Do library research to find out which is which.    ∠ of incidence is made with path of approaching ball, ∠ of reflection with path after ball hits wall.

# ■ Chapter 7 Review ■

**1–4.** Which symbol, $<$, $=$, or $>$, should replace the ▨?

**7.1**

**1.** If $n$ ▨ 9, $n + c = 9$ for some positive number $c$.  $<$

**2.** If $x = -3 + 7$, then $x$ ▨ $-3$.  $>$

**Assignment Guide**
*Oral:* 1–4
*Written:* Min. 5–23
        Reg. 5–24
        Max. 5–24

**3.** If $s$ ▨ 5, $s$ is not less than or equal to 5.  $>$

**4.** If $t$ is not equal to 3, $t$ ▨ 3 or $t$ ▨ 3.  $<$ ; $>$

**5–8.** Solve.

**5.** $p + 6 < 8$
$p < 2$

**6.** $2y > 7$
$y > \frac{7}{2}$

**7.** $x - 8 < 3$
$x < 11$

**8.** $\frac{1}{3}r > 8$
$r > 24$

**9–16.** Which symbol, $<$, $=$, or $>$, should replace the ▨?

**7.2**

**9.** If $\overline{MN}$ is shorter than $\overline{PD}$, then $MN$ ▨ $PD$.  $<$

**10.** If $\angle 3$ is larger than $\angle 1$, then $m\angle 1$ ▨ $m\angle 3$.  $<$

**11.** If $\triangle ABC$ has a $60°$ exterior angle at $A$, then $m\angle B$ ▨ 60.  $<$

**12.** If $RS = RT + TS$, then $RS$ ▨ $TS$.  $>$

**13.** In $\triangle RST$, if $RS > ST$, then $m\angle T$ ▨ $m\angle R$.  $>$

**14.** In $\triangle XVW$, if $m\angle W > m\angle V$, then $XW$ ▨ $XV$.  $<$

**7.3**

**15.** If $\overline{DT} \perp \ell$ at $T$ and $\overline{DS}$ intersects $\ell$ at $S$, $DT$ ▨ $DS$.  $<$

**16.** If $\overline{SM} \perp \overline{MR}$, then $SR$ ▨ $SM$ and $MR$ ▨ $SR$.  $>$ ; $<$

**17–20.** Can the given numbers be lengths of the sides of a triangle?

**7.4**

**17.** 3, 7, 11
No

**18.** 9, 7, 3
Yes

**19.** 5, 9, 5
Yes

**20.** 2, 7, 5
No

**21–23.** Which symbol, $<$, $=$, or $>$, should replace the ▨?

**7.5**

**21.** If $P$ were located so that $m\angle CAP$ ▨ $m\angle DAP$; $P$ would be closer to $C$ than to $D$.  $<$

**22.** If $BC > DE$, then $m\angle 1$ ▨ $m\angle 3$.  $>$

**23.** If $m\angle 3 > m\angle 1$, then $BC$ ▨ $DE$.  $<$

Ex. 21–23

**24.** Copy $S$, $T$, and $\ell$. Draw the shortest path from $S$ to $\ell$ to $T$.

$S \cdot$      Ex. 24

**7.6**

**Assignment Guide**
*Written:* Min. 1–21
Reg. 1–22
Max. 1–22

**1–4.** Which symbol, <, =, or >, should replace the ▨ ?

**1.** A positive number can be added to $x$ to get $y$ if $x$ ▨ $y$.  <

**2.** If $n$ is not less than or equal to 8, $n$ ▨ 8.  >

**3.** If $AB$ ▨ $PQ$, then $\overline{AB}$ is longer than $\overline{PQ}$.  >

**4.** If $\angle S$ is larger than $\angle T$, then $m\angle T$ ▨ $m\angle S$.  <

**5.** If $\overline{GH} \perp \ell$ at $H$, then $GH$ is the $\underline{\text{Distance}}$ from $G$ to $\ell$.

**6.** In $\triangle ABC$, $AB + BC > AC$ according to the $\underline{\triangle \text{ Inequality}}$ Thm.

**7.** Solve:    **a.** $x - 13 < 2$    **b.** $\frac{3}{5}t > 36$   $t > 60$
$$x < 15$$

**8.** Can $\triangle DEF$ have sides with the given lengths?

   **a.** 13, 5, 7   No          **b.** 8, 7, 14   Yes

**9–21.** Refer to the figures. Which symbol, <, =, or >, should replace the ▨ ?

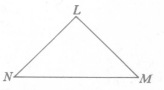

**9.** $m\angle S$ ▨ $m\angle 1$     <     **10.** $m\angle 6$ ▨ $m\angle 3$     >

**11.** $RT + TS$ ▨ $RS$  =     **12.** $RV + VS$ ▨ $RS$ >

**13.** If $VT > TS$, then $m\angle 4$ ▨ $m\angle S$. <

**14.** If $m\angle S < m\angle 2$, then $VS$ ▨ $VR$.  >

**15.** If $\overline{VR} \perp \overline{VS}$, then $VR$ ▨ $RS$.   <

**16.** If $RV = SV$ and $m\angle 3$ ▨ $m\angle 4$,
then $T$ is closer to $S$ than to $R$.   >

**17.** If $\overline{RT} \cong \overline{TS}$ and $m\angle 5 < m\angle 6$, then $RV$ ▨ $SV$.  <

**18.** If $\overline{RS} \cong \overline{MN}$, $\overline{VR} \cong \overline{LM}$, and $m\angle M < m\angle 2$, then $VS$ ▨ $LN$.  >

**19.** If $\overline{RS} \cong \overline{MN}$, $\overline{VR} \cong \overline{LM}$, and $LN > VS$, then $m\angle 2$ ▨ $m\angle M$.  <

**20.** If $m\angle 5 < 90$, $m\angle 4$ ▨ 90.  <    **21.** If $m\angle RVS < 95$, $m\angle 3$ ▨ 95.  <

**22.** Refer to the figure. Which point is on the path of the ball?  G

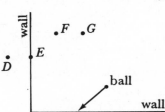

# ■ Cumulative Review: Chapters 1–7 ■

**Suggested Class Time**

| Course | Min. | Reg. | Max. |
|--------|------|------|------|
| Days   | 3    | 2    | 2    |

**1–4.** What postulate or theorem leads to the conclusion about the figure?

**Ch. 1**

*1–2. Answers below*

**1.** Every point on $\ell$ is in $s$.

**2.** $N$ and $\ell$ determine a plane.

**3.** $s$ and $n$ intersect at $\overleftrightarrow{PE}$.
Two planes intersect at exactly one line.

**4.** There is a point in $s$ not on $\ell$.
A plane contains at least three noncollinear pts.

Ex. 1–4

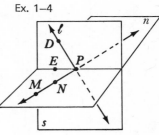

**5.** A _____ is accepted as true without proof.  Postulate

**6.** _____ reasoning is based on examples.  Inductive

**7.** A <u>Theorem</u> states a hypothesis and its logical conclusion.

**8.** <u>Deductive</u> reasoning is based on postulates and definitions.

**9.** If the coordinates of $A$ and $B$ are 3 and 7, $AB =$ _____4_____.

**Assignment Guide**
*Oral:* 1–20
*Written:*
Min. (day 1) 21–35
    (day 2) 36–48; 51–56
    (day 3) 57–65; 68–80
Reg. (day 1) 21–38
    (day 2) 39–79 odd
Max. (day 1) 21–38
    (day 2) 39–79 odd

**10–15.** Refer to the figure for Exercises 1–4.

**10.** Points $M$, $N$, and ___$P$___ are collinear.

**11.** $\overleftrightarrow{MN}$ and line $\ell$ intersect at ___$P$___.

**12.** $\overrightarrow{NP}$ and ___$\overrightarrow{NM}$___ are opposite rays.

**13.** Line $\ell$ intersects plane $n$ at ___$P$___.

**14.** $\overleftrightarrow{MN}$ and plane $s$ intersect at ___$P$___.

**15.** If $N$ is the ___Midpoint___ of $\overline{MP}$, then $MN = NP$.

**16.** Is a half plane a convex set?  Yes

**Ch. 2**

**17.** In a plane, how many lines through a given point are perpendicular to a given line?  Exactly 1

1. If 2 pts. on a line are in a plane, the line is in the plane.
2. A line and a pt. not on the line determine a plane.

**18–22.** Refer to the figure. $B$ is on $\overleftrightarrow{AE}$.

**18.** Name a point in the interior of $\angle ABD$.  C

**19.** Name 2 angles adjacent to $\angle CBD$.  $\angle ABC$, $\angle DBE$

**20.** If $\overrightarrow{BD}$ is the bisector of $\angle CBE$, find $m\angle DBE$.  37

**21.** If $m\angle ABD = 151$, find (**a**) $m\angle ABC$ and (**b**) $m\angle DBE$.
114                29

**22.** If $m\angle ABD = 153$, name (**a**) all acute angles, (**b**) all obtuse angles, and (**c**) all right angles.  a. $\angle CBD$, $\angle DBE$, $\angle CBE$
b. $\angle ABC$, $\angle ABD$
c. None

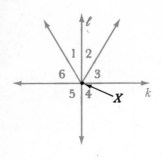

**23–26.** $\ell \perp k$. What theorem leads to the conclusion about the figure?

**23.** $\angle X_{16}$, $\angle X_{23}$, $\angle 4$, and $\angle 5$ are right angles.
Two $\perp$ lines form 4 rt. $\angle$s.

**24.** $\angle 4 \cong \angle 5$   Rt. $\angle$s are $\cong$.

**25.** If $\angle 1 \cong \angle 2$, then $\angle 6 \cong \angle 3$.
Complements of $\cong$ $\angle$s are $\cong$.

**26.** If $\angle 1 \cong \angle 2$, then $\angle X_{56} \cong \angle_{34}$.
Supplements of $\cong$ $\angle$s are $\cong$.

**Ch. 3**

**27.** Give the hypothesis and the conclusion of the following statement:
If two angles are complementary, the sum of their measures is 90.
*Hypothesis*          *Conclusion*

**28.** Change the following statement to if-then form: All rational numbers are real numbers.
If a number is a rational number, then it is a real number.

**29.** Draw an Euler diagram for the statement in Exercise 28.

**29.**

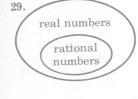

**30.** If $\triangle TIP \cong \triangle LUM$, complete each statement.
   **a.** $\overline{IP} \cong \underline{\ UM\ }$        **b.** $\angle P \cong \underline{\ \angle M\ }$        **c.** $\overline{TP} \cong \underline{\ LM\ }$

**31–34.** Give a reason for each statement.

Given: $\overline{FI} \cong \overline{IH}$, $\angle FIS \cong \angle HIS$

Prove: $\overline{FS} \cong \overline{HS}$

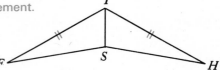

| Proof:   STATEMENTS | | REASONS |
|---|---|---|
| 1. $\overline{FI} \cong \overline{IH}$, $\angle FIS \cong \angle HIS$ | 1. **31.** | Given |
| 2. $\overline{SI} \cong \overline{SI}$ | 2. **32.** | Seg. is $\cong$ to itself. |
| 3. $\triangle FIS \cong \triangle HIS$ | 3. **33.** | SAS Post. |
| 4. $\overline{FS} \cong \overline{HS}$ | 4. **34.** | Corres. parts of $\cong$ $\triangle$s are $\cong$. |

**35.** Line $\ell$ is the perpendicular bisector of $\overline{MN}$.
Find the values of $x$ and $y$.  $x = 12$, $y = 20$

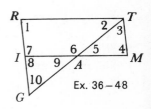

Ex. 35

**Ch. 4**

**36–48.** In the figure, $\overline{TR} \parallel \overline{IM}$ and $A$ is on $\overline{GT}$.

**36.** $\angle 2$ and $\underline{\ \angle 9\ }$ are corresponding angles.

**37.** $\angle 5$ and $\underline{\ \angle 2\ }$ are alternate interior angles.

**38.** $\angle 1$ and $\underline{\ \angle 7\ }$ are supplementary.

Ex. 36–48

**39.** If $\overline{IR} \perp \overline{RT}$, $\overline{IR} \perp$ ___$\overline{IM}$___.

**40.** If $\overline{TR} \cong \overline{IM}$, $TRIM$ is a ___$\square$___.

**41.** $TRIA$ is a ___Trapezoid___.

**42.** If $RI = IG$, then $TA =$ ___$AG$___.

**43.** If $\angle 3 \cong$ ___$\angle 10$___, $\overline{TM} \parallel \overline{RG}$.

**44.** $m\angle 2 + m\angle 6 =$ ___$180$___

**45.** $m\angle 1 + m\angle 2 + m\angle 10 =$ ___$180$___

**46.** $m\angle 6 = m\angle 4 + m$ ___$\angle 3$___

**47.** How many lines through $G$ are parallel to $\overleftrightarrow{RT}$? Exactly 1

**48.** $IA = \frac{1}{2}RT$ if $\overline{IA}$ is a ___Midline___ of $\triangle RGT$.

**49.** Given: $\overline{PO} \parallel \overline{HS}$, $\overline{PO} \cong \overline{HS}$, $\overline{PS} \perp \overline{HO}$

Prove: $POSH$ is a rhombus.

**50.** Given: Rhombus $POSH$

Prove: $\angle OPQ$ is acute.

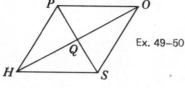

Ex. 49–50

**51.** Is this figure a polygon? Why?

No; 2 sides do not intersect another side at their endpts.

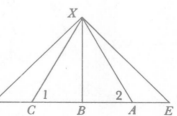

Ex. 51

**52–56.** $ABCDEFGH$ is a regular octagon.

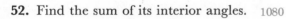

**52.** Find the sum of its interior angles. 1080

**53.** Find the sum of its exterior angles, one at each vertex. 360

**54.** Find the measure of each interior angle. 135

**55.** Find the measure of each exterior angle. 45

**56.** If $AB = 6$, find the perimeter of the octagon. 48

**57–60.** Using the given information, what postulate or theorem can be used to prove $\triangle XBC \cong \triangle XBA$?

**57.** $\overline{XB} \perp \overleftrightarrow{AC}$, $\overline{XC} \cong \overline{XA}$ HL Thm.

**58.** $\overrightarrow{XB}$ is the bisector of $\angle CXA$, $\angle 1 \cong \angle 2$ AAS Thm.

**59.** $\angle XBC$ and $\angle XBA$ are right angles, $\angle 1 \cong \angle 2$ LA Thm.

**60.** $\triangle XDA \cong \triangle XEC$, $\overline{CB} \cong \overline{BA}$ SSS Post.

**49.** 1. $\overline{PO} \parallel \overline{HS}$, $\overline{PO} \cong \overline{HS}$ (Given)
2. $POSH$ is a $\square$ (Quad. is $\square$ if 2 sides are $\parallel$ and $\cong$.)
3. $\overline{PS} \perp \overline{HO}$ (Given)
4. $POSH$ is a rhombus. (If diagonals are $\perp$, $\square$ is a rhombus.)

## Ch. 5

**50.** 1. $POSH$ is a rhombus. (Given)
2. $\overline{PS} \perp \overline{HO}$ (Diagonals of rhombus are $\perp$.)
3. $\angle PQO$ is a rt. $\angle$. (Def. of $\perp$)
4. $\triangle PQO$ is a rt. $\triangle$. (Def. of rt. $\triangle$)
5. $\angle OPQ$ is acute. (If 1 $\angle$ of $\triangle$ is rt., other $\angle$s are acute.)

## Ch. 6

**66.** *Sketch of Proof:* Given $\overline{CS} \cong \overline{ES}$, so $m\angle C_{12} = m\angle E_{34}$ ($\angle$s opp. $\cong$ sides of $\triangle$ are $\cong$). By $\angle$ Add. Post., $m\angle C_{12} = m\angle 1 + m\angle 2$ and $m\angle E_{34} = m\angle 3 + m\angle 4$. $m\angle 1 = m\angle 2$ and $m\angle 3 = m\angle 4$ (Def. of $\angle$ bis.), so $m\angle 1 = m\angle 3$ by subst., add., and mult. $\angle S \cong \angle S$, so $\triangle CRS \cong \triangle ETS$ (ASA Post.) and $\overline{CR} \cong \overline{ET}$ (Corres. parts of $\cong$ $\triangle$s are $\cong$).

**67.** *Sketch of Proof:* Given $\overline{CS} \cong \overline{ES}$, so $m\angle C_{12} = m\angle E_{34}$ ($\angle$s opp. $\cong$ sides of $\triangle$ are $\cong$). By $\angle$ Add. Post., $m\angle C_{12} = m\angle 1 + m\angle 2$ and $m\angle E_{34} = m\angle 3 + m\angle 4$. $m\angle 1 = m\angle 2$ and $m\angle 3 = m\angle 4$ (Def. of $\angle$ bis.),

## Ch. 7

so $m\angle 2 = m\angle 4$ by subst., add., and mult. $\overline{CE} \cong \overline{CE}$, so $\triangle CET \cong \triangle ECR$ (ASA Post.) and $\overline{CR} \cong \overline{ET}$ (Corres. parts of $\cong$ $\triangle$s are $\cong$.)

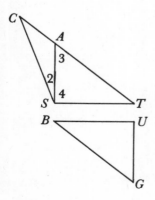

**61.** Give a counterexample to show the following statement is false: If two angles are supplementary, both angles are right angles.

*Typical answer:* $m\angle A = 120$ and $m\angle B = 60$

**62.** Write the converse of the statement in Exercise 61. Is it true?

If 2 $\angle$s are rt. $\angle$s, they are supplementary; yes

**63.** Can the statements below be connected by *if and only if* to form a true statement?   Yes

Two triangles are equiangular.   Two triangles are equilateral.

**64.** In an indirect proof, you assume the Opposite of the fact you want to prove.

**65.** Draw a sketch to illustrate the Median Concurrence Theorem.

*See figure for Ex. 1, p. 231.*

**66–67.** Use the given plan to write a proof.

**Given:** $\triangle CES$ with $\overrightarrow{CR}$ and $\overrightarrow{ET}$ the bisectors of $\angle C$ and $\angle E$, $\overline{CS} \cong \overline{ES}$

**Prove:** $\overline{CR} \cong \overline{ET}$

**66.** [*Plan:* Show $\triangle CRS \cong \triangle ETS$.]

**67.** [*Plan:* Show $\triangle CET \cong \triangle ECR$.]

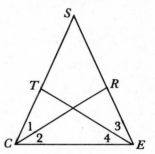

**68.** If _____ can be added to $c$ to get $d$, then $c < d$.   A positive number

**69.** If $\overline{PD}$ is _____ than $\overline{RS}$, then $RS > PD$.   Shorter

**70.** If $m\angle A > m\angle B$, then $\angle A$ _____ $\angle B$.   Is larger than

**71.** Solve:    **a.** $t - 14 > 2$  $t > 16$    **b.** $\frac{2}{3}n < 5$  $n < \frac{15}{2}$

**72–80.** Which symbol, $<$, $=$, or $>$, should replace the 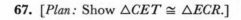 ?

**72.** $m\angle 3$ ▨ $m\angle C$    $>$

**73.** $m\angle 4$ ▨ $m\angle CST$    $<$

**74.** $CA + AT$ ▨ $CT$    $=$

**75.** If $m\angle 4 = 90$, $ST$ ▨ $AT$.    $<$

**76.** $CS + ST$ ▨ $CT$    $>$

**77.** If $ST > AS$, $m\angle 3$ ▨ $m\angle T$.    $>$

**78.** If $\overline{CS} \cong \overline{ST}$ and $m\angle 4 > m\angle 2$, then $AT$ ▨ $CA$.    $>$

**79.** If $\overline{UG} \cong \overline{SA}$, $\overline{BU} \cong \overline{ST}$, and $m\angle 4 > m\angle U$, then $AT$ ▨ $BG$.    $>$

**80.** If $\overline{AT} \cong \overline{BG}$, $\overline{BU} \cong \overline{AS}$, and $ST > GU$, then $m\angle 3$ ▨ $m\angle B$.    $>$

# PERPENDICULAR

## LINES AND PLANES 8

Which supports of the rings structure seem to be perpendicular to the plane of the floor?

# When Are a Line and a Plane Perpendicular?

**8.1**

You can easily make the models below.

| Model of vertical line and horizontal plane | Model of nonvertical line and horizontal plane |
|---|---|

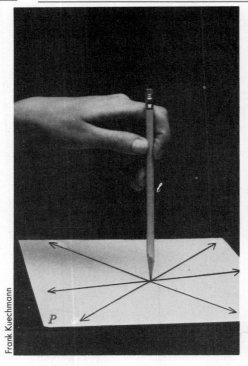

Frank Kuechmann

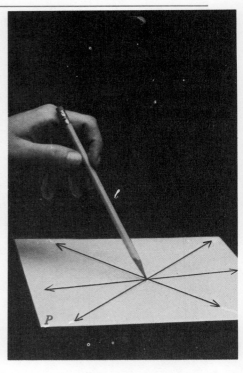

Line $\ell$ appears to be perpendicular to plane $P$ and to *every* line in $P$ that passes through the intersection of $\ell$ and $P$.

Line $\ell$ does not appear to be perpendicular to plane $P$ or to every line in $P$ that passes through the intersection of $\ell$ and $P$. (But $\ell$ could be perpendicular to one of these lines. Try it.)

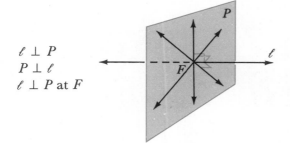

$\ell \perp P$
$P \perp \ell$
$\ell \perp P$ at $F$

These models lead us to define *perpendicular* for a line and a plane as follows: Line $\ell$ and plane $P$ are **perpendicular** if and only if they intersect and $\ell$ is perpendicular to every line in $P$ that contains the point of intersection. The point of intersection is called the **foot** of the perpendicular.

Earlier, we drew perpendicular lines in a plane to intersect at right angles. See figure I. Now, when we draw perpendicular lines in space, we might *not* draw them to intersect at right angles. See figure II. This is because we are drawing 3-dimensional figures on a 2-dimensional surface.

Keep this in mind, and you should have no trouble with the figures in the book or with drawing your own figures. But if you do have trouble, make a simple model like those on page 266.

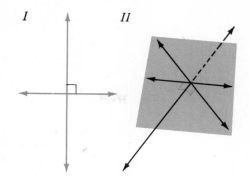

I    II

## Exercises 8.1

Ⓐ **1–4.** Refer to the figure.

**1.** Is $\ell \perp r$?  Yes

**2.** Name the foot of the perpendicular $\ell$.  F

**3.** Is $\ell \perp s$?  No

**4.** Is $\ell \perp \overleftrightarrow{XY}$? To $\overleftrightarrow{XF}$?  No; yes

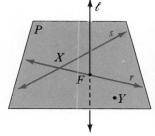

$\ell \perp P$ at $F$.

$P$ contains lines $r$ and $s$ and point $Y$.

$\ell$ intersects $r$ at $F$.

**5–8.** Refer to the figure.

**5.** Can $k$ be perpendicular to $t$ but not to $M$?  Yes

**6.** Can $k$ be perpendicular to $M$ but not to $t$?  No

**7.** If $k \perp M$ at $Z$, what line in $M$ must $k$ be perpendicular to?  $t$

**8.** If $k$ is perpendicular to every line in $M$ containing $Z$, is $k \perp M$? Why?

Yes; definition of $\perp$ line and plane

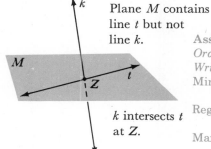

Plane $M$ contains line $t$ but not line $k$.

$k$ intersects $t$ at $Z$.

**Assignment Guide**
*Oral:* 1–10
*Written:*
Min. 11–23 odd;
       Alg. Rev., p. 269
Reg. 11–24; Alg. Rev., p. 269, odd
Max. 11–25

**9–10.** $\overleftrightarrow{AX} \perp p$; $p$ contains $W$, $X$, $Y$, and $Z$. Use the figure to

**9.** Name all pairs of perpendicular lines.

$\overleftrightarrow{AX} \perp \overleftrightarrow{XY}$, $\overleftrightarrow{AX} \perp \overleftrightarrow{XZ}$, $\overleftrightarrow{AX} \perp \overleftrightarrow{XW}$

**10.** Name all right angles.

$\angle AXY$, $\angle AXZ$, $\angle AXW$

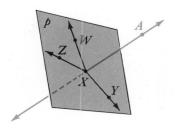

Ⓑ **11–18.** Plane $t$ contains points $B$, $C$, and $D$. Also, $\overleftrightarrow{AB} \perp t$. Is each statement true or not necessarily true?

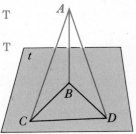

**11.** $\overleftrightarrow{CB} \perp \overleftrightarrow{AB}$    T      **12.** $\overleftrightarrow{CB} \perp \overleftrightarrow{BD}$   Not nec. T

**13.** $\overleftrightarrow{CD} \perp \overleftrightarrow{AC}$        **14.** $\overleftrightarrow{AD} \perp \overleftrightarrow{CD}$   Not nec. T
     Not nec. T

**15.** $m\angle CBA = 90$      **16.** $m\angle ABD = 90$
        T                 T

**17.** $m\angle ADC = 90$      **18.** $m\angle CBD = 90$
     Not nec. T           Not nec. T

**19–20.** Refer to the figure.

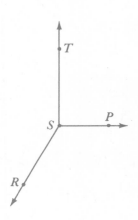

**19.** If $\overleftrightarrow{PS}$ is perpendicular to the plane containing points $R$, $S$, and $T$, which angles must be right angles?   $\angle PST$, $\angle PSR$

**20.** If $\overleftrightarrow{RS}$ is perpendicular to the plane containing points $S$, $T$, and $P$, which angles must be right angles?   $\angle RST$, $\angle RSP$

**21.** Sketch a plane perpendicular to a vertical line.
     *See line $\ell$ and plane $P$ in the fig. for Ex. 1–4, page 267.*
**22.** Sketch a plane perpendicular to a horizontal line.
     *See line $\ell$ and plane $P$ at bottom of page 266.*

**23–24.** *Review:* Draw a figure and state the reason for each conclusion.

**23.** *Given:* Lines $\ell$ and $k$ both contain point $P$.

     *Conclusion:* Only one plane contains lines $\ell$ and $k$. *See page 32.*

**24.** *Given:* Points $A$ and $B$ are in plane $r$.

     *Conclusion:* $\overleftrightarrow{AB}$ is in plane $r$. *See page 28.*    **Ex. 25**

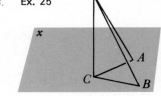

**25.** *1.* Plane $x$ contains $A$, $B$, and $C$; $\overleftrightarrow{FC} \perp x$, $\overline{FA} \cong \overline{FB}$ (Given)

Ⓒ **25.** **Given:** Plane $x$ contains $A$, $B$, and $C$;
         $\overleftrightarrow{FC} \perp x$; $\overline{FA} \cong \overline{FB}$

    **Prove:** $\overline{CA} \cong \overline{CB}$

*2.* $\overleftrightarrow{FC} \perp \overline{CA}$, $\overleftrightarrow{FC} \perp \overline{CB}$ (Def. of $\perp$ line and plane)

*3.* $\angle FCA$, $\angle FCB$ are rt. $\angle$s. (Def. of $\perp$)

*4.* $\triangle FCA$, $\triangle FCB$ are rt. $\triangle$s. (Def. of rt. $\triangle$)

*5.* $\overline{FC} \cong \overline{FC}$ (Seg. is $\cong$ to itself.)

*6.* $\triangle FCA \cong \triangle FCB$ (HL Thm.)

*7.* $\overline{CA} \cong \overline{CB}$ (Corres. parts of $\cong$ $\triangle$s are $\cong$.)

**26.** Using a model like the one on page 266, draw two intersecting lines on the paper. Try to hold the pencil at the point of intersection so the pencil is perpendicular to both lines but not to the plane. Is it possible?   No

Choose a term from the list to answer the question or to complete the statement.

**a.** congruent     **b.** converse     **c.** geometry     **d.** hexagon

**e.** hypotenuse     **f.** isosceles     **g.** measure     **h.** polygon

**i.** rhombus     **j.** unit

1. What did the acorn say when it grew up?

2. What did the girl who received a wool scarf from her boyfriend say?

3. What did the people say when their parrot flew away?

4. What did the witch say after getting rid of the magic spell?

5. What is "mister" in French?

6. What did the bus driver say when asked why the bus hadn't stopped at Main Street?

7. What did the warden call the poetry on the jail-cell wall?

8. About the plant growing in the prison yard, the warden said, "A _____."

9. Explaining verb tenses, the teacher said, "I see the leaves, _____, I have seen the leaves."

10. When asked if the tall coffee urn was being used, the cook replied, "_____."

Can you make up some of your own?

*ANSWERS:* 1. c 2. j 3. h 4. d 5. g 6. i 7. b 8. a 9. f 10. e

---

**Factor to remove the greatest common monomial factor.**

**1.** $4a + 4b$    $4(a + b)$    **2.** $6r + 12s$   $6(r + 2s)$    **3.** $12m - 18n$   $6(2m - 3n)$

**4.** $ca - cb$    $c(a - b)$    **5.** $abc - abd$   $ab(c - d)$    **6.** $x^2 - xy$   $x(x - y)$

**7.** $2x^2 + 2xy$    $2x(x + y)$    **8.** $\pi r^2 + \pi rs$   $\pi r(r + s)$    **9.** $2\pi r^2 + 2\pi rh$   $2\pi r(r + h)$

**10.** $\frac{1}{2}b_1 h + \frac{1}{2}b_2 h$   $\frac{1}{2}h(b_1 + b_2)$    **11.** $\frac{1}{3}B_1 r + \frac{1}{3}B_2 r + \frac{1}{3}B_3 r$   $\frac{1}{3}r(B_1 + B_2 + B_3)$

*Algebra Review*

**Review this skill:**

- factoring out a common monomial factor

GEOM FUNNY    269

# 8.2    The Basic Theorem for Perpendiculars

**Suggested Class Time**

| Course | Min. | Reg. | Max. |
|--------|------|------|------|
| Days   | 1    | 1    | 1    |

In Section 8.1 we defined a line $\ell$ to be perpendicular to a plane $P$ if and only if they intersect and $\ell$ is perpendicular to all lines in $P$ containing the point of intersection. This definition would be awkward to use in proving a plane and a line perpendicular. We now prove the Basic Theorem for Perpendiculars, which will be much easier to use.

**Basic Theorem for Perpendiculars**

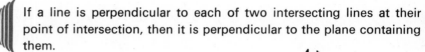

If a line is perpendicular to each of two intersecting lines at their point of intersection, then it is perpendicular to the plane containing them.

Given: Lines $\ell$ and $n$ in plane $P$ intersect at point $X$, $\overleftrightarrow{AX} \perp \ell$, $\overleftrightarrow{AX} \perp n$

Prove: $\overleftrightarrow{AX} \perp P$

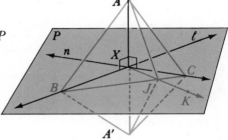

[*Plan:* Show $\overleftrightarrow{AX} \perp \overleftrightarrow{XK}$ ($\overleftrightarrow{XK}$ is any line in $P$ containing $X$). To do this, draw $\overline{XA'} \cong \overline{XA}$ and prove $\triangle ABC \cong \triangle A'BC$. Next prove $\triangle ABJ \cong \triangle A'BJ$. Then $JA = JA'$, so $\overleftrightarrow{XJ}$ is a $\perp$ bisector of $\overline{AA'}$. Since $J$ is on $\overleftrightarrow{XK}$, $\overleftrightarrow{AX} \perp \overleftrightarrow{XK}$.]

| Proof:    STATEMENTS | REASONS |
|---|---|
| 1. Lines $\ell$ and $n$ in plane $P$ intersect at $X$, $\overleftrightarrow{AX} \perp \ell$, $\overleftrightarrow{AX} \perp n$. | 1. Given |
| 2. Choose any point $K$ in $P$ (not on $\ell$ or $n$) and draw $\overleftrightarrow{XK}$ in $P$. | 2. Two points determine a line, and if two points are in a plane, the line they determine is in that plane. |
| 3. Choose any points $B$ on $\ell$ and $C$ on $n$ so $B$ and $C$ are on opposite sides of $\overleftrightarrow{XK}$. Then draw $\overleftrightarrow{BC}$ intersecting $\overleftrightarrow{XK}$ at $J$. | 3. Plane Separation Postulate (p. 45) since $B$ and $C$ are in opposite half planes with edge $\overleftrightarrow{XK}$. |
| 4. Choose $A'$ on $\overleftrightarrow{AX}$ so $AX = A'X$. | 4. Point Plotting Thm. (p. 27) |
| 5. Draw $\overline{AB}$, $\overline{AC}$, $\overline{AJ}$, $\overline{A'B}$, $\overline{A'C}$, and $\overline{A'J}$. | 5. Two pts. determine a line. |

270      CHAPTER 8      PERPENDICULAR LINES AND PLANES

**6.** $\overleftrightarrow{XB}$ is a $\perp$ bisector of $\overline{AA'}$, $\overleftrightarrow{XC}$ is a $\perp$ bisector of $\overline{AA'}$.

**6.** Def. of $\perp$ bisector

**7.** $\overline{BA} \cong \overline{BA'}$, $\overline{CA} \cong \overline{CA'}$

**7.** A pt. on a $\perp$ bisector of a seg. is equidistant from the endpoints of the seg.

**8.** $\overline{BC} \cong \overline{BC}$

**8.** A segment is $\cong$ to itself.

**9.** $\triangle ABC \cong \triangle A'BC$

**9.** SSS Postulate

**10.** $\angle ABC \cong \angle A'BC$

**10.** Corres. parts of $\cong$ $\triangle$s are $\cong$.

**11.** $\overline{BJ} \cong \overline{BJ}$

**11.** A segment is $\cong$ to itself.

**12.** $\triangle ABJ \cong \triangle A'BJ$

**12.** SAS Postulate

**13.** $\overline{JA} \cong \overline{JA'}$

**13.** Corres. parts of $\cong$ $\triangle$s are $\cong$.

**14.** $\overleftrightarrow{XJ}$ is a $\perp$ bisector of $\overline{AA'}$.

**14.** Two pts. equidistant from the endpoints of a seg. determine a $\perp$ bisector (steps 4 and 13).

**15.** $\overleftrightarrow{AX} \perp \overleftrightarrow{XJ}$, so $\overleftrightarrow{AX} \perp \overleftrightarrow{XK}$.

**15.** Def. of $\perp$ bisector

**16.** $\overleftrightarrow{AX} \perp P$

**16.** $\overleftrightarrow{AX}$ is perpendicular to *any* line in plane $P$ containing $X$.

**Assignment Guide**
*Oral:* 1–2
*Written:* Min.  3–15 odd
Reg.  3–16
Max.  3–17

# Exercises 8.2

(A) **1.** If $\overleftrightarrow{XC} \perp \overleftrightarrow{AC}$ and $\overleftrightarrow{XC} \perp \overleftrightarrow{DC}$, is $\overleftrightarrow{XC} \perp r$? Why?

Yes; Basic Thm. for $\perp$s

**2.** State the Basic Theorem for Perpendiculars.

*See page 270.*

Ex. 1

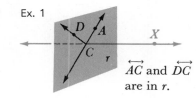

$\overleftrightarrow{AC}$ and $\overleftrightarrow{DC}$ are in $r$.

(B) **3–6.** *WXYZ* is a square. $\overleftrightarrow{AX} \perp \overline{XW}$

**3.** Name all perpendicular segments.
(*Example:* $\overline{XW} \perp \overline{WZ}$) $\overline{XW} \perp \overline{WZ}$, $\overline{WZ} \perp \overline{ZY}$, $\overline{ZY} \perp \overline{YX}$, $\overline{AX} \perp \overline{XW}$, $\overline{XY} \perp \overline{XW}$

**4.** Name all planes that can be determined by the lines in the figure. (*Example:* the plane containing $X$, $W$, $Y$, and $Z$) Also the plane containing $A$, $X$, and $Y$ and the plane containing $A$, $X$, and $W$

**5.** Is $\overleftrightarrow{AX}$ perpendicular to the plane containing $X$, $W$, $Y$, and $Z$? Not necessarily

**6.** Is $\overleftrightarrow{XW}$ perpendicular to the plane containing $A$, $X$, and $Y$? Yes

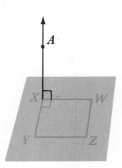

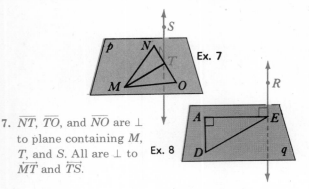

Ex. 7

7. $\overline{NT}$, $\overline{TO}$, and $\overline{NO}$ are $\perp$ to plane containing $M$, $T$, and $S$. All are $\perp$ to $\overleftrightarrow{MT}$ and $\overleftrightarrow{TS}$.

Ex. 8

7. $\triangle MNO$ is isosceles, $MN = MO$, $NT = OT$, and $\overleftrightarrow{ST} \perp \overline{NO}$ at $T$. $S$ is not in plane $p$. Are any segments perpendicular to planes? Why?

8. $\angle DAE$ is a right angle, and $\overleftrightarrow{RE} \perp \overline{AE}$. Point $R$ is not in plane $q$. Are any segments perpendicular to planes? Why?  No. No given seg. is $\perp$ to 2 intersecting lines.

17. 1. Planes $e$, $f$ intersect at $\overleftrightarrow{AB}$, $\overleftrightarrow{RQ}$ is in $f$, $\overleftrightarrow{WX}$ is in $e$, $\overleftrightarrow{RQ} \perp \overleftrightarrow{AB}$, $\overleftrightarrow{WX} \perp f$ (Given)
2. $\overleftrightarrow{WX} \perp \overleftrightarrow{RQ}$ (Def. of $\perp$ line and plane)
3. $\overleftrightarrow{RQ} \perp e$ (Basic Thm. for $\perp$s)

18. 1. $m\angle NGP = 90$, plane $r$ contains $P$, $G$, $A$; $\overline{NA} \cong \overline{NP}$, $\overline{PG} \cong \overline{AG}$ (Given)
2. $\overline{NG} \cong \overline{NG}$ (Seg. is $\cong$ to itself.)
3. $\triangle NGP \cong \triangle NGA$ (SSS Postulate)
4. $\angle NGP \cong \angle NGA$ (Corres. parts of $\cong \angle$s are $\cong$.)
5. $m\angle NGA = 90$ (Def. of $\cong \triangle$s )
6. $\overline{NG} \perp \overleftrightarrow{AG}$, $\overline{NG} \perp \overleftrightarrow{PG}$ (Def. of $\perp$)
7. Plane $r$ contains $\overleftrightarrow{AG}$ and $\overleftrightarrow{PG}$. (If 2 pts. are in a plane, the line through them is in the plane.)
8. $\overleftrightarrow{NG} \perp r$ (Basic Thm. for $\perp$s)

| 9–16. | plane | a | b | c |
|---|---|---|---|---|
| | contains points | R, S, E, Y | S, E, T, M | E, Y, P, M |

$\overleftrightarrow{EY} \perp \overleftrightarrow{EM}$, $\overleftrightarrow{EM} \perp \overleftrightarrow{ES}$, $\overleftrightarrow{ES} \perp \overleftrightarrow{EY}$. True or False?

9. $a \perp \overleftrightarrow{EM}$  T  10. $c \perp \overleftrightarrow{ES}$  T

11. $b \perp \overleftrightarrow{ES}$  F  12. $b \perp \overleftrightarrow{EY}$  T

13. $\overleftrightarrow{EY} \perp \overleftrightarrow{ET}$  T  14. $\overleftrightarrow{ES} \perp \overleftrightarrow{EP}$  T

15. $\overleftrightarrow{ET} \perp \overleftrightarrow{EM}$  F  16. $\overleftrightarrow{EM} \perp \overleftrightarrow{ER}$  T

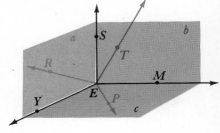

Ex. 17

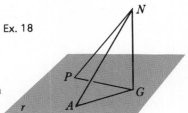

Ex. 18

© 17. **Given:** Planes $e$ and $f$ intersect at $\overleftrightarrow{AB}$, $\overleftrightarrow{RQ}$ is in $f$, $\overleftrightarrow{WX}$ is in $e$, $\overleftrightarrow{RQ} \perp \overleftrightarrow{AB}$, $\overleftrightarrow{WX} \perp f$

**Prove:** $\overleftrightarrow{RQ} \perp e$

18. **Given:** $m\angle NGP = 90$; plane $r$ contains $P$, $G$, and $A$; $\overline{NA} \cong \overline{NP}$; $\overline{PG} \cong \overline{AG}$

**Prove:** $\overleftrightarrow{NG} \perp r$

19. A table leg is attached to a tabletop with two right-angle brackets as shown. Is the leg perpendicular to the top? Why?

19. Yes. Each bracket represents a pair of $\perp$ lines, one in the table leg and one in the plane of the tabletop. The bracket lines in the plane intersect. Think of the table leg as a line through this intersection and apply the Basic Thm. for $\perp$s.

Frank Kuechmann

# Theorems on Perpendicular Lines and Planes

The Perpendicular Line Postulate (page 60) states that in any plane containing a given line and point, there is exactly one line through the point perpendicular to the given line. The next two postulates deal with perpendicular lines and planes in space in a similar manner.

**Suggested Class Time**

| Course | Min. | Reg. | Max. |
|--------|------|------|------|
| Days   | 1    | 1    | 1    |

**a.** Through a given point, there is exactly one plane perpendicular to a given line.

**b.** Through a given point, there is exactly one line perpendicular to a given plane.

Perpendicular Line and Plane Postulates

Only plane $p$ is perpendicular to $\overleftrightarrow{AB}$ at $X$. The only plane containing $Y$ and perpendicular to $\overleftrightarrow{AB}$ is $q$.

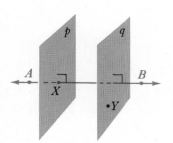

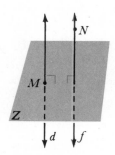

Only line $d$ is perpendicular to $Z$ at $M$. The only line containing $N$ and perpendicular to $Z$ is $f$.

If a line and a plane are perpendicular, they intersect at a point, and the plane contains every line perpendicular to the given line at that point.

Theorem

Given: $\ell \perp E$ at $P$, $j \perp \ell$ at $P$, $k \perp \ell$ at $P$

Prove: Plane $E$ contains lines $j$ and $k$.

**Proof:**

| STATEMENTS | REASONS |
|------------|---------|
| 1. $\ell \perp E$ at $P$, $j \perp \ell$ at $P$, $k \perp \ell$ at $P$ | 1. Given |
| 2. $\ell$ is perpendicular to the plane determined by $j$ and $k$. Call this plane $F$. | 2. If a line is $\perp$ to each of 2 intersecting lines, it is $\perp$ to the plane they determine. |
| 3. $E$ and $F$ are the same plane. | 3. Through a given pt., there is exactly one plane $\perp$ to a given line. |
| 4. $E$ contains $j$ and $k$. | 4. $j$ and $k$ are in $F$, and $F = E$. |

Recall that the perpendicular bisector of a segment is perpendicular to the segment at its midpoint. The **perpendicular bisecting plane** of a segment is the plane perpendicular to the segment at its midpoint.

 A point is in the perpendicular bisecting plane of a segment if and only if it is equidistant from the endpoints of the segment.

NOTE: Because of the if-and-only-if statement, there are two parts to this theorem.

**Part a.**

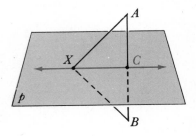

Given: Point $X$ is in $p$, the perpendicular bisecting plane of $\overline{AB}$.

Prove: $XA = XB$

[*Plan*: Show $X$ is on a perpendicular bisector of $\overline{AB}$.]

Proof:

| STATEMENTS | REASONS |
|---|---|
| 1. Point $X$ is in $p$, the perpendicular bisecting plane of $\overline{AB}$. | 1. Given |
| 2. Let $C$ be the midpoint of $\overline{AB}$. | 2. Every segment has a midpoint. |
| 3. $\overleftrightarrow{XC}$ is in $p$. | 3. If 2 pts. are in a plane, the line they determine is in that plane. |
| 4. $\overleftrightarrow{AB} \perp \overleftrightarrow{XC}$ | 4. If a line is $\perp$ to a plane, it is $\perp$ to every line in the plane through its foot. |
| 5. In the plane determined by $X$ and $\overleftrightarrow{AB}$, $\overleftrightarrow{XC}$ is the $\perp$ bisector of $\overline{AB}$. | 5. Def. of $\perp$ bisector |
| 6. $XA = XB$ | 6. If a pt. is on the $\perp$ bisector of a seg., it is equidistant from the endpoints of the segment. |

You'll be asked to complete the proof of part **b** in Exercises 21–27.

**Assignment Guide**
*Oral:* 1–8
*Written:* Min. 9–19 odd
Reg. 9–19 odd;
21–27
Max. 9–19 odd;
21–28

Ⓐ **1–4.** $\overleftrightarrow{AB} \perp p$ at $B$, and $E$ is in $p$.

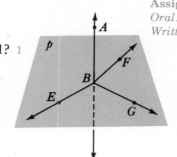

**1.** How many planes are perpendicular to $\overleftrightarrow{AB}$ at $A$? 1

**2.** How many lines are perpendicular to $p$ at $E$? 1

**3.** If $\overleftrightarrow{AB} \perp \overleftrightarrow{BF}$, is $\overleftrightarrow{BF}$ in $p$? Yes

**4.** If $\overleftrightarrow{AB} \perp \overleftrightarrow{GB}$, is $G$ in $p$? Yes

**5–8.** Plane $e$ is the perpendicular bisecting plane of $\overline{PR}$.
Points $A$, $B$, $C$, and $D$ are in $e$. Complete each statement.

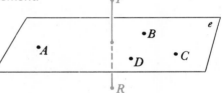

**5.** $AP = $ _____ $AR$

**6.** $PC = $ _____ $RC$

**7.** $RC = $ _____ $PC$

**8.** $DR = $ _____ $DP$

Ⓑ **9–12.** Planes $a$ and $b$ intersect at $\overleftrightarrow{RS}$;
$\overleftrightarrow{XY} \perp b$; $Y$ and $Z$ are in $b$; and $W$, $Y$,
and $X$ are in $a$.

**9.** Is $\overleftrightarrow{XY} \perp \overleftrightarrow{YZ}$? Yes

**10.** Is $\overleftrightarrow{XY} \perp \overleftrightarrow{YW}$?
Not necessarily

**11.** Is $\overleftrightarrow{RS} \perp \overleftrightarrow{YZ}$?
Not necessarily

**12.** Is $\overleftrightarrow{RS} \perp \overleftrightarrow{XY}$? Yes

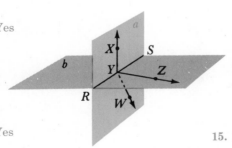

**13–16.** $\overleftrightarrow{AB} \perp$ plane $p$ at $A$. Plane $p$ contains $G$.

**13.** If $\overleftrightarrow{AF} \perp \overleftrightarrow{AB}$, does $p$ contain $F$? Why?
Yes; $p$ contains every line $\perp$ to $\overleftrightarrow{AB}$ at $A$.

**14.** If point $E$ is not in $p$, is $\overleftrightarrow{AE} \perp \overleftrightarrow{AB}$? No

**15.** Could $\overleftrightarrow{BF}$ be perpendicular to plane $p$? Why?

**16.** Plane $q$ contains points $G$, $A$, and $E$. If $\overleftrightarrow{AB} \perp q$
at $A$, is $E$ in plane $p$? Why?

**15.** No; $\overleftrightarrow{BA} \perp p$, and through a given pt. there
is exactly 1 line $\perp$ to a given plane.

**16.** Yes; There is exactly 1 plane $\perp$ to $\overleftrightarrow{AB}$
at $A$, so $p$ and $q$ are the same plane.

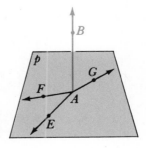

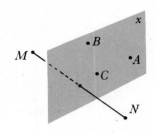

**17–20.** x is the perpendicular bisecting plane of $\overline{MN}$. A, B, and C are in x. Are these statements always true?

**17.** $AN = MA$  Yes

**18.** $\overline{MN} \perp \overline{AC}$
No

**19.** $\overline{MN} \perp \overline{BC}$  No

**20.** $MA = CN$
No

**21–27.** Give a reason for each statement.

Given: $XA = XB$

Prove: Point $X$ is in $p$, the perpendicular bisecting plane of $\overline{AB}$.

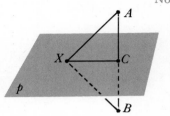

Proof:

| STATEMENTS | | REASONS |
|---|---|---|
| 1. $XA = XB$ | 1. | **21.** Given |
| 2. In the plane determined by $X$, $A$, and $B$, $X$ is on the $\perp$ bisector of $\overline{AB}$. | 2. | **22.** A pt. equidist. from the endpts. of a seg. is on the $\perp$ bis. of the seg. |
| 3. Let $C$ be the midpoint of $\overline{AB}$. | 3. | **23.** Every seg. has a midpt. |
| 4. $\overleftrightarrow{XC} \perp \overline{AB}$ | 4. | **24.** Def. of $\perp$ bis. |
| 5. Let $p$ be the perpendicular bisecting plane of $\overline{AB}$. | 5. | **25.** Through a given pt. ($C$), there is exactly 1 plane $\perp$ to a given line. |
| 6. $p$ contains $\overleftrightarrow{XC}$. | 6. | **26.** *At left* |
| 7. $X$ is in $p$, the perpendicular bisecting plane of $\overline{AB}$. | 7. | **27.** If a line is in a plane, every pt. on the line is in the plane. |

**26.** If a line and a plane are $\perp$, they intersect at a pt. and the plane contains every line $\perp$ to the given line at that pt.

**28.** 1. A, W, X, Y, Z, B not all coplanar; $AW = BW$, $AX = BX$, $AY = BY$, $AZ = BZ$ (Given)
2. W, X, Y, Z are in the $\perp$ bis. plane of $\overline{AB}$. ($\perp$ Bis. Pl. Thm.)
3. W, X, Y, and Z are coplanar. (Def. of coplanar)

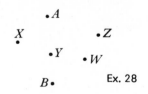

Ex. 28

© **28.** Given: $A$, $W$, $X$, $Y$, $Z$, and $B$ are not all coplanar, $AW = BW$, $AX = BX$, $AY = BY$, $AZ = BZ$

Prove: $W$, $X$, $Y$, and $Z$ are coplanar.

**29.** Plane $p$ contains $\triangle XYZ$. Line $\ell \perp p$ at $A$, and $\overline{AX} \cong \overline{AY} \cong \overline{AZ}$. $B$ is any point on $\ell$. Prove that $\overline{BX} \cong \overline{BY} \cong \overline{BZ}$. *Answer on page 278*

Ex. 29

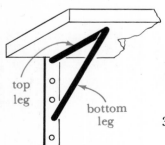

top leg

bottom leg

**30.** A shelf bracket is made as shown. The top leg is perpendicular to the wall. Can the bottom leg be perpendicular to the wall?

No, through a given pt. there is exactly 1 line $\perp$ to a given plane.

# BUILDING THINGS "PLUMB" RIGHT

The plumb line, spirit level, and try square are carpenters' tools. They are used to make things horizontal (level) or vertical (plumb) and to make things perpendicular to each other.

The plumb line consists of a weight (bob) attached to a piece of heavy string. When the weight is hung from the string and the string stops swaying, the plumb line is vertical, or plumb.

plumb line

Frank Kuechmann

spirit level

The spirit level is a piece of wood or metal containing two or three tubes of liquid. The tubes have markings, and when the bubble in a tube is exactly between the markings, the spirit level is horizontal or vertical.

try square

A try square is shown at left. Each edge is perpendicular to the edge it touches.

1. If the floor is level, how could you use a try square to make sure the uprights of the shelf unit are plumb and the shelf is level?

2. If the floor is not level, how could you use a plumb line and a try square to make sure the shelves are level?

1. Use ⊥ edges of try square to see that uprights are ⊥ to 2 intersecting lines in the floor and also in the shelf.

2. Use plumb line to make uprights vertical. Use try square to check shelf as described in Ex. 1.

## 8.4  More About Perpendicular Lines and Planes

**Suggested Class Time**

| Course | Min. | Reg. | Max. |
|--------|------|------|------|
| Days   | 1    | 1    | 1    |

**Theorem**

The next two theorems round out the important ideas about perpendicular lines and planes.

Two lines perpendicular to the same plane are coplanar. (In Chapter 13, we prove that these lines are parallel.)

Given: $\overleftrightarrow{AB} \perp p$ at $A$, $\overleftrightarrow{CD} \perp p$ at $C$

Prove: $\overleftrightarrow{AB}$ and $\overleftrightarrow{CD}$ are coplanar.

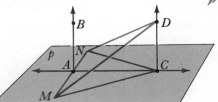

[*Plan:* Use auxiliary segment $\overline{MN}$ where $MA = NA$. Show that $\overleftrightarrow{AB}$ and $\overleftrightarrow{AC}$ are in plane $t$, the perpendicular bisecting plane of $\overline{MN}$. Then show that $D$ is also in $t$, so $\overleftrightarrow{AB}$ and $\overleftrightarrow{CD}$ are coplanar.]

Proof:

| STATEMENTS | REASONS |
|---|---|
| 1. $\overleftrightarrow{AB} \perp p$ at $A$, $\overleftrightarrow{CD} \perp p$ at $C$. | 1. Given |
| 2. $\overleftrightarrow{AC}$ is in plane $p$. | 2. If 2 pts. are in a plane, so is the line containing them. |
| 3. In plane $p$, let $\overline{MN}$ be $\perp$ to $\overleftrightarrow{AC}$ at $A$ and let $MA = NA$. | 3. Perp. Line Post. (p. 60) and the Point Plotting Thm. (p. 27) |
| 4. $\overleftrightarrow{AB} \perp \overline{MN}$ at $A$. | 4. A line $\perp$ to a plane is $\perp$ to every line in the plane through its foot. |
| 5. $\overleftrightarrow{AB}$ and $\overleftrightarrow{AC}$ determine a plane (call it $t$), and $\overline{MN} \perp t$ at $A$. | 5. Two intersecting lines determine a plane, and $\overline{MN}$ is $\perp$ to $\overleftrightarrow{AB}$ and $\overleftrightarrow{AC}$ at $A$. |
| 6. Plane $t$ (determined by $\overleftrightarrow{AB}$ and $\overleftrightarrow{AC}$) is the $\perp$ bisecting plane of $\overline{MN}$. | 6. Def. of $\perp$ bisecting plane |

(Now we show that point $D$ is in $t$, so $\overleftrightarrow{CD}$ is in $t$.)

| STATEMENTS | REASONS |
|---|---|
| 7. $\overleftrightarrow{CD} \perp \overleftrightarrow{CN}$, $\overleftrightarrow{CD} \perp \overleftrightarrow{CM}$ | 7. If a line is $\perp$ to a plane, it is $\perp$ to every line in the plane through its foot. |
| 8. $\overline{CN} \cong \overline{CM}$ | 8. Perp. Bisecting Plane Theorem |

*Answer for page 276*

29. 1. $p$ contains $\triangle XYZ$; $\ell \perp p$ at $A$; $\overline{AX} \cong \overline{AY} \cong \overline{AZ}$ (Given)
2. $\overline{BA} \perp \overline{AX}$, $\overline{BA} \perp \overline{AY}$, $\overline{BA} \perp \overline{AZ}$ (Def. of $\perp$ line and plane)
3. $\angle BAX$, $\angle BAY$, $\angle BAZ$ are rt. $\angle$s. (Def. of rt. $\angle$)
4. $\triangle BAX$, $\triangle BAY$, $\triangle BAZ$ are rt. $\triangle$s. (Def. of rt. $\triangle$)
5. $\overline{BA} \cong \overline{BA}$ (Seg. is $\cong$ to itself.)
6. $\triangle BAX \cong \triangle BAY \cong \triangle BAZ$ (LL Thm.)
7. $\overline{BX} \cong \overline{BY} \cong \overline{BZ}$ (Corres. parts of $\cong$ $\triangle$s are $\cong$.)

278  CHAPTER 8  PERPENDICULAR LINES AND PLANES

| STATEMENTS | REASONS |
|---|---|
| 9. $\overline{CD} \cong \overline{CD}$ | 9. A segment is $\cong$ to itself. |
| 10. $\angle DCN$ and $\angle DCM$ are rt. $\angle$s, $\triangle DCN$ and $\triangle DCM$ are rt. $\triangle$s. | 10. Def. of $\perp$ lines and rt. $\triangle$s |
| 11. $\triangle DCN \cong \triangle DCM$ | 11. LL Theorem |
| 12. $\overline{DN} \cong \overline{DM}$ | 12. Corres. parts of $\cong$ $\triangle$s are $\cong$. |
| 13. $D$ is in $t$, the $\perp$ bisecting plane of $\overline{MN}$. | 13. Perp. Bisecting Plane Theorem |
| 14. $\overleftrightarrow{CD}$ is in $t$. | 14. If 2 pts. are in a plane, so is the line containing them. |
| 15. $\overleftrightarrow{CD}$ and $\overleftrightarrow{AB}$ are coplanar. | 15. Steps 5 and 14 |

Poles that are perpendicular to the ground are often braced with support wires as shown in the photo. Which is shorter, the pole or the wire? The next theorem proves the answer.

Courtesy American Airlines

The shortest segment to a plane from a point not in the plane is the perpendicular segment.

**Theorem**

Given: $\overline{AB} \perp p$ at $B$,
  $C$ is any point in $p$ other than $B$.

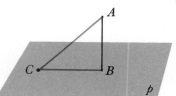

Prove: $AB < AC$

**Proof:**

| STATEMENTS | REASONS |
|---|---|
| 1. $\overline{AB} \perp p$ at $B$. | 1. Given |
| 2. $\overleftrightarrow{CB}$ is in plane $p$. | 2. If 2 pts. are in a plane, so is the line containing them. |
| 3. $\overline{AB} \perp \overline{CB}$ | 3. Def. of a $\perp$ line and plane. |
| 4. $\angle ABC$ is a right $\angle$, $\triangle ABC$ is a right $\triangle$. | 4. Def. of $\perp$ lines and right $\triangle$s |
| 5. $m\angle ACB < 90$ | 5. The other $\angle$s of a rt. $\triangle$ are acute. |
| 6. $AB < AC$ | 6. In a $\triangle$, the side opp. the smaller of 2 $\angle$s is shorter. |

Assignment Guide
*Oral:* 1–4
*Written:* Min. 5–8; 11–12
       Reg. 5–9; 11–12
       Max. 5–12

Now we can define **the distance from a point to a plane** as the length of the segment perpendicular to the plane from the point.

## *Exercises 8.4* ▮▮▮▮▮▮▮▮▮▮▮▮▮▮▮▮▮▮▮▮▮▮▮▮▮▮▮▮▮▮▮▮▮▮▮▮▮▮▮▮▮

**9.** *1.* $\ell$ and $k$ in $p$,
$\overleftrightarrow{WZ} \perp \ell, \overleftrightarrow{WZ} \perp k$
(Given)
*2.* $\overleftrightarrow{WZ} \perp p$ (Basic Thm.
for ⊥s)
*3.* $\overline{XY}$ the shortest seg.
from $Y$ to $p$ (Given)
*4.* $\overline{XY} \perp p$ (Shortest seg.
from a pt. to a plane is
the ⊥ seg.)
*5.* $\overline{XY}$ and $\overline{WZ}$ are
coplanar. (2 lines ⊥
to a plane are
coplanar.)     Ex. 5–8

Ⓐ **1–4.** $\overleftrightarrow{AB} \perp p$ at $B$, $\overleftrightarrow{CD} \perp p$ at $D$.

**1.** Are $\overleftrightarrow{AB}$ and $\overleftrightarrow{CD}$ coplanar? Yes

**2.** Is $CB < CD$? No

**3.** Name the shortest segment from $C$ to plane $p$. $\overline{CD}$

**4.** Define the distance from point $A$ to plane $p$.
The length of the segment from $A$ perpendicular to $p$

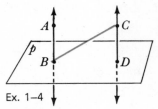
Ex. 1–4

Ⓑ **5–8.** Points $D$ and $C$ are in plane $p$. $\overline{AC} \perp p$.

**5.** Can $m\angle ADC > 90$? Why?    No; in
$\triangle ADC$, $m\angle C = 90$, so other $\angle$s are acute.

**6.** Can $AD = 7$ and $AC = 9$? No

**7.** If the distance from $A$ to plane $p$ is 12, find $AC$.
12

**8.** If $AC = 5.8$, find the distance from $A$ to plane $p$.
5.8

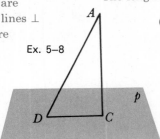
Ex. 5–8

**10.** *1.* $\overline{WZ}$ shortest seg. from
$W$ to $p$ (Given)
*2.* $\overline{WZ} \perp p$ (Shortest seg.
to a plane from a pt. is
the ⊥ seg.)
*3.* $XY$ distance from $Y$ to
$p$ (Given)
*4.* $\overline{XY} \perp p$ (Def. of dist.
from pt. to plane)
*5.* $\overline{WZ}$ and $\overline{XY}$ are
coplanar. (2 lines ⊥
to same plane are
coplanar.)

**9.** Given: Lines $\ell$ and $k$ are in plane $p$,
$\overleftrightarrow{WZ} \perp k$, $\overleftrightarrow{WZ} \perp \ell$, $\overline{XY}$ is the
shortest segment from $Y$ to plane $p$.
Prove: $\overline{XY}$ and $\overline{WZ}$ are coplanar.

**10.** Given: $\overline{WZ}$ is the shortest segment from
$W$ to plane $p$, $XY$ is the distance
from $Y$ to plane $p$.
Prove: $\overline{WZ}$ and $\overline{XY}$ are coplanar.

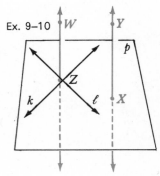
Ex. 9–10

**11.** Yes; 2 lines (the posts) ⊥
to the same plane (the
ground) are in the same
plane (the sign).

Ⓒ **11.** Two posts are
anchored perpen-
dicular to the
ground, which is
flat. Will a sign
fit flat against
both posts? Why?

**12.** Which is longer, the 2 × 4 or its brace?
Its brace

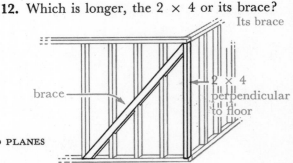

# Transformations: Reflections in Space

We use mirror images as models for reflections in space. In the photo a point and its image are connected by a segment. The mirror appears to be the perpendicular bisecting plane of that segment. We define reflections in space in a manner similar to the definition of reflections in a plane.

Frank Kuechmann

Reflections in a Plane

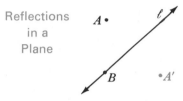

Reflections in Space

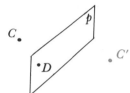

**Suggested Class Time**

| Course | Min. | Reg. | Max. |
|--------|------|------|------|
| Days | 0 | 1 | 1 |

The reflection image of point $A$ over *reflecting line* $\ell$ is $A'$. Line $\ell$ is the perpendicular bisector of $\overline{AA'}$, and points $A$ and $A'$ are the same distance from line $\ell$.

The reflection image of point $B$ is $B$.

The **reflection image** of point $C$ over *reflecting plane* $p$ is point $C'$. Plane $p$ is the perpendicular bisecting plane of $\overline{CC'}$, and points $C$ and $C'$ are the same distance from plane $p$.

The reflection image of point $D$ is $D$.

The images of points $A$, $B$, $C$, and $E$ over reflecting plane $p$ are points $A'$, $B'$, $C'$, and $E'$.

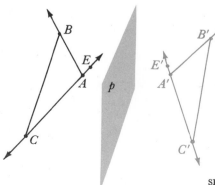

Notice that

1. $m\angle CAB = m\angle C'A'B'$

2. $A$ is between $C$ and $E$.
   $A'$ is between $C'$ and $E'$.

3. $A$, $C$, and $E$ are collinear.
   $A'$, $C'$, and $E'$ are collinear.

4. $AB = A'B'$

5. $A$, $B$, $C$, and $E$ are coplanar.
   $A'$, $B'$, $C'$, and $E'$ are coplanar.

Reflections in space preserve

1. betweenness of points
2. collinearity of points
3. distance between points
4. angle measure
5. coplanarity of points

In the figures on page 281 consider triangles $ABC$ and $A'B'C'$. The orientation of $\triangle ABC$ is counterclockwise, while the orientation of $\triangle A'B'C'$ is clockwise. This leads to the following conclusion:

Reflections in space reverse orientation.

## Exercises 8.5

**Assignment Guide**
*Oral:* Reg. & Max. 1–8
*Written:* Reg. & Max. 9–14

Ⓐ **1–4.** Plane $p$ is the reflecting plane. Point $E$ is in $p$. From the drawing tell which point is the reflection image of

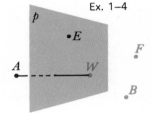

Ex. 1–4

1. $A$   *W*
2. $Z$   *F*
3. $B$   *D*
4. $E$   *E*

5. Describe reflecting line $\ell$ if $A'$ is the image of $A$ over $\ell$.
   *$\ell$ is the $\perp$ bisector of $\overline{AA'}$.*

6. Describe reflecting plane $p$ if $A'$ is the image of $A$ over $p$.
   *$p$ is the $\perp$ bisecting plane of $\overline{AA'}$.*

7. Name 5 properties preserved by reflections in space.
   *See list above.*

8. Name 1 property not preserved by reflections in space.   Orientation

Ⓑ **9.** Sketch a point and a plane. Then sketch the image of the point when reflected over the plane.   *See page 281.*

10. Sketch a line and a plane. Then sketch the image of the line when reflected over the plane.   *See page 281.*

11. If a line and a plane are perpendicular, will their reflection images in space be perpendicular?   Yes

12. If 3 noncoplanar segments have the same length, will their reflection images in space have the same length?   Yes

**13–14.** Use the photos. Can a reflecting plane be placed so that each half is the image of the other?

13.
Camerique

Yes

14.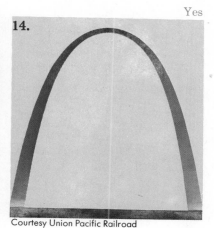
Courtesy Union Pacific Railroad

Yes

© **15.** Make a model of a segment or a triangle and its reflection image in space. HINT: You may find pipe cleaners, wire, string, and a shoe box helpful.

## GEOMETRIC CHEMISTRY

You probably know that each molecule of a compound is made up of the same atoms. But did you know that the molecules of two different compounds can also contain the same atoms? Such compounds are called *isomers*. The molecules of isomers differ in their geometry—the way the atoms are arranged.

For example, lactic acid exists in two forms: *d*-lactic acid is produced by muscles when they work, while *l*-lactic acid is found in sour milk. The molecules can be pictured as follows.

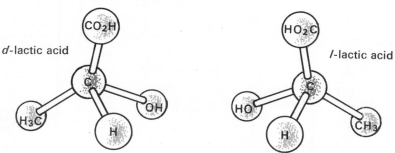

The atoms in each molecule are the same, but the molecular geometry is different. In this case, one molecule is the reflection image of the other over a plane.

# ■ Chapter 8 Review ■

**8.1**

1. By the definition of a perpendicular line and plane, when is a line $\ell$ perpendicular to a plane $p$?  *See page 266.*

**8.2**

**Assignment Guide**
*Written:* Min. 1–16
Reg. 1–18
Max. 1–18

2–3. *ABCD* is a rectangle in plane $p$, $\overrightarrow{BF} \perp \overrightarrow{AB}$, and $\overrightarrow{BF} \perp \overrightarrow{BC}$. Give a reason for each statement.

2. $\overrightarrow{BF} \perp$ plane $p$   Basic Thm. for ⊥s

3. $\overrightarrow{AB} \perp$ the plane containing $F$, $B$, and $C$.
   Basic Thm. for ⊥s

**8.3**

4–10. $\overleftrightarrow{EF} \perp q$ at $F$; $H$ and $J$ are in $q$; planes $p$ and $q$ intersect at $\overleftrightarrow{KL}$; $E$, $F$, and $G$ are in $p$.

4. Is $\overleftrightarrow{EF} \perp \overleftrightarrow{FJ}$?  Yes

5. Is $\overleftrightarrow{FH} \perp \overleftrightarrow{FG}$?  Not nec.

6. Is $\overleftrightarrow{EF} \perp \overleftrightarrow{KL}$?  Yes

7. Is $\overleftrightarrow{GF} \perp$ plane $q$?  No

8. Find $m\angle EFJ$.  90

9. Find $m\angle HFE$.  90

10. How many planes are perpendicular to $\overleftrightarrow{GF}$ at $G$?  1

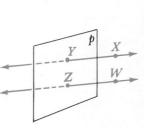

11–13. Plane $n$ is the perpendicular bisecting plane of $\overline{RS}$. Plane $n$ contains points $A$, $B$, and $C$.

11. Does $RC = SC$?  Yes

12. Is $\overleftrightarrow{BC}$ a perpendicular bisector of $\overline{RS}$?  Not nec.

13. If $RX = SX$, must point $X$ be in plane $n$? Why?
   Yes; ⊥ Bisecting Plane Thm.

**8.4**

14–16. $\overleftrightarrow{XY} \perp p$ at $Y$, $\overrightarrow{ZW} \perp p$ at $Z$.

14. Are $\overleftrightarrow{XY}$ and $\overrightarrow{ZW}$ coplanar?  Yes

15. Name the shortest segment to $p$ from $W$.
   $\overline{ZW}$

16. Define the distance from $W$ to plane $p$.
   The length of the seg. from $W$ ⊥ to $p$

**8.5**

17–18. $A'$ is the image of $A$ over reflecting plane $p$.

17. Describe plane $p$.   ⊥ bis. plane of $\overline{AA'}$

18. If the distance from $A$ to $p$ is 8, find the distance from $A'$ to $p$.  8

**1–3.** Complete each statement.

**1.** If $\ell \perp P$ at $A$, then $\ell$ is perpendicular to
_____ lines in $P$ _____ $A$.   All; containing

**2.** If lines $x$ and $y$ are in $P$, $\ell \perp x$,
and $\ell \perp y$, then ____ $\ell$ ____ $\perp$ ____ $P$ ____.

**3.** If $\ell$ intersects $P$ at $A$, then there will always
be ____ 1 ____ line(s) in $P$ perpendicular to $\ell$.

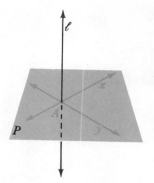

**Assignment Guide**
*Written:* Min. 1–8
Reg. 1–14
Max. 1–14

**4–6.** True or False?

**4.** All the points in space equidistant from points $A$ and $B$ are coplanar.   T

**5.** Two distinct lines perpendicular to the same plane are coplanar.   T

**6.** Two planes can be perpendicular to a given line at a given point.   F

**7–8.** $\overleftrightarrow{AD} \perp p$ at $D$, $\overleftrightarrow{BC} \perp p$ at $C$.

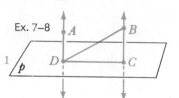

Ex. 7–8

**7.** How many planes contain points $A$, $B$, $C$, and $D$?   1

**8.** Which is greater, $BC$ or $BD$?   $BD$

**9–12.** Complete this proof.

**Given:** Plane $e$ contains $X$, $Y$, and $B$; $\overleftrightarrow{XB} \perp j$;
$\overleftrightarrow{YB} \perp k$; $j$ and $k$ intersect at $\overleftrightarrow{AB}$.

**Prove:** $\overleftrightarrow{AB} \perp e$

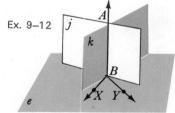

Ex. 9–12

**Proof:**

| STATEMENTS | | REASONS |
|---|---|---|
| 1. $j \perp \overleftrightarrow{XB}$, $k \perp \overleftrightarrow{YB}$ | 1. __9.__ | Given |
| 2. $\overleftrightarrow{XB} \perp \overleftrightarrow{AB}$ | 2. __10.__ | Def. of $\perp$ line and plane |
| 3. $\overleftrightarrow{YB} \perp \overleftrightarrow{AB}$ | 3. __11.__ | Def. of $\perp$ line and plane |
| 4. $\overleftrightarrow{AB} \perp$ plane $e$ | 4. __12.__ | Basic Thm. for $\perp$s |

**13.** If the distance from $A$ to plane $p$ is 8, and the distance from $C$ to $p$
is 8, can $C$ be the image of $A$ over reflecting plane $p$?   Yes

**14.** If two lines are perpendicular, will their reflection images in space
be perpendicular?   Yes

Courtesy Burroughs Wellcome Co.

# 9
# AREAS OF
# POLYGONS

Bill Miller

The topic of this chapter is one of the most useful in geometry. Since you have worked with area formulas in earlier courses, much of the material will be familiar. We will review area formulas, use them in solving problems, and show how they can be proved. Also, we will prove the Pythagorean Theorem—probably the best known theorem in geometry and all of mathematics.

# Areas of Rectangles  9.1

A **polygonal region** consists of a polygon and its interior. Some examples are shown below.

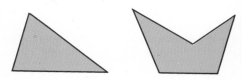

Camerique

Earlier, you saw that for every pair of points there is a unique number, called the *distance* between them. Also, for every angle there is a unique number, called its *degree measure*. Similarly,

> For every polygonal region there is a unique positive real number, called the **area** of the region.

Area Postulate

Since congruent triangles have the same size and shape, the following postulate is suggested:

> If two triangles are congruent, then the triangular regions determined by them have the same area.

Area Postulate for Congruent Triangles

Another postulate about area is suggested by the following figures:

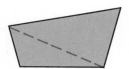 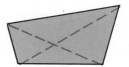 

> A polygonal region can be separated into nonoverlapping regions, the sum of whose areas is equal to the area of the given region.

Area Addition Postulate

SECTION 9.1     AREAS OF RECTANGLES     287

1 unit of length     1 square unit of area

To measure the area of a polygonal region, we must have a unit of area. The most convenient unit is the square unit. If we measure distance in centimeters, we measure area in square centimeters, and so on.

NOTE: For convenience, we often refer to the area of a polygon rather than the area of a polygonal region. Just remember that area always refers to a region, even if not exactly stated that way.

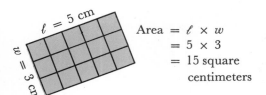

Area $= \ell \times w$
$\phantom{Area} = 5 \times 3$
$\phantom{Area} = 15$ square centimeters

Suppose a rectangle has consecutive sides that are 5 centimeters (cm) and 3 centimeters long. The measure of the longer side is its length; the measure of the shorter side is its width. The figure at the left suggests that the area is length times width. We state this as a postulate.

**Area Postulate for a Rectangle**

The area ($A$) of a rectangle is the product of its length ($\ell$) and its width ($w$).

$$A = \ell w$$

**Example 1:** Find the area of a rectangle with the given length and width.

**a.** 7 m and 5 m

$A = \ell w$
$A = 7 \cdot 5$
$A = 35$ m²

**b.** 32 mm and 3 cm

$A = \ell w$
$A = 32 \cdot 30$
$A = 960$ mm²

◀ Since length and width must be in the same units, change 3 cm to 30 mm.

NOTE: m² means square meters, cm² means square centimeters, and so on.

**Example 2:** A rectangle has a width of 16 and an area of 400. Find the length.

$A = \ell w$
$400 = \ell \cdot 16$
$25 = \ell$

If no units are listed as here, assume that the same unit has been used for length and width, and the proper square unit has been used for area.

Since a square is a rectangle, the following theorem results:

**Area Theorem for a Square**

The area ($A$) of a square is the square of the length ($s$) of a side.

$$A = s^2$$

Ⓐ **1.** What is the formula for the area of a rectangle? What does each letter stand for? *See page 288.*

*See page 288.*

**2.** What is the formula for the area of a square? What does each letter stand for? *See page 288.*

*See page 288.*

**Assignment Guide**
*Oral:* 1–12
*Written:* Min. 13–41 odd
Reg. 13–45 odd
Max. 13–49 odd

**3–6.** If the length and width of a rectangle are in the given unit, in what unit would the area be?

**3.** centimeter (cm) **4.** kilometer (km) **5.** millimeter (mm) **6.** meter (m)
 cm² km² mm² m²

**7.** If two triangles are congruent, which postulate tells you they have the same area? Area Post. for ≅ △s

**8.** If two triangles have the same area, are they necessarily congruent? No

**9–10.** Area A = 20, and Area B = 8.

**9.** Which postulate tells you that the area of the figure shaded in green is 28? Area Add. Post.

**10.** Is the area 28 if the rectangles overlap as in the given figure? No

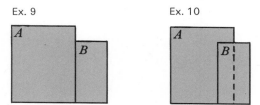

Ex. 9          Ex. 10

**11.** In Example 1b, could the area be found by changing 32 mm to 3.2 cm and leaving 3 cm unchanged? What would the area be?
Yes; 9.6 cm²

**12.** If a rectangle has length 30 cm and width 0.2 m, what is its area in cm²? In m²? 600 cm²; 0.06 m²

Ⓑ **13–28.** Find the area of each rectangle (or square).

**13.** $\ell = 19$ m, $w = 13$ m
247 m²

**14.** $\ell = 28$ cm, $w = 22$ cm
616 cm²

**15.** $\ell = 4.5$ km, $w = 2.5$ km
11.25 km²

**16.** $\ell = 7.5$ m, $w = 2.25$ m
16.875 m²

**17.** $\ell = 6$ cm, $w = 33$ mm
(Find $A$ in mm².) 1980 mm²

**18.** $\ell = 2$ m, $w = 120$ cm
(Find $A$ in cm².) 24 000 cm²

**19.** $\ell = 6$ cm, $w = 33$ mm
(Find $A$ in cm².) 19.8 cm²

**20.** $\ell = 2$ m, $w = 120$ cm
(Find $A$ in m².) 2.4 m²

**21.** $\ell = 23$ mm, $w = 1.5$ cm
345 mm² or 3.45 cm²

**22.** $\ell = 6.2$ m, $w = 415$ cm
25.73 m² or 257 300 cm²

**23.** square with $s = 2.3$ m
5.29 m²

**24.** square with $s = 1.8$ cm
3.24 cm²

**25.** square with $s = 1\frac{1}{3}$
$1\frac{7}{9}$

**26.** square with $s = 6\frac{1}{2}$
$42\frac{1}{4}$

**27.** square with $s = 1.52$
2.3104

**28.** square with $s = 3.4$  11.56

**29–34.** Find the missing length or width of each rectangle.

**29.** $A = 228, \ell = 19$  $w = 12$    **30.** $A = 3066, w = 42$   $\ell = 73$

**31.** $A = 100, w = 2.5$  $\ell = 40$    **32.** $A = 19.04, \ell = 5.6$  $w = 3.4$

**33.** $A = \frac{1}{8}, \ell = \frac{1}{2}$   $w = \frac{1}{4}$    **34.** $A = 6\frac{1}{4}, w = 2$  $\ell = 3\frac{1}{8}$

**35.** What happens to the area of a rectangle when

  **a.** the length is doubled?  Doubles
  **b.** the width is doubled?  Doubles
  **c.** both the length and width are doubled?  Quadruples

**36.** What happens to the area of a square when

  **a.** the side is doubled?  Quadruples
  **b.** the side is tripled?  Is mult. by 9
  **c.** the side is halved?  Is mult. by $\frac{1}{4}$

**37.** How many square centimeters are in a square meter?  10 000

**38.** How many square meters are in a square kilometer?  1 000 000

**39.** How many square meters of paneling are needed to panel a wall that is 3.5 meters high by 5.2 meters wide?  18.2

**40.** How many square-centimeter tiles are needed to tile a tabletop that is 31 cm by 48 cm?  1488

**41.** How many square meters of artificial turf are needed to cover a soccer field that is 101 m by 64 m?  6464

**49.** *Plan:* Show $\triangle ABC \cong$ $\triangle CDA$ by the theorem on page 141. The areas of the $\triangle$s are equal by the Area Postulate for $\cong \triangle$s. Then use the Area Addition Post. and substitution to show 2 area $\triangle ABC =$ area $ABCD$. So area $\triangle ABC = \frac{1}{2}$ area $ABCD$.

**50.** *Plan:* Show that the diagonals and sides of $SOFA$ form 4 $\triangle$s that are $\cong$ by the SSS Post. or by the LL Thm. The areas are equal by the Area Post. for $\cong \triangle$s. Then use the Area Addition Post. and substitution to show 4 area $ARF =$ area $SOFA$. So area $\triangle ARF = \frac{1}{4}$ area $SOFA$.

**42.** The National Aeronautics and Space Administration is studying plans to launch an unmanned spacecraft to meet with Halley's Comet when it next approaches the sun in 1986. A giant square sail, 800 meters on a side, would be used to propel the spacecraft by means of sunlight. What would be the area of the sail?  640 000 m²

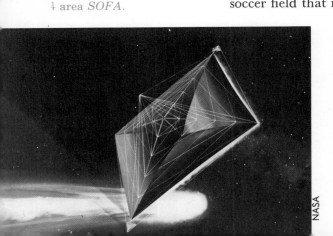
NASA

**43–48.** Find the area of each shaded region.   All angles are right angles.

**43.**
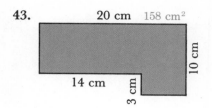
20 cm   158 cm²
10 cm
14 cm
3 cm

**44.**
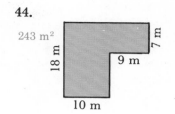
243 m²
18 m
7 m
9 m
10 m

**45.**
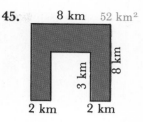
8 km   52 km²
3 km
8 km
2 km   2 km

**46.**
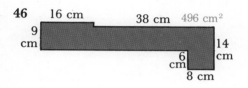
16 cm
38 cm   496 cm²
9 cm
14 cm
6 cm
8 cm

**47.**
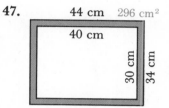
44 cm   296 cm²
40 cm
30 cm
34 cm

**48.**
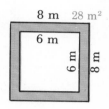
8 m   28 m²
6 m
6 m
8 m

**49.** Given: Parallelogram $ABCD$ with diagonal $\overline{AC}$

Prove: Area $\triangle ABC = \frac{1}{2}$ area $ABCD$

Ex. 49
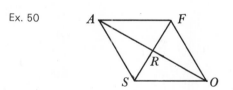

**50.** Given: Rhombus $SOFA$ with diagonals $\overline{SF}$ and $\overline{AO}$ intersecting at $R$

Prove: Area $\triangle ARF = \frac{1}{4}$ area $SOFA$

Ex. 50
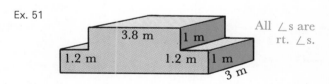

© **51.** A housing for an industrial machine is shaped as shown at the right. How many square meters of sheet metal are needed for the surface of the housing? (There is no bottom.)
50.6 m²

Ex. 51
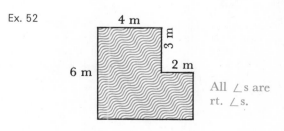
3.8 m   1 m
1.2 m   1.2 m   1 m
3 m
All ∠s are rt. ∠s.

**52.** The floor plan of a living-dining area is shown at the right. The walls and the ceiling are to be painted. If the height of the ceiling is 2.5 meters, how many square meters of surface must be painted? (Ignore the fact that doors and windows will not be painted.)
90 m²

Ex. 52
4 m
3 m
2 m
6 m
All ∠s are rt. ∠s.

# 9.2 Areas of Triangles and Parallelograms

The Area Postulate for a Rectangle is useful in finding the areas of other figures such as right triangles and parallelograms.

**Area Theorem for a Right Triangle**

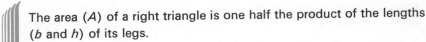

The area ($A$) of a right triangle is one half the product of the lengths ($b$ and $h$) of its legs.

$$A = \tfrac{1}{2}bh$$

**Suggested Class Time**

| Course | Min. | Reg. | Max. |
|--------|------|------|------|
| Days | 1 | 1 | 1 |

**Given:** Right $\triangle ABC$ with legs of lengths $b$ and $h$, $m\angle A = 90$

**Prove:** Area $\triangle ABC = \tfrac{1}{2}bh$

**Sketch of Proof:** Draw a line through $C$ parallel to $\overline{AB}$ and a line through $B$ parallel to $\overline{AC}$. Let $D$ be their point of intersection.

Now we have rectangle ($\square$) $ABDC$. Also, we know $\triangle ABC \cong \triangle DCB$. (Why?) So we can reason as follows:

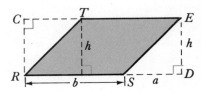

*Answer for page 295*

**41.** *1.* $\overline{CD} \parallel \overline{AB}$, $\overline{BD} \parallel \overline{AC}$ (Parallel Post.)
*2.* $ABDC$ is a $\square$. (Def. of $\square$)
*3.* $m\angle A = 90$ (Given)
*4.* $ABDC$ is a $\square$. (Def. of $\square$)

| | |
|---|---|
| area $\square ABDC = bh$ | Area Post. for a $\square$ |
| area $\triangle ABC$ + area $\triangle DCB = bh$ | Area Addition Post. |
| area $\triangle ABC$ + area $\triangle ABC = bh$ | Area Post. for $\cong$ $\triangle$s (Substitute area $\triangle ABC$ for area $\triangle DCB$.) |
| 2 area $\triangle ABC = bh$ | Addition |
| area $\triangle ABC = \tfrac{1}{2}bh$ | Multiply both sides by $\tfrac{1}{2}$. |

Any side of a parallelogram may be called its *base*. Then the *corresponding height* is the distance from the base to the opposite side.

**Area Theorem for a Parallelogram**

The area ($A$) of a parallelogram is the length ($b$) of its base times the corresponding height ($h$).

$$A = bh$$

**Given:** Parallelogram $RSET$ with base of length $b$ and height $h$

**Prove:** Area $RSET = bh$

**Sketch of Proof:** Extend $\overline{RS}$ and draw the perpendicular from $E$ to this extended line. Let $D$ be the point of intersection. Likewise, extend $\overline{ET}$ and draw the perpendicular from $R$ to the extended line. Let $C$ be the point of intersection. Now we have a rectangle $RDEC$. Also, by the HL Theorem we can prove $\triangle RTC \cong \triangle ESD$. So we can reason as follows:

| | |
|---|---|
| area $\square RDEC = (b+a)h$ | Area Post. for a $\square$ |
| area $\triangle RTC +$ area $\square RSET +$ area $\triangle ESD = (b+a)h$ | Area Addition Post. |
| area $\triangle ESD +$ area $\square RSET +$ area $\triangle ESD = (b+a)h$ | Area Post. for $\cong \triangle$s |
| $\frac{1}{2}ah +$ area $\square RSET + \frac{1}{2}ah = (b+a)h$ | Area Thm. for a Rt. $\triangle$ |
| area $\square RSET + ah = bh + ah$ | Use algebra. |
| area $\square RSET = bh$ | |

Any side of a triangle may be called its *base*. Then the length of the altitude to that base is the *corresponding height*.

---

The area ($A$) of a triangle is one half times the length of its base times the corresponding height.

$$A = \tfrac{1}{2}bh$$

Area Theorem
for a Triangle

**Given:** $\triangle ABC$ with base of length $b$ and height $h$

**Prove:** Area $\triangle ABC = \frac{1}{2}bh$

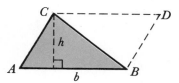

*Answer for page 295*

**Sketch of Proof:** Through $C$ draw a line parallel to $\overline{AB}$. Through $B$ draw a line parallel to $\overline{AC}$. Let $D$ be the point where these two lines intersect. Then $ABDC$ is a parallelogram. So area $\square ABDC = bh$. Since $\overline{BC}$ is a diagonal of $\square ABDC$, $\triangle ABC \cong \triangle DCB$. So area $\triangle ABC = \frac{1}{2}$ area $ABDC$, or area $\triangle ABC = \frac{1}{2}bh$.

In finding the area of a triangle, any side can be the base. Of course, you must know the length of the altitude to that side before you can find the area. The altitude to a given side can (**a**) be in the interior of the triangle, (**b**) coincide with another side, or (**c**) be in the exterior of the triangle.

**42.** *1.* $\square RSET$ (Given)
*2.* $\overleftrightarrow{RS} \parallel \overleftrightarrow{TE}$ (Def. of $\square$)
*3.* $\overline{ED} \perp \overleftrightarrow{RS},\ \overline{RC} \perp \overleftrightarrow{TE}$
  ($\perp$ Line Post.)
*4.* $\overline{RC} \perp \overleftrightarrow{RS}$ (In a plane, a line $\perp$ to 1 of 2 $\parallel$ lines is $\perp$ to the other.)
*5.* $\overline{RC} \parallel \overline{ED}$ (In a plane, lines $\perp$ to the same line are $\parallel$.)
*6.* $RDEC$ is a $\square$. (Def. of $\square$)
*7.* $\angle C$ is a rt. $\angle$. (Def. of $\perp$)
*8.* $RDEC$ is a $\square$. (Def. of $\square$)

(a) 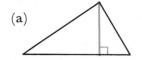  (b)   (c)

**Examples:** Find the area of each figure.

**1.** Find the area of a triangle where $b = 12$ m and $h = 5$ m.

$$A = \tfrac{1}{2}bh$$
$$A = \tfrac{1}{2} \cdot 12 \cdot 5$$
$$A = 30 \text{ m}^2$$

**2.** Find the area of a parallelogram where $b = 3.2$ cm and $h = 40$ mm.

$$A = bh$$
$$A = (3.2)(4) \quad \blacktriangleleft 40 \text{ mm} = 4 \text{ cm}$$
$$A = 12.8 \text{ cm}^2$$

## Exercises 9.2

**Assignment Guide**
*Oral:* 1–14
*Written:* Min. 15–37 odd
     Reg. 15–39 odd
     Max. 15–43 odd

Ⓐ **1–2.** Give the formula for the area of each figure and tell what each letter stands for.

**1.** a parallelogram  *See page 292.*      **2.** a triangle  *See page 293.*

**3–8.** For the given base, what is the corresponding height?

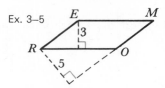  Ex. 3–5     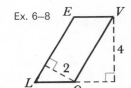 Ex. 6–8

**3.** $\overline{RO}$   3    **4.** $\overline{OM}$   5

**5.** $\overline{RE}$   5    **6.** $\overline{LO}$   4

**7.** $\overline{LE}$   2    **8.** $\overline{OV}$   2

**9–14.** For each triangle, name the altitude to the given side.

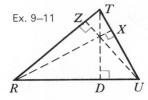  Ex. 9–11     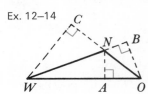 Ex. 12–14

**9.** $\overline{RU}$ $\overline{TD}$ **10.** $\overline{UT}$ $\overline{RX}$

**11.** $\overline{RT}$ $\overline{UZ}$ **12.** $\overline{WN}$ $\overline{OB}$

**13.** $\overline{WO}$ $\overline{NA}$ **14.** $\overline{ON}$ $\overline{WC}$

Ⓑ **15–18.** Find the area of each parallelogram.

**15.**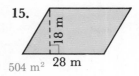
504 m²   28 m

**16.**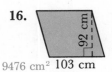
9476 cm²   103 cm

**17.**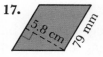
45.82 cm² or 4582 mm²

**18.**
45.76 cm² or 4576 mm²

**19–22.** Find the area of each triangle.

**19.**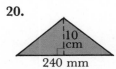
180 mm
162 cm² or 16 200 mm²

**20.**
240 mm
120 cm² or 12 000 mm²

**21.** 27

**22.** $6\tfrac{3}{4}$

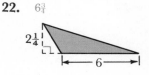

**23–30.** Find the area of each triangle.

**23.** $b = 3\frac{2}{3}$, $h = 1\frac{1}{2}$     $2\frac{3}{4}$

**24.** $b = 2\frac{1}{6}$, $h = 3$     $3\frac{1}{4}$

**25.** $b = 5$, $h = 2\frac{2}{5}$     6

**26.** $b = 6\frac{1}{4}$, $h = 3\frac{1}{2}$   $10\frac{15}{16}$

**27.** $b = 3.8$, $h = 2.4$     4.56

**28.** $b = 1.5$, $h = 9.4$
               7.05

**29.** $b = 1.66$, $h = 3.42$   2.8386

**30.** $b = 8.12$, $h = 5.63$
             22.8578

**31–38.** Find the area of each parallelogram.

**31.** $b = 8$, $h = 3\frac{1}{2}$     28

**32.** $b = 10$, $h = 2\frac{3}{4}$   $27\frac{1}{2}$

**33.** $b = 2\frac{1}{3}$, $h = 2\frac{1}{3}$     $5\frac{4}{9}$

**34.** $b = 6\frac{1}{4}$, $h = 3\frac{1}{2}$   $21\frac{7}{8}$

**35.** $b = 4.3$, $h = 6.3$    27.09

**36.** $b = 1.9$, $h = 3.8$
               7.22

**37.** $b = 1.25$, $h = 3.48$    4.35

**38.** $b = 7.29$, $h = 3.57$
            26.0253

**39–40.** In $\triangle ABC$, $\overline{CD}$ is the altitude to $\overline{AB}$, and $\overline{AE}$ is the altitude to $\overline{BC}$.

**39.** If $AB = 12$, $CD = 8$, $AE = 9$, find $BC$.    $10\frac{2}{3}$

**40.** If $AB = 5$, $AE = 11$, $BC = 7$, find $CD$.   15.4

© **41.** For the figure at the top of page 292, prove $ABDC$ is a rectangle.
*Answer on page 292*

**42.** For the figure at the bottom of page 292, prove $RDEC$ is a rectangle.
*Answer on page 292*

**43.** How many square meters of tent material are needed to make a tent like that at the right? (There is no floor, so two triangles and two rectangles are involved. Neglect the material needed for hems and seams.)     10.2 m²

Ex. 43

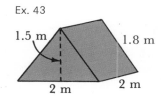

1.5 m       1.8 m

2 m      2 m

**44.** A steel storage shed has dimensions as shown in the figure. How many square meters of sheet metal are needed to cover the ends, the sides, and the roof? (Neglect the amount cut out for windows and doors.)
      312 m²

Ex. 44

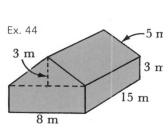

3 m       5 m     3 m     15 m     8 m

H. Armstrong Roberts

# 9.3 Areas of Trapezoids and Rhombuses

**Suggested Class Time**

| Course | Min. | Reg. | Max. |
|---|---|---|---|
| Days | 1 | 1 | 1 |

Remember that a trapezoid has two parallel sides called *bases* and two nonparallel sides. The distance between the parallel sides is called the *height* of the trapezoid.

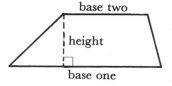

**Area Theorem for a Trapezoid**

The area ($A$) of a trapezoid is one half times the height ($h$) times the sum of the lengths ($b_1$ and $b_2$) of its bases.

$$A = \tfrac{1}{2}h(b_1 + b_2)$$

Given: Trapezoid $ABCD$ with bases of lengths $b_1$ and $b_2$, and height $h$

Prove: Area $ABCD = \tfrac{1}{2}h(b_1 + b_2)$

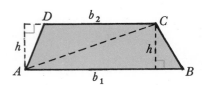

Sketch of Proof: Draw auxiliary segment $AC$ so that $\triangle ABC$ and $\triangle ACD$ are formed. By the Area Addition Postulate, the area of $ABCD$ equals the sum of the areas of $\triangle ABC$ and $\triangle ACD$.

We know area $\triangle ABC = \tfrac{1}{2}b_1h$ and area $\triangle ACD = \tfrac{1}{2}b_2h$. (Both triangles have the same height $h$.) So area $ABCD = \tfrac{1}{2}b_1h + \tfrac{1}{2}b_2h$.

Then area $ABCD = \tfrac{1}{2}h(b_1 + b_2)$.

Another quadrilateral that we sometimes use is the rhombus. The proof of the next theorem is asked for in Exercise 30.

**Area Theorem for a Rhombus**

The area ($A$) of a rhombus is one half times the product of the lengths ($d_1$ and $d_2$) of its diagonals.

$$A = \tfrac{1}{2}d_1d_2$$

**Examples:**

1. Find the area of a trapezoid having bases of lengths 14 and 20 and height 8.

$A = \tfrac{1}{2}h(b_1 + b_2)$
$A = \tfrac{1}{2} \cdot 8 \cdot (14 + 20)$
$A = 136$

2. Find the area of a rhombus with diagonals of lengths 4 and $2\tfrac{1}{2}$.

$A = \tfrac{1}{2}d_1d_2$
$A = \tfrac{1}{2} \cdot 4 \cdot 2\tfrac{1}{2}$
$A = 5$

Ⓐ    1. What is the formula for the area of a trapezoid? What does each letter stand for?   *See page 296.*

2. What is the formula for the area of a rhombus? What does each letter stand for?   *See page 296.*

**Assignment Guide**
*Oral:* 1–10
*Written:*
Min. 11–27 odd;
       Quiz, p. 299
Reg. 11–27 odd; 32–34;
       Quiz, p. 299
Max. 11–29 odd; 32–35;
       Quiz, p. 299

**3–6.** For the given trapezoid, is the length of a base or the height listed?

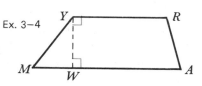

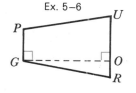

Ex. 5–6

Ex. 3–4

3. *MA*   Base      4. *YW*   Height      5. *OG*   Height      6. *UR*   Base

7. Can a trapezoid also be a rhombus?   No

8. Can a parallelogram also be a rhombus?   Yes

**9–10.** Refer to the figure where *DAVE* is a rhombus.

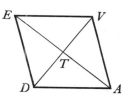

9. What is $m\angle ETV$? $m\angle ATV$?   90; 90

10. If $DV = 6$ and $AE = 8$, what is area *DAVE*?   24

Ⓑ   **11–16.** Find the area of each trapezoid.

11.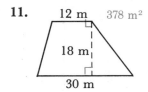
12 m   378 m²
18 m
30 m

12.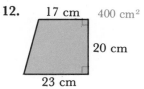
17 cm   400 cm²
20 cm
23 cm

13.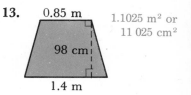
0.85 m   1.1025 m² or 11 025 cm²
98 cm
1.4 m

14.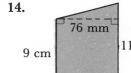
76 mm   76.95 cm² or 7695 mm²
9 cm   11.25 cm

15.
2.4   10.2
3.8   4.7

16.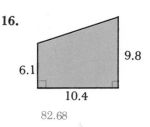
9.8
6.1
10.4
82.68

**29.** *Sketch of Proof:* In trapezoid $ABCD$, $\overline{AB} \parallel \overline{CD}$. Since parallel lines are equidistant, the heights of $\triangle ADB$ and of $\triangle BCA$ are equal. Call the height $h$. But both $\triangle$s have base $\overline{AB}$, so area $\triangle ADB$ = area $\triangle BCA$ = $\frac{1}{2}AB \cdot h$. Using the Area Add. Post. and substitution, area $\triangle AEB$ + area $\triangle ADE$ = area $\triangle AEB$ + area $\triangle BCE$. Subtracting area $\triangle AEB$ from both sides, area $\triangle ADE$ = area $\triangle BCE$.

**30.** *Sketch of Proof:* $ABCD$ is a rhombus, so $\overline{AC} \perp \overline{DB}$ and $DE = BE = \frac{1}{2}d_2$. Then $\triangle ADC$ and $\triangle ABC$ both have height $\frac{1}{2}d_2$ and base length $AC = d_1$. So area $\triangle ABC = \frac{1}{2}d_1(\frac{1}{2}d_2)$ $= \frac{1}{4}d_1d_2$, and area $\triangle ADC = \frac{1}{2}d_1(\frac{1}{2}d_2) =$ $\frac{1}{4}d_1d_2$. But area $ABCD$ = area $\triangle ABC$ + area $\triangle ADC = \frac{1}{4}d_1d_2 +$ $\frac{1}{4}d_1d_2 = \frac{1}{2}d_1d_2$.

**17–20.** Find the area of each rhombus.

**17.**  117

**18.** 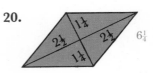 308

**19.** 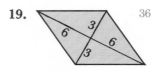 36

**20.** 6$\frac{1}{4}$

**21–24.** Find the area of each trapezoid.

**21.** $h = 21.2$, $b_1 = 18.3$, $b_2 = 15.8$   361.46

**22.** $h = 5.25$, $b_1 = 3.83$, $b_2 = 5.14$   23.54625

**23.** $h = 3\frac{1}{4}$, $b_1 = 4\frac{1}{2}$, $b_2 = 3\frac{1}{4}$   $12\frac{19}{32}$

**24.** $h = 9\frac{1}{2}$, $b_1 = 10\frac{1}{4}$, $b_2 = 12\frac{1}{4}$   $106\frac{7}{8}$

**25–28.** Find the area of each rhombus.

**25.** $d_1 = 4\frac{1}{4}$, $d_2 = 3\frac{1}{2}$   $7\frac{7}{16}$    **26.** $d_1 = 1\frac{1}{8}$, $d_2 = 1\frac{3}{8}$   $\frac{99}{128}$

**27.** $d_1 = 5.6$, $d_2 = 8.3$   23.24    **28.** $d_1 = 10.6$, $d_2 = 12.4$   65.72

Ex. 29

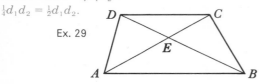

**29.** **Given:** Trapezoid $ABCD$ with bases $\overline{AB}$ and $\overline{CD}$, diagonals $\overline{AC}$ and $\overline{BD}$ intersect at $E$.

**Prove:** Area $\triangle ADE$ = area $\triangle BCE$

[*Plan:* Prove area $\triangle ADB$ = area $\triangle BCA$. Then subtract area $\triangle AEB$ from both.]

Ex. 30

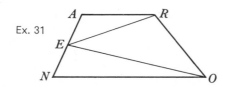

**30.** **Given:** Rhombus $ABCD$ with diagonals of lengths $d_1$ and $d_2$

**Prove:** Area $ABCD = \frac{1}{2}d_1d_2$

Ex. 31

© **31.** **Given:** Trapezoid $NORA$, $\overline{NO} \parallel \overline{AR}$, $E$ is the midpoint of $AN$.

**Prove:** Area $\triangle EOR = \frac{1}{2}$ area $NORA$

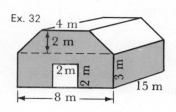

Ex. 32

**32.** The sides and ends of a barn are to be painted. How many square meters of surface need to be covered? See the figure at the left. The door will not be painted. 158

**31.** *Sketch of Proof:* Draw a seg. through $E \perp$ to $\overrightarrow{AR}$ and $\overline{NO}$. Call its length $h$. Then $h$ is the height of *NORA*, and area *NORA* is $\frac{1}{2}h(AR + NO)$. $E$ is the midpt. of $\overline{AN}$, so it is also the midpt. of

**33.** The cross section of a swimming pool is shown at the right. If the sides and bottom are to be painted, find the surface area to be covered. (The pool is 18 feet wide.) 1608 ft²

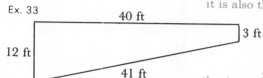

Ex. 33

the $\perp$ seg. The height of $\triangle EAR$ from $E$ to $\overline{AR}$ and of $\triangle ENO$ from $E$ to $\overline{NO}$ is $\frac{1}{2}h$. Then area $\triangle EAR = \frac{1}{2}AR(\frac{1}{2}h)$, area $\triangle ENO = \frac{1}{2}NO(\frac{1}{2}h)$. The sum of the areas is $\frac{1}{2} \cdot \frac{1}{2}h(AR + NO)$ or $\frac{1}{2}$ area *NORA*. Since area *NORA* is the sum of the areas of 3 $\triangle$s, the area of the third $\triangle$, $\triangle EOR$, is also $\frac{1}{2}$ area *NORA*.

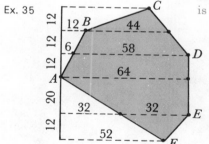

Ex. 34

**34.** A glazier is cutting glass to fit a window shaped like that at the left. The glass is cut from a rectangular sheet of plate glass that is 180 cm by 120 cm. How much glass will be wasted? 6600 cm²

**35.** A surveyor needs to find the area of a plot shaped like *ABCDEF*. A north-south line is determined through $A$, and east-west lines are determined through $C$, $B$, $D$, $A$, $E$, and $F$. Measurements are then made along these lines. Find the area of *ABCDEF*. 2760

Ex. 35

---

Find the area of each figure.

**1.** a rectangle with length 9 and width $6\frac{1}{2}$  $58\frac{1}{2}$

**2.** a triangle with base of length 6.8 and height 8  27.2

**3.** a trapezoid with bases of lengths 17 and 21 and height 22  418

**4.** a rhombus with diagonals of lengths 14 and 21  147

*Quick Quiz* for Sections 9.1 to 9.3

# GEOMETRY AT WORK

## SCIENTIFIC AND TECHNICAL JOBS

About $2\frac{1}{2}$ million people in the United States have scientific or technical jobs. These include various kinds of engineers, scientists, and technicians, as well as drafters and surveyors. The training needed by these workers ranges from college degrees for some scientists to on-the-job training for some technicians.

High-school graduates with courses in science and mathematics are more likely to get scientific and technical jobs.

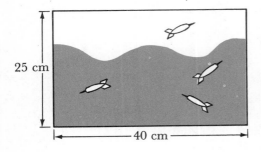

25 cm

40 cm

Scientific and technical workers might sometimes use an experiment to find the area of an irregular region like the green region at the left. You can estimate the area of such a region by throwing darts. (A scientific worker wouldn't use darts but might simulate such an experiment with a computer.) Suppose there are 75 hits in the green region out of a total of 100 hits in the rectangular region. The area of the rectangular region is $25 \cdot 40 = 1000$ square centimeters. Solving the proportion below approximates the area of the green region.

$$\frac{75}{100} = \frac{x}{1000} \qquad x = 750$$

Photri

# Square Roots and Radicals

In the next section, we discuss the Pythagorean Theorem. Since square roots are important in using this theorem, we will review the basic ideas about square roots now.

> For real numbers $r$ and $x$, $r$ is a square root of $x$ if and only if $r^2 = x$.

**Example 1:** Find the square roots of 36.

Since $6^2 = 36$, 6 is a square root of 36. We write $\sqrt{36} = 6$. Also $(-6)^2 = 36$. So $-6$ is a square root of 36. We write $-\sqrt{36} = -6$.

You may remember that $\sqrt{36}$ is called a *radical*. The word *radical* comes from a Latin word meaning "root." The sign $\sqrt{\phantom{x}}$ is thought to be a form of the letter $r$. In this section we are dealing only with square roots. But radicals can be used for other roots such as $\sqrt[3]{8}$ or $\sqrt[5]{10}$.

Two theorems from algebra are very important in working with radicals.

> If $a$ and $b$ are nonnegative real numbers,
> $$\sqrt{ab} = \sqrt{a} \cdot \sqrt{b} \quad \text{and} \quad \sqrt{\frac{a}{b}} = \frac{\sqrt{a}}{\sqrt{b}} \quad (b \neq 0)$$

**Example 2:** Change each radical expression to *simplest form*.

   **a.** $\sqrt{32}$        **b.** $\sqrt{\frac{7}{9}}$        **c.** $\dfrac{\sqrt{3}}{\sqrt{2}}$

   **a.** $\sqrt{32} = \sqrt{16} \cdot \sqrt{2} = 4\sqrt{2}$

   **b.** $\sqrt{\frac{7}{9}} = \dfrac{\sqrt{7}}{\sqrt{9}} = \dfrac{\sqrt{7}}{3}$

   **c.** $\dfrac{\sqrt{3}}{\sqrt{2}} = \dfrac{\sqrt{3}}{\sqrt{2}} \cdot \dfrac{\sqrt{2}}{\sqrt{2}} = \dfrac{\sqrt{6}}{2}$    ◀ This is called rationalizing the denominator.

These examples show that a radical expression is *not* in simplest form if

**a.** the number under the square-root sign contains a perfect-square factor.

**b.** the number under the square-root sign is a fraction.

**c.** a radical appears in the denominator.

Sometimes it is helpful to change a fraction so that its denominator is a perfect square before the radical is simplified.

**Example 3:** $\sqrt{\frac{1}{8}} = \sqrt{\frac{2}{16}} = \frac{\sqrt{2}}{\sqrt{16}} = \frac{\sqrt{2}}{4}$

It should be clear that not all square roots are integers. For example, $\sqrt{14}$ is between 3 and 4 since $3^2 = 9$ and $4^2 = 16$. Approximations to the square roots of integers from 1 to 150 are given in a table on page 562. For integers larger than 150, you can still use the table in some cases, as in the following example:

**Example 4:** Find $\sqrt{300}$ to the nearest tenth.

$$\sqrt{300} = \sqrt{100} \cdot \sqrt{3} = 10\sqrt{3}$$

From the table, $\sqrt{3} \approx 1.732$. ($\approx$ means "is approximately equal to.") So $\sqrt{300} = 10\sqrt{3} \approx 10(1.732)$ or 17.32.

To the nearest tenth, $\sqrt{300} \approx 17.3$.

## *Exercises 9.4*

**Assignment Guide**
*Oral:* 1–4
*Written:*
Min. 5–47 odd; Alg. Rev.,
   p. 303, odd
Reg. 5–47 odd; Alg. Rev.,
   p. 303, odd
Max. 5–51 odd

Ⓐ **1.** How many square roots does each positive real number have?  2

**2.** Which square roots are not integers?  b, d

   **a.** $\sqrt{4}$      **b.** $\sqrt{6}$      **c.** $\sqrt{25}$      **d.** $\sqrt{50}$      **e.** $\sqrt{100}$

**3.** Which expressions are not in simplest form?  a, b, c

   **a.** $\sqrt{50}$      **b.** $\sqrt{\frac{2}{3}}$      **c.** $\frac{\sqrt{2}}{\sqrt{3}}$      **d.** $\sqrt{17}$      **e.** $\frac{\sqrt{2}}{3}$

**4.** Name the largest perfect-square factor of the number under each square-root sign.

   **a.** $\sqrt{12}$  4      **b.** $\sqrt{75}$  25      **c.** $\sqrt{48}$  16      **d.** $\sqrt{200}$  100      **e.** $\sqrt{72}$  36

Ⓑ **5–14.** Use the table on page 562 to find each positive square root.

   **5.** $\sqrt{17}$  4.123    **6.** $\sqrt{23}$  4.796    **7.** $\sqrt{40}$  6.325    **8.** $\sqrt{61}$  7.810    **9.** $\sqrt{35}$
                                                                                    5.916

   **10.** $\sqrt{78}$  8.832    **11.** $\sqrt{99}$  9.950    **12.** $\sqrt{75}$  8.660    **13.** $\sqrt{32}$  5.657    **14.** $\sqrt{92}$
                                                                                                        9.592

**15–44.** Simplify. Do not use the table on page 562.

**15.** $\sqrt{16}$    4    **16.** $\sqrt{36}$    6    **17.** $\sqrt{64}$    8    **18.** $\sqrt{100}$   10    **19.** $\sqrt{81}$     9

**20.** $\sqrt{49}$    7    **21.** $\sqrt{\frac{1}{25}}$   $\frac{1}{5}$   **22.** $\sqrt{\frac{4}{9}}$   $\frac{2}{3}$   **23.** $\sqrt{\frac{25}{49}}$   $\frac{5}{7}$   **24.** $\sqrt{\frac{1}{100}}$   $\frac{1}{10}$

**25.** $\sqrt{18}$   $3\sqrt{2}$   **26.** $\sqrt{50}$   $5\sqrt{2}$   **27.** $\sqrt{32}$   $4\sqrt{2}$   **28.** $\sqrt{72}$   $6\sqrt{2}$   **29.** $\sqrt{200}$   $10\sqrt{2}$

**30.** $\sqrt{98}$   $7\sqrt{2}$   **31.** $\sqrt{125}$   $5\sqrt{5}$   **32.** $\sqrt{54}$   $3\sqrt{6}$   **33.** $\sqrt{48}$   $4\sqrt{3}$   **34.** $\sqrt{108}$   $6\sqrt{3}$

**35.** $\sqrt{\frac{3}{4}}$   $\frac{1}{2}\sqrt{3}$   **36.** $\sqrt{\frac{5}{16}}$   $\frac{1}{4}\sqrt{5}$   **37.** $\sqrt{\frac{3}{25}}$   $\frac{1}{5}\sqrt{3}$   **38.** $\sqrt{\frac{2}{49}}$   $\frac{1}{7}\sqrt{2}$   **39.** $\dfrac{\sqrt{2}}{\sqrt{6}}$   $\frac{1}{3}\sqrt{3}$

**40.** $\dfrac{\sqrt{3}}{\sqrt{5}}$   $\frac{1}{5}\sqrt{15}$   **41.** $\dfrac{1}{\sqrt{3}}$   $\frac{1}{3}\sqrt{3}$   **42.** $\dfrac{\sqrt{3}}{\sqrt{8}}$   $\frac{1}{4}\sqrt{6}$   **43.** $\sqrt{\frac{1}{5}}$   $\frac{1}{5}\sqrt{5}$   **44.** $\sqrt{\frac{2}{7}}$   $\frac{1}{7}\sqrt{14}$

**45–48.** Find a decimal approximation to the nearest tenth. Refer to the table on page 562. (First simplify each radical.)

**45.** $\sqrt{180}$   13.4     **46.** $\sqrt{162}$   12.7     **47.** $\sqrt{192}$   13.9     **48.** $\sqrt{200}$   14.1

© **49.** Make a list of the squares of integers from 11 to 20. Memorize them. Then find these square roots.

$\sqrt{196}$   14     $\sqrt{144}$   12     $\sqrt{225}$   15     $\sqrt{324}$   18     $\sqrt{121}$   11

$\sqrt{169}$   13     $\sqrt{256}$   16     $\sqrt{361}$   19     $\sqrt{289}$   17     $\sqrt{400}$   20

**50.** A tile setter has 500 square tiles to use for constructing the largest square patio possible. If only whole tiles are to be used, how many tiles will be left after the patio is constructed?    16

**51.** A builder is told that the floor of a building must be square with area 324 m². What must the floor dimensions be?    18 m by 18 m

Solve each quadratic equation. Find answers in simplified radical form when the results are not rational.

**1.** $6^2 + b^2 = 10^2$   $b = \pm 8$   **2.** $10^2 + 5^2 = x^2$ ⟵ **Example:**

**3.** $a^2 + 12^2 = 15^2$   $a = \pm 9$   **4.** $13^2 = x^2 + 5^2$   $x = \pm 12$    $125 = x^2$

**5.** $15^2 + 20^2 = x^2$   $x = \pm 25$   **6.** $9^2 + x^2 = 41^2$   $x = \pm 40$    $x = \pm 5\sqrt{5}$

**7.** $3^2 + 9^2 = z^2$   $z = \pm 3\sqrt{10}$   **8.** $7^2 + b^2 = (7\sqrt{2})^2$   $b = \pm 7$

*Algebra Review*

**Review this skill:**

• solving quadratic equations

# Pythagorean Theorem and Its Converse

**Suggested Class Time**

| Course | Min. | Reg. | Max. |
|--------|------|------|------|
| Days   | 1    | 1    | 1    |

The Pythagorean Theorem is probably the most famous theorem in mathematics. The theorem takes its name from the Greek mathematician named Pythagoras. It is not known whether Pythagoras or one of his followers was the first to prove the theorem. The following proof is just one of over 200 ways that have been used to prove the theorem.

**Pythagorean Theorem**

 In a right triangle, the square of the length of its hypotenuse is equal to the sum of the squares of the lengths of its legs.

Given: Right $\triangle ABC$ with hypotenuse of length $c$ and legs of lengths $a$ and $b$

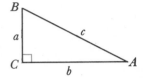

Prove: $c^2 = a^2 + b^2$

Sketch of proof: First, take a square with sides of length $a + b$. In the square draw four right triangles with legs of lengths $a$ and $b$.

**1.** By the LL Theorem, each right triangle is congruent to the given $\triangle ABC$. Therefore, each triangle has a hypotenuse of length $c$.

**2.** Now we must prove that the quadrilateral formed by the four hypotenuses is a square. In the figure,

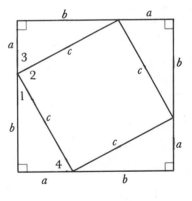

$$m\angle 1 + m\angle 2 + m\angle 3 = 180$$

Also, $m\angle 4 = m\angle 3$.

So, $m\angle 1 + m\angle 2 + m\angle 4 = 180$.

Since $m\angle 1 + m\angle 4 = 90$ (Why?),

$$m\angle 2 = 90.$$

Likewise, the other angles of the quadrilateral are right angles.

**3.** By the Area Addition Postulate, the area of the large square is equal to the area of the small square, plus the sum of the areas of the four congruent triangles. This gives

$$(a + b)^2 = c^2 + 4 \cdot \tfrac{1}{2}ab$$

Therefore, $a^2 + 2ab + b^2 = c^2 + 2ab$

and $\qquad a^2 + b^2 = c^2$

The converse of the Pythagorean Theorem is also true.

 If the square of the length of one side of a triangle is equal to the sum of the squares of the lengths of the other two sides, then the triangle is a right triangle, with the right angle opposite the longest side.  **Converse of Pythagorean Theorem**

Given: $\triangle ABC$ with $c^2 = a^2 + b^2$

Prove: $\triangle ABC$ is a right triangle.

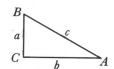 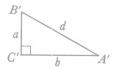

Proof: Let $A'B'C'$ be a right triangle with legs of length $a$ and $b$ and hypotenuse of length $d$. Then $d^2 = a^2 + b^2$ by the Pythagorean Theorem. Since $c^2 = a^2 + b^2$, then $c^2 = d^2$ or $c = d$. (Actually, $c = \pm d$, but the length of a side of a triangle cannot be negative.) By the SSS Postulate, $\triangle ABC \cong \triangle A'B'C'$. Therefore, $\angle C \cong \angle C'$. Since $\angle C'$ is a right angle, so is $\angle C$.

**Examples:**

**1.** Find the length of the hypotenuse of a right triangle having legs of lengths 9 and 12.

$c^2 = 9^2 + 12^2$

$c^2 = 81 + 144 = 225$

$c = 15$

NOTE: This quadratic equation has two roots. But we disregard the negative root since we are finding the length of a side of a triangle.

**2.** In right $\triangle ABC$, find the length $a$ of one leg if the hypotenuse has length $c = 8$ and the other leg has length $b = 4$.

$$8^2 = a^2 + 4^2$$

$$64 = a^2 + 16$$

$$48 = a^2$$

$$\sqrt{48} = a$$

$$\sqrt{16} \cdot \sqrt{3} = a$$

$$4\sqrt{3} = a$$

**3.** Can the following be lengths of the sides of a right triangle?

$$6, 8, 11$$

$$11^2 \stackrel{?}{=} 6^2 + 8^2$$

$$121 \stackrel{?}{=} 36 + 64$$

$$121 \neq 100$$

No, these could not be the lengths of the sides of a right triangle.

# Exercises 9.5

**Assignment Guide**
*Oral:* 1–10
*Written:*
Min. 11–31 odd
Reg. 11–23 odd; 25–32
Max. 11–23 odd; 25–33

(A) **1.** Can the Pythagorean Theorem be applied to any triangle?   No

**2.** If the sides of a right triangle have lengths $x$, $y$, and $z$ with $z$ the greatest length, what equation must be true?   $z^2 = x^2 + y^2$

**3–6.** State an equation that can be used to find the missing length for each triangle.

$x^2 = 4^2 + 7^2$ **3.** 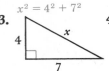   $y^2 = 3^2 + 3^2$ **4.**    $9^2 = a^2 + 5^2$ **5.**    $8^2 = b^2 + 4^2$ **6.**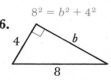

**7–10.** The lengths of three sides of a triangle are given. Can the triangle be a right triangle?

**7.** 3, 4, 5   Yes     **8.** 4, 5, 6   No     **9.** 6, 8, 10   Yes     **10.** 3, 3, 5   No

(B) **11–18.** For right $\triangle ABC$, the lengths of two of the three sides are given. Find the length of the third side. Leave answers in simplified radical form where answers are not rational.

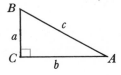

**11.** $a = 5$, $b = 12$     13         **12.** $a = 8$, $b = 15$     17

**13.** $a = 4$, $b = 4$     $4\sqrt{2}$     **14.** $a = 5$, $b = 10$     $5\sqrt{5}$

**15.** $c = 41$, $a = 40$     9         **16.** $c = 20$, $a = 16$     12

**17.** $c = 16$, $b = 9$     $5\sqrt{7}$     **18.** $c = 12$, $b = 8$     $4\sqrt{5}$

**19–24.** Determine if a triangle with sides of the given lengths is a right triangle.

**19.** 9, 12, 15   Yes     **20.** 15, 20, 25   Yes     **21.** 5, 8, 9     No

**22.** 10, 24, 26   Yes     **23.** 16, 30, 34   Yes     **24.** 20, 40, 60   No

**25.** A 40-meter radio tower is braced with a cable that is tied 30 meters from the base. How long must the cable be? (Disregard the amount of cable needed for tying.)   50 m

Ex. 25

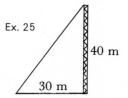

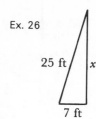

Ex. 26

25 ft / x

7 ft

**26.** A 25-foot ladder leans against a building so that the foot of the ladder is 7 feet from the base of the building. How high up on the building does the ladder reach? 24 ft

**27.** A surveyor wants to find the distance from point $A$ to point $B$. Since the distance cannot be measured directly, a right triangle is laid off as in the figure. $AC = 21$ m and $BC = 35$ m. How long is $AB$? 28 m

Ex. 27

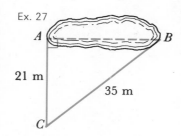

A                    B

21 m

35 m

C

Ex. 28

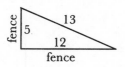

18 km

x

24 km

**28.** A ship is 18 kilometers south and 24 kilometers east of its starting point. How far is the ship from its starting point? 30 km

**29.** In laying out wood forms into which concrete will be poured, cement masons often use a 3-4-5 triangle. Is $\angle ABC$ a right angle? Why?
Yes; Converse of Pythagorean Thm.

Ex. 29

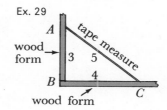

A

tape measure

wood form →

3    5

B    4    C

wood form

Ex. 30

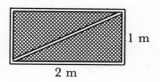

fence

5    13

12

fence

**30.** A fence installer wants to square off the corner of a fence. A triangle is measured as shown. Does the corner form a right angle? Why?
Yes; Converse of Pythagorean Thm.

**31.** A baseball diamond (square) is 90 feet on each side. If the catcher throws from home plate to second base, how far is the ball thrown (to the nearest tenth of a foot)? 127.3 ft

Ex. 31

2nd

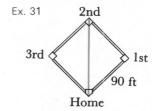

3rd            1st

90 ft

Home

Ex. 32

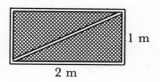

1 m

2 m

**32.** A rectangular gate is braced with a board connecting opposite corners. If the gate is 2 meters by 1 meter, how long must the brace be (to the nearest hundredth of a meter)? 2.24 m

Ex. 33

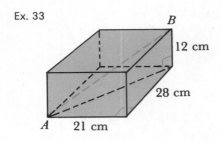

12 cm

28 cm

21 cm

© **33.** A box has a length, width, and height of 28 cm, 21 cm, and 12 cm. How long is a diagonal of the box? (A diagonal joins opposite corners, such as $A$ and $B$ in the figure.) HINT: Apply the Pythagorean Theorem twice. *37 cm*

Ex. 34

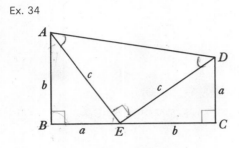

**34.** President James Garfield discovered a proof of the Pythagorean Theorem in 1876 while he was a member of the House of Representatives, five years before he became President. The proof involves finding the area of $ABCD$ in two different ways, first using three triangles and then as a trapezoid. Show that $c^2 = a^2 + b^2$.

*Answer on page 309*

# THE WHEEL OF THEODORUS

Theodorus was a Greek philosopher who lived about 425 B.C. It is said that he discovered the construction below. Therefore, it is called the "wheel of Theodorus."

Notice how the "wheel of Theodorus" enables us to construct segments having measures of $\sqrt{1}$, $\sqrt{2}$, $\sqrt{3}$, $\sqrt{4}$, $\sqrt{5}$, $\cdots$.

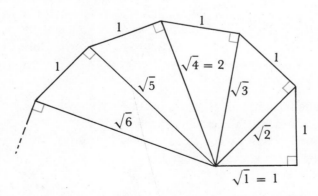

Construct a wheel of your own. What is the measure of the last segment that can be constructed before the wheel overlaps? $\sqrt{17}$

If you construct a wheel (or parts of it) by using unit segments that are 1 decimeter long, you can estimate $\sqrt{2}$, $\sqrt{3}$, $\sqrt{5}$, and so on, to the nearest hundredth by measuring to the nearest millimeter.

# INDUSTRIAL PRODUCTION

Millions of people in the United States work in industrial production. These workers are employed mostly in factories. Semiskilled workers, such as assemblers and certain machine operators, may need only brief on-the-job training. Skilled workers, such as patternmakers and machinists, may have to complete a 3- or 4-year apprenticeship program.

For most jobs in industrial production a high-school diploma is not required. But many employers prefer high-school graduates who have taken such courses as machine shop and blueprint reading. A knowledge of geometry can also be very helpful in getting a good job and in successfully completing the training program.

A welder might have to solve a problem like the following:

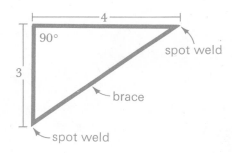

How long a metal rod is needed for the brace ?　5

34. area $\triangle ABE$ + area $\triangle AED$ + area $\triangle DCE$
$$= \text{area trapezoid } ABCD$$
$$\tfrac{1}{2}ab + \tfrac{1}{2}c \cdot c + \tfrac{1}{2}ab = \tfrac{1}{2}(a + b)(a + b)$$
$$ab + \tfrac{1}{2}c^2 = \tfrac{1}{2}(a^2 + 2ab + b^2)$$
$$ab + \tfrac{1}{2}c^2 = \tfrac{1}{2}a^2 + ab + \tfrac{1}{2}b^2$$
$$\tfrac{1}{2}c^2 = \tfrac{1}{2}a^2 + \tfrac{1}{2}b^2$$
$$c^2 = a^2 + b^2$$

Joe Tritsch

## 9.6 Special Right Triangles

| Suggested Class Time | | | |
|---|---|---|---|
| Course | Min. | Reg. | Max. |
| Days | 2 | 1 | 1 |

Isosceles Right Triangle

30-60-90° Triangle

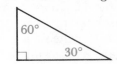

The two triangles at the left have properties that are sometimes quite useful.

**Isosceles Right Triangle Theorem**

In an isosceles right triangle, the length of the hypotenuse is $\sqrt{2}$ times the length of either leg.

Given: Isosceles right $\triangle ABC$ with
$m\angle C = 90$, $BC = AC = x$,
$BA = c$

Prove: $c = x\sqrt{2}$

Proof: By the Pythagorean Theorem, $c^2 = x^2 + x^2$. So $c^2 = 2x^2$. Then $c = \sqrt{2}x$ or $c = x\sqrt{2}$. (We can ignore the negative root since the side of a triangle must have a positive length.)

**30-60-90° Triangle Theorem**

In a 30-60-90° triangle, the length of the side opposite the 30° angle is half the length of the hypotenuse. The length of the side opposite the 60° angle is $\sqrt{3}$ times the length of the side opposite the 30° angle.

Given: Right $\triangle ABC$ with $m\angle A = 30$,
$m\angle B = 60$, $m\angle C = 90$.
$AB = c$, $BC = a$, $CA = b$

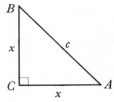

Prove: $a = \frac{1}{2}c$ and $b = a\sqrt{3}$

Proof: From $C$, draw $\overline{CD}$ so that $m\angle BCD = 60$. Let $CD = x$. By the Isosceles Triangle Theorem, $BD = x$.

Since $m\angle BCA = 90$ and $m\angle BCD = 60$, it follows that $m\angle ACD = 30$. Therefore, $\angle DCA \cong \angle CAD$, and $\triangle DCA$ is isosceles. Since $CD = x$, then $DA = x$.

$$\text{So } c = x + x = 2x \text{ or } \tfrac{1}{2}c = x.$$

Now in $\triangle BCD$, $m\angle BCD = m\angle CBD = 60$. Then $m\angle BDC = 60$. So $\triangle BCD$ is equilateral, and $a = x$. Since $\frac{1}{2}c = x$, then $\frac{1}{2}c = a$ or $a = \frac{1}{2}c$.

By the Pythagorean Theorem, ▶ $c^2 = a^2 + b^2$

Since $a = \frac{1}{2}c$, ▶ $c^2 = (\frac{1}{2}c)^2 + b^2$

$c^2 = \frac{1}{4}c^2 + b^2$

$\frac{3}{4}c^2 = b^2$

$\frac{\sqrt{3}}{2}c = b$

Substituting $2a$ for $c$, ▶ $\sqrt{3}a = b$ or $b = a\sqrt{3}$

**Examples:** Find the missing length(s) in each triangle.

1.

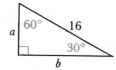

2.

By the 30-60-90° Triangle
Theorem, $a = \frac{1}{2} \cdot 16 = 8$ and
$b = 8\sqrt{3}$.

By the Isosceles Right
Triangle Theorem, $x = 4\sqrt{2}$.

## Exercises 9.6

Ⓐ 1. In an isosceles right triangle, the length of the hypotenuse equals the length of either leg multiplied by __$\sqrt{2}$__ .

2. In a 30-60-90° triangle, the length of the side opposite the 30° angle is __Half__ the length of the hypotenuse.

3. In a 30-60-90° triangle, the length of the side opposite the 60° angle equals the length of the side opposite the 30° angle multiplied by __$\sqrt{3}$__ .

4. In an isosceles right triangle, each acute angle has a measure of __45__ .

Ⓑ **5–12.** Given the length of a leg of an isosceles right triangle, find the length of the hypotenuse.

5. 7   $7\sqrt{2}$

6. 10   $10\sqrt{2}$

7. $\frac{1}{2}$   $\frac{1}{2}\sqrt{2}$

8. $\frac{1}{4}$   $\frac{1}{4}\sqrt{2}$

9. $\sqrt{2}$   2

10. $\sqrt{3}$   $\sqrt{6}$

11. $3\sqrt{3}$   $3\sqrt{6}$

12. $5\sqrt{2}$   10

Assignment Guide
*Oral:* 1–4
*Written:*
Min. (day 1) 5–27 odd
  (day 2) 29–40
Reg. 5–39 odd
Max. 5–39 odd
*Constructions:* 41–43

**13-20.** Given the length of the hypotenuse of a 30-60-90° triangle, find the length of **(a)** the side opposite the 30° angle and **(b)** the side opposite the 60° angle.

**13.** 14   **a.** 7   **b.** $7\sqrt{3}$    **14.** 20   **a.** 10   **b.** $10\sqrt{3}$    **15.** 1   **a.** $\frac{1}{2}$   **b.** $\frac{1}{2}\sqrt{3}$    **16.** 3   **a.** $\frac{3}{2}$   **b.** $\frac{3}{2}\sqrt{3}$

**17.** $\frac{1}{2}$   **a.** $\frac{1}{4}$   **b.** $\frac{1}{4}\sqrt{3}$    **18.** $\frac{1}{3}$   **a.** $\frac{1}{6}$   **b.** $\frac{1}{6}\sqrt{3}$    **19.** $\sqrt{2}$   **a.** $\frac{1}{2}\sqrt{2}$   **b.** $\frac{1}{2}\sqrt{6}$    **20.** $\sqrt{3}$   **a.** $\frac{1}{2}\sqrt{3}$   **b.** $\frac{3}{2}$

**21-24.** Given the length of the hypotenuse of an isosceles right triangle, find the length of a leg.

**21.** 10   $5\sqrt{2}$     **22.** 12   $6\sqrt{2}$     **23.** $4\sqrt{2}$   4     **24.** $\sqrt{10}$   $\sqrt{5}$

**25-28.** Given the length of the side opposite the 30° angle in a 30-60-90° triangle, find the length of **(a)** the side opposite the 60° angle and **(b)** the hypotenuse.

**25.** 6   **a.** $6\sqrt{3}$   **b.** 12    **26.** 18   **a.** $18\sqrt{3}$   **b.** 36    **27.** $\sqrt{3}$   **a.** 3   **b.** $2\sqrt{3}$    **28.** $8\sqrt{3}$   **a.** 24   **b.** $16\sqrt{3}$

**29-32.** Find the missing length(s) in each triangle.

**29.** 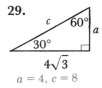   $a = 4, c = 8$

**30.** 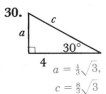   $a = \frac{4}{3}\sqrt{3},$   $c = \frac{8}{3}\sqrt{3}$

**31.** 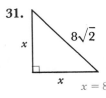   $x = 8$

**32.** 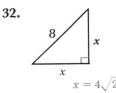   $x = 4\sqrt{2}$

**33-36.** Find the length of the altitude in each triangle.

**33.**

**34.**

**35.**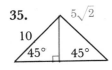

**36.**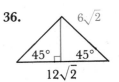

**37-40.** Find each answer to the nearest tenth. $\sqrt{2} \approx 1.414$, $\sqrt{3} \approx 1.732$

Ex. 37

Ex. 38

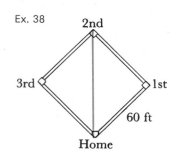

**37.** A brace is made for a bookshelf as shown in the figure. How long must the brace be?   39.6 cm

**38.** A softball diamond (square) is 60 feet on a side. If the ball is thrown from home plate to second base, how far must it be thrown?   84.8 ft

**39.** A ramp is inclined so that it makes a 60° angle with the ground. How long must the ramp be so that it reaches a point that is 42 cm above the ground? 48.5 cm

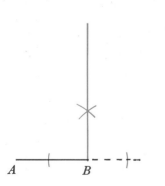

Ex. 39

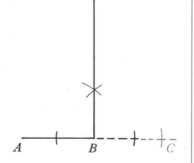

Ex. 40

**40.** At the General Motors Proving Ground in Milford, Michigan, there is a hill with a 30° incline (see figure) for testing tracked vehicles like bulldozers. On this hill, for every meter that a vehicle moves horizontally, how much would it move vertically? 0.6 m

Courtesy Caterpillar Tractor Co.

## construction: a 30-60-90° triangle

**1.** Pick a unit length $AB$ and construct a perpendicular at one endpoint of $\overline{AB}$.

**2.** Extend $\overline{AB}$ and construct $\overline{BC}$ so that $\overline{AB} \cong \overline{BC}$.

**3.** With $A$ as center and radius $AC$, construct an arc intersecting the perpendicular at $D$. $\triangle DAB$ is a 30-60-90° triangle.

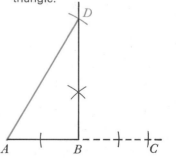

© **41.** Construct a 15° angle. HINT: Construct a 30-60-90° triangle and then bisect one of the angles.

**42.** Construct a 75° angle. HINT: Use the construction in Exercise 41.

**43.** Construct a 105° angle.

# Transformations: Size Changes

In Chapter 10, we discuss figures with the same shape but different sizes. The material in this section will be useful at that time.

©1975, Universal Press Syndicate.

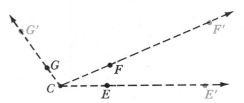

Look at the figure shown at the left. Rays are drawn from point $C$ through $E$, $F$, and $G$. Then points $E'$, $F'$, and $G'$ are marked off so that each one is 3 times as far from $C$ as $E$, $F$, and $G$ are.

We say $E'$, $F'$, and $G'$ are the images of $E$, $F$, and $G$ under a *size change* with magnitude 3 and center $C$. In general,

> Let $C$ be a point and let $k$ be a *positive* real number. For any point $A$, let $A'$ be the point on $\overrightarrow{CA}$ whose distance from $C$ is $k$ times the distance from $C$ to $A$. That is, $A'C = k \cdot AC$. This transformation is called a **size change** with magnitude $k$ and center $C$.

**Example 1:**

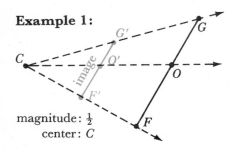

magnitude: $\frac{1}{2}$
center: $C$

**Example 2:**

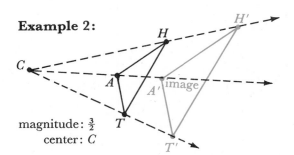

magnitude: $\frac{3}{2}$
center: $C$

Notice that when $k < 1$, the size change is a *contraction*. The image points are closer to the center than the original points are. When $k > 1$, the size change is an *expansion*, and the image points are farther from the center than the original points are.

The preceding examples show that some properties remain the same under a size change. For instance, in Example 1, $G$, $O$, and $F$ are collinear, and their images under the size change are collinear. Also $O$ is between $G$ and $F$, and $O'$ is between $G'$ and $F'$ under the size change.

In Example 2, $\angle H$ and $\angle H'$ have the same measure. So do $\angle A$ and $\angle A'$, as well as $\angle T$ and $\angle T'$.

Consequently, the following should seem reasonable:

Each size change preserves

     **a.** collinearity,    **b.** betweenness, and    **c.** angle measure.

## Exercises 9.7

(A) **1.** In a size change of magnitude 2, the distance from each image point to the center is <u>Twice</u> the distance from each original point to the center.

**2.** $P'$ is the image of $P$ under a size change of magnitude $\frac{1}{4}$, center $A$. If $AP = 4$, then $AP' = $ <u> 1 </u>.

**3.** $E'$ is the image of $E$ under a size change of magnitude 4, center $A$. If $AE' = 8$, then $AE = $ <u> 2 </u>.

**4.** Which of the following properties are *not* preserved under a size change?   b

    **a.** collinearity           **b.** distance           **c.** angle measure

**5.** In a contraction, which point is farther from the center, the image or the original point?   Original point

**6.** A size change with magnitude greater than 1 is called a(n) <u>Expansion</u>.

(B) **7–10.** $C$ is the center of a size change. A point and its image (in orange) are given. Find the magnitude.

**7.**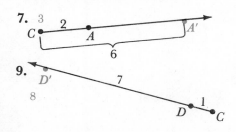

**8.**

**9.**

**10.**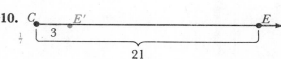

**Assignment Guide**
*Oral:* 1–6
*Written:*
Min. 7–21 odd; Alg. Rev., p. 316, odd
Reg. 7–21 odd; Alg. Rev., p. 316, odd
Max. 7–23

**11–14.** For each exercise, copy the given figure. Draw the image of each point under a size change with center $C$ and the given magnitude.

**11.** 2

**12.** $\frac{1}{2}$

**13.** $\frac{1}{4}$

**14.** $\frac{3}{2}$

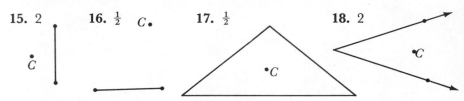

**15–18.** For each exercise, copy the given figure. Draw the image under a size change with center $C$ and the given magnitude.

**15.** 2     **16.** $\frac{1}{2}$     $C$•     **17.** $\frac{1}{2}$     **18.** 2

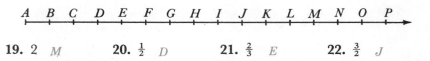

**19–22.** The points $A$ through $P$ are equally spaced on the ray shown. Consider a size change with center $A$. What is the image of $G$ when the transformation has the given magnitude?

$$A \quad B \quad C \quad D \quad E \quad F \quad G \quad H \quad I \quad J \quad K \quad L \quad M \quad N \quad O \quad P$$

**19.** 2  $M$         **20.** $\frac{1}{2}$  $D$         **21.** $\frac{2}{3}$  $E$         **22.** $\frac{3}{2}$  $J$

© **23.** What happens in a size change when $k = 1$? In particular, what are the images of $A$, $B$, $C$, and $D$ under a size change with center $Q$, magnitude 1?

$B$•                    •$D$

•$C$

$A$•                    •$Q$

Each point is its own image.

---

*Algebra Review*

**Review this skill:**

• *reducing fractions to lowest terms*

Reduce each fraction to lowest terms.

**1.** $\frac{2}{4}$  $\frac{1}{2}$     **2.** $\frac{5}{25}$  $\frac{1}{5}$     **3.** $\frac{10}{100}$  $\frac{1}{10}$     **4.** $\frac{36}{81}$  $\frac{4}{9}$

**5.** $\frac{12}{48}$  $\frac{1}{4}$     **6.** $\frac{19}{76}$  $\frac{1}{4}$     **7.** $\frac{3x}{3y}$  $\frac{x}{y}$     **8.** $\frac{4a}{5a}$  $\frac{4}{5}$

**9.** $\frac{16x^2}{24x}$  $\frac{2x}{3}$     **10.** $\frac{5y^3}{15y}$  $\frac{y^2}{3}$     **11.** $\frac{7xy}{49x^4y}$  $\frac{1}{7x^3}$     **12.** $\frac{10a^2b^2}{25a^5b}$

$\frac{2b}{5a^3}$

# ■ Chapter 9 Review ■

**1–4.** Find the area of each rectangle or square. ($\ell$ stands for length, $w$ for width, and $s$ for length of a side of a square.)

**9.1**

Assignment Guide
*Written:* 1–31 odd

**1.** $\ell = 16$ cm, $w = 14$ cm
224 cm²

**2.** $\ell = 3.5$ cm, $w = 20$ mm
7 cm² or 700 mm²

**3.** $s = 1\frac{1}{2}$  $2\frac{1}{4}$

**4.** $s = 5.6$  31.36

**5.** A rectangle has an area of 450 and a length of 25. Find the width.  18

**6–8.** Find the area of each triangle.

**9.2**

**6.** 238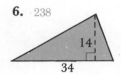

**7.** 90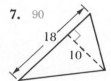

**8.**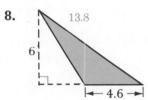

**9–10.** Find the area of each parallelogram.

**9.** $b = 6.3$, $h = 1.9$  11.97

**10.** $b = 3\frac{1}{4}$, $h = 7$  $22\frac{3}{4}$

**11–13.** Find the area of each trapezoid.

**9.3**

**11.**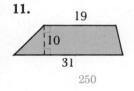
250

**12.**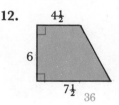
36

**13.**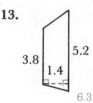

**14–16.** Find the area of each rhombus.

**14.**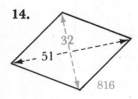
816

**15.**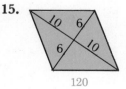
120

**16.**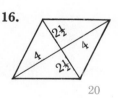
20

**17–20.** Simplify each radical.

**9.4**

**17.** $\sqrt{27}$  $3\sqrt{3}$

**18.** $\sqrt{\frac{5}{36}}$  $\frac{1}{6}\sqrt{5}$

**19.** $\sqrt{\frac{1}{3}}$  $\frac{1}{3}\sqrt{3}$

**20.** $\dfrac{2}{\sqrt{3}}$  $\frac{2}{3}\sqrt{3}$

**21–22.** Use the table on page 562 to find each square root to the nearest tenth. You will first have to simplify each radical.

**21.** $\sqrt{300}$   17.3       **22.** $\sqrt{250}$   15.8

**9.5**

**23–25.** Find the missing length in each right triangle.

**23.** 50

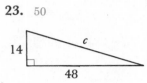

**24.** 20

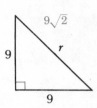

**25.**

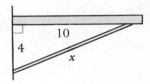

**26.** A carpenter makes a brace for a shelf as shown. How long must the brace be? (Leave the answer in simplified radical form.)   $2\sqrt{29}$

**9.6**

**27–29.** Find the missing lengths.

**27.** $b = 9$, $a = 9\sqrt{3}$

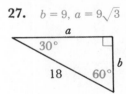

**28.**

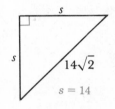

$x = 4\sqrt{3}$, $y = 8$

**29.**

$s = 14$

**30.** A square frame has a diagonal brace as shown. If the square is 30 centimeters on a side, how long is the brace?   $30\sqrt{2}$ cm

**9.7**

**31–32.** $C$ is the center of a size change. A point and its image are given. Find the magnitude.

**31.** 4

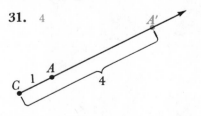

**32.** $\frac{1}{2}$

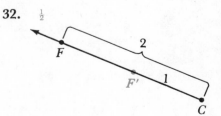

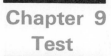

1. A rectangular lot has a length of 38 m and a width of 21 m. Find its area.  798 m²

2. A square is 4.5 m on a side. What is its area?  20.25 m²

3. A triangle has a base of $4\frac{1}{2}$, and its height is 10. What is its area?

$22\frac{1}{2}$

4. A parallelogram has a base of 60, and its height is 73. What is its area?  4380

5. A trapezoid has bases of 32 and 41. The height is 24. Find its area.

876

6. A rhombus has diagonals of $8\frac{1}{2}$ and 16. Find its area.  68

**Assignment Guide**
*Written:* 1–16

 **7–10.** Simplify each radical.

7. $\sqrt{125}$  $5\sqrt{5}$     **8.** $\sqrt{\frac{1}{8}}$  $\frac{1}{4}\sqrt{2}$     **9.** $\sqrt{\frac{64}{81}}$  $\frac{8}{9}$     **10.** $\dfrac{2}{\sqrt{5}}$  $\frac{2}{5}\sqrt{5}$

**11–12.** Use the Pythagorean Theorem to find the missing length in each right triangle.

**11.** 20

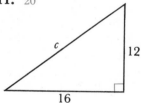

**12.** 30

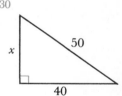

13. Can the lengths of the sides of a right triangle be 27, 36, and 45? Give a reason.     Yes; Converse of Pythagorean Thm.

**14–15.** Find the missing lengths.

**14.** $s = 12, r = 6\sqrt{3}$

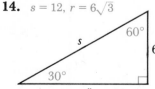

**15.**

16. $C$ is the center of a size change. A point and its image are given. Find the magnitude.  5

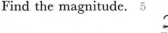

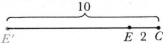

# MINI-CHAPTER: RUBBER-SHEET GEOMETRY

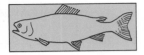

If the picture of a fish at the left were drawn on a rubber sheet, some interesting results would occur if you could stretch, shrink, and distort the sheet (without tearing it).

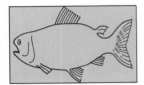  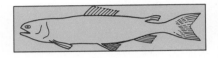

Even though the creatures above are different in many ways, they are still fish.

A whole branch of mathematics called *topology* deals with the ways that surfaces can be twisted, bent, pulled, stretched, or otherwise deformed from one shape into another. A topologist is interested in the properties that remain unchanged after all these transformations have taken place.

When you look at a doughnut and a coffee cup, you probably don't see that they have anything in common. Yet to a topologist, they are equivalent. One could be transformed into the other by twisting, bending, and shaping. But in either case, there is one hole. A topologist would say that both have *genus one*. Notice how some objects that look very different can have the same genus.

GENUS 0 (no holes)     GENUS 1     GENUS 2

Which objects have genus 0? Genus 1? Genus 2? Genus 3 or more?

## EXPERIMENT 1

At a party you may have played a game where you were tied to another person by two cords or ropes as shown in the photograph. The object was to get loose from your partner without untying or cutting the cords. Try it! HINT: Loop your cord under the wrist loop of your partner. Then pull your cord over the hand of your partner.

Frank Kuechmann

## EXPERIMENT 2

A German mathematician named Augustus Moebius discovered an interesting object that has only one surface. It is called a Moebius strip in his honor. To make one, take an ordinary strip of paper. First give the strip a half twist and then connect the ends to form a closed ring.

fig. 1

An ordinary sheet of paper has two surfaces. You could color one side red and the other side green. Use colored pencils and try to color a Moebius strip that way. What happens?

An interesting thing happens if you try to "halve" a Moebius strip. Try it. See figure 1.     Result is 1 large ring.

fig. 2

Next make another Moebius strip and make the cut one third of the way in from the edge. See figure 2. What happens this time?     Result is 1 large ring and 1 small ring linked together.

MINI–CHAPTER: RUBBER–SHEET GEOMETRY     321

Copy the map shown at the left and color it so that no two bordering states have the same color. Use a minimum of colors.

If you use more than four colors, something is wrong. Mapmakers have known for years that only four colors are needed for a flat map.

Yet mathematicians always want to prove things. So for years they looked for a proof of this fact. The four-color map theorem was one of the great unsolved problems in mathematics till just recently. Finally in 1976, a group of mathematicians at the University of Illinois proved that four colors are enough to color any flat map. However, they had to use computers in order to prove it.

## Jordan Curves and Mazes

Would you guess that figures 1 and 2 below have something in common? One is a simple circle. The other is a circle that has been bent out of shape but is still a plane figure that does not intersect itself. We call such a figure a Jordan curve. Like a circle, it has an inside and and an outside. To get from the inside to the outside, the figure must be crossed at least once.

A is inside the circle.

B is actually outside the curve.

fig. 1

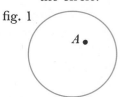

fig. 2

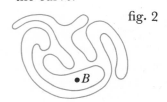

A quick way to tell if a point is inside or outside a Jordan curve is to connect it by a straight line to the outside. If the line crosses the curve an even number of times, the point is outside the curve. If the line crosses the curve an odd number of times, the point is inside the curve.

The figure at the left is a Jordan curve. Decide if points A and B are inside or outside the curve.

A is inside, B is outside.

A maze is another kind of figure that looks like a Jordan curve. However, it is very different because it has an entrance or exit. So a maze can be said to have no inside. All the paths in a maze connect to the outside without crossing any boundaries.

Mazes made of shrubbery were once very popular in Europe. The one shown at the right is in Williamsburg, Virginia. It is a reproduction of the most famous garden maze, at Hampton Court, England.

The maze shown below is a diagram of the Hampton Court maze. The goal is to get to the open area in the center. To get to the center, use this rule: Place either hand on any wall and then take no paths that require you to lift your hand from the wall.

Colonial Williamsburg Foundation

# 10 SIMILAR POLYGONS

You are familiar with objects that have the *same shape* but not the same size—enlargements or reductions of photos, scale models of airplanes or buildings, and so on.

In geometry, figures that are exactly the same shape—whether or not they are the same size—are called **similar figures.**

◆ Some polygons are similar.       ◆ Some triangles are similar.

◆ All squares are similar.        ◆ All equilateral triangles are similar.

*Ratios* are used to compare sizes of similar figures.

# Ratio and Proportion

Suppose your school team won 8 out of 10 meets and lost 2. You might describe their record by using any of these *ratios*:

meets won to total meets: 8 to 10 or $\frac{8}{10}$ or 8:10

meets lost to total meets: 2 to 10 or $\frac{2}{10}$ or 2:10

meets won to meets lost: 8 to 2 or $\frac{8}{2}$ or 8:2

A **ratio** is a comparison of numbers by division. A ratio can be written in any of the ways above, but we will usually use a fraction. Equivalent fractions express **equivalent ratios**.

Photri

**Example 1: a.** $\frac{8}{10} = \frac{4}{5}$ **b.** $\frac{8}{2} = \frac{4}{1}$ **c.** $\frac{2}{3} = \frac{4}{6}$ **d.** $\frac{3}{4} = \frac{6}{8} = \frac{9}{12}$

When a ratio is expressed by a fraction that cannot be reduced, the fraction and the ratio are in *lowest terms*.

A true statement that ratios are equal is a **proportion.** (The equations in the example above are proportions.) Here are some expressions used in talking about proportions. Assume $b \neq 0$ and $d \neq 0$.

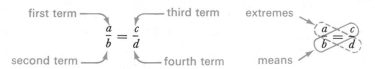

The multiplication and division properties of $=$ can be used to show that, if no term is zero, the five equations below are equivalent.

| Given proportion | Switch means | Switch extremes | Invert both sides | Cross multiply | |
|---|---|---|---|---|---|
| $\frac{a}{b} = \frac{c}{d}$ | $\frac{a}{c} = \frac{b}{d}$ | $\frac{d}{b} = \frac{c}{a}$ | $\frac{b}{a} = \frac{d}{c}$ | $ad = bc$ | In a proportion, the product of the extremes equals the product of the means. |

**Example 2:**

| Given proportion | Switch means | Switch extremes | Invert both sides | Cross multiply |
|---|---|---|---|---|
| $\frac{2}{5} = \frac{4}{10}$ | $\frac{2}{4} = \frac{5}{10}$ | $\frac{10}{5} = \frac{4}{2}$ | $\frac{5}{2} = \frac{10}{4}$ | $2 \cdot 10 = 5 \cdot 4$ |

48. *Sketch of Proof:* Consec.
∠s of □ are supp.,
so corres. ∠s of □s
*ABCD* and *EFGH* are ≅
(Given ∠A ≅ ∠E and
supplements of ≅ ∠s
are ≅). Since opp.
sides of □ are ≅ and
$\frac{AB}{EF} = \frac{BC}{FG}$ (Given),
$\frac{AB}{EF} = \frac{CD}{GH} = \frac{BC}{FG} = \frac{AD}{EH}$
(Subst.).

49. *Sketch of Proof:* □s
are □s, and opp. sides
of □ are ≅, so $\frac{HI}{NO} =$
$\frac{IJ}{OP} = \frac{JK}{PQ} = \frac{KH}{QN}$. All
∠s of □ are rt. ∠s,
so corres. ∠s of *HIJK*
and *NOPQ* are ≅.

If one term of a proportion contains a variable, solving for the variable is called *solving the proportion.*

**Example 3:** Solve.

**a.** $\frac{x}{3} = \frac{4}{5}$

$x = \frac{12}{5}$   Multiply both sides by 3.

**b.** $\frac{y}{5} = \frac{12}{15}$

$\frac{y}{5} = \frac{4}{5}$   Reduce $\frac{12}{15}$.

$y = 4$   Multiply both sides by 5.

**c.** $\frac{2}{n} = \frac{3}{8}$

$16 = 3n$   Cross multiply.

$\frac{16}{3} = n$   Divide both sides by 3.

**d.** $\frac{3m}{4} = \frac{5}{2}$

$3m = 10$   Multiply both sides by 4.

$m = \frac{10}{3}$   Divide both sides by 3.

The properties of equality also let us use any two equations to set up a proportion. Assume $c \neq 0$ and $d \neq 0$.

If $a = b$ and $c = d$, ▶ then $\frac{a}{c} = \frac{b}{d}$.

**Example 4:** If $x = 2$ and $y = 3$, ▶ then $\frac{x}{y} = \frac{2}{3}$.

# Exercises 10.1

**Assignment Guide**
*Oral:* 1–12
*Written:*
Min. (day 1) 13–37 odd
(day 2) 14–38 even
Reg. 13–37 odd
Max. 13–51 odd

Ⓐ **1.** A ratio compares two numbers by ___Division___.

**2.** Equivalent ratios are expressed by equivalent ___Fractions___.

**3.** A ratio in lowest terms is expressed by a ___Fraction___ in lowest terms.

**4–10.** Let $\frac{m}{n} = \frac{5}{3}$.

**4.** This equation is an example of a ___Proportion___.

**5.** The means are ___n, 5___.

**6.** The extremes are ___m, 3___.

**7.** The second term is ___n___.

**8.** The fourth term is ___3___.

**9.** $\frac{3}{n} = \frac{5}{m}$

**10.** $5n = 3m$

**11.** If $\frac{r}{5} = \frac{4}{10}$, then $r = \underline{2}$.

**12.** If $s = 3$ and $4 = t$, then $\frac{s}{4} = \frac{3}{t}$.

**13–16.** Reduce each ratio to lowest terms.

**13.** $\frac{3}{12}$ $\frac{1}{4}$     **14.** $\frac{4}{24}$ $\frac{1}{6}$     **15.** $\frac{28}{50}$ $\frac{14}{25}$     **16.** $\frac{12}{60}$ $\frac{1}{5}$

**17–20.** Write four equivalent equations, as in Example 2.

**17.** $\frac{s}{t} = \frac{4}{5}$     **18.** $\frac{p}{r} = \frac{3}{7}$     **19.** $4g = 3h$     **20.** $7n = 6k$

**21–26.** Use the given equations to find a ratio equivalent to $\frac{x}{y}$.

**21.** $x = 3, y = 7$ $\frac{3}{7}$     **22.** $x = 9, y = 5$ $\frac{9}{5}$     **23.** $x = 12, 5 = y$ $\frac{12}{5}$

**24.** $11 = x, y = 3$ $\frac{11}{3}$     **25.** $2x = 13, 2y = 15$ $\frac{13}{15}$     **26.** $3x = 4, 3y = 7$ $\frac{4}{7}$

**27–38.** Solve.

**27.** $\frac{n}{5} = \frac{3}{8}$ $n = \frac{15}{8}$     **28.** $\frac{r}{6} = \frac{2}{5}$ $r = \frac{12}{5}$     **29.** $\frac{s}{7} = \frac{3}{14}$ $s = \frac{3}{2}$     **30.** $\frac{t}{5} = \frac{7}{15}$ $t = \frac{7}{3}$

**31.** $\frac{4}{m} = \frac{5}{9}$ $m = \frac{36}{5}$     **32.** $\frac{5}{7} = \frac{3}{x}$ $x = \frac{21}{5}$     **33.** $\frac{c}{5} = \frac{24}{18}$ $c = \frac{20}{3}$     **34.** $\frac{d}{3} = \frac{15}{25}$ $d = \frac{9}{5}$

**35.** $\frac{3}{5} = \frac{18}{e}$ $e = 30$     **36.** $\frac{24}{f} = \frac{4}{7}$ $f = 42$     **37.** $\frac{2a}{5} = \frac{4}{7}$ $a = \frac{10}{7}$     **38.** $\frac{5b}{2} = \frac{6}{7}$ $b = \frac{12}{35}$

Ⓒ **39–46.** Let $\frac{a}{c} = \frac{b}{d}$. Show that each statement is true.

**39.** If $a = b$, then $c = d$. Substitute $a$ for $b$ and solve for $c$.     **40.** If $c = d$, then $a = b$.

**41.** If $a = c$, then $b = d$. Substitute $a$ for $c$ and solve for $b$.     **42.** If $b = c$, then $b^2 = ad$.

**43.** $\frac{5a}{c} = \frac{5b}{d}$ Multiply both sides of equation by 5.     **44.** $\frac{3a}{3c} = \frac{b}{d}$ Multiply $\frac{a}{c}$ by 1 in the form $\frac{3}{3}$.

**45.** $\frac{a + c}{c} = \frac{b + d}{d}$     **46.** $\frac{a - c}{c} = \frac{b - d}{d}$

**47–48.** Show that the given proportion lets you conclude that $\frac{a}{c} = \frac{b}{d}$.

**47.** $\frac{a + c}{c} = \frac{b + d}{d}$
Reverse steps for Ex. 45.     **48.** $\frac{a - c}{c} = \frac{b - d}{d}$
Reverse steps for Ex. 46.

**49–52.** Write as a ratio in lowest terms. For example, $3\% = \frac{3}{100}$.

**49.** $23\%$ $\frac{23}{100}$     **50.** $147\%$ $\frac{147}{100}$     **51.** $2.5\%$ $\frac{1}{40}$     **52.** $0.01\%$ $\frac{1}{10000}$

**17.** $\frac{s}{4} = \frac{t}{5}$, **18.** $\frac{p}{3} = \frac{r}{7}$,

$\frac{5}{t} = \frac{4}{s}$,     $\frac{7}{r} = \frac{3}{p}$,

$\frac{t}{s} = \frac{5}{4}$,     $\frac{r}{p} = \frac{7}{3}$,

$5s = 4t$     $7p = 3r$

**19.** $\frac{4}{3} = \frac{h}{g}$, **20.** $\frac{7}{6} = \frac{k}{n}$,

$\frac{4}{h} = \frac{3}{g}$,     $\frac{7}{k} = \frac{6}{n}$,

$\frac{g}{3} = \frac{h}{4}$,     $\frac{n}{6} = \frac{k}{7}$,

$\frac{3}{4} = \frac{g}{h}$     $\frac{6}{7} = \frac{n}{k}$

**40.** Substitute $c$ for $d$ and solve for $a$.

**42.** Substitute $b$ for $c$ and cross multiply.

**45.** 1. $\frac{a}{c} = \frac{b}{d}$

2. $\frac{a}{c} + 1 = \frac{b}{d} + 1$

3. $\frac{a}{c} + \frac{c}{c} = \frac{b}{d} + \frac{d}{d}$

4. $\frac{a + c}{c} = \frac{b + d}{d}$

**46.** Similar to Ex. 45, except subtract 1.

# Dogs prefer the taste of new improved Gravy Train® 3 to 1.

<sub>DOG FOOD</sub>

Photri

In tests, we gave dogs Gravy Train and new improved Gravy Train. And you know what happened? 3 out of 4 dogs preferred the new to the old. That's 3 to 1.

Reprinted courtesy General Foods Corp.

This advertisement compares a new product and an older product from the same company.

Which of the ratios below is $\frac{3}{4}$? Which is $\frac{3}{1}$?   b; a

a. dogs that preferred the new product to dogs that preferred the old product

b. dogs that preferred the new product to total dogs tested

c. total dogs tested to dogs that preferred the old product

If only 4 dogs were tested, how many preferred the new product? The old?
3; 1

If 48 dogs were tested, how many preferred the new product? The old?
36; 12

If 27 of the dogs tested preferred the new product, how many dogs were tested?  36

AN INDUSTRY study shows three out of four buyers of 1977 model cars are equipping them with the larger, often optional V-8 engines. Only one out of five chooses a 6-cylinder engine and one out of 20 a 4-cylinder.

Reprinted courtesy Chicago Tribune

• • •

This newspaper item from early 1977 shows one reason why the world's supply of gasoline is rapidly being used up.

What is the ratio of  a.  V-8 buyers to all buyers?  $\frac{3}{4}$

b.  6-cylinder buyers to all buyers?  $\frac{1}{5}$

c.  4-cylinder buyers to all buyers?  $\frac{1}{20}$

Out of every 20 car buyers, how many buy each type of car?
{ V-8: 15, 6-cylinder: 4, 4-cylinder: 1

What is the ratio of  a.  V-8 buyers to 6-cylinder buyers?  $\frac{15}{4}$

b.  4-cylinder buyers to V-8 buyers?  $\frac{1}{15}$

# What Are Similar Polygons?

**10.2**

Suppose you draw a polygon, photograph it, and then have photo prints of two different sizes made. The photos should show polygons of exactly the same shape. This means that

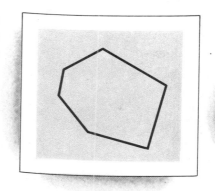

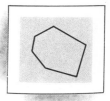

- Any angle of the polygon is the same size on both photos.

- If a side of the polygon on one photo is half as long as on the other photo, all sides compare the same way.

The polygons in the two photos are *similar*.

As in the case of *congruent* polygons, there is a one-to-one correspondence between the vertices of *similar* polygons. This leads to pairs of corresponding angles and pairs of corresponding sides.

is similar to

| ABCDE ~ RSTUV | |
|---|---|
| ∠A and ∠R | $\overline{AB}$ and $\overline{RS}$ |
| ∠B and ∠S | $\overline{BC}$ and $\overline{ST}$ |
| ∠C and ∠T | $\overline{CD}$ and $\overline{TU}$ |
| ∠D and ∠U | $\overline{DE}$ and $\overline{UV}$ |
| ∠E and ∠V | $\overline{EA}$ and $\overline{VR}$ |

corresponding angles

corresponding sides

**Similar polygons** are polygons for which corresponding angles are congruent and the ratios of corresponding sides are equal. NOTE: *Ratio of sides* means "ratio of their lengths."

**Example 1:** △ABC ~ △DEF

| Congruent angles | Equal ratios |
|---|---|
| ∠A ≅ ∠D | $\dfrac{AB}{DE} = \dfrac{8}{6} = \dfrac{4}{3}$ |
| ∠B ≅ ∠E | $\dfrac{BC}{EF} = \dfrac{16}{12} = \dfrac{4}{3}$ |
| ∠C ≅ ∠F | $\dfrac{AC}{DF} = \dfrac{20}{15} = \dfrac{4}{3}$ |

Notice that corresponding vertices are listed above and below one another.

$$\frac{AB}{DE} = \frac{BC}{EF} = \frac{AC}{DF}$$

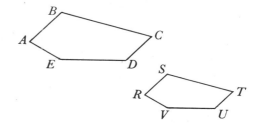

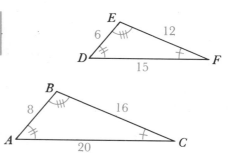

**Example 2:**

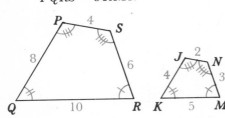

PQRS ~ JKMN

| Congruent angles | Equal ratios |
|---|---|
| $\angle J \cong \angle P$ | $\dfrac{JK}{PQ} = \dfrac{4}{8} = \dfrac{1}{2}$ |
| $\angle K \cong \angle Q$ | $\dfrac{KM}{QR} = \dfrac{5}{10} = \dfrac{1}{2}$ |
| $\angle M \cong \angle R$ | $\dfrac{MN}{RS} = \dfrac{3}{6} = \dfrac{1}{2}$ |
| $\angle N \cong \angle S$ | $\dfrac{NJ}{SP} = \dfrac{2}{4} = \dfrac{1}{2}$ |

$$\dfrac{JK}{PQ} = \dfrac{KM}{QR} = \dfrac{MN}{RS} = \dfrac{NJ}{SP}$$

When the ratios of corresponding sides are equal, as above, we say the sides are **proportional.** The common ratio is called the **ratio of similarity**. In Examples 1 and 2, the ratio of similarity is

| | |
|---|---|
| $\frac{4}{3}$ for $\triangle ABC \sim \triangle DEF$ | $\frac{1}{2}$ for $JKMN \sim PQRS$ |
| $\frac{3}{4}$ for $\triangle DEF \sim \triangle ABC$ | $\frac{2}{1}$ for $PQRS \sim JKMN$ |

If two polygons are congruent, their corresponding angles are congruent. And since corresponding sides have the same length, they are proportional, with ratio of similarity $\frac{1}{1}$. Therefore,

**Theorem** — Congruent polygons are similar polygons.

If two figures are similar and we know the measures of some of their parts, we may be able to find the measures of the other parts.

**Example 3:** If $\triangle MNP \sim \triangle TUV$, find the five missing measures.

1. **∠P** $\angle P$ corresponds to $\angle V$, so $m\angle P = 31$.
2. **∠T** $\angle T$ corresponds to $\angle M$, so $m\angle T = 24$.
3. **∠U** $\angle U$ corresponds to $\angle N$, so $m\angle U = 125$.

4. **MP** Corresponding sides are proportional, so

$$\dfrac{MN}{TU} = \dfrac{MP}{TV}$$

Substitute $\quad \dfrac{10}{15} = \dfrac{n}{24}$

Solve $\quad 240 = 15n$

$$n = 16$$

So $MP = 16$.

5. **UV** Use another proportion.

$$\dfrac{MN}{TU} = \dfrac{NP}{UV}$$

Substitute $\quad \dfrac{10}{15} = \dfrac{8}{t}$

Solve $\quad 10t = 120$

$$t = 12$$

So $UV = 12$.

**Assignment Guide**
*Oral:* 1–14
*Written:*
Min. (day 1) 15–39 odd
    (day 2) 16–40 even
Reg. 15–45 odd
Max. 15–47 odd

Ⓐ **1–14.** Suppose $\triangle KMN \sim \triangle PDR$ and $\dfrac{KM}{PD} = \dfrac{1}{3}$.

**1.** Name the corresponding sides.
$\overline{KM}, \overline{PD}; \overline{MN}, \overline{DR}; \overline{KN}, \overline{PR}$

**2.** Name the congruent angles.
$\angle K, \angle P; \angle M, \angle D; \angle N, \angle R$

**3.** What is the ratio of each side of $\triangle KMN$ to the corresponding side of $\triangle PDR$? $\frac{1}{3}$

**4.** What is the ratio of each side of $\triangle PDR$ to the corresponding side of $\triangle KMN$? $\frac{3}{1}$

**5.** Each side of $\triangle PDR$ is ___3___ times as long as the corresponding side of $\triangle KMN$.

**6.** Each side of $\triangle KMN$ is ___$\frac{1}{3}$___ times as long as the corresponding side of $\triangle PDR$.

**7.** If $KM = 2$, then $PD = $ ___6___.

**8.** If $MN = 5$, then $DR = $ ___15___.

**9.** If $PD = 12$, then $KM = $ ___4___.

**10.** If $PR = 6$, then $KN = $ ___2___.

**11.** If $KN = \frac{1}{3}$, $PR = $ ___1___.

**12.** If $DR = 1$, $MN = $ ___$\frac{1}{3}$___.

**13.** If $m\angle M = 43$, $m$ ___$\angle D$___ $= 43$.

**14.** If $\overline{KN} \perp \overline{MN}$, ___$\overline{PR}$___ $\perp$ ___$\overline{DR}$___.

Ex. 1–14

Ⓑ **15–26.** Refer to the figures.

**15.** For $\triangle AED \sim \triangle ABC$, the ratio of similarity is ___$\frac{3}{4}$___.

**16.** For $\triangle ABC \sim \triangle AED$, the ratio of similarity is ___$\frac{4}{3}$___.

**17.** If $\triangle AED \sim \triangle ABC$, then $AD = $ ___$\frac{3}{4}$___ $\cdot AC$.

**18.** If $\dfrac{AE}{AB} = \dfrac{1}{2}$, then $\triangle AED$ (is, <u>is not</u>) similar to $\triangle ABC$.

**19.** For $RSTV \sim WXTY$, the ratio of similarity is ___$\frac{2}{1}$___.

**20.** For $WXTY \sim RSTV$, the ratio of similarity is ___$\frac{1}{2}$___.

Ex. 15–26

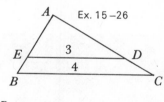

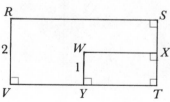

**21.** If $\dfrac{RS}{WX} = \dfrac{3}{2}$, then $RSTV$ (is, <u>is not</u>) similar to $WXTY$.

**22.** If $RSTV \sim WXTY$, then $WX = $ ___$\frac{1}{2}$___ $\cdot RS$.

**23.** If $RSTV \sim WXTY$, then $ST = $ ___2___ $\cdot XT$.

**24.** If $RSTV \sim WXTY$, then $VT = $ ___2___ $\cdot YT$.

**25.** If $WX = 3$ and $RS = 4$, then $RSTV$ (is, <u>is not</u>) similar to $WXTY$.

**26.** If $VT = 6$ and $YT = 3$, then $RSTV$ (<u>is</u>, is not) similar to $WXTY$.

**27–30.** Find all missing measures.

**27.** $u = 24$, $z = 25$,
$m \angle T = 40$, $m \angle V = 57$,
$m \angle Y = 83$

**28.** $c = 32$, $d = 15$,
$m \angle C = 105$, $m \angle D = 46$,
$m \angle E = 29$

**29.** $v = 49$, $x = 24$,
$y = 32$, $m \angle M = 120$,
$m \angle N = 60$, $m \angle S = 90$,
$m \angle T = 90$

**30.** $a = 25$, $n = 48$,
$w = 20$, $m \angle A = 90$,
$m \angle B = 53$, $m \angle V = 127$,
$m \angle W = 90$

**27.** $\triangle TUV \sim \triangle XYZ$

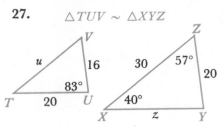

**28.** $\triangle ABC \sim \triangle DEF$

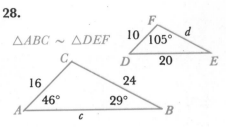

**29.**

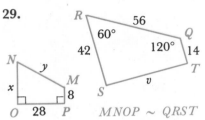

$MNOP \sim QRST$

**30.** $ABCD \sim TUVW$

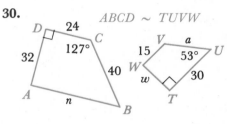

**31.** If a photographic negative 24 mm wide by 35 mm long is enlarged to make a picture 12 cm wide, how long will the picture be? 17.5 cm

**32.** If a photographic negative 24 mm wide by 35 mm long is enlarged to make a picture 28 cm long, how wide will the picture be? 19.2 cm

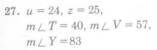

Courtesy Revell, Inc.

**33–40.** The ratio of a full-size car to its scale model is $\frac{25}{2}$. Complete the tables.

| | Corresponding measures | | | | Corresponding measures | |
|---|---|---|---|---|---|---|
| | on car | on model | | | on car | on model |
| **33.** | 2.5 m | 0.2 m | | **34.** | 250 cm | 20 cm |
| **35.** | 225 cm | 18 cm | | **36.** | 0.45 m | 0.036 m |
| **37.** | 90° | 90° | | **38.** | 90° | 90° |
| **39.** | 45° | 45° | | **40.** | $32\frac{1}{2}°$ | $32\frac{1}{2}°$ |

**41–44.** In the figure, $\triangle JPN \sim \triangle JMK$. HINT: Redraw the triangles so they don't overlap.

**41.** If $JP = 3$, $JM = 5$, and $JK = 4$, then $JN = \underline{\quad \frac{12}{5} \quad}$.

**42.** If $PN = 3$, $MK = 5$, and $JN = 2$, then $JK = \underline{\quad \frac{10}{3} \quad}$.

**43.** Find $m \angle M$. 43          **44.** Find $m \angle K$. 69

**45.** Given: $\angle A \cong \angle M$, $\overline{AB} \cong \overline{BC}$,
$\overline{MN} \cong \overline{NP}$, $\dfrac{AB}{MN} = \dfrac{AC}{MP}$

Prove: $\triangle ABC \sim \triangle MNP$

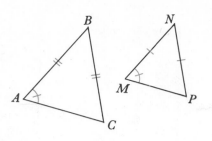

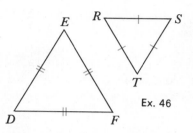

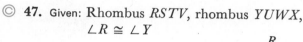

Ex. 46

**46.** Given: $\triangle DEF$ and $\triangle RST$
are equilateral.

Prove: $\triangle DEF \sim \triangle RST$

© **47.** Given: Rhombus $RSTV$, rhombus $YUWX$,
$\angle R \cong \angle Y$

Prove: $RSTV \sim YUWX$

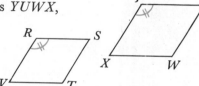

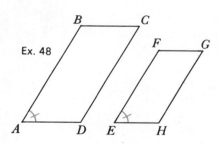

Ex. 48

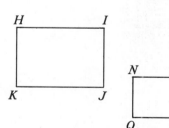

**48.** Given: $\square ABCD$, $\square EFGH$,
$\angle A \cong \angle E$, $\dfrac{AB}{EF} = \dfrac{BC}{FG}$

Prove: $\square ABCD \sim \square EFGH$

**49.** Given: $\square HIJK$, $\square NOPQ$,
$\dfrac{IJ}{OP} = \dfrac{KJ}{QP}$

Prove: $\square HIJK \sim \square NOPQ$

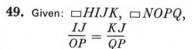

**50.** A tape measure that was originally 20 m long
has stretched uniformly to 20.1 m. This tape
is to be used to lay out a rectangular foundation 8 m wide by 12 m long. What will the
dimensions of the foundation read on the tape?
8.04 m, 12.06 m

**51.** The *pitch* of a roof is found by dividing the rise
by the span. If a roof has pitch $\frac{3}{8}$ and a total
rise of 9 feet, what is the rafter length?   15 ft

Ex. 51

**45.** *Sketch of Proof:* $\triangle ABC$
and $\triangle MNP$ are isos.,
so $\angle A \cong \angle C$, $\angle M \cong$
$\angle P$. Given $\angle A \cong \angle M$,
so $\angle M \cong \angle C$ and $\angle C \cong$
$\angle P$ ($\angle$s $\cong$ to same
$\angle$ are $\cong$) and $\angle B \cong$
$\angle N$ (Third $\angle$s of each
$\triangle$ are $\cong$). $\dfrac{AB}{MN} = \dfrac{AC}{MP}$
(Given) and $AB = BC$,
$MN = NP$ (Def. of $\cong$
segs.), so $\dfrac{BC}{NP} = \dfrac{AC}{MP}$
(Subst.).

**46.** *Sketch of Proof:* Since
$\triangle DEF$ and $\triangle RST$ are
equilateral, $DE =$
$EF = DF$ and $RS =$
$ST = RT$. So $\dfrac{DE}{RS} =$
$\dfrac{EF}{ST} = \dfrac{DF}{RT}$. Each $\angle$ of
both $\triangle$s has meas. 60,
so corres. $\angle$s are $\cong$.

**47.** *Sketch of Proof:* A rhombus has 4 $\cong$ sides, so
$\dfrac{RS}{YU} = \dfrac{ST}{UW} = \dfrac{TV}{WX} = \dfrac{VR}{XY}$.
A rhombus is a $\square$ and
consec. $\angle$s of a $\square$ are
supp., so corres. $\angle$s of
$\square$s $RSTV$ and $YUWX$
are $\cong$ (Given $\angle R \cong \angle Y$
and supplements of $\cong$
$\angle$s are $\cong$).

**48–49.** *Answers on p. 326*

# 10.3  Similar Triangles

Corresponding angles of the triangles shown here are congruent. Do the triangles appear to be similar? Can you draw a triangle that is not similar to these but whose angles are congruent to the angles of these triangles? The next postulate answers this question.

**AAA Similarity Postulate**

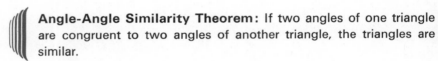

**Angle-Angle-Angle Similarity Postulate:** If the three angles of one triangle are congruent to the three angles of another triangle, the triangles are similar.

But if two angles of one triangle are congruent to two angles of another, the remaining angles are congruent. So one pair of angles mentioned in the postulate above is not needed. That is,

**AA Similarity Theorem**

**Angle-Angle Similarity Theorem:** If two angles of one triangle are congruent to two angles of another triangle, the triangles are similar.

The next two theorems are corollaries of the AA Similarity Theorem.

**Theorem**

In $\triangle ABC$ (see figure below), when line $\ell$ intersects side $\overline{AB}$ at $D$ and side $\overline{BC}$ at $E$,

    **a.** If $\ell \parallel \overline{AC}$, then $\triangle ABC \sim \triangle DBE$.

    **b.** If $\triangle ABC \sim \triangle DBE$, then $\ell \parallel \overline{AC}$.

*Answers for page 336*

**19.** *Given:* $\triangle ABC \sim \triangle DBE$
*Prove:* $\ell \parallel \overline{AC}$
*Proof:*
*1.* $\triangle ABC \sim \triangle DBE$
  (Given)
*2.* $\angle 1 \cong \angle 2$ (Def. of $\sim$ polygons)
*3.* $\ell \parallel \overline{AC}$ (If corres. $\angle$s are $\cong$, lines are $\parallel$.)

**20.** Part **a** is same as proof at right and part **b** is same as Ex. 19, except alt. int. $\angle$s are used in both.

**Part a.**  Given: $\ell \parallel \overline{AC}$

    Prove: $\triangle ABC \sim \triangle DBE$

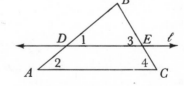

**Proof:**

| STATEMENTS | REASONS |
|------------|---------|
| **1.** $\ell \parallel \overline{AC}$ | **1.** Given |
| **2.** $\angle 1 \cong \angle 2$, $\angle 3 \cong \angle 4$ | **2.** If 2 lines are $\parallel$, corres. $\angle$s are $\cong$. ($\overleftrightarrow{AB}$ is a transversal of $\ell$ and $\overleftrightarrow{AC}$, and so is $\overleftrightarrow{BC}$.) |
| **3.** $\triangle ABC \sim \triangle DBE$ | **3.** AA Similarity Theorem |

This proves part **a** of the theorem. The proof of part **b,** the converse, is Exercise 19.

The proof of the theorem below is outlined in Exercises 21–24.

 Triangles similar to the same triangle are similar to each other.  **Theorem**

## Exercises 10.3

Ⓐ **1.** If $\triangle XYZ \sim \triangle RTS$ and $\triangle HIJ \sim \triangle RTS$, is $\triangle XYZ \sim \triangle HIJ$? Why?

Yes; $\triangle$s $\sim$ to same $\triangle$ are $\sim$.

**2–6.** Refer to the figure.

**2.** If $\overleftrightarrow{DR} \parallel \overleftrightarrow{PM}$, $\triangle PTM \sim \underline{\triangle DTR}$.

**3.** If $\triangle DRT \sim \triangle PMT$, then $\overline{PM} \parallel \underline{\overline{DR}}$.

**4.** If $\triangle DTR \sim \triangle PTM$, then $\dfrac{PT}{DT} = \underline{\dfrac{TM}{TR}} = \underline{\dfrac{PM}{DR}}$.

**5.** If $\angle DRT \cong \underline{\angle M}$, $\triangle RTD \sim \triangle MTP$.

**6.** If $\triangle DTR \sim \triangle PTM$, $\angle TDR \cong \underline{\angle P}$.

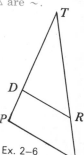

Ex. 2–6

**7.** Which triangles below are similar?   a and d, c and h, e and f

**a.**   **b.**   **c.**   **e.**   **g.**   **h.**

  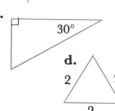 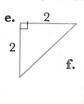 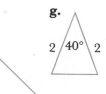 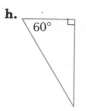

**d.**   **f.**

**8.** Which of these statements result from the AA Similarity Theorem?

**a.** All equilateral triangles are similar.

**b.** All isosceles triangles are similar.

**c.** All right triangles are similar.

**d.** All isosceles right triangles are similar.

**e.** All 30-60-90° triangles are similar.

**Assignment Guide**
*Oral:* 1–8
*Written:*
Min. 9–12; 21–24; Alg.
   Rev., p. 337
Reg. 9–17 odd; 21–24;
   Alg. Rev., p. 337
Max. 9–19 odd; 20–25

*Answers for page 336*

**13.** *1.* $k \parallel n$ (Given)

*2.* $\angle AFD \cong \angle ECD$, $\angle FAD \cong \angle CED$ (If lines are $\parallel$, alt. int. $\angle$s are $\cong$.)

*3.* $\triangle ADF \sim \triangle EDC$ (AA Sim. Thm.)

**14.** *1–3. Same as Ex. 13*

*4.* $\dfrac{DC}{DF} = \dfrac{ED}{AD}$ (Def. of $\sim$ polygons)

**11.** *1.* $\ell \parallel n$ (Given)
   *2.* $\triangle ABD \sim \triangle ACE$ (If line $\parallel$ to 1 side of $\triangle$ intersects other 2 sides, $\sim \triangle$ is formed.)

**12.** *1.* $k \parallel \ell$ (Given)
   *2.* $\triangle BCD \sim \triangle ACF$ (Same as Reason 2 for Ex. 11)

**13–14.** *Answers on p. 335*

**15.** *1.* $\overline{CD} \perp \overline{CT}$, $\overline{BP} \perp \overline{CT}$ (Given)
   *2.* $\overline{CD} \parallel \overline{BP}$ (In plane, lines $\perp$ to same line are $\parallel$.)
   *3.* $\triangle SPR \sim \triangle VDR$ (Same as Reason 2 for Ex. 11)

**16.** *1.* $\overline{RP} \perp \overline{CD}$, $\overline{RP} \perp \overline{BP}$ (Given)
   *2.* $\overline{CD} \parallel \overline{BP}$ (Same as Reason 2 for Ex. 15)
   *3.* $\triangle TSB \sim \triangle TVC$ (Same as Reason 2 for Ex. 11)

**17.** *1.* $\angle 1 \cong \angle 2$ (Given)
   *2.* $\overline{CD} \parallel \overline{BP}$ (If alt. int. $\angle$s are $\cong$, lines are $\parallel$.)
   *3.* $\triangle RDV \sim \triangle RPS$ (Same as Reason 2 for Ex. 11)
   *4.* $\dfrac{RV}{RS} = \dfrac{RD}{RP}$ (Def. of $\sim$ polygons)

**18.** *Answer on page 337*

**19–20.** *Answers on p. 334*

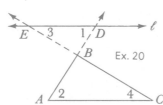

Ex. 20

Ⓑ **9–10.** Which triangles are similar?

**9.**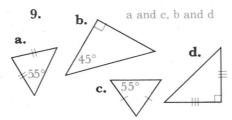

a and c, b and d

**10.**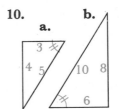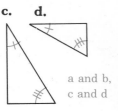

a and b, c and d

**11–18.** Refer to the figures below.

**11.** Given: $\ell \parallel n$

   Prove: $\triangle ABD \sim \triangle ACE$

**12.** Given: $k \parallel \ell$

   Prove: $\triangle BCD \sim \triangle ACF$

**13.** Given: $k \parallel n$

   Prove: $\triangle ADF \sim \triangle EDC$

**14.** Given: $k \parallel n$

   Prove: $\dfrac{DC}{DF} = \dfrac{ED}{AD}$

Ex. 11–14

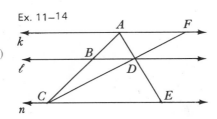

Ex. 15–18

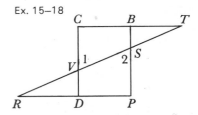

**15.** Given: $\overline{CD} \perp \overline{CT}, \overline{BP} \perp \overline{CT}$

   Prove: $\triangle SPR \sim \triangle VDR$

**16.** Given: $\overline{RP} \perp \overline{CD}, \overline{RP} \perp \overline{BP}$

   Prove: $\triangle TSB \sim \triangle TVC$

**17.** Given: $\angle 1 \cong \angle 2$

   Prove: $\dfrac{RV}{RS} = \dfrac{RD}{RP}$

**18.** Given: $\angle 1 \cong \angle 2$

   Prove: $\dfrac{CT}{BT} = \dfrac{VT}{ST}$

**19.** Prove part **b** of the second theorem on page 334. (Use the figure with part **a.**)

**20.** Prove that the second theorem on page 334 is true if the line intersects the lines containing the sides of the triangle. (See the figure at the left.)

**21–24.** Complete this proof that triangles similar to the same triangle are similar to each other.

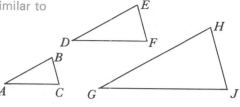

Given: $\triangle ABC \sim \triangle DEF$, $\triangle ABC \sim \triangle GHJ$

Prove: $\triangle DEF \sim \triangle GHJ$

Proof:

| STATEMENTS | | REASONS |
|---|---|---|
| 1. $\angle A \cong \angle D$, $\angle B \cong \angle E$, $\angle A \cong \angle G$, $\angle B \cong \angle H$ | 1. __**21.**__ | Def. of $\sim$ polygons |
| 2. $\angle D \cong \angle G$, $\angle E \cong \angle H$ | 2. __**22.**__ | $\angle$s $\cong$ to same $\angle$ are $\cong$. |
| 3. __**23.**__ $\triangle DEF \sim \triangle GHJ$ | 3. __**24.**__ | AA Sim. Thm. |

© **25.** Why, in the projection system shown, are segments in the image on the screen proportional to segments in the picture? HINT: The picture, lens, and screen are parallel.

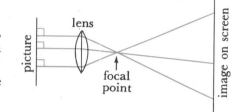

25. The segs. on the picture and at the lens are opp. sides of a ▱ (so they are $\cong$). And the segs. at the lens and on the screen are corres. parts of $\sim$ $\triangle$s.

**26–27.** *Answers on p. 338*

**26.** Prove that if the sides of one triangle are parallel to the sides of another triangle, the triangles are similar. HINT: Use a line containing a side of one triangle both as a transversal and as a line parallel to a side of the other triangle.

**27.** Prove that if the lines containing the sides of one triangle are perpendicular to the lines containing the sides of another triangle, the triangles are similar. HINT: Extend the sides of the triangles to form four right triangles. Use vertical and complementary angles.

*Answer for page 336*
18. 1. $\angle 1 \cong \angle 2$ (Given)
   2. $\overline{CD} \parallel \overline{BP}$ (Same as Reason 2 for Ex. 17)
   3. $\triangle CTV \sim \triangle BTS$ (Same as Reason 2 for Ex. 11)
   4. $\dfrac{CT}{BT} = \dfrac{VT}{ST}$ (Def. of $\sim$ polygons)

---

Simplify.

*Algebra Review*

**1.** $(2x + 5) + (7x + 3)$
$9x + 8$

**2.** $(3y - 2) + (8y + 4)$
$11y + 2$

**3.** $(9n - 3) + (2n - 4)$
$11n - 7$

**4.** $(2a^2 + 4a + 1) + (3a^2 + 7a - 2)$
$5a^2 + 11a - 1$

**5.** $(x^2 - 2) + (3x^2 + 2)$
$4x^2$

**6.** $(c^2 - 2c + 3) + (c - 5)$
$c^2 - c - 2$

**7.** $(5n + 2) - (2n + 5)$
$3n - 3$

**8.** $(4a - 6) - (3a - 2)$
$a - 4$

**9.** $(3y^2 - 5) - (y^2 - 5)$
$2y^2$

**10.** $(6x^2 + 7x - 3) - (2x^2 - 4x + 5)$
$4x^2 + 11x - 8$

**11.** $(6v^2 + 4) - (3v + 2)$
$6v^2 - 3v + 2$

**12.** $(5t^2 - 2t + 3) - (t - 3)$
$5t^2 - 3t + 6$

**Review these skills:**

• adding polynomials

• subtracting polynomials

## 10.4   Proving Triangles Similar

**Suggested Class Time**

| Course | Min. | Reg. | Max. |
|--------|------|------|------|
| Days   | 2    | 1    | 1    |

In earlier chapters, we considered different ways to prove triangles *congruent* (SAS, SSS, ASA, and AAS). In the preceding section, we stated that triangles can be proved *similar* by AAA. But this is more than is needed, since we can prove the AA Similarity Theorem. Now we consider other ways to prove triangles similar.

**SAS Similarity Theorem**

**Side-Angle-Side Similarity Theorem:** If two sides of one triangle are proportional to two sides of another triangle and the included angles are congruent, then the triangles are similar.

*Answers for page 337*

**26.**

*Given:* $\overline{AB} \parallel \overline{DE}$, $\overline{BC} \parallel \overline{EF}$, $\overline{AC} \parallel \overline{DF}$

*Prove:* $\triangle ABC \sim \triangle DEF$

*Sketch of Proof:* $\overline{AC} \parallel \overline{DF}$, so $\triangle DEF \sim \triangle MEN$ (If line $\parallel$ to 1 side of $\triangle$ intersects the other 2 sides, or the lines containing them, $\sim \triangle$ is formed). Given $\overline{AB} \parallel \overline{DE}$ and $\overline{BC} \parallel \overline{EF}$, so $\angle A \cong \angle 1$ and $\angle 2 \cong \angle 3$ (Corres. $\angle$s are $\cong$). $\triangle ABC \sim \triangle MEN$ (AA Sim. Thm.), and $\triangle ABC \sim \triangle DEF$ ($\triangle$s $\sim$ to same $\triangle$ are $\sim$).

**27.**

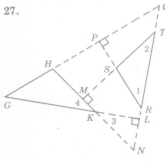

*(Continued on page 339)*

Given: $\dfrac{DE}{AB} = \dfrac{DF}{AC}$, $\angle A \cong \angle D$

Prove: $\triangle ABC \sim \triangle DEF$

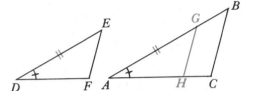

Proof:

| STATEMENTS | REASONS |
|------------|---------|
| 1. On $\overrightarrow{AB}$, let $AG = DE$, so $\overline{AG} \cong \overline{DE}$. | 1. Point Plotting Theorem (p. 27) |
| 2. Through $G$, draw $\overline{GH} \parallel \overline{BC}$. | 2. Parallel Postulate |
| 3. $\triangle AGH \sim \triangle ABC$ | 3. If a line $\parallel$ to one side of a $\triangle$ intersects the other two sides, a similar $\triangle$ is formed. |
| 4. $\dfrac{AG}{AB} = \dfrac{AH}{AC}$ | 4. Definition of similar polygons |
| 5. $\dfrac{DE}{AB} = \dfrac{DF}{AC}$ | 5. Given |
| 6. $\dfrac{AG}{AB} = \dfrac{DF}{AC}$ | 6. Substitution (steps 1 and 5) |
| 7. $\dfrac{AH}{AC} = \dfrac{DF}{AC}$ | 7. Substitution (steps 4 and 6) |
| 8. $AH = DF$, so $\overline{AH} \cong \overline{DF}$. | 8. Multiply both sides by $AC$. |
| 9. $\angle A \cong \angle D$ | 9. Given |
| 10. $\triangle AGH \cong \triangle DEF$ | 10. SAS Postulate (steps 1, 8, and 9) |
| 11. $\triangle AGH \sim \triangle DEF$ | 11. $\cong$ polygons are $\sim$. |
| 12. $\triangle ABC \sim \triangle DEF$ | 12. $\triangle$s $\sim$ to the same $\triangle$ are $\sim$. |

Similar triangles are triangles for which

corresponding angles are congruent  The AAA Postulate says this alone gives similar triangles.

and corresponding sides are proportional. We can now prove that this alone gives similar triangles.

 **Side-Side-Side Similarity Theorem:** If the sides of one triangle are proportional to the corresponding sides of another triangle, the triangles are similar.

SSS Similarity Theorem

Given: $\dfrac{SR}{OM} = \dfrac{ST}{OP} = \dfrac{RT}{MP}$

Prove: $\triangle RST \sim \triangle MOP$

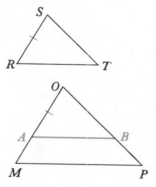

[*Plan:* Let $\overline{OA} \cong \overline{SR}$ and $\overline{AB} \parallel \overline{MP}$. Then $\triangle AOB \sim \triangle MOP$. Use proportions from this similarity and the given information to prove $\triangle RST \cong \triangle AOB$ by SSS.]

The proof of this theorem is in Exercise 39.

Do we need an ASA Similarity Theorem or an AAS Similarity Theorem for triangles? In each of these cases, two pairs of corresponding angles are congruent. This is enough to prove the triangles similar by AA. So neither theorem is needed.

The figures at the right show why triangles *cannot* be proved similar by SSA—just as triangles cannot be proved congruent by SSA.

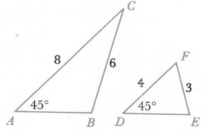

27. (*Continued from p. 338*)
Given: $\overleftrightarrow{TR} \perp \overleftrightarrow{GK}$, $\overleftrightarrow{TS} \perp \overleftrightarrow{HK}$,
$\overleftrightarrow{SR} \perp \overleftrightarrow{HG}$
Prove: $\triangle GHK \sim \triangle RST$
Sketch of Proof: *GLQ, RPQ, TMN,*
*KLN* are rt. $\triangle$s. $\angle$s $G$ and $Q$, 1
and $Q$, 2 and $N$, 3 and $N$ are acute
$\angle$s of rt. $\triangle$s and are complementary
$\angle G \cong \angle 1$, $\angle 2 \cong \angle 3$ (Com-
plements of same $\angle$ are $\cong$), and
$\angle 4 \cong \angle 3$ (Vert. $\angle$s are $\cong$), so
$\angle 4 \cong \angle 2$ ($\angle$s are $\cong$ to same $\angle$),
$\triangle GHK \sim \triangle RST$ by AA Sim. Thm.

$\angle A \cong \angle D$ and $\dfrac{AC}{DF} = \dfrac{BC}{EF}$

But $\triangle ABC \not\sim \triangle DEF$

⎩ is not similar to

# Exercises 10.4

## Assignment Guide
*Oral:* 1–16
*Written:*
Min. (day 1) 17–26
    (day 2) 31–36; Quiz,
    p. 343
Reg. 17–35 odd; Quiz,
    p. 343
Max. 17–35 odd; 39;
    Quiz, p. 343
*Constructions:* 37–38

Ⓐ **1–3.** *Multiple choice:* List *all* possible choices.

    **a.** SAS    **b.** SSS    **c.** ASA    **d.** AAS    **e.** SSA    **f.** AA

**1.** We stated a postulate or theorem for proving triangles congruent by $\underline{\text{a, b, c, d}}$.

**2.** We stated a theorem for proving triangles similar by $\underline{\text{a, b, f}}$.

**3.** Because of the AA Similarity Theorem, a(n) $\underline{\text{c, d}}$ Similarity Theorem is not needed.

**4–10.** State each postulate or theorem.

**4.** SAS Postulate
    *See page 97.*

**5.** SAS Similarity Theorem
    *See page 338.*

**6.** SSS Postulate
    *See page 97.*

**7.** SSS Similarity Theorem
    *See page 339.*

**8.** ASA Postulate
    *See page 97.*

**9.** AA Similarity Theorem
    *See page 334.*

**10.** AAS Theorem
    *See page 178.*

25. 1. $\dfrac{BC}{EC} = \dfrac{AC}{DC}$ (Given)
    2. $\angle ACB \cong \angle DCE$
       (Vert. $\angle$s are $\cong$.)
    3. $\triangle ACB \sim \triangle DCE$
       (SAS Sim. Thm.)

26. 1. $\angle A \cong \angle D$ (Given)
    2. $\angle ACB \cong \angle DCE$
       (Vert. $\angle$s are $\cong$.)
    3. $\triangle ACB \sim \triangle DCE$
       (AA Sim. Thm.)

27. 1. $GF = \frac{1}{2}GC$, $GE = \frac{1}{2}GD$, $EF = \frac{1}{2}DC$
    (Given)
    2. $\dfrac{GF}{GC} = \dfrac{1}{2}$, $\dfrac{GE}{GD} = \dfrac{1}{2}$, $\dfrac{EF}{DC} = \dfrac{1}{2}$ (Divide both sides of each given equation by the same number.)
    3. $\dfrac{GF}{GC} = \dfrac{GE}{GD} = \dfrac{EF}{DC}$ (Subst.)
    4. $\triangle GFE \sim \triangle GCD$ (SSS Sim. Thm.)

**11–16.** Given the figures and the information below, can you conclude that $\triangle ABC \sim \triangle DEF$? If so, by which theorem?

Ex. 11–16

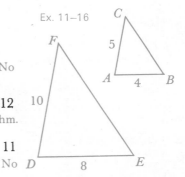

**11.** $\angle A \cong \angle D$
Yes; SAS Sim. Thm.

**12.** $\angle B \cong \angle E$   No

**13.** $\dfrac{BC}{EF} = \dfrac{1}{2}$
Yes; SSS Sim. Thm.

**14.** $BC = 6$, $EF = 12$
Yes; SSS Sim. Thm.

**15.** $\dfrac{BC}{EF} = \dfrac{3}{5}$    No

**16.** $BC = 6$, $EF = 11$    No

Ⓑ **17–18.** Which triangles are similar?

**17.**    a, b, c

**18.** a, b

**19–24.** Given the figures and the information below, can you conclude that $\triangle KMN \sim \triangle RPS$? If so, by which theorem?

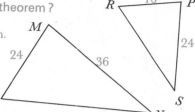

**19.** $m\angle M = 80, m\angle P = 80$  Yes; SAS Sim. Thm.

**20.** $m\angle M = 80, m\angle R = 80$  No

**21.** $m\angle M = 80, m\angle R + m\angle S = 100$
  Yes; SAS Sim. Thm.

**22.** $\dfrac{RS}{KN} = \dfrac{2}{3}$    **23.** $RS = 26, KN = 40$  No
Yes; SSS Sim. Thm.

**24.** $KN = MN, RS = PS$  Yes; SSS Sim. Thm.

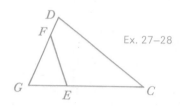

Ex. 25–26

**25.** Given: $\dfrac{BC}{EC} = \dfrac{AC}{DC}$

  Prove: $\triangle ACB \sim \triangle DCE$

**26.** Given: $\angle A \cong \angle D$

  Prove: $\triangle ACB \sim \triangle DCE$

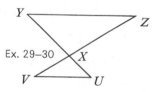

Ex. 27–28

**27.** Given: $GF = \frac{1}{2}GC$,
  $GE = \frac{1}{2}GD$,
  $EF = \frac{1}{2}DC$

  Prove: $\triangle GFE \sim \triangle GCD$

**28.** Given: $GF = \frac{1}{2}DC$,
  $GE = \frac{1}{2}DG$,
  $EF = \frac{1}{2}GC$

  Prove: $\triangle GFE \sim \triangle DCG$

28–30. Ans. on pp. 342–343

**29.** Given: $\overline{YZ} \parallel \overline{UV}$

  Prove: $\dfrac{XY}{XU} = \dfrac{YZ}{UV}$

**30.** Given: $\dfrac{XY}{XU} = \dfrac{XZ}{XV}$

  Prove: $\overline{YZ} \parallel \overline{UV}$

Ex. 29–30

**31–36.** If something cannot be measured directly, it may be possible to find its approximate size by using similar triangles to make an *indirect measurement*, as shown in the figures.

**31.** If the shadow of the tree is 14 m ▶ long and the shadow of the person, who is 1.8 m tall, is 4 m long, how tall is the tree?      6.3 m

**32.** If the shadow of the tree is 20 m long and the shadow of the person, who is 190 cm tall, is 250 cm long, how tall is the tree?      15.2 m

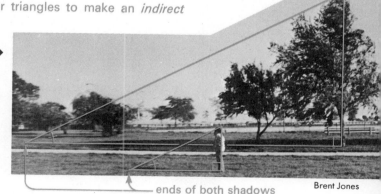

ends of both shadows

Brent Jones

**33.** A pole 3 m high has a shadow 5 m long when the shadow of a nearby building is 110 m long. How tall is the building?  66 m

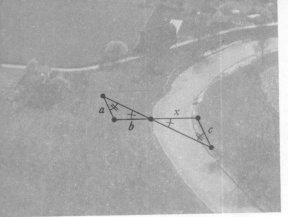

**34.** A flagpole 4 m high has a shadow 6 m long when the shadow of a nearby monument is 45 m long. How tall is the monument?  30 m

◄ **35.** By measurement, $a = 9$ m, $b = 15$ m, and $c = 12$ m. How long is $x$?  20 m

◄ **36.** By measurement, $a = 8$ m, $b = 12$ m, and $c = 15$ m. How long is $x$?  22.5 m

**37–38.** *Constructions:* Use the SAS Similarity Theorem as a basis for the construction. Then repeat the construction using the SSS Similarity Theorem.

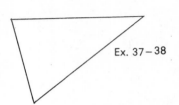

Ex. 37–38

**37.** Construct $\triangle XYZ \sim \triangle RST$ so that $XY = 2RS$.
*See pages 36 and 100.*

**38.** Construct $\triangle XYZ \sim \triangle RST$ so that $XY = 3RS$.
*See pages 36 and 100.*

© **39.** Copy the figure and restatement of the SSS Similarity Theorem on page 339. Then complete the proof.

| Proof:  STATEMENTS | REASONS |
|---|---|
| *1.* On $\overrightarrow{OM}$, let $OA = SR$, so $\overline{OA} \cong \overline{SR}$. | 1. _____ On $\overrightarrow{OM}$ there is exactly 1 pt. $A$ whose distance from $O$ is a given pos. no. |
| **2.** Through $A$, draw $\overline{AB} \parallel \overline{MP}$. | 2. _____ Parallel Post. (p. 125) |
| **3.** $\triangle AOB \sim \triangle MOP$ | 3. _____ If line $\parallel$ to 1 side of $\triangle$ intersects other 2 sides, $\sim \triangle$ is formed. |
| **4.** $\dfrac{OA}{OM} = \dfrac{OB}{OP} = \dfrac{AB}{MP}$ | 4. _____ Def. of $\sim$ polygons |
| **5.** $\dfrac{SR}{OM} = \dfrac{ST}{OP} = \dfrac{RT}{MP}$ | 5. _____ Given |
| **6.** $\dfrac{OA}{OM} = \dfrac{SR}{OM}$ | 6. Divide both sides of $OA = SR$ by $OM$ (see step 1). |
| **7.** $\dfrac{OB}{OP} = \dfrac{ST}{OP}, \dfrac{AB}{MP} = \dfrac{RT}{MP}$ | 7. _____ Subst. (steps 4–6) |
| **8.** $OB = ST$, so $\overline{OB} \cong \overline{ST}$. $AB = RT$, so $\overline{AB} \cong \overline{RT}$. | 8. _____ Mult. both sides of 1st equation in step 7 by $OP$, 2nd equation by $MP$. |
| **9.** $\triangle RST \cong \triangle AOB$ | 9. _____ SSS Post. (steps 1 and 8) |
| **10.** $\triangle RST \sim \triangle AOB$ | 10. _____ $\cong$ polygons are $\sim$. |
| **11.** $\triangle RST \sim \triangle MOP$ | 11. _____ $\triangle$s $\sim$ to same $\triangle$ are $\sim$ (steps 3 and 10). |

*Answers for page 341*

**28.** *1.* $GF = \frac{1}{2}DC$, $GE = \frac{1}{2}DG$, $EF = \frac{1}{2}GC$ (Given)

2. $\dfrac{GF}{DC} = \dfrac{1}{2}, \dfrac{GE}{DG} = \dfrac{1}{2}, \dfrac{EF}{GC} = \dfrac{1}{2}$ (Divide both sides of each given equation by the same number.)

3. $\dfrac{GF}{DC} = \dfrac{GE}{DG} = \dfrac{EF}{GC}$ (Subst.)

4. $\triangle GFE \sim \triangle DCG$ (SSS Sim. Thm.)

**29.** *1.* $\overline{YZ} \parallel \overline{UV}$ (Given)

2. $\angle Y \cong \angle U$, $\angle Z \cong \angle V$ (If lines are $\parallel$, alt. int. $\angle$s are $\cong$.)

3. $\triangle XYZ \sim \triangle XUV$ (AA Sim. Thm.)

4. $\dfrac{XY}{XU} = \dfrac{YZ}{UV}$ (Def. of $\sim$ polygons)

**1–5.** Let $\dfrac{3}{n} = \dfrac{5}{x}$.

**1.** Name the means. $\;n, 5$      **2.** Name the extremes. $\;3, x$

**3.** The given equation is an example of a $\underset{n}{\underline{\text{Proportion}}}$.

**4.** $3x = \underline{\;\;5n\;\;}$          **5.** $\frac{3}{5} = \underline{\;\;\frac{n}{x}\;\;}$

**6.** Solve: $\dfrac{5}{4} = \dfrac{t}{12}$   $t = 15$      **7.** If $p = 2$ and $6 = r$, $\dfrac{p}{6} = \underline{\;\;\frac{2}{r}\;\;}$

**8–11.** For $\triangle PDC \sim \triangle RST$, the ratio of similarity is $\frac{2}{3}$.

**8.** $\dfrac{PD}{RS} = \underline{\;\;\frac{2}{3}\;\;}$      **9.** If $m\angle S = 35$, $\underline{\;\;m\angle D\;\;} = 35$.

**10.** $\dfrac{RT}{PC} = \underline{\;\;\frac{3}{2}\;\;}$      **11.** If $DC = 6$, then $ST = \underline{\;\;9\;\;}$.

**12–14.** State each similarity theorem.

**12.** AA *See page 334.*    **13.** SAS *See page 338.*    **14.** SSS *See page 339.*

## GET THE PICTURE?

GEOMETRY AROUND YOU

Each picture on a strip of motion-picture film is called a *frame*. When the picture is projected onto a flat screen, parallel to the film plane, the outlines of the frame and of the projected picture are similar rectangles. The ratio of frame height to frame width depends on the type of camera and the film size. Some frame ratios are shown below. Notice that 16 mm film is used for both commercial and home movies.

| film size | commercial movies | | | home movies |
| | wide screen | | normal screen | |
| | 70 mm | 35 mm | 35 mm, | 16 mm, 8 mm |
|---|---|---|---|---|
| frame height<br>frame width | $\frac{2}{5}$ | $\frac{4}{7}$ | | $\frac{3}{4}$ |

If the picture is to fit the screen closely, how wide does a screen of the given height have to be for each frame ratio above?

**1.** 9 m   22.5 m; 15.75 m; 12 m    **2.** 10 m   25 m; 17.5 m; 13.34 m    **3.** 7 m   17.5 m; 12.25 m; 9.34 m    **4.** 18.4 m   46 m; 32.2 m; 24.54 m

When a movie is shown on television, part of the picture may be lost because the outline of the screen on the TV set is not similar to the outline of the film frame. Two commonly used height-to-width ratios for TV screens are $\frac{3}{4}$ and $\frac{4}{5}$. Which is best for showing normal-screen movies? For 70 mm wide-screen movies? For 35 mm wide-screen movies?

$\frac{3}{4}$ TV screen ratio is best for showing all movies.

*Answer for page 341.*

**30.** 1. $\dfrac{XY}{XU} = \dfrac{XZ}{XV}$ (Given)
   2. $\angle YXZ \cong \angle UXV$ (Vert. $\angle$s are $\cong$.)
   3. $\triangle XYZ \sim \triangle XUV$ (SAS Sim. Thm.)
   4. $\angle Y \cong \angle U$ (Def. of $\sim$ polygons)
   5. $\overline{YZ} \parallel \overline{UV}$ (If alt. int. $\angle$s are $\cong$, lines are $\parallel$.)

# 10.5 Similar Right Triangles

In Chapter 5, we considered special theorems for proving *right* triangles *congruent* (LL, HL, HA, and LA). There are also special ways to prove that *right* triangles are *similar*.

**LL Similarity Theorem**

**Leg-Leg Similarity Theorem**: If the legs of one right triangle are proportional to the legs of another right triangle, then the triangles are similar.

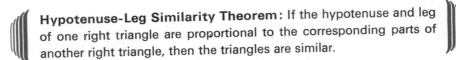

Given: $\angle C$ and $\angle F$ are right angles,
$$\frac{AC}{DF} = \frac{BC}{EF}$$

Prove: $\triangle ABC \sim \triangle DEF$

Proof:

| STATEMENTS | REASONS |
|------------|---------|
| 1. $\angle C$ and $\angle F$ are rt. $\angle$s. | 1. Given |
| 2. $\angle C \cong \angle F$ | 2. All rt. $\angle$s are $\cong$. |
| 3. $\dfrac{AC}{DF} = \dfrac{BC}{EF}$ | 3. Given |
| 4. $\triangle ABC \sim \triangle DEF$ | 4. SAS Similarity Theorem |

The next theorem is proved in Exercise 44.

**HL Similarity Theorem**

**Hypotenuse-Leg Similarity Theorem**: If the hypotenuse and leg of one right triangle are proportional to the corresponding parts of another right triangle, then the triangles are similar.

Do we need an HA Similarity Theorem or an LA Similarity Theorem for right triangles? In each of these cases, a pair of acute angles are congruent. Since the right angles are also congruent, the two triangles are similar by AA. So neither of these theorems is needed. We can, however, prove two other theorems about right-triangle similarity.

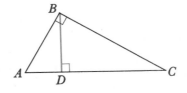

An altitude to the hypotenuse of a right triangle forms two smaller right triangles. They may not look much like the original triangle, but they are in fact the same shape. The three triangles are shown separately in the next figure.

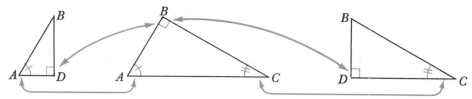

The right angles are congruent.

The common angles are congruent.

So, by the AA Similarity Theorem, $\triangle ADB \sim \triangle ABC \sim \triangle BDC$. That is,

right angles ↓

common angles

 In a right triangle, the sides and the altitude to the hypotenuse form two triangles that are similar to the given triangle and to each other. **Theorem**

Since the triangles are similar, corresponding sides are proportional.

$$\triangle ADB \sim \triangle BDC \qquad \triangle ABC \sim \triangle BDC \qquad \triangle ADB \sim \triangle ABC$$

corresponding sides ▶ $\dfrac{AD}{BD} = \dfrac{BD}{CD}$ $\qquad \dfrac{AC}{BC} = \dfrac{BC}{DC}$ $\qquad \dfrac{AD}{AB} = \dfrac{AB}{AC}$

corresponding sides ▶

When both *means* of a proportion are the same number, as in the proportions above, that number is called the **geometric mean** of the extremes. The three proportions can now be described in one theorem.

 For any right triangle and the altitude to its hypotenuse,

**a.** The altitude is the geometric mean of the segments into which it separates the hypotenuse.

**b.** Each leg is the geometric mean of the hypotenuse and the adjacent segment of the hypotenuse.

**Theorem**

**Examples:**

**1.**

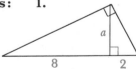

$\dfrac{2}{a} = \dfrac{a}{8}$    By part **a** above

$a^2 = 16$    Cross multiply.

$a = 4$    Take the (positive) square root of both sides.

**2.**

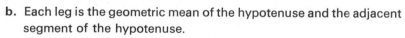

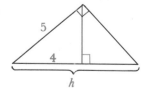

$\dfrac{4}{5} = \dfrac{5}{h}$    By part **b** above

$4h = 25$    Cross multiply.

$h = \frac{25}{4}$    Divide both sides by 4.

# Exercises 10.5 ▏▎▌▌▊▊▋▊▊▊▎▌▎▊▍▊▊▊▍▊▊▍▊▊▎▊▊▎▊▊▍▊▊▍▊▊▍▎▊▊▎▌▍▎▊▍▎▍

**Assignment Guide**
*Oral:* 1–18
*Written:*
Min. 19–26; 27–31 odd
Reg. 19–26; 27–31 odd
Max. 19–26; 27–31 odd; 43–44
*Constructions:* 33–42

Ⓐ **1–3.** *Multiple choice:* List *all* possible choices.

**a.** LL      **b.** HL      **c.** HA      **d.** LA

**1.** We stated a theorem for proving right triangles congruent by $\underline{\text{a, b, c, d}}$.

**2.** We stated a theorem for proving right triangles similar by $\underline{\text{a, b}}$.

**3.** Because of the AA Similarity Theorem, a(n) $\underline{\text{c, d}}$ Similarity Theorem is not needed.

**4–9.** State each theorem.

**4.** LL Theorem
   *See page 186.*

**5.** LL Similarity Theorem
   *See page 344.*

**6.** HL Theorem
   *See page 186.*

**7.** HL Similarity Theorem
   *See page 344.*

**8.** HA Theorem
   *See page 185.*

**9.** LA Theorem
   *See page 185.*

**10–15.** Given the figures and the information below, can you conclude that $\triangle ABC \sim \triangle DEF$? If so, by which theorem?

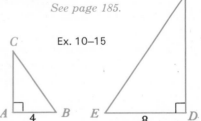
Ex. 10–15

**10.** $\dfrac{AC}{DF} = \dfrac{1}{2}$
   Yes; LL Sim. Thm.

**11.** $\dfrac{BC}{EF} = \dfrac{1}{2}$
   Yes; HL Sim. Thm.

**12.** $\dfrac{AC}{DF} = \dfrac{3}{5}$
   No

**13.** $AC = 5$, $DF = 10$
   Yes; LL Sim. Thm.

**14.** $\angle B \cong \angle E$
   Yes; AA Sim. Thm.

**15.** $BC = 6$, $EF = 12$
   Yes; HL Sim. Thm.

**16–18.** Refer to the figure.

Ex. 16–18

**16.** $\dfrac{e}{h} = \dfrac{?}{f}$   $h$

**17.** $\dfrac{e}{a} = \dfrac{?}{e+f}$   $a$

**18.** $\dfrac{f}{?} = \dfrac{?}{e+f}$   $b; b$

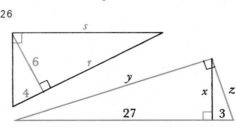
Ex. 19–26

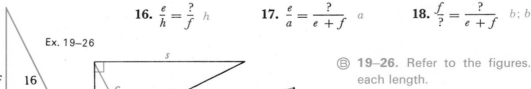

Ⓑ **19–26.** Refer to the figures. Find each length.

**19.** $a$       **20.** $x$       **21.** $b$       **22.** $y$
   8            9          $4\sqrt{5}$      $9\sqrt{10}$

**23.** $c$       **24.** $z$       **25.** $r$       **26.** $s$
   $8\sqrt{5}$      $3\sqrt{10}$      9          $3\sqrt{13}$

27–30. *Answers on p. 348*

**27.** **Given:** $\angle Y$ and $\angle V$ are rt. $\angle$s.
**Prove:** $\triangle XYZ \sim \triangle XVW$

Ex. 27

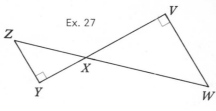

**28.** **Given:** $\overline{AC} \perp \overline{DE}$, $\dfrac{AC}{BC} = \dfrac{DC}{EC}$
**Prove:** $\triangle ADC \sim \triangle BEC$

Ex. 28–30

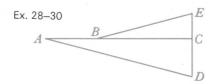

**29.** **Given:** $\overline{AC} \perp \overline{DE}$, $\dfrac{AD}{BE} = \dfrac{DC}{EC}$
**Prove:** $\triangle ADC \sim \triangle BEC$

**30.** **Given:** $\overline{AC} \perp \overline{DE}$, $\angle D \cong \angle E$
**Prove:** $\triangle ACD \sim \triangle BCE$

**31.** The person is 166 cm tall and stands 90 cm from the mirror. If the mirror is 495 cm from the base of the tower, how high is the tower?        913 cm

Ex. 31–32

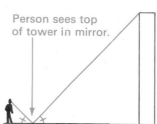

Person sees top of tower in mirror.

**32.** The person is 160 cm tall and stands 120 cm from the mirror, which is 675 cm from the base of the tower. How high is the tower?        900 cm

Brent Jones

## construction: **the geometric mean of two segments**

**1.** Given:
$\overline{AB}, \overline{CD}$

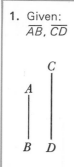

**2.** On any line $\ell$, construct $\overline{A'B'} \cong \overline{AB}$ and $\overline{B'D'} \cong \overline{CD}$. Construct $\overrightarrow{B'P} \perp \overline{A'D'}$ at $B'$.

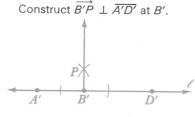

**3.** Construct $M$, the midpoint of $\overline{A'D'}$. From $M$, mark off $\overline{MT} \cong \overline{MD'}$. $\angle A'TD'$ is a right angle.

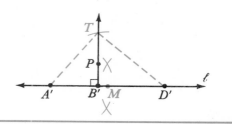

**33–36.** Refer to right $\triangle A'TD'$ in step 3 above.

**33.** The geometric mean of $A'B'$ and $B'D'$ is ___TB'___.

**34.** The geometric mean of $A'B'$ and $A'D'$ is ___TA'___.

**35.** The geometric mean of $B'D'$ and $A'D'$ is ___TD'___.

**36.** The geometric mean of $AB$ and $CD$ in step 1 is ___TB'___.

**37–40.** Draw $\overline{MN}$, $\overline{RS}$, and $\overline{TV}$ so that $MN = 8$ cm, $RS = 5$ cm, and $TV = 3$ cm. Then construct the geometric mean of the lengths listed.

**37.** $MN, RS$   **38.** $MN, TV$   **39.** $MN + TV, RS$   **40.** $MN + RS, TV$

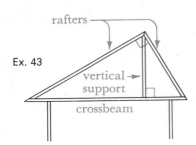

Ex. 43

rafters

vertical support

crossbeam

Ⓒ **41–42.** For the lengths listed, identify the geometric mean in one of the constructions for Exercises 37–40.

**41.** *MN + RS, MN*
In Ex. 37, length of longer leg

**42.** *MN + TV, TV*
In Ex. 38, length of shorter leg

**43.** The rafters of this roof meet at a right angle. The vertical support is 15 feet long and rests on a 34-foot crossbeam. How far from the ends of the crossbeam is the base of the support?  25 ft and 9 ft

**44.** Copy and complete this proof of the HL Similarity Theorem.

Given: $\angle C$ and $\angle F$ are right angles,
$$\frac{DE}{AB} = \frac{DF}{AC}$$

Prove: $\triangle ABC \sim \triangle DEF$

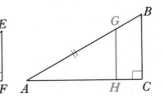

**Proof:**

| STATEMENTS | REASONS |
|---|---|
| 1. On $\overrightarrow{AB}$, let $AG = DE$, so $\overline{AG} \cong \overline{DE}$. | 1. Point Plotting Theorem (p. 27) |
| 2. Through $G$, draw $\overline{GH} \parallel \overline{BC}$. | 2. <u>Parallel</u> Post. (p. 125) |
| 3. $\triangle AGH \sim \triangle ABC$ | 3. <u>_____</u> If line $\parallel$ to 1 side of $\triangle$ intersects other 2 sides, $\sim \triangle$ is formed. |
| 4. $\angle GHA \cong \angle C$ | 4. <u>Def. of $\sim$</u> polygons |
| 5. $\angle GHA$ is a rt. $\angle$. | 5. Def. of $\cong \angle$s and given $\angle C$ is a rt. $\angle$. |
| 6. $\frac{AG}{AB} = \frac{AH}{AC}$ | 6. <u>Def. of $\sim$</u> polygons |
| 7. $\frac{DE}{AB} = \frac{DF}{AC}$ | 7. <u>Given</u> |
| 8. $\frac{AG}{AB} = \frac{DF}{AC}$ | 8. Subst. (steps 1 and 7) |
| 9. $\frac{AH}{AC} = \frac{DF}{AC}$ | 9. <u>Subst.</u> (steps 6 and 8) |
| 10. $AH = DF$, so $\overline{AH} \cong \overline{DF}$. | 10. <u>Multiply</u> both sides of equation in step 9 by $AC$. |
| 11. $\triangle AGH \cong \triangle DEF$ | 11. HL Theorem (steps 1 and 10) |
| 12. $\triangle AGH \sim \triangle DEF$ | 12. <u>$\cong$ polygons</u> are $\sim$. |
| 13. $\triangle ABC \sim \triangle DEF$ | 13. <u>$\triangle$s $\sim$ to same $\triangle$ are $\sim$</u> (steps 3 and 12). |

# MECHANICS AND REPAIRERS

One of the fastest growing groups of skilled workers includes mechanics and repairers—the people who keep cars, airplanes, home appliances, and other machinery working properly. These workers are trained in vocational and technical schools or on the job, often in apprenticeship programs.

Employers look for high-school graduates who have courses in mathematics, chemistry, physics, blueprint reading, and machine shop.

Mechanics and repairers must often use diagrams to recognize repair parts. A knowledge of similar figures can be helpful.

Can you match the parts in each photo with the diagram?

10, 13, 17–20

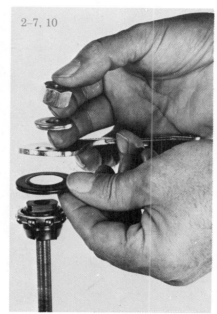

2–7, 10

Copyright, Schwinn Bicycle Co., Chicago, Ill.

8, 11, 12

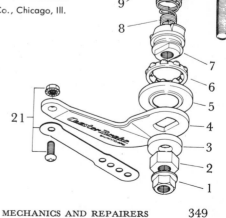

# 10.6 Triangle Similarity Summarized

| Suggested Class Time | | | |
|---|---|---|---|
| Course | Min. | Reg. | Max. |
| Days | 1 | 1 | 1· |

**TRIANGLES CAN BE PROVED SIMILAR BY**

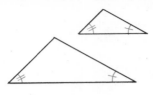

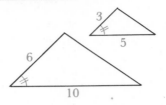

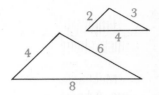

| Angle-Angle Similarity Theorem | Side-Angle-Side Similarity Theorem | Side-Side-Side Similarity Theorem |
|---|---|---|

**RIGHT TRIANGLES CAN BE PROVED SIMILAR BY**

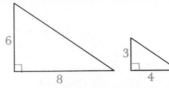

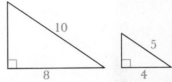

Leg-Leg Similarity Theorem          Hypotenuse-Leg Similarity Theorem

Triangles **cannot** be proved similar by Side-Side-Angle.

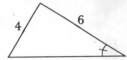

We also saw that certain cases for which we stated a congruence postulate or theorem (ASA, AAS, HA, and LA) did not have to be extended to similarity. These cases are covered by the AA Similarity Theorem.

**Assignment Guide**
*Oral:* 1–6
*Written:* Min. 7–9
        Reg. 7–10
        Max. 7–11

# Exercises 10.6

7. *1.* $\overline{WX} \parallel \overline{YZ}$ (Given)
  *2.* $\angle XWY \cong \angle WYZ$, $\angle WXZ \cong \angle XZY$ (If lines are ∥, alt. int. ∠s are ≅.)
  *3.* $\triangle WNX \sim \triangle YNZ$ (AA Sim. Thm.)

8. *1.* $\square HIJK$ (Given)
  *2.* $\angle K$, $\angle J$ are rt. ∠s. ($\square$ has 4 rt. ∠s.)
  *3.* $\triangle HRK$, $\triangle RIJ$ are rt. △s. (Def. of rt. △)

*(Continued on page 351)*

Ⓐ **1–6.** Using the given information, which theorem can be used to prove $\triangle ABC \sim \triangle DEF$?

**1.** $\angle A \cong \angle D$, $\angle C \cong \angle F$
    AA Sim. Thm.

**2.** $\dfrac{AB}{DE} = \dfrac{BC}{EF} = \dfrac{AC}{DF}$   SSS Sim. Thm.

**3.** $\dfrac{BC}{EF} = \dfrac{AC}{DF}$, $\angle C \cong \angle F$   SAS Sim. Thm.

Ex. 1–6

**4.** $\angle C$ and $\angle F$ are rt. ∠s, $\dfrac{AB}{DE} = \dfrac{BC}{EF}$
    HL Sim. Thm.

**5.** $\angle C$ and $\angle F$ are rt. ∠s, $\angle B \cong \angle E$
    AA Sim. Thm.

**6.** $\angle C$ and $\angle F$ are rt. ∠s, $\dfrac{AC}{DF} = \dfrac{BC}{EF}$
    LL Sim. Thm.

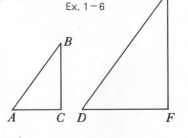

**7. Given:** Trapezoid $WXYZ$ with $\overline{WX} \parallel \overline{YZ}$

**Prove:** $\triangle WNX \sim \triangle YNZ$

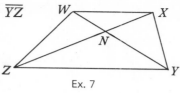

Ex. 7

**8. Given:** $\square HIJK$, $\dfrac{HR}{RI} = \dfrac{RK}{IJ}$

**Prove:** $\triangle HRK \sim \triangle RIJ$

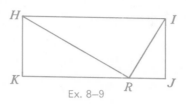

Ex. 8–9

**9. Given:** $\square HIJK$, $\dfrac{HI}{RH} = \dfrac{IR}{HK} = \dfrac{RH}{KR}$

**Prove:** $\angle HRI$ is a rt. $\angle$.

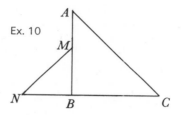

Ex. 10

**10. Given:** $\overline{AB} \perp \overline{NC}$ at $B$, $\dfrac{BN}{BC} = \dfrac{BM}{BA}$

**Prove:** $\angle N \cong \angle C$

**11. Given:** $R$ is the midpoint of $\overline{XY}$, $S$ is the midpoint of $\overline{ZY}$.

**Prove:** $\triangle RYS \sim \triangle XYZ$

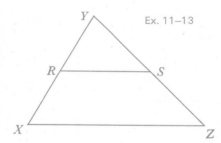

Ex. 11–13

**12. Given:** $\dfrac{RY}{XY} = \dfrac{SY}{ZY}$

**Prove:** $\triangle RYS \sim \triangle XYZ$

**13. Given:** $XY = \tfrac{5}{2}RY$, $ZY = \tfrac{5}{2}SY$

**Prove:** $\triangle RYS \sim \triangle XYZ$

**14. Given:** $\square FGHI$

**Prove:** $\triangle HGJ \sim \triangle KIH$

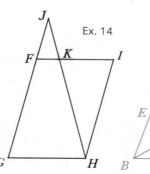

Ex. 14

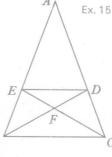

Ex. 15

© **15. Given:** $\triangle ADB \cong \triangle AEC$

**Prove:** $\triangle ABC \sim \triangle AED$

**8.** *(Continued from page 350)*
4. $\dfrac{HR}{RI} = \dfrac{RK}{IJ}$ (Given)
5. $\triangle HRK \sim \triangle RIJ$ (HL Sim. Thm.)

**9.** 1. $\dfrac{HI}{RH} = \dfrac{IR}{HK} = \dfrac{RH}{KR}$ (Given)
2. $\triangle HRI \sim \triangle RKH$ (SSS Sim. Thm.)
3. $m\angle HRI = m\angle RKH$ (Def. of $\sim$ polygons)
4. $HIJK$ is a $\square$. (Given)
5. $m\angle RKH = 90$ ($\square$ has 4 rt. $\angle$s.)
6. $m\angle HRI = 90$ (Subst.)
7. $\angle HRI$ is a rt. $\angle$. (Def. of rt. $\angle$)

**10.** 1. $\overline{AB} \perp \overline{NC}$ (Given)
2. $\angle MBN$, $\angle ABC$ are rt. $\angle$s. (Def. of $\perp$)
3. $\triangle MBN$, $\triangle ABC$ are rt. $\triangle$s. (Def. of rt. $\triangle$)
4. $\dfrac{BN}{BC} = \dfrac{BM}{BA}$ (Given)
5. $\triangle MBN \sim \triangle ABC$ (LL Sim. Thm.)
6. $\angle N \cong \angle C$ (Def. of $\sim$ polygons)

**11.** 1. $R$, $S$ are midpts. of $\overline{XY}$, $\overline{ZY}$. (Given)
2. $\overline{RS}$ is midline of $\triangle XYZ$. (Def. of midline)
3. $\overline{RS} \parallel \overline{XZ}$ (Midline of $\triangle$ is $\parallel$ to base.)
4. $\triangle RYS \sim \triangle XYZ$ (If line $\parallel$ to side of $\triangle$ intersects other 2 sides, $\sim \triangle$ is formed.)

**12.** *Sketch of Proof:* Using given and $\angle Y \cong$ to itself, $\triangle RYS \sim \triangle XYZ$ by SAS Sim. Thm.

**13–15.** *Ans. on pp. 356–357*

# 10.7 Parallel Lines, Proportional Segments

On page 154, we proved that if a line parallel to one side of a triangle bisects either of the other two sides, it bisects both of them. Now we will show that no matter where this parallel line intersects the other two sides, the corresponding segments on the sides are proportional.

Gene Kuechmann

**Suggested Class Time**

| Course | Min. | Reg. | Max. |
|--------|------|------|------|
| Days   | 1    | 1    | 1    |

*Answer for page 355*

**39.** *Reverse order of statements at right. Add step 6.*

1. *Given*
2. *Add 1 to both sides.*
3. *Def. of + of fractions*
4. *Def. of between*
5. *Substitution*
6. *(∠A ≅ ∠A) ∠ is ≅ to itself.*
7. *SAS Sim. Thm.*
8. *Part **b**, 2nd Thm., p. 334*

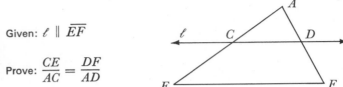

Given: $\ell \parallel \overline{EF}$

Prove: $\dfrac{CE}{AC} = \dfrac{DF}{AD}$

Proof: STATEMENTS | REASONS

1. $\ell \parallel \overline{EF}$ | 1. Given
2. $\triangle AEF \sim \triangle ACD$ | 2. If a line $\parallel$ to 1 side of a $\triangle$ intersects the other 2 sides, a $\sim \triangle$ is formed.
3. $\dfrac{AE}{AC} = \dfrac{AF}{AD}$ | 3. Definition of $\sim$ polygons
4. $AE = AC + CE$, $AF = AD + DF$ | 4. Definition of between
5. $\dfrac{AC + CE}{AC} = \dfrac{AD + DF}{AD}$ | 5. Substitution (steps 3 and 4)
6. $\dfrac{AC}{AC} + \dfrac{CE}{AC} = \dfrac{AD}{AD} + \dfrac{DF}{AD}$ | 6. Definition of addition of fractions
7. $\dfrac{CE}{AC} = \dfrac{DF}{AD}$ | 7. Subtract 1 from both sides. $\left(\dfrac{AC}{AC} = \dfrac{AD}{AD} = 1\right)$

The converse of the statement proved above can also be proved (see Exercise 39). The two are combined here in one theorem.

**Proportional Segments Theorem for a Triangle**

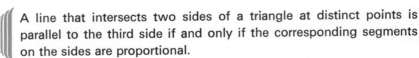

A line that intersects two sides of a triangle at distinct points is parallel to the third side if and only if the corresponding segments on the sides are proportional.

The next theorem is a corollary of the one above.

**Proportional Segments Theorem for Parallels**

Three parallel lines intercept proportional corresponding segments on any two transversals.

Given: $k \parallel \ell \parallel n$, transversals $s$ and $t$

Prove: $\dfrac{AC}{CE} = \dfrac{BD}{DF}$

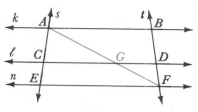

**Proof:**

| STATEMENTS | REASONS |
|---|---|
| **1.** Join $A$ and $F$. | **1.** 2 points determine a line. |
| **2.** In $\triangle AEF$, $\dfrac{AC}{CE} = \dfrac{AG}{GF}$.<br><br>In $\triangle FBA$, $\dfrac{BD}{DF} = \dfrac{AG}{GF}$. | **2.** Proportional Segments Theorem for a $\triangle$ |
| **3.** $\dfrac{AC}{CE} = \dfrac{BD}{DF}$ | **3.** Substitution |

The Proportional Segments Theorem for Parallels can be extended to any number of parallel lines and any number of transversals. But when there are more than two segments on each transversal, fractions are not the best way to express the ratios. For example,

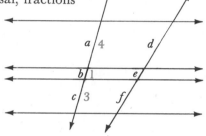

The ratios can be described by using fractions $\quad \dfrac{a}{b} = \dfrac{4}{1}, \dfrac{b}{c} = \dfrac{1}{3}, \dfrac{a}{c} = \dfrac{4}{3}$

or by using **continued ratios.** $\quad a:b:c = 4:1:3$

If the lines are parallel, $\qquad a:b:c = d:e:f = 4:1:3.$

Continued ratios can be used to set up proportions to be solved, but care must be taken to use *corresponding terms*.

**Example:** If $d:e:f = 4:1:3$ and $e = 1.5$, find $d$ and $f$.

$d{:}e{:}f = 4{:}1{:}3 \quad \dfrac{d}{e} = \dfrac{4}{1}$ ◀ Write a proportion. ▶ $\dfrac{e}{f} = \dfrac{1}{3} \quad d{:}e{:}f = 4{:}1{:}3$

$\dfrac{d}{1.5} = \dfrac{4}{1}$ ◀ Substitute 1.5 for $e$. ▶ $\dfrac{1.5}{f} = \dfrac{1}{3}$

$d = 6$ ◀ Solve the proportion. ▶ $f = 4.5$

# Exercises 10.7

Ⓐ **1.** Compare the lengths of the segments on $r$, in the second figure above. Are the segments in the ratio $4:1:3$? Yes

**2.** Compare the lengths of the segments on $s$, $t$, and $\overleftrightarrow{AF}$, at the top of the page. Do the results seem to agree with the theorem? Yes

*Assignment Guide*
*Oral:* 1–14
*Written:*
Min. 15–27 odd
Reg. 15–27 odd
Max. 15–27 odd; 39–41
*Constructions:* 29–38

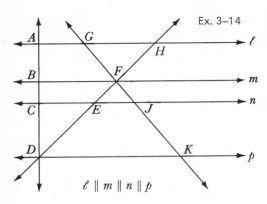

Ex. 3–14

$\ell \parallel m \parallel n \parallel p$

**3–5.** For each segment, name the corresponding segments on the other transversals in the figure.

**3.** $\overline{AB}$     **4.** $\overline{FJ}$     **5.** $\overline{ED}$
$\overline{GF}, \overline{HF}$     $\overline{BC}, \overline{FE}$     $\overline{CD}, \overline{JK}$

**6–9.** Refer to the figure. Name two ratios equal to the given ratio.

**6.** $\dfrac{HF}{FE}$    **7.** $\dfrac{GF}{FK}$    **8.** $\dfrac{CD}{AC}$    **9.** $\dfrac{DE}{EF}$

$\dfrac{AB}{BC}, \dfrac{GF}{FJ}$   $\dfrac{AB}{BD}, \dfrac{HF}{FD}$   $\dfrac{ED}{HE}, \dfrac{JK}{GJ}$   $\dfrac{DC}{CB}, \dfrac{KJ}{JF}$

**10–12.** Refer to the figure. State a proportion for all sides of the given triangles.

**10.** $\triangle DAH, \triangle DBF$     **11.** $\triangle DCE, \triangle DAH$     **12.** $\triangle DFK, \triangle EFJ$
$\dfrac{DA}{DB} = \dfrac{AH}{BF} = \dfrac{HD}{FD}$    $\dfrac{DC}{DA} = \dfrac{CE}{AH} = \dfrac{ED}{HD}$    $\dfrac{DF}{EF} = \dfrac{FK}{FJ} = \dfrac{KD}{JE}$

**13.** Use the figure to name two continued ratios equal to $AB:BC:CD$.
$GF:FJ:JK$ and $HF:FE:ED$

**14.** If $KJ:JF:FG = 3:1:2$, what other segments in the figure are in this same continued ratio?
$DC:CB:BA$ and $DE:EF:FH$

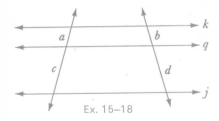

Ex. 15–18

Ⓑ **15–18.** If $k \parallel q \parallel j$ in the figure, use the given information to find the length of the fourth segment.

**15.** $a = 3, b = 2, c = 6$
$d = 4$
**16.** $b = 3, c = 12, d = 9$
$a = 4$

**17.** $c = 6\frac{2}{3}, d = 5, b = 3$
$a = 4$
**18.** $b = 2, a = 3, c = 7\frac{1}{2}$
$d = 5$

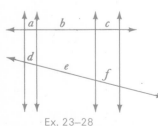

Ex. 19–22

**19–22.** $r \parallel s \parallel t$ in the figure.

**19.** If $AB = 2$, $BC = 5$, and $EB = 3$, $BD = \underline{\quad 7\frac{1}{2} \quad}$.

**20.** If $BD = 6$, $BE = 3$, and $BC = 5$, $AB = \underline{\quad 2\frac{1}{2} \quad}$.

**21.** If $BE = 3$, $DE = 8$, and $EG = 10$, $EF = \underline{\quad 3\frac{3}{4} \quad}$.

**22.** If $EF = 3$, $BE = 2$, and $EG = 12$, $ED = \underline{\quad 8 \quad}$.

Ex. 23–28

**23–28.** The vertical lines in the figure are parallel; $a:b:c = 1:5:2$.

**23.** If $a = 3$, find $b$ and $c$. $b = 15$, **24.** If $c = 4$, find $a$ and $b$. $a = 2$,
$c = 6$          $b = 10$

**25.** $e:f:d = \underline{\quad 5:2:1 \quad}$     **26.** $f:e:d = \underline{\quad 2:5:1 \quad}$

**27.** If $e = 2.5$, find $d$ and $f$.     **28.** If $f = 0.5$, find $d$ and $e$.
$d = 0.5, f = 1$          $d = 0.25, e = 1.25$

# construction: separate a segment into segments in a given ratio

| | | |
|---|---|---|
| **1.** Given: Any segment $\overline{AB}$ to be separated into segments in the ratio 4:3:1 | **2.** Construct $\overrightarrow{AP}$. Mark off $4 + 3 + 1$ or 8 congruent segments on $\overrightarrow{AP}$, starting at $A$. | **3.** Join $B$ and $C$. At the end of 4 segments on $\overrightarrow{AP}$ construct a parallel to $\overline{BC}$. Count off 3 more segments and construct a parallel to $\overline{BC}$. |

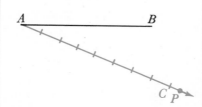
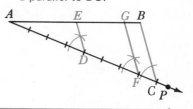

**29.** How is it decided how many congruent segments to mark off on $\overrightarrow{AP}$?

Add terms in ratio.

**30.** Why isn't a parallel to $\overline{BC}$ constructed at every point marked on $\overrightarrow{AP}$?

Unnecessary

**31.** How are the points chosen at which to construct parallels?

Endpts. of segs. on $\overline{AC}$ that are in given ratio

**32.** Why is $AE:EG:GB = 4:3:1$?

∥ lines intercept proportional corres. segs. on $\overline{AC}$ and $\overline{AB}$.

**33–38.** Construct a segment of the given length. Then use the construction above to separate it into segments in the given ratio.

**33.** 6 cm, 4:2:1    **34.** 9 cm, 2:3:2    **35.** 10 cm, 2:3:4

**36.** 11 cm, 2:5:3    **37.** 12 cm, 2:3:5:4    **38.** 13 cm, 3:2:4:5

© **39.** Prove that if a line intersects two sides of a triangle at distinct points so that the corresponding segments on the sides are proportional, then the line is parallel to the third side. HINT: Copy the figure on page 352; interchange the *Given* and *Prove*; reverse the order of the statements (but one more statement is needed).

*Answer on page 352*

**40.** Two nonenlarging projection systems are shown. Explain why, in each case, ratios of segments in the image on the screen are equal to the ratios of segments in the picture.

∥ lines intercept transversals at proportional segs.

**41.** Prove that the bisector of an angle of a triangle separates the opposite side into segments proportional to the sides they intersect.

HINT: Let $\overleftrightarrow{AE} \parallel \overline{CD}$. Write a proportion using lengths of segments on $\overline{BE}$ and $\overline{BA}$. Then prove $CE = CA$.

**41.** *Given:* $\triangle ABC$, $\overrightarrow{CD}$ is bis. of $\angle ACB$.

*Prove:* $\dfrac{BC}{BD} = \dfrac{CA}{DA}$

*Sketch of Proof:* By ∥ Post., let $\overleftrightarrow{AE} \parallel \overleftrightarrow{CD}$, then $\dfrac{BC}{CE} = \dfrac{BD}{DA}$ (Prop. Segs. Thm. for △s).

$\angle 1 \cong \angle 3$, $\angle 2 \cong \angle 4$ (Alt. int., corres. ∠s), $\angle 1 \cong \angle 2$ (Def. of ∠ bis.), so $\angle 3 \cong \angle 4$ (∠s $\cong$ to same ∠ are $\cong$). Sides opp. $\cong$ ∠s of △ are $\cong$, so $CE = CA$, $\dfrac{BC}{CA} = \dfrac{BD}{DA}$ (Subst.), and $\dfrac{BC}{BD} = \dfrac{CA}{DA}$ (Switch means).

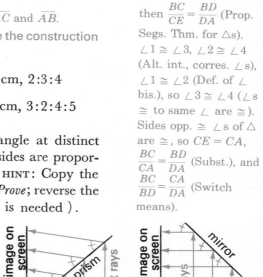

image on screen    prism    light rays

picture    Ex. 40

image on screen    mirror    light rays

picture

Ex. 41

# Areas of Similar Figures

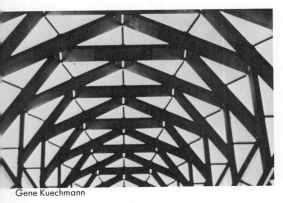

Gene Kuechmann

Some of the oldest puzzle problems in geometry have to do with "doubling" the size of a figure. Choose a small triangle in the photograph. Then try to choose a triangle that is twice as large.

The puzzle, of course, is in the words. When is one triangle *twice as large as* another? When its sides are twice as long? Or when its area is twice as large? Do these mean the same or different things?

In the figures below, let $\triangle ABC \sim \triangle DEF$.

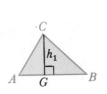

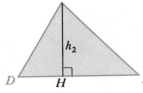

$$\text{area } \triangle ABC = \tfrac{1}{2}AB \cdot h_1$$

$$\text{area } \triangle DEF = \tfrac{1}{2}DE \cdot h_2$$

$$\frac{\text{area } \triangle ABC}{\text{area } \triangle DEF} = \frac{\tfrac{1}{2}AB \cdot h_1}{\tfrac{1}{2}DE \cdot h_2}$$

$$= \frac{AB}{DE} \cdot \frac{h_1}{h_2}$$

*Answers for page 351*

**13.** *1.* $XY = \tfrac{5}{2}RY$, $ZY = \tfrac{5}{2}SY$ (Given)

*2.* $\dfrac{XY}{RY} = \dfrac{5}{2}$, $\dfrac{ZY}{SY} = \dfrac{5}{2}$ (Divide both sides of each given equation by same number.)

*3.* $\dfrac{XY}{RY} = \dfrac{ZY}{SY}$ (Subst.)

*4.* $\angle Y \cong \angle Y$ ($\angle$ is $\cong$ to itself.)

*5.* $\triangle RYS \sim \triangle XYZ$ (SAS Sim. Thm.)

**14.** *1.* $\square FGHI$ (Given)

*2.* $\overline{FI} \parallel \overline{GH}$, $\overline{GF} \parallel \overline{HI}$ (Def. of $\square$)

*3.* $\angle IKH \cong \angle GHJ$, $\angle KHI \cong \angle J$ (If lines are $\parallel$, alt. int. $\angle$s are $\cong$.)

*4.* $\triangle HGJ \sim \triangle KIH$ (AA Sim. Thm.)

But $\triangle BGC \sim \triangle EHF$ by the AA Similarity Theorem, so $\dfrac{h_1}{h_2} = \dfrac{BC}{EF}$

We are given that $\triangle ABC \sim \triangle DEF$, so $\dfrac{BC}{EF} = \dfrac{AB}{DE}$

By substitution, $\dfrac{h_1}{h_2} = \dfrac{AB}{DE}$

Substituting this last result in the area proportion above, we have

$$\frac{\text{area } \triangle ABC}{\text{area } \triangle DEF} = \left(\frac{AB}{DE}\right)^2 \quad \text{and} \quad \frac{\text{area } \triangle ABC}{\text{area } \triangle DEF} = \left(\frac{h_1}{h_2}\right)^2$$

In fact, if $\overline{CG}$ and $\overline{FH}$ were corresponding medians or angle bisectors or any other corresponding segments related to the triangles, they would have the same ratio as the altitudes. So the ratio of the areas equals the square of the ratio of *any* two corresponding segments related to the triangles.

In the figures on page 357, $d$ and $e$ are lengths of the corresponding diagonals of similar quadrilaterals. The corresponding triangles can be proved similar using the SAS Similarity Theorem.

So $\dfrac{\text{area } \triangle MNO}{\text{area } \triangle QRS} = \left(\dfrac{d}{e}\right)^2 = \dfrac{d^2}{e^2}$ and $\dfrac{\text{area } \triangle MPO}{\text{area } \triangle QTS} = \left(\dfrac{d}{e}\right)^2 = \dfrac{d^2}{e^2}$

Cross multiply ▶ $e^2(\text{area } \triangle MNO) = d^2(\text{area } \triangle QRS)$

$e^2(\text{area } \triangle MPO) = d^2(\text{area } \triangle QTS)$

$e^2(\text{area } \triangle MNO) + e^2(\text{area } \triangle MPO) = d^2(\text{area } \triangle QRS) + d^2(\text{area } \triangle QTS)$

$e^2(\text{area } \triangle MNO + \text{area } \triangle MPO) = d^2(\text{area } \triangle QRS + \text{area } \triangle QTS)$

$e^2(\text{area } MNOP) = d^2(\text{area } QRST)$

$\dfrac{\text{area } MNOP}{\text{area } QRST} = \dfrac{d^2}{e^2} = \left(\dfrac{d}{e}\right)^2$

This reasoning can be extended to similar polygons with any number of sides, using any two corresponding segments, so we have this theorem:

 The ratio of the areas of two similar polygons is the square of the ratio of any two corresponding segments.

**Ratio of Areas Theorem**

**Examples:** $\triangle ABC \sim \triangle DEF$ (See the figure on page 356.)

**1.** If $AB = 6$ and $DE = 9$, find $\dfrac{\text{area } \triangle ABC}{\text{area } \triangle DEF}$.

$\dfrac{\text{area } \triangle ABC}{\text{area } \triangle DEF} = \left(\dfrac{AB}{DE}\right)^2$

$= \left(\dfrac{6}{9}\right)^2$

$= \left(\dfrac{2}{3}\right)^2 = \dfrac{4}{9}$

**2.** If area $\triangle ABC = 50$ and area $\triangle DEF = 128$, find $\dfrac{BC}{EF}$.

$\left(\dfrac{BC}{EF}\right)^2 = \dfrac{\text{area } \triangle ABC}{\text{area } \triangle DEF}$

$= \dfrac{50}{128}$

$= \dfrac{25}{64}$

So, $\dfrac{BC}{EF} = \sqrt{\dfrac{25}{64}} = \dfrac{\sqrt{25}}{\sqrt{64}} = \dfrac{5}{8}$

**3.** If $AC = 8$, $DF = 12$, and area $\triangle ABC = 80$, find area $\triangle DEF$.

$\dfrac{\text{area } \triangle ABC}{\text{area } \triangle DEF} = \left(\dfrac{AC}{DF}\right)^2$ ▶ $\dfrac{80}{\text{area } \triangle DEF} = \left(\dfrac{8}{12}\right)^2$ ▶ $\dfrac{80}{\text{area } \triangle DEF} = \left(\dfrac{2}{3}\right)^2$

$\dfrac{80}{\text{area } \triangle DEF} = \dfrac{4}{9}$

$4(\text{area } \triangle DEF) = 720$

$\text{area } \triangle DEF = 180$

# Exercises 10.8

**Assignment Guide**
*Oral:* 1–12
*Written:*
Min. 13–18; Alg. Rev.,
    p. 359, odd
Reg. 13–23 odd; Alg. Rev.,
    p. 359, odd
Max. 13–25 odd

Ⓐ **1–2.** Refer to $\triangle ABC$ and $\triangle DEF$, page 356. Why is the statement true?

**1.** $\angle BGC \cong \angle EHF$
All rt. $\angle$s are $\cong$.

**2.** $\angle B \cong \angle E$
Def. of $\sim$ polygons

**3–7.** Refer to the figures and equations at the top of page 357.

**3.** Why are corresponding angles at $N$ and $R$ and at $P$ and $T$ congruent?
Def. of $\sim$ polygons

**4.** Why are corresponding sides of $\triangle MNO$ and $\triangle QRS$, as well as of $\triangle MPO$ and $\triangle QTS$, proportional?
Def. of $\sim$ polygons

**5.** What five pairs of lengths besides $d$ and $e$ could have been used?

$$5.\ \frac{MN}{QR}, \frac{NO}{RS}, \frac{OP}{ST}, \frac{PM}{TQ}, \frac{NP}{RT}$$

**6.** If $NP = 3$ and $RT = 5$, find the ratio of the areas. $\frac{9}{25}$

**7.** If the areas are 16 and 25, find the ratio of corresponding sides. $\frac{4}{5}$

**8–12.** Let $ABCDE$ and $MNOPR$ be similar polygons. Give your answers in lowest terms.

**8.** If $BC = 1$ and $NO = 3$, find the ratio of the areas. $\frac{1}{9}$

**9.** If $BC = 2$ and $NO = 4$, find the ratio of the areas. $\frac{1}{4}$

**10.** If the areas are 9 and 16, find the ratio of corresponding sides. $\frac{3}{4}$

**11.** If the areas are 4 and 5, find the ratio of corresponding sides. $\frac{2}{\sqrt{5}} = \frac{2\sqrt{5}}{5}$

**12.** If the areas are 10 and 20, find the ratio of corresponding sides. $\frac{1}{\sqrt{2}} = \frac{\sqrt{2}}{2}$

**26.** *1.* $\triangle DAB \sim \triangle CPE$,
corres. $\angle$ bisectors
$\overrightarrow{AN}$ and $\overrightarrow{PT}$ (Given)

*2.* $m\angle D = m\angle C$,
$m\angle DAB = m\angle CPE$
(Def. of $\sim$ polygons)

*3.* $\frac{1}{2}m\angle DAB = \frac{1}{2}m\angle CPE$
(Mult. both sides of
equation by $\frac{1}{2}$.)

*4.* $m\angle DAN = \frac{1}{2}m\angle DAB$,
$m\angle CPT = \frac{1}{2}m\angle CPE$
(Def. of $\angle$ bis.)

*5.* $m\angle DAN = m\angle CPT$
(Subst.)

*6.* $\triangle DAN \sim \triangle CPT$
(AA Sim. Thm.)

*7.* $\frac{AN}{PT} = \frac{AD}{PC}$ (Def. of
$\sim$ polygons)

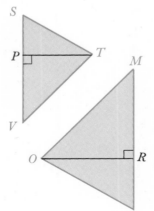

Ⓑ **13–18.** In the figure, $\triangle STV \sim \triangle LOM$. Use the given information to find the missing values.

| | $\dfrac{ST}{LO}$ | area $\triangle STV$ | area $\triangle LOM$ | $TP$ | $OR$ |
|---|---|---|---|---|---|
| **13.** | $\frac{3}{5}$ ? | 45 | 125 | ? 6 | 10 |
| **14.** | $\frac{4}{7}$ ? | 32 | 98 | ? 8 | 14 |
| **15.** | $\frac{5}{6}$ | ? 50 | 72 | 10 | ? 12 |
| **16.** | $\frac{3}{4}$ | ? 27 | 48 | 9 | ? 12 |
| **17.** | $\frac{5}{3}$ ? | 50 | ? 18 | 20 | 12 |
| **18.** | $\frac{4}{5}$ ? | 48 | ? 75 | 12 | 15 |

**19–20.** Refer to the figure for Exercises 13–18. Let $\triangle STV \sim \triangle LOM$. Find the ratio of corresponding medians in lowest terms.

**19.** area $\triangle STV = 20$    $\dfrac{\sqrt{5}}{3}$     **20.** area $\triangle STV = 45$    $\dfrac{\sqrt{15}}{4}$
     area $\triangle LOM = 36$             area $\triangle LOM = 48$

**21–24.** Let $RSTUV$ and $KMNOP$ be similar polygons.

**21.** If $RS = \sqrt{3}$ and $KM = 2\sqrt{2}$, the ratio of the areas is $\underline{\quad}^{\frac{3}{8}}\underline{\quad}$.

**22.** If $UV = 2\sqrt{5}$ and $OP = \sqrt{11}$, the ratio of the areas is $\underline{\quad}^{\frac{20}{11}}\underline{\quad}$.

**23.** If the areas are 124 and 225, the ratio of corresponding sides is $\underline{\quad}^{\frac{2\sqrt{31}}{15}}\underline{\quad}$.

**24.** If the areas are 125 and 169, the ratio of corresponding diagonals is $\underline{\quad}^{\frac{5\sqrt{5}}{13}}\underline{\quad}$.

© **25.** Given: $\triangle MOP \sim \triangle QRS$, corresponding medians $\overline{OK}$ and $\overline{RL}$

     Prove: $\dfrac{OK}{RL} = \dfrac{OM}{RQ}$    *Answer on page 360*

**26.** Given: $\triangle DAB \sim \triangle CPE$, corresponding angle bisectors $\overrightarrow{AN}$ and $\overrightarrow{PT}$

     Prove: $\dfrac{AN}{PT} = \dfrac{AD}{PC}$    *Answer on page 358*

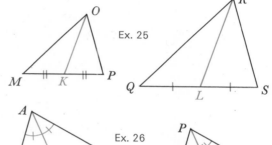
Ex. 25

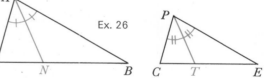
Ex. 26

---

Divide as indicated.

**1.** $\dfrac{5x^2 + 15x}{5x}$   $x + 3$

**2.** $\dfrac{3n^3 - n^2}{n^2}$   $3n - 1$

**3.** $\dfrac{y^4 + y^2 + y}{y}$   $y^3 + y + 1$

**4.** $\dfrac{12a^3 - 4a^2}{-2a^2}$   $-6a + 2$

**5.** $\dfrac{8r^3 + 3r}{4r}$   $2r^2 + \frac{3}{4}$

**6.** $\dfrac{14m^2n^2 - 21mn}{7mn}$   $2mn - 3$

**7.** $\dfrac{18a^3b^4 + 12a^2b^3}{6ab^2}$   $3a^2b^2 + 2ab$

**8.** $\dfrac{x^2 + 4x + 4}{x + 2}$   $x + 2$

**9.** $\dfrac{y^2 + 3y - 28}{y - 4}$   $y + 7$

**10.** $\dfrac{6s^2 - 5s + 1}{2s - 1}$   $3s - 1$

**11.** $\dfrac{t^3 - 7t + 6}{t - 2}$   $t^2 + 2t - 3$

**12.** $\dfrac{27y^2 + 3y + 4}{3y + 1}$

**13.** $(x^3 + 3x^2 + 3x + 1) \div (x + 1)$   $x^2 + 2x + 1$

**14.** $(x^3 - 8) \div (x - 2)$   $x^2 + 2x + 4$

**15.** $(9c^3 - 12c^2 + c + 2) \div (3c - 2)$   $3c^2 - 2c - 1$

**16.** $(y^3 + 8) \div (y + 2)$   $y^2 - 2y + 4$

*Algebra Review*

**Review these skills:**

- dividing a polynomial by a monomial
- dividing a polynomial by a binomial

**12.** $9y - 2 + \dfrac{6}{3y + 1}$

# 10.9 Similarity Transformations

**Suggested Class Time**

| Course | Min. | Reg. | Max. |
|--------|------|------|------|
| Days   | 0    | 0    | 1    |

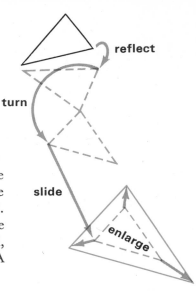

reflect

turn

slide

enlarge

Each of these transformations preserves angle measure:

| reflection | slide |
|------------|-------|
| turn | size change |

If you applied any number of these transformations, in any order, as at the right, angle measures would be preserved. Since the angles of each image triangle are congruent to the angles of the original, all of the triangles are similar by the AA Similarity Theorem.

*Answer for page 359*

25. *1.* △MOP ~ △QRS, corres. medians $\overline{OK}$, $\overline{RL}$ (Given)

2. $\frac{OM}{RQ} = \frac{MP}{QS}$, $\angle M \cong \angle Q$ (Def. of ~ polygons)

3. $MK = \frac{1}{2}MP$, $QL = \frac{1}{2}QS$ (Defs. of median and midpt.)

4. $\frac{OM}{RQ} = \frac{\frac{1}{2}MP}{\frac{1}{2}QS}$ (Mult. $\frac{MP}{QS}$ by 1; $\frac{\frac{1}{2}}{\frac{1}{2}} = 1$)

5. $\frac{OM}{RQ} = \frac{MK}{QL}$ (Subst., steps 3 and 4)

6. △MOK ~ △QRL (SAS Sim. Thm.)

7. $\frac{OK}{RL} = \frac{OM}{RQ}$ (Def. of ~ polygons)

> Any combination of reflections, turns, slides, and size changes is a **similarity transformation**.

The magnitude of the size change (or size changes) involved in a similarity transformation determines the ratio of similarity of the figures.

**Examples:** 1. △DEF is the image of △ABC under a similarity transformation that involves one size change of magnitude 4. The ratio of similarity of △DEF to △ABC is $\frac{4}{1}$.

2. △MOP is the image of △RST under a similarity transformation that involves one size change of magnitude $\frac{1}{3}$. The ratio of similarity of △MOP to △RST is $\frac{1}{3}$.

3. A similarity transformation involving size changes of magnitudes 6 and $\frac{2}{3}$ applied to △FST gives image △HRD. The ratio of similarity of △HRD to △FST is $\frac{2}{3} \cdot \frac{6}{1}$, or $\frac{4}{1}$.

# Exercises 10.9

**Assignment Guide**
*Oral:* Max. 1–4
*Written:* Max. 5–17 odd

Ⓐ **1.** Which of the transformations applied to the triangle above preserve congruence?   Reflection, slide, turn

**2.** Which preserve similarity?   All

**3.** If a similarity transformation does not involve a size change, what is the ratio of similarity of the given figure to its image?   ┆

**4.** If a similarity transformation involves one size change, of magnitude $k$, what is the ratio of similarity of the image to the given figure? Of the given figure to its image?  $\dfrac{k}{1}, \dfrac{1}{k}$

Ⓑ **5–12.** Each similarity transformation involves a size transformation. Complete the chart.

| | Given triangle | Image | Magnitude of size change | |
|---|---|---|---|---|
| **5.** | $\triangle BDC$ | $\triangle ABC$ | ? | $\frac{5}{3}$ |
| **6.** | $\triangle ADB$ | $\triangle ABC$ | ? | $\frac{5}{4}$ |
| **7.** | $\triangle BDC$ | $\triangle ADB$ | ? | $\frac{4}{3}$ |
| **8.** | $\triangle ADB$ | $\triangle BDC$ | ? | $\frac{3}{4}$ |
| **9.** | $\triangle RVS$ | ? $\triangle SVT$ | $\frac{12}{5}$ | |
| **10.** | $\triangle SVR$ | ? $\triangle TSR$ | $\frac{13}{5}$ | |
| **11.** | $\triangle RST$ | ? $\triangle RVS$ | $\frac{5}{13}$ | |
| **12.** | $\triangle TSR$ | ? $\triangle TVS$ | $\frac{12}{13}$ | |

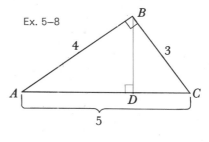

Ex. 5–8

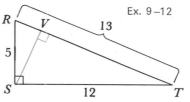

Ex. 9–12

Ⓒ **13–20.** Refer to the figures above. Which transformation described below, combined with a size change and applied to the given triangle, gives the image named ?

**a.** 90° turn around $D$ clockwise

**b.** 90° turn around $V$ counterclockwise

**c.** reflection over $\overleftrightarrow{BC}$ and turn around $C$ of $m\angle C$ counterclockwise

**d.** reflection over $\overleftrightarrow{RS}$ and turn around $R$ of $m\angle R$ counterclockwise

**e.** reflection over $\overleftrightarrow{AB}$ and turn around $A$ of $m\angle A$ clockwise

**f.** reflection over $\overleftrightarrow{ST}$ and turn around $T$ of $m\angle T$ clockwise

| | Given △ | Image | | | Given △ | Image |
|---|---|---|---|---|---|---|
| **13.** c | $\triangle BDC$ | $\triangle ABC$ | | **14.** b | $\triangle SVR$ | $\triangle TVS$ |
| **15.** e | $\triangle ADB$ | $\triangle ABC$ | | **16.** f | $\triangle RST$ | $\triangle SVT$ |
| **17.** a | $\triangle ADB$ | $\triangle BDC$ | | **18.** d | $\triangle RVS$ | $\triangle RST$ |

| Suggested Class Time | | | |
|---|---|---|---|
| Course | Min. | Reg. | Max. |
| Days | 1 | 1 | 1 |

**10.1**

**Assignment Guide**
*Written:* Min. 1–49 odd
Reg. 1–49 odd
Max. 1–51 odd

**1–6.** Let $\frac{a}{b} = \frac{4}{10}$.

**1.** $\frac{a}{b}$ and $\frac{4}{10}$ are _____ ratios. Equivalent

**2.** Name the means and extremes. Means: $b$, 4; extremes: $a$, 10

**3.** $\frac{4}{10}$ (is, is not) in lowest terms.

**4.** $4b = \underline{\ 10a\ }$

**5.** $\frac{a}{4} = \underline{\ \frac{b}{10}\ }$

**6.** $\frac{10}{b} = \underline{\ \frac{4 \cdot}{a}\ }$

**7.** If $m = 3$ and $n = 5$, then $\frac{m}{n} = \underline{\ \frac{3}{5}\ }$.

**8.** Solve:
**a.** $\frac{x}{4} = \frac{9}{5}$    **b.** $\frac{13}{y} = \frac{2}{3}$
$x = 7\frac{1}{5}$    $y = 19\frac{1}{2}$

**10.2**

**9.** Define *similar polygons*. *See page 329.*

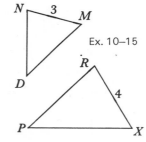

Ex. 10–15

**10–15.** Refer to the figures. Let $\triangle DMN \sim \triangle PXR$.

**10.** Name the corresponding angles and sides.
$\angle D, \angle P; \angle M, \angle X; \angle N, \angle R; \overline{DM}, \overline{PX}; \overline{MN}, \overline{XR}; \overline{DN}, \overline{PR}$

**11.** For $\triangle DMN \sim \triangle PXR$, the ratio of similarity is _____. $\frac{3}{4}$

**12.** $MN = \underline{\ \frac{3}{4}\ } \cdot XR$    **13.** If $ND = 5$, $RP = \underline{\ 6\frac{2}{3}\ }$.

**14.** $DM = \underline{\ \frac{3}{4}\ } \cdot PX$    **15.** If $m\angle N = 75$, $\underline{\ m\angle R\ } = 75$.

**10.3**

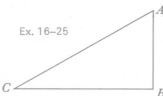

Ex. 16–25

**16–25.** Refer to the figures. Does the given information mean that $\triangle STV \sim \triangle ABC$?

**16.** $\angle A \cong \angle S$    No

**17.** $\angle B \cong \angle T, \angle C \cong \angle V$    Yes

**18.** $\angle A \cong \angle S, \overline{AB} \perp \overline{BC}, \overline{VT} \perp \overline{TS}$    Yes

**19.** $\triangle ABC \sim \triangle FGK$, $\triangle STV \sim \triangle FGK$    Yes

**10.4**

**20.** $\frac{AB}{ST} = \frac{BC}{TV}$    No

**21.** $\frac{AB}{ST} = \frac{AC}{SV}, \angle A \cong \angle S$    Yes

**22.** $\frac{AB}{ST} = \frac{BC}{TV} = \frac{AC}{SV}$    Yes

**23.** $\frac{AB}{ST} = \frac{BC}{TV}, \angle C \cong \angle V$    No

**10.5**

**24.** $m\angle B = m\angle T = 90$, $\frac{AB}{ST} = \frac{BC}{TV}$    Yes

**25.** $\overline{AB} \perp \overline{BC}, \overline{VT} \perp \overline{TS}$, $\frac{AC}{SV} = \frac{AB}{ST}$    Yes

**26–31.** Refer to the figure.

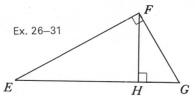

Ex. 26–31

**26.** $\triangle EFH \sim$ _$\triangle FGH$_ $\sim$ _$\triangle EGF$_

**27.** $FH$ is the _____ of $EH$ and $HG$.
Geometric mean

**28.** The geometric mean of $EH$ and $EG$ is _$EF$_.

**29.** $FG$ is the geometric mean of $HG$ and _$EG$_.

**30.** If $FH = 6$ and $HG = 4$, then $EH =$ _9_.

**31.** If $FG = 16$ and $EG = 64$, then $HG =$ _4_.

**32–41.** Is the given abbreviation a part of the name of a similarity theorem in this book? If your answer is yes, state the theorem.                          **10.6**

**32.** SAS Yes.
See p. 338.

**33.** HL Yes.
See p. 344.

**34.** ASA No

**35.** LL Yes.
See p. 344.

**36.** SSA No

**37.** AAS No

**38.** HA No

**39.** SSS Yes.
See p. 339.

**40.** LA No

**41.** AA Yes.
See p. 334.

**42–47.** $k \parallel \ell \parallel n \parallel s$ in the figure.                          **10.7**

Ex. 42–47

**42.** $\dfrac{a}{b} =$ _$\dfrac{d}{e}$_

**43.** $\dfrac{c}{b} =$ _$\dfrac{f}{e}$_

**44.** $d{:}e{:}f =$ _$a{:}b{:}c$_

**45.** $c{:}b{:}a =$ _$f{:}e{:}d$_

**46.** If $a{:}b{:}c = 3{:}2\tfrac{1}{2}{:}1$, then $d{:}e{:}f =$ _$3{:}2\tfrac{1}{2}{:}1$_.

**47.** If $a{:}b{:}c = 3{:}2\tfrac{1}{2}{:}1$ and $b = 10$, find $a$ and $c$.
$a = 12,\ c = 4$

**48–49.** Refer to the figure for Exercises 16–25.                          **10.8**

**48.** If $\triangle STV \sim \triangle ABC$ and $\dfrac{ST}{AB} = \dfrac{2}{3}$, then $\dfrac{\text{area } \triangle STV}{\text{area } \triangle ABC} =$ _$\tfrac{4}{9}$_.

**49.** If $\dfrac{\text{area } \triangle ABC}{\text{area } \triangle STV} = \dfrac{36}{25}$, then corresponding altitudes of $\triangle ABC$ and $\triangle STV$ have the ratio _$\tfrac{6}{5}$_.

**50.** Define *similarity transformation*. See page 360.                          **10.9**

**51.** If $\triangle VSY$ is the image of $\triangle PMT$ under a similarity transformation that involves a size change of magnitude $\tfrac{1}{2}$, then $\dfrac{VS}{PM} =$ _$\tfrac{1}{2}$_.

**1–3.** Let $\dfrac{c}{d} = \dfrac{2}{3}$.

**1.** $\dfrac{c}{d} = \dfrac{2}{3}$ is a __Proportion__.

**2.** $\dfrac{2}{3}$ is in __Lowest__ terms.

**3.** If $d = 2$, then 2 is the _____ of $c$ and 3. Geometric mean

**4.** In similar polygons, corresponding angles are __$\cong$__ and the ratios of corresponding __sides__ are equal.

**5.** For $\triangle AMN \sim \triangle BDC$, if the ratio of similarity is $\frac{3}{5}$, then $\dfrac{AM}{BD} = $ __$\frac{3}{5}$__.

**6.** Solve: $\dfrac{d}{7} = \dfrac{3}{14}$ $\;d = \frac{3}{2}$

Ex. 7–16

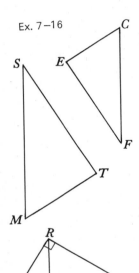

**7–12.** Refer to the figures. Using the given information, which theorem would be used to prove that $\triangle CFE \sim \triangle MST$?

**7.** $\angle F \cong \angle S$, $\angle E \cong \angle T$
 AA Sim. Thm.

**8.** $\overline{ST} \perp \overline{MT}$, $\overline{CE} \perp \overline{EF}$, $\angle F \cong \angle S$
 AA Sim. Thm.

**9.** $\dfrac{CF}{MS} = \dfrac{FE}{ST} = \dfrac{CE}{MT}$
 SSS Sim. Thm.

**10.** $\triangle CFE \sim \triangle DPR$, $\triangle DPR \sim \triangle MST$
 $\triangle s \sim$ to same $\triangle$ are $\sim$.

**11.** $\dfrac{CF}{MS} = \dfrac{FE}{ST}$, $\angle F \cong \angle S$
 SAS Sim. Thm.

**12.** $\overline{ST} \perp \overline{TM}$, $\overline{CE} \perp \overline{EF}$, $\dfrac{CE}{MT} = \dfrac{EF}{TS}$
 LL Sim. Thm.

**13–16.** Refer to the figures. Let $\triangle CEF \sim \triangle MTS$.

**13.** If $\dfrac{CE}{MT} = \dfrac{5}{7}$ and $ST = 21$, then $FE = $ __15__.

**14.** If $m\angle F = 32$, __$m\angle S$__ $= 32$.

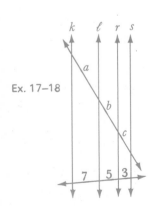

**15.** If $GR = 9$ and $PG = 27$, then $DG = $ __3__.

**16.** If $DR = 2$ and $RP = 5$, then $\dfrac{\text{area } \triangle DGR}{\text{area } \triangle RGP} = $ __$\frac{4}{25}$__.

Ex. 17–18

**17–18.** Refer to the figure. Let $k \parallel \ell \parallel r \parallel s$.

**17.** $a:b:c = $ __7:5:3__

**18.** If $c = 6$, find $a$ and $b$. $a = 14$, $b = 10$

**19.** If $\triangle A'B'C'$ is the image of $\triangle ABC$ under a similarity transformation that involves one size change, and for $\triangle A'B'C' \sim \triangle ABC$ the ratio of similarity is $\frac{2}{5}$, the size change has a magnitude of _____. $\frac{2}{5}$

**20.** Given: $TU = 1$, $TW = 2$, $TV = 4$
 Prove: $\triangle TUW \sim \triangle TWV$

# MINI-CHAPTER: TRIGONOMETRY

$\angle A$ is any acute angle. $B$ and $D$ are any two points on one side of $\angle A$.

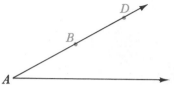

Draw $\overline{BC}$ and $\overline{DE}$ perpendicular to the other side of $\angle A$.

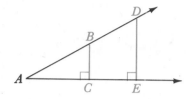

20. 1. $TU = 1$, $TW = 2$, $TV = 4$ (Given)
2. $\dfrac{TU}{TW} = \dfrac{1}{2}$, $\dfrac{TW}{TV} = \dfrac{1}{2}$
(Use given equations to form proportions.)
3. $\dfrac{TU}{TW} = \dfrac{TW}{TV}$ (Subst.)
4. $\angle T \cong \angle T$ ($\angle$ is $\cong$ to itself.)
5. $\triangle TUW \sim \triangle TWV$ (SAS Sim. Thm.)

By the AA Similarity Theorem, $\triangle ACB \sim \triangle AED$

By the definition of similar polygons, $\dfrac{BC}{DE} = \dfrac{AB}{AD}$

By the properties of proportions (p. 325), $\dfrac{BC}{AB} = \dfrac{DE}{AD}$ ◄ corresponding sides
◄ corresponding sides

▲ sides of $\triangle ACB$ ▲ sides of $\triangle AED$

This shows that

> If two triangles are similar, the ratio of any two sides of one triangle equals the ratio of the corresponding sides of the other.

Look again at the ratio of the sides of right triangles $ACB$ and $AED$. Since the triangles are different sizes, this ratio does not depend on the size of the right triangle, but only on $m\angle A$.

Side opposite $\angle A$ in each right triangle ▶ $\dfrac{BC}{AB} = \dfrac{DE}{AD}$
Hypotenuse of each right triangle ▶

This ratio is called the **sine** of $m\angle A$, abbreviated $\sin \angle A$.

**Example:** $\sin \angle P = \frac{24}{25}$

$\sin \angle D = \frac{7}{25}$

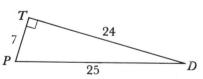

Use right triangle $MNP$ to find $\sin \angle M$. Then use each of the other two right triangles to find $\sin \angle M$. Are the results equal?

Find $\sin \angle MPN$. Find the sines of the angles corresponding to $\angle MPN$ in the other two triangles. (These three angles are congruent, so they have the same sine.)

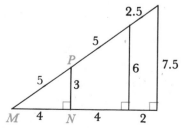

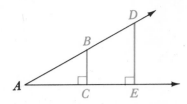

We used the ratios of the sides opposite $\angle A$ and the hypotenuses of right triangles $ACB$ and $AED$ to define sine of $m\angle A$. The ratios of the other pairs of corresponding sides are also equal, and these other ratios are also given special names. NOTE: The leg that is not *opposite $\angle A$ is adjacent* to $\angle A$.

These are called **trigonometric ratios.**

| Name | Abbreviation | Ratio |
|------|--------------|-------|
| sine of $m\angle A$ | sin $\angle A$ | $\dfrac{\text{side opposite } \angle A}{\text{hypotenuse}}$ |
| cosine of $m\angle A$ | cos $\angle A$ | $\dfrac{\text{side adjacent to } \angle A}{\text{hypotenuse}}$ |
| tangent of $m\angle A$ | tan $\angle A$ | $\dfrac{\text{side opposite } \angle A}{\text{side adjacent to } \angle A}$ |

As before, the ratio of sides means the ratio of their lengths.

**Exercises:** Find the sine, cosine, and tangent of each acute angle.

| $\angle$ | sin | cos | tan |
|------|------|------|------|
| 1. $X$ | $\frac{7}{25}$ | $\frac{24}{25}$ | $\frac{7}{24}$ |
| | 0.280 | 0.960 | 0.292 |
| $Z$ | $\frac{24}{25}$ | $\frac{7}{25}$ | $\frac{24}{7}$ |
| | 0.960 | 0.280 | 3.429 |
| 2. $U$ | $\frac{3}{5}$ | $\frac{4}{5}$ | $\frac{3}{4}$ |
| | 0.600 | 0.800 | 0.750 |
| $W$ | $\frac{4}{5}$ | $\frac{3}{5}$ | $\frac{4}{3}$ |
| | 0.800 | 0.600 | 1.333 |
| 3. $R$ | $\frac{4}{5}$ | $\frac{3}{5}$ | $\frac{4}{3}$ |
| | 0.800 | 0.600 | 1.333 |
| $T$ | $\frac{3}{5}$ | $\frac{4}{5}$ | $\frac{3}{4}$ |
| | 0.600 | 0.800 | 0.750 |
| 4. $M$ | $\frac{\sqrt{3}}{2}$ | $\frac{1}{2}$ | $\sqrt{3}$ |
| | 0.866 | 0.500 | 1.732 |
| $P$ | $\frac{1}{2}$ | $\frac{\sqrt{3}}{2}$ | $\frac{\sqrt{3}}{3}$ |
| | 0.500 | 0.866 | 0.577 |
| 5. $H$ | $\frac{\sqrt{3}}{2}$ | $\frac{1}{2}$ | $\sqrt{3}$ |
| | 0.866 | 0.500 | 1.732 |
| $K$ | $\frac{1}{2}$ | $\frac{\sqrt{3}}{2}$ | $\frac{\sqrt{3}}{3}$ |
| | 0.500 | 0.866 | 0.577 |

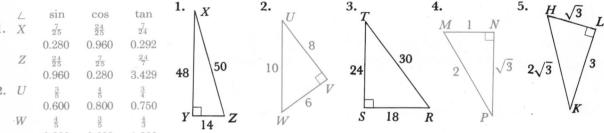

**Example:** $\tan \angle X = \frac{14}{48} = \frac{7}{24}$ ◀ in lowest terms

Is $\sin \angle P = \sin \angle K$ in the figures above? Is $\sin \angle M = \sin \angle H$? $m\angle P = 30$ and $m\angle M = 60$. What is $m\angle K$? $m\angle H$?

Trigonometric ratios are usually expressed using decimals rather than fractions. In most cases the decimal is an approximation, but for convenience we will use the symbol $=$ throughout.

**Examples:** $\sin 30° = \frac{1}{2} = 0.5$

$\sin 60° = \frac{1}{2}\sqrt{3} = 0.866$ (to the nearest thousandth)

**Exercises:** Give the sine, cosine, and tangent of each acute angle of figures 1–5 above as a decimal approximation to the nearest thousandth.

Because every angle with the same measure has the same sine, the same cosine, and the same tangent, a table can be made showing angle measures and decimal approximations for the corresponding trigonometric ratios. The table on page 368 lists approximations to the nearest thousandth for angle measures in degrees from 1° to 89°.

### USING A TABLE OF APPROXIMATIONS

**1.** To find cos 27° ▶ Find 27 in the column headed $m\angle A$. Then look across the row to the column headed cos $\angle A$. (cos 27° = 0.891)

**2.** To find $x$, given tan $x = 2.356$ ▶ Find 2.356 in the column headed tan $\angle A$. Then look across the row to the column headed $m\angle A$. ($x = 67°$)

## Exercises

Use the table to find each approximation.

**1.** sin 39° 0.629  **2.** cos 64° 0.438  **3.** tan 23° 0.424  **4.** sin 45° 0.707

**5.** cos 45° 0.707  **6.** tan 75° 3.732  **7.** sin 57° 0.839  **8.** cos 17° 0.956

Use the table to find each angle measure.

**9.** sin $x = 0.485$ 29°  **10.** cos $y = 0.225$ 77°  **11.** tan $a = 6.314$ 81°

**12.** sin $r = 0.990$ 82°  **13.** cos $b = 0.990$ 8°  **14.** tan $z = 0.306$ 17°

You have seen that for a given angle measure there is exactly one value for the sine, cosine, or tangent. Conversely, a given value for sin $x$, cos $x$, or tan $x$ corresponds to exactly one $x$ between 0° and 90°.

In the table, find sin 87° and sin 88°. In view of the statement above, how can both of the statements below be true?

$$\sin 87° = 0.999 \qquad \sin 88° = 0.999$$

Some hand-held calculators give approximations for trigonometric ratios. These approximations may include nine or more digits following the decimal point and may cover many more angle measures than our table does. So if you do these exercises using a calculator, you should get a more accurate result than you can get using the table. (The usefulness of this additional accuracy would depend on the accuracy of the original measurements and the use to be made of the result.)

## SINES, COSINES, AND TANGENTS

| $m\angle A$ | sin $\angle A$ | cos $\angle A$ | tan $\angle A$ | $m\angle A$ | sin $\angle A$ | cos $\angle A$ | tan $\angle A$ |
|---|---|---|---|---|---|---|---|
| 1° | 0.017 | 1.000 | 0.017 | 46° | 0.719 | 0.695 | 1.036 |
| 2 | .035 | 0.999 | .035 | 47 | .731 | .682 | 1.072 |
| 3 | .052 | .999 | .052 | 48 | .743 | .669 | 1.111 |
| 4 | .070 | .998 | .070 | 49 | .755 | .656 | 1.150 |
| 5 | .087 | .996 | .087 | 50 | .766 | .643 | 1.192 |
| 6 | .105 | .995 | .105 | 51 | .777 | .629 | 1.235 |
| 7 | .122 | .993 | .123 | 52 | .788 | .616 | 1.280 |
| 8 | .139 | .990 | .141 | 53 | .799 | .602 | 1.327 |
| 9 | .156 | .988 | .158 | 54 | .809 | .588 | 1.376 |
| 10 | .174 | .985 | .176 | 55 | .819 | .574 | 1.428 |
| 11 | .191 | .982 | .194 | 56 | .829 | .559 | 1.483 |
| 12 | .208 | .978 | .213 | 57 | .839 | .545 | 1.540 |
| 13 | .225 | .974 | .231 | 58 | .848 | .530 | 1.600 |
| 14 | .242 | .970 | .249 | 59 | .857 | .515 | 1.664 |
| 15 | .259 | .966 | .268 | 60 | .866 | .500 | 1.732 |
| 16 | .276 | .961 | .287 | 61 | .875 | .485 | 1.804 |
| 17 | .292 | .956 | .306 | 62 | .883 | .469 | 1.881 |
| 18 | .309 | .951 | .325 | 63 | .891 | .454 | 1.963 |
| 19 | .326 | .946 | .344 | 64 | .899 | .438 | 2.050 |
| 20 | .342 | .940 | .364 | 65 | .906 | .423 | 2.145 |
| 21 | .358 | .934 | .384 | 66 | .914 | .407 | 2.246 |
| 22 | .375 | .927 | .404 | 67 | .921 | .391 | 2.356 |
| 23 | .391 | .921 | .424 | 68 | .927 | .375 | 2.475 |
| 24 | .407 | .914 | .445 | 69 | .934 | .358 | 2.605 |
| 25 | .423 | .906 | .466 | 70 | .940 | .342 | 2.747 |
| 26 | .438 | .899 | .488 | 71 | .946 | .326 | 2.904 |
| 27 | .454 | .891 | .510 | 72 | .951 | .309 | 3.078 |
| 28 | .469 | .883 | .532 | 73 | .956 | .292 | 3.271 |
| 29 | .485 | .875 | .554 | 74 | .961 | .276 | 3.487 |
| 30 | .500 | .866 | .577 | 75 | .966 | .259 | 3.732 |
| 31 | .515 | .857 | .601 | 76 | .970 | .242 | 4.011 |
| 32 | .530 | .848 | .625 | 77 | .974 | .225 | 4.331 |
| 33 | .545 | .839 | .649 | 78 | .978 | .208 | 4.705 |
| 34 | .559 | .829 | .675 | 79 | .982 | .191 | 5.145 |
| 35 | .574 | .819 | .700 | 80 | .985 | .174 | 5.671 |
| 36 | .588 | .809 | .727 | 81 | .988 | .156 | 6.314 |
| 37 | .602 | .799 | .754 | 82 | .990 | .139 | 7.115 |
| 38 | .616 | .788 | .781 | 83 | .993 | .122 | 8.144 |
| 39 | .629 | .777 | .810 | 84 | .995 | .105 | 9.514 |
| 40 | .643 | .766 | .839 | 85 | .996 | .087 | 11.430 |
| 41 | .656 | .755 | .869 | 86 | .998 | .070 | 14.301 |
| 42 | .669 | .743 | .900 | 87 | .999 | .052 | 19.081 |
| 43 | .682 | .731 | .933 | 88 | .999 | .035 | 28.636 |
| 44 | .695 | .719 | .966 | 89 | 1.000 | .017 | 57.290 |
| 45 | .707 | .707 | 1.000 | | | | |

## APPLICATIONS OF TRIGONOMETRIC RATIOS

Trigonometry is used in surveying, navigation, astronomy, and a number of other fields. Here are some typical applications.

How high is the kite?

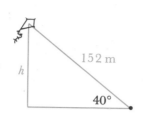

$$\frac{h}{152} = \sin 40°$$
$$h = 152 \sin 40°$$
$$= 152 (0.643)$$
$$= 97.736 \text{ m high}$$

If a jet airplane takes off at an 18° angle to the runway, how high is the jet when it is over a point that is 170 m from its takeoff point?

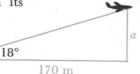

$$\frac{a}{170} = \tan 18°$$
$$a = 170 \tan 18°$$
$$= 170 (0.325)$$
$$= 55.25 \text{ m high}$$

Leo de Wys, Inc.

### Exercises

Use a trigonometric ratio to solve each exercise. Give your answers to the nearest hundredth or the nearest degree.

1. If a sudden wind lifted the kite shown above so the string made a 60° angle with the ground, how high would the kite be?   131.63 m

2. If you swam to the opposite shore on the line perpendicular to the near shore, how far would you swim?   70 m

3. If you rowed a boat back on the line that makes a 35° angle with the near shore, how far would you row?   122.10 m

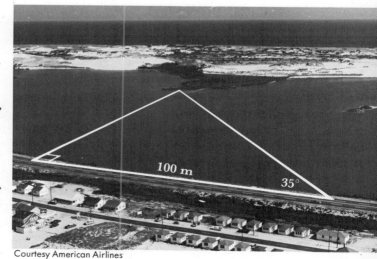

Courtesy American Airlines

**4.** How far above the water is the roadway of the bridge?

45.62 m

**5.** How far above the roadway does the bridge tower extend?

72.20 m

**6.** How far is the rider from the base of the rock formation?

1971.83 m

**7.** How far from the rider is an eagle that is sitting on top of the rock formation?   2019.23 m

**8.** How far is the submarine from the wreck on the ocean floor?

100 m

**9.** If the submarine drops vertically to the ocean floor from its present position, how far from the wreck will it be?

86.66 m

Ex. 8–9

**10.** How far does the cable car drop vertically as it slides 21 m down the cable? How far does it drop for each foot it slides?

16.09 m; 0.77 ft

**11.** How far does the cable car travel horizontally as it slides 21 m down the cable? How far does it travel horizontally for each foot it slides?

13.50 m; 0.64 ft

Photos courtesy American Airlines

**12.** If a straight road were built from the fork at $X$ to the intersection at $Z$, how long would the new road be?  894.68 m

**13.** How long would a road be from the intersection at $Z$ to the highway at $Y$?  420.28 m

Ex. 14

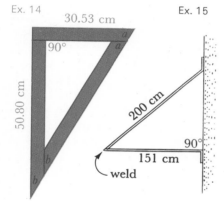

30.53 cm

90°

50.80 cm

$a$
$a$

Ex. 15

200 cm

151 cm

90°

weld

**14.** The wooden triangle is to be used as a shelf support. At what angles should the wood pieces be cut at $a$ and $b$?  59°, 31°

**15.** Two pieces of metal are to be welded into a wall bracket as shown. At what angle should the pieces be joined?  41°

Ex. 16–17

70 m

65°

**16.** How far is it from the pier on the right to the ferry dock in the distance?  165.48 m

**17.** How much closer to the ferry dock is the pier on the left than the pier on the right?  15.33 m

**18–19.** When a car's brakes are the only thing keeping it from rolling downhill, the force on the brakes is $w \sin x°$, where $w$ is the weight of the car.

**18.** Find the force on the brakes of a 3000-pound car parked on a 7° hill. NOTE: The force is in pounds.  366 lb

**19.** Find the force on the brakes of a 2800-pound car parked on a 12° hill.  582.4 lb

Ex. 18–19

$x°$

**20.** A wheelchair ramp should not rise more than 1 cm for every 12 cm of horizontal distance covered. Can the ramp make an angle as large as 5° with the level ground?　　No

**21.** A wheelchair ramp from the street to a curb 17.74 cm high is 2.54 m long. What angle does the ramp make with the street?　　4°

◀**22–23.** To find the horizontal distance between two points on a hill, a surveyor may first measure the actual distance and then measure the angle of depression. Trigonometric ratios may then be used to find both the horizontal distance and how much lower one point is than the other.

**22.** If $d = 10$ m and $m\angle P = 5$, find $x$ and $y$.
$x = 9.96$ m, $y = 0.87$ m

**23.** If $d = 10$ m and $m\angle P = 6$, find $x$ and $y$.
$x = 9.95$ m, $y = 1.05$ m

**24–25.** To intercept 100% of the solar energy that strikes it, a flat solar-energy collector should be perpendicular to the sun's rays. If it is not, the percent ($n$) of solar energy it intercepts can be found by using the formula $n = 100 \cos x°$.

Ex. 24–25

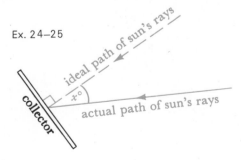

**24.** If the angle between the actual path of the sun's rays and the collector is 73°, what percent of the solar energy is intercepted?
95.6%

**25.** If the sun's rays hit the ground at a 35° angle and the collector leans at a 45° angle, what percent of the solar energy is intercepted?
98.5%

Ex. 26

**26.** In a TV picture tube, the beams put out by the electron gun (at the back of the tube) form the picture on the screen. In older picture tubes, the deflection angle of the electron beams was 56°. Now that angle might be 114°. For a screen that is 16 inches from top to bottom, as shown, how much "thinner" from back to front can the TV set be made by using the larger deflection angle?　　9.84 in.

deflection angle

16 in.

screen

electron gun

# ■ Cumulative Review: Chapters 8–10 ■

**1.** State the definition of a perpendicular line and plane. *See page 266.*   **Ch. 8**

**2–8.** Refer to the figure.

**2.** If $\overleftrightarrow{AX} \perp \overleftrightarrow{BX}$ and $\overleftrightarrow{AX} \perp \overleftrightarrow{CX}$, is $\overleftrightarrow{AX} \perp p$? Why?
   Yes; Basic Thm. for ⊥s (p. 270)

**3.** How many planes are perpendicular to $\overleftrightarrow{MG}$ at $G$?   Ex. 2–11

   Exactly one

**4.** If $\overleftrightarrow{AX} \perp p$, is $\overleftrightarrow{AY} \perp p$? If so, why?  No

**5.** If $\overleftrightarrow{GM} \perp p$ and $\overleftrightarrow{GM} \perp \overleftrightarrow{MP}$, is $\overleftrightarrow{MP}$ in $p$? If so, why?
   Yes; def. of ⊥ line and plane

**6.** If $\overleftrightarrow{GM} \perp p$ and $\overleftrightarrow{AX} \perp p$, are $G$, $M$, $A$, and $X$ coplanar?  Yes

**7.** If $\overleftrightarrow{AX} \perp p$, is $AX > AY$?  No

**8.** When is $AX$ the distance from $A$ to plane $p$? When $\overleftrightarrow{AX} \perp p$

**9–11.** Refer to the figure. Plane $p$ is the perpendicular bisecting plane of $\overline{AZ}$. Complete each statement.

**9.** $YA = $ ___YZ___       **10.** $SA = $ ___SZ___

**11.** If $NA = NZ$, then $N$ is ___In plane___ $p$

**12–13.** Find the area of each rectangle or square. ($\ell$ stands for length, $w$ for width, and $s$ for length of a side of a square.)   **Ch. 9**

**12.** $\ell = 45$ m, $w = 42$ m       **13.** $s = 3\frac{1}{2}$  $12\frac{1}{4}$
   1890 m²

Assignment Guide
*Written:*
Min. (day 1) 1–20
     (day 2) 21–30; 33–40
Reg. 1–39 odd
Max. 1–39 odd

**14.** A triangle has a base with length 18.2 and a corresponding height of 14. What is the area of the triangle?   127.4

**15.** A parallelogram has a base with length $21\frac{1}{2}$ and a corresponding height of 6. Find its area.   129

**16.** A trapezoid has bases of lengths 14 and 22. The height is 9. Find its area.   162

**17–20.** Simplify each radical.

**17.** $\sqrt{45}$  $3\sqrt{5}$   **18.** $\sqrt{\frac{2}{25}}$  $\frac{\sqrt{2}}{5}$   **19.** $\sqrt{\frac{1}{5}}$  $\frac{\sqrt{5}}{5}$   **20.** $\frac{3}{\sqrt{7}}$  $\frac{3\sqrt{7}}{7}$

**21.** A right triangle has legs of lengths 4 and 6. Find the length of the hypotenuse. (Leave your answer in simplified radical form.) $2\sqrt{13}$

**22.** A triangle has sides of lengths 10, 24, and 26. Is it a right triangle?

Yes

**23–24.** Find the missing lengths.

**23.** 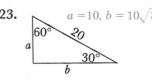 $a = 10, \; b = 10\sqrt{3}$

**24.** 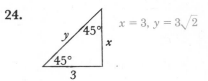 $x = 3, \; y = 3\sqrt{2}$

**Ch. 10**

**25–28.** Let $\dfrac{n}{3} = \dfrac{2}{t}$.

**25.** $nt = \underline{\quad 6 \quad}$

**26.** If $n = 2$, $t = \underline{\quad 3 \quad}$.

**27.** $\dfrac{n}{2} = \underline{\quad \frac{3}{t} \quad}$

**28.** $\dfrac{t}{3} = \underline{\quad \frac{2}{n} \quad}$

**29.** Solve: **a.** $\dfrac{r}{3} = \dfrac{4}{24}$ $r = \frac{1}{2}$ **b.** $\dfrac{2s}{5} = \dfrac{6}{7}$ $s = 2\frac{1}{7}$

**30–39.** Refer to the figures.

Ex. 30–39

**30.** Given: $\angle D \cong \angle AFW$

Prove: $\triangle DAB \sim \triangle FAW$

**31.** Given: $\dfrac{AF}{AD} = \dfrac{AW}{AB}$

Prove: $\triangle DAB \sim \triangle FAW$

**32.** Given: $\angle A$ is a rt. $\angle$, $\angle RST$ is a rt. $\angle$, $\angle AWF \cong \angle B$, $\angle AWF \cong \angle R$

Prove: $\dfrac{RS}{BA} = \dfrac{ST}{AD}$

**33.** $\triangle TVS \sim \underline{\triangle SVR} \sim \underline{\triangle TSR}$

**34.** $(RS)^2 = RT \cdot \underline{\;RV\;}$

**35.** $(SV)^2 = RV \cdot \underline{\;VT\;}$

**36.** If $ST = 2\sqrt{3}$ and $VT = 2$, then $RT = \underline{\quad 6 \quad}$.

**37.** If $\overline{FW} \parallel \overline{DB}$, then $\triangle ADB \sim \underline{\triangle AFW}$.

**38.** If $\triangle BDA \sim \triangle WFA$, then $\overline{DB} \parallel \underline{\;\overline{FW}\;}$.

**39.** If $RS = 3$ and $RT = 4$, then $\dfrac{\text{area } \triangle RSV}{\text{area } \triangle RTS} = \underline{\quad \frac{9}{16} \quad}$.

**40.** If $d : e : f = 4 : 3 : 2$ and $f = 4$, find $d$ and $e$. $d = 8, \; e = 6$

**30.** *1.* $\angle D \cong \angle AFW$ (Given)
*2.* $\angle A \cong \angle A$ ($\angle$ is $\cong$ to itself.)
*3.* $\triangle DAB \sim \triangle FAW$ (AA Sim. Thm.)

**31.** *1.* $\dfrac{AF}{AD} = \dfrac{AW}{AB}$ (Given)
*2.* $\angle A \cong \angle A$ ($\angle$ is $\cong$ to itself.)
*3.* $\triangle DAB \sim \triangle FAW$ (SAS Sim. Thm.)

**32.** *1.* $\angle A$, $\angle RST$ are rt. $\angle$s. (Given)
*2.* $\angle A \cong \angle RST$ (All rt. $\angle$s are $\cong$.)
*3.* $\angle AWF \cong \angle B$, $\angle AWF \cong \angle R$ (Given)
*4.* $\angle R \cong \angle B$ ($\angle$s $\cong$ to same $\angle$ are $\cong$.)
*5.* $\triangle RST \sim \triangle BAD$ (AA Sim. Thm.)
*6.* $\dfrac{RS}{BA} = \dfrac{ST}{AD}$ (Def. of $\sim$ polygons)

# CIRCLES AND SPHERES

Zefa

# 11.1 Definitions

**Suggested Class Time**

| Course | Min. | Reg. | Max. |
|--------|------|------|------|
| Days   | 1    | 1    | 1    |

A basketball hoop is nearly a circle. In a plane, a **circle** is the set of all points at a fixed distance, the *radius*, from a given point, the *center*.

A basketball is nearly a sphere. In space, a **sphere** is the set of all points at a fixed distance, the *radius*, from a given point, the *center*.

We will define the basic terms relating to circles and spheres at the same time, since the definitions are almost identical.

The Los Angeles Lakers

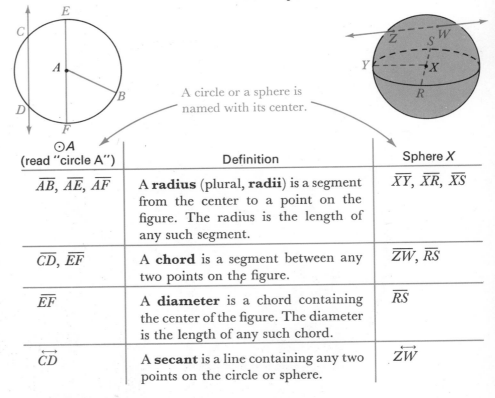

A circle or a sphere is named with its center.

| $\odot A$ (read "circle A") | Definition | Sphere $X$ |
|---|---|---|
| $\overline{AB}$, $\overline{AE}$, $\overline{AF}$ | A **radius** (plural, **radii**) is a segment from the center to a point on the figure. The radius is the length of any such segment. | $\overline{XY}$, $\overline{XR}$, $\overline{XS}$ |
| $\overline{CD}$, $\overline{EF}$ | A **chord** is a segment between any two points on the figure. | $\overline{ZW}$, $\overline{RS}$ |
| $\overline{EF}$ | A **diameter** is a chord containing the center of the figure. The diameter is the length of any such chord. | $\overline{RS}$ |
| $\overleftrightarrow{CD}$ | A **secant** is a line containing any two points on the circle or sphere. | $\overleftrightarrow{ZW}$ |

Notice that the term *radius* has been defined in two ways, as a segment and as the length of a segment. Similarly, two definitions have been given for *diameter*. It will be clear from the context which meaning is intended. For example, when we say that all radii of a circle are congruent, we mean the radii as segments. When we say that two spheres each have a radius of 3, we mean the radius as the length of a segment.

## Exercises 11.1

Ⓐ **1.** Define *circle*. *See page 376.*  **2.** Define *sphere*. *See page 376.*

**3–10.** What name best applies to each of the following?

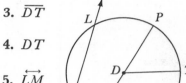

**3.** $\overline{DT}$

**4.** $DT$

**5.** $\overleftrightarrow{LM}$

**6.** $\overline{PO}$

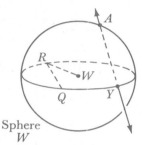

**7.** $\overrightarrow{AY}$

**8.** $\overline{RQ}$

**9.** $\overline{AY}$

**10.** $\overline{WR}$

Sphere W

**Assignment Guide**
*Oral:* 1–10
*Written:*
Min. 11–22; Alg. Rev., p. 378, odd
Reg. 11–22; Alg. Rev., p. 378, odd
Max. 11–22
*Constructions:* 23–27

| | |
|---|---|
| 3. Radius | 7. Secant |
| 4. Radius | 8. Chord |
| 5. Secant | 9. Chord |
| 6. Diameter | 10. Radius |

Ⓑ **11–18.** Use the appropriate figure to name the following:

**11.** a radius
$\overline{FO}$ (or $\overline{FP}$ or $\overline{FM}$)

**12.** three chords
$\overline{EA}$, $\overline{PM}$, $\overline{RN}$

**13.** a diameter
$\overline{PM}$

**14.** a secant
$\overleftrightarrow{EA}$

Ex. 11–14

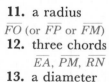

**15.** two radii
$\overline{MI}$, $\overline{MG}$ (or $\overline{MT}$)

**16.** three chords
$\overline{JS}$, $\overline{DC}$, $\overline{GI}$

**17.** two secants
$\overleftrightarrow{CD}$, $\overleftrightarrow{JS}$

**18.** a diameter
$\overline{GI}$

Ex. 15–18

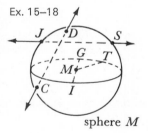

sphere M

**19–22.** True or False?

**19.** All radii of a circle are congruent.  T

**20.** A diameter of a sphere is also a secant of the sphere.  F

**21.** A radius of a sphere is also a chord of the sphere.  F

**22.** A chord of a circle is always a diameter of the circle.  F

**23–24.** Construct a circle with

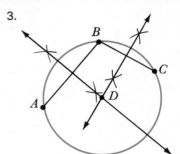

**23.** diameter $AB$          **24.** radius $AC$

---

## construction: a circle given 3 points on the circle

| **1.** Given: Points $A$, $B$, and $C$. | **2.** | **3.** |
|---|---|---|
| 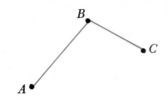 | | |
| Construct any 2 segments with endpoints $A, B, C$. | Construct the perpendicular bisectors of the segments. | $D$ is the center of the circle with $\overline{DA}$, $\overline{DB}$, and $\overline{DC}$ as radii. |

---

© **25–27.** Copy points $A$, $B$, and $C$ and construct a circle containing them.

**25.**  $B \bullet$          **26.**  $A \bullet$  **27.**          $\bullet B$

                                                    $A \bullet$

$A \bullet$          $C \bullet$      $B \bullet$      $\bullet C$          $\bullet C$

—o-o-o-o-o-o-o-o— **Settling the Circle** —o-o-o-o-o-o-o-o—

Settlers coming to south-central Ohio in 1810 found two earthwork enclosures built by prehistoric Mound Builders. One was in the shape of a square, and the other was in the shape of a circle. The people decided to settle within the circle and call their community Circleville.

---

### Algebra Review

**Review this skill:**

- *multiplying and dividing rational expressions*

Multiply or divide. Express each answer in simplest form.

**1.** $\frac{4}{7} \cdot \frac{5}{6}$  $\frac{10}{21}$     **2.** $\frac{3}{4} \div \frac{3}{5}$  $1\frac{1}{4}$     **3.** $\frac{5}{6} \cdot \frac{12}{25}$  $\frac{2}{5}$     **4.** $\frac{4}{9} \div \frac{2}{21}$  $4\frac{2}{3}$

**5.** $\frac{a}{2} \cdot \frac{a}{6}$  $\frac{a^2}{12}$     **6.** $\frac{5}{d} \div \frac{6}{d}$  $\frac{5}{6}$     **7.** $\frac{2m^3}{r} \cdot \frac{r^2}{4m}$  $\frac{m^2 r}{2}$

**8.** $\frac{s^3}{t} \div \frac{s}{t}$  $s^2$     **9.** $\frac{14}{g^4} \cdot \frac{g}{24}$  $\frac{7}{12g^3}$     **10.** $\frac{6}{z^3 w} \div \frac{w^2}{15}$  $\frac{90}{z^3 w^3}$

**11.** $\frac{x^3 y}{3x} \cdot \frac{2}{x^2 y^2}$  $\frac{2}{3y}$     **12.** $\frac{16a^2 b^3}{6a} \cdot \frac{9a^2 b}{4b}$  $6a^3 b^3$     **13.** $\frac{7c^2 n}{m^2 n^2} \div \frac{21cm^4}{n^5}$  $\frac{cn^4}{3m^6}$

Any circle $C$ is in some plane $p$. A circle separates that plane into two sets of points, the interior and exterior of the circle. The **interior** of a circle contains all the points in the plane whose distance from the center is less than the radius. The **exterior** of a circle contains all the points in the plane whose distance from the center is greater than the radius.

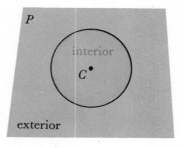

In the photo think of the pizza as a circle and its interior. If we make a cut in the pizza, not through the center, the cut could be thought of as a chord of a circle. If we now cut through the center of the pizza and bisect the first cut, the second cut will be perpendicular to the first. This is a model for part **a** of the Chord Theorem.

| Suggested Class Time | | | |
|---|---|---|---|
| Course | Min. | Reg. | Max. |
| Days | 1 | 1 | 1 |

a. The segment containing the center of a circle and bisecting a chord that is not a diameter is perpendicular to the chord.

b. The perpendicular from the center of a circle to a chord bisects the chord.

c. In the plane of a circle, the perpendicular bisector of a chord contains the center of the circle.

Chord Theorem

## Part a.

Given: $\odot P$, chord $\overline{AB}$, $\overline{PM}$ bisects $\overline{AB}$.

Prove: $\overline{PM} \perp \overline{AB}$

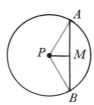

Proof: Since $\overline{PM}$ bisects $\overline{AB}$, $\overline{AM} \cong \overline{MB}$. We can draw radii $\overline{PA}$ and $\overline{PB}$, and $\overline{PA} \cong \overline{PB}$ because radii of a circle are congruent. $\overline{PM} \cong \overline{PM}$, so $\triangle PMA \cong \triangle PMB$ by the SSS Postulate. Then $\angle PMA \cong \angle PMB$ because they are corresponding parts. Also, $\angle PMA$ and $\angle PMB$ are supplementary because they are adjacent and their noncommon sides are opposite rays. Because they are supplementary and congruent, $\angle PMA$ and $\angle PMB$ are right angles. Therefore, $\overline{PM} \perp \overline{AB}$.

**Part b.**

Given: $\odot P$, chord $\overline{AB}$, $\overline{PM} \perp \overline{AB}$

Prove: $AM = MB$

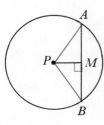

You'll be asked to prove part **b** in Exercise 27. Part **c** is proved in Exercises 15–18.

Dr. E.R. Degginger

Notice that the wheels in the photo are congruent, and the spokes of each wheel are the same length. Think of the wheels as a model for congruent circles. **Congruent circles** are circles whose radii are congruent.

**Congruent Chords Theorem**

In the same circle or in congruent circles, chords are congruent if and only if they are equidistant from the center(s) of the circle(s).

**Part a.**

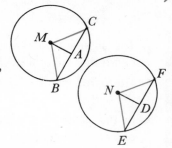

Given: $\odot M \cong \odot N$, $MA$ the distance to $\overline{BC}$, $ND$ the distance to $\overline{EF}$, $MA = ND$

Prove: $\overline{BC} \cong \overline{EF}$

Proof: Since $MA$ is the distance to $\overline{BC}$ and $ND$ is the distance to $\overline{EF}$, $\overline{MA} \perp \overline{BC}$ and $\overline{ND} \perp \overline{EF}$. So $\triangle MAC$ and $\triangle NDF$ are right $\triangle$s. Also $\overline{MC} \cong \overline{NF}$ since they are radii of congruent circles, and we are given $MA = ND$. Therefore, $\triangle MAC \cong \triangle NDF$ by the HL Theorem, so $\overline{AC} \cong \overline{DF}$. By the Chord Theorem, $\overline{MA}$ bisects $\overline{BC}$ and $\overline{ND}$ bisects $\overline{EF}$. Since $\overline{AC} \cong \overline{DF}$, $\overline{BC} \cong \overline{EF}$.

**Part b.**

Given: $\odot M \cong \odot N$, $MA$ the distance to $\overline{BC}$, $ND$ the distance to $\overline{EF}$, $\overline{BC} \cong \overline{EF}$    (See figure for part **a**.)

Prove: $MA = ND$

You'll be asked to prove part **b** in Exercise 28.

*Answer for page 382*

27. 1. $\odot P$, chord $\overline{AB}$, $\overline{PM} \perp \overline{AB}$ (Given)
2. Draw $\overline{PA}$, $\overline{PB}$. (2 pts. determine a line.)
3. $\overline{PA} \cong \overline{PB}$ (Radii of a $\odot$ are $\cong$.)
4. $\overline{PM} \cong \overline{PM}$ (Seg. is $\cong$ to itself.)
5. $\angle PMA$, $\angle PMB$ are rt. $\angle$s. (Def. of $\perp$)
6. $\triangle PMA$, $\triangle PMB$ are rt. $\triangle$s. (Def. of rt. $\triangle$)
7. $\triangle PMA \cong \triangle PMB$ (HL Thm.)
8. $\overline{AM} \cong \overline{MB}$, so $AM = MB$ (Corres. parts of $\cong$ $\triangle$s are $\cong$.)

Ⓐ **1–7.** Refer to the figure.

**Assignment Guide**
*Oral:* 1–8
*Written:* Min. 9–18
Reg. 9–24
Max. 9–25

**1.** Name 3 points in the interior of ⊙*A*.
$A, J, M$

**2.** Name 1 point in the exterior of ⊙*A*.

**3.** If $\overline{AJ} \perp \overline{EF}$, $\overline{FJ} \cong$ ___$\overline{JE}$___.

**4.** If $MB = MD$, why is $\overline{AC} \perp \overline{BD}$?
Chord Thm., part **a**

**5.** If $\overleftrightarrow{GJ}$ is the ⊥ bisector of $\overline{EF}$, why does $\overleftrightarrow{GJ}$ contain point *A*?
Chord Thm., part **c**

**6.** If $AM = AJ$, name 2 congruent chords.
$\overline{BD}, \overline{FE}$

**7.** If $\overline{BD} \cong \overline{EF}$, $AM =$ ___$AJ$___.

**8.** Define *congruent circles*. *See page 380.*

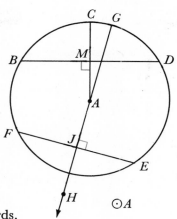
⊙*A*

Ⓑ **9–14.** State a reason for each conclusion. Refer to the figures.

**9.** *Given:* ⊙*C*, $\overline{CO} \perp \overline{MT}$
*Conclusion:* $MO = OT$
Chord Thm., part **b**

**10.** *Given:* ⊙*C* ≅ ⊙*D*, $CO = DA$, $\overline{CO} \perp \overline{MT}$, $\overline{DA} \perp \overline{HF}$
*Conclusion:* $\overline{MT} \cong \overline{HF}$
≅ Chords Thm.

**11.** *Given:* ⊙*C* ≅ ⊙*D*
*Conclusion:* $\overline{CT} \cong \overline{DH}$
≅ ⊙s have ≅ radii.

**12.** *Given:* ⊙*D*, $FA = AH$
*Conclusion:* $\overline{DA} \perp \overline{FH}$   Chord Thm., part **a**

**13.** *Given:* ⊙*C*, $\overleftrightarrow{GO}$ is the ⊥ bisector of $\overline{MT}$.
*Conclusion:* $\overleftrightarrow{GO}$ contains *C*.   Chord Thm., part **c**

**14.** *Given:* ⊙*C* ≅ ⊙*D*, $\overline{MT} \cong \overline{FH}$, $\overline{CO} \perp \overline{MT}$, $\overline{DA} \perp \overline{FH}$
*Conclusion:* $CO = DA$   ≅ Chords Thm.

Ex. 9–14

⊙*C*

⊙*D*

*Answer for page 382*

**28.** 1. ⊙*M* ≅ ⊙*N*; *MA, ND* are distances to $\overline{BC}$, $\overline{EF}$; $\overline{BC} \cong \overline{EF}$ (Given)
2. Draw $\overline{MB}, \overline{MC}, \overline{NE}, \overline{NF}$. (2 pts. determine a line.)
3. $\overline{MB} \cong \overline{NE}, \overline{MC} \cong \overline{NF}$ (Radii of ≅ ⊙s are ≅.)
4. △*MBC* ≅ △*NEF* (SSS Post.)
5. ∠*MCB* ≅ ∠*NFE* (Corres. parts of ≅ △s are ≅.)
6. $\overline{MA} \perp \overline{BC}, \overline{ND} \perp \overline{EF}$ (Def. of distance from pt. to line)
7. ∠*MAC*, ∠*NDF* are rt. ∠s. (Def. of ⊥)
8. △*MAC*, △*NDF* are rt. △s. (Def. of rt. △)
9. △*MAC* ≅ △*NDF* (HA Thm.)
10. $\overline{MA} \cong \overline{ND}$, so $MA = ND$ (Corres. parts of ≅ △s are ≅.)

**18.** In a plane, pt. equidistant from endpts. of seg. is on ⊥ bis. of seg.

**25.** *1.* ⊙$C$, $\overline{CD} \perp \overline{AE}$, $\overline{CB} \perp \overline{AF}$, $CD = CB$ (Given)
*2.* $\overline{AE} \cong \overline{AF}$, so $AE = AF$ (In a ⊙, chords equidistant from the center are ≅.)
*3.* $\overline{CD}$ bisects $\overline{AE}$, $\overline{CB}$ bisects $\overline{AF}$. (The ⊥ from center of ⊙ to a chord bisects it.)
*4.* $AD = \frac{1}{2}AE$, $FB = \frac{1}{2}AF$ (Def. of bisect)
*5.* $\frac{1}{2}AE = \frac{1}{2}AF$ (Mult. both sides of equation in step 2 by $\frac{1}{2}$.)
*6.* $AD = FB$ (Subst.)

**26.** *1.* ⊙$C$, $\overline{CD} \perp \overline{AE}$, $\overline{CB} \perp \overline{AF}$, $DE = BF$ (Given)
*2.* Same as step 3 for Ex. 25
*3.* $DE = \frac{1}{2}AE$, $BF = \frac{1}{2}AF$ (Def. of bisect)
*4.* $\frac{1}{2}AE = \frac{1}{2}AF$ (Subst.)
*5.* $AE = AF$ (Mult. both sides by 2.)
*6.* $CD = CB$ (In a ⊙, ≅ chords are equidistant from center.)

Ex. 25–26

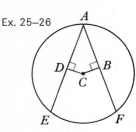

---

**15–24.** Complete these proofs.

**Given:** ⊙$C$, $\overleftrightarrow{DX}$ is the perpendicular bisector of chord $\overline{AB}$.

**Prove:** $\overleftrightarrow{DX}$ contains point $C$.

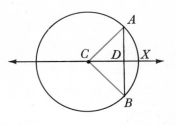

**Proof:**

| STATEMENTS | REASONS |
|---|---|
| *1.* ⊙$C$, $\overleftrightarrow{DX}$ the ⊥ bisector of chord $\overline{AB}$ | *1.* **15.** Given |
| *2.* Draw $\overline{CA}$ and $\overline{CB}$. | *2.* **16.** 2 pts. determine line. |
| *3.* $\overline{CA} \cong \overline{CB}$ | *3.* **17.** Radii of ⊙ are ≅. |
| *4.* $C$ is on the ⊥ bisector of $\overline{AB}$, $\overleftrightarrow{DX}$. | *4.* **18.** *At left* |

**Given:** ⊙$X$ contains points $Q$, $R$, and $S$.

**Prove:** Points $Q$, $R$, and $S$ are not collinear.

*[Plan:* Use an indirect proof.*]*

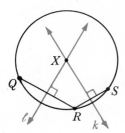 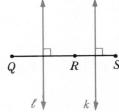

**Proof:**

| STATEMENTS | REASONS |
|---|---|
| *1.* ⊙$X$ contains points $Q$, $R$, and $S$. | *1.* **19.** Given |
| *2.* Assume $Q$, $R$, and $S$ are collinear. | *2.* **20.** Assump. for ind. prf. |
| *3.* Draw $\ell$, the ⊥ bisector of $\overline{QR}$. Draw $k$, the ⊥ bisector of $\overline{RS}$. | *3.* **21.** In plane, seg. has exactly 1 ⊥ bis. |
| *4.* $\ell \parallel k$ | *4.* **22.** In plane, lines ⊥ to same line are ∥. |
| *5.* But, $\ell$ intersects $k$ at point $X$. | *5.* **23.** Chord Thm., part **c** |
| *6.* So, $Q$, $R$, and $S$ are not collinear. | *6.* **24.** Prin. of Ind. Reas. |

**25. Given:** ⊙$C$, $\overline{CD} \perp \overline{AE}$, $\overline{CB} \perp \overline{AF}$, $CD = CB$

**Prove:** $AD = FB$

**26. Given:** ⊙$C$, $\overline{CD} \perp \overline{AE}$, $\overline{CB} \perp \overline{AF}$, $DE = BF$

**Prove:** $CD = CB$

© **27.** Prove part **b** of the Chord Theorem.
*Answer on page 380*

**28.** Prove part **b** of the Congruent Chords Theorem.
*Answer on page 381*

Use the figures and restatements on page 380.

Consider a line and a circle in a plane. They may have 0, 1, or 2 points of intersection.

**0 points of intersection**

**1 point of intersection**

**2 points of intersection**

In a plane, a line that intersects a circle at exactly one point is **tangent** to the circle. The line is called a *tangent line*, and the point of intersection is called the *point of tangency*. Segments and rays may also be tangent to a circle.

In a plane, if a line contains a point in the interior of a circle, it intersects the circle in two points.

In the center figure above, notice that the radius drawn to the point of tangency is perpendicular to the tangent. We prove this as part of the next theorem.

 A line is perpendicular to a radius at its outer endpoint if and only if it is tangent to the circle.  **Tangent Line Theorem**

**Part a.** If a line is perpendicular to a radius at its outer endpoint, then it is tangent to the circle.

You'll be asked to complete the proof of part **a** in Exercises 23–26.

**Part b.** If a line is tangent to a circle, then it is perpendicular to a radius at its outer endpoint.

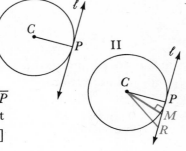

Given: Line $\ell$ is tangent to $\odot C$ at $P$.

Prove: $\overline{CP} \perp \ell$

[*Plan:* Use an indirect proof. Assume $\overline{CP}$ is not perpendicular to $\ell$, so some segment $\overline{CM} \perp \ell$, which leads to a contradiction.]

Proof: Assume $\overline{CP}$ is not perpendicular to $\ell$. We can draw one line, $\overleftrightarrow{CM}$, perpendicular to $\ell$ and containing $C$. See figure II. Choose $R$ on the ray opposite $\overrightarrow{MP}$, so that $\overline{MR} \cong \overline{MP}$. To prove $\triangle CMR \cong \triangle CMP$ we know that (**1**) $\overline{CM} \cong \overline{CM}$, (**2**) $\angle CMR$ and $\angle CMP$ are right angles because $\overline{CM} \perp \ell$, and (**3**) $\overline{MR} \cong \overline{MP}$. $\triangle CMR \cong \triangle CMP$ by the **LL** Theorem.

Therefore, $\overline{CR} \cong \overline{CP}$ because they are corresponding parts of congruent triangles. So $\overline{CR}$, like $\overline{CP}$, must be a radius, and $R$ must be on $\odot C$. Then both $R$ and $P$ would be on line $\ell$ and $\odot C$. This contradicts the given fact that $\ell$ is a tangent line. Therefore, the assumption that $\overline{CP}$ is not perpendicular to $\ell$ is false. A tangent is perpendicular to a radius at its outer endpoint.

Now consider the possible ways two circles can intersect.

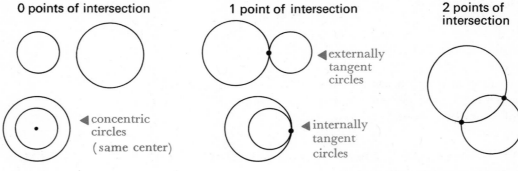

**0 points of intersection**

◄ concentric circles (same center)

**1 point of intersection**

◄ externally tangent circles

◄ internally tangent circles

**2 points of intersection**

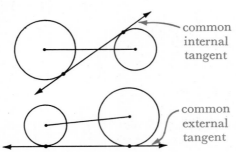

common internal tangent

common external tangent

A line tangent to more than one circle is called a **common tangent.** If a common tangent intersects the segment that joins the centers of the circles, it is a *common internal tangent.*

If a common tangent does not intersect the segment that joins the centers of the circles, it is a *common external tangent.*

**Assignment Guide**
*Oral:* 1–8
*Written:*
Min. 9–22
Reg. 9–21 odd; 23–27
Max. 9–21 odd; 23–27;
29
*Constructions:* 31–34

Ⓐ **1–5.** Use the appropriate figure at the right to name the following:

**1.** a segment tangent to ⊙P  $\overline{MD}$

**2.** a point of tangency  M

**3.** two perpendicular segments
   $\overline{MD}, \overline{MP}$

**4.** a common internal tangent  ℓ

**5.** a common external tangent  k

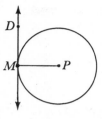

Ex. 1–3

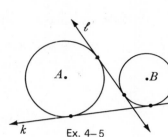

Ex. 4–5

**6–8.** Describe the circles with the appropriate term below.

**a.** externally tangent        **b.** concentric        **c.** internally tangent

**6.** b

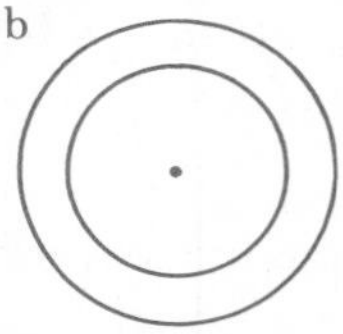

**7.** c

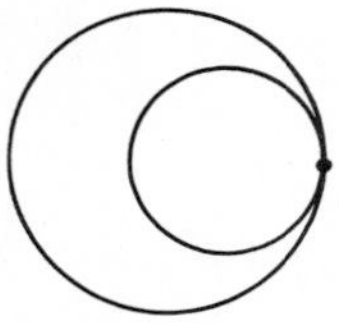

**8.** a

*Answer for page 386*
**30.** *Given:* B in exterior of
      ⊙X; $\overline{AB}, \overline{CB}$
      tangent to ⊙X
      at A, C
*Prove:* $\overline{AB} \cong \overline{CB}$
*Proof:*
1. $\overline{AB}, \overline{CB}$ tangent to
   ⊙X at A, C (Given)
2. Draw $\overline{XA}, \overline{XB}, \overline{XC}$.
   (2 pts. determine a
   line.)
3. $\overline{XA} \perp \overline{AB}, \overline{XC} \perp$
   $\overline{CB}$ (A radius is ⊥
   to tangent at pt. of
   tangency.)
4. ∠XAB, ∠XCB are
   rt. ∠s. (Def. of ⊥)
5. △XAB, △XCB are
   rt. △s. (Def. of rt.
   △)
6. $\overline{XB} \cong \overline{XB}$ (Seg. is
   ≅ to itself.)
7. $\overline{XA} \cong \overline{XC}$ (Radii of
   ⊙ are ≅.)
8. △XAB ≅ △XCB
   (HL Thm.)
9. $\overline{AB} \cong \overline{CB}$ (Corres.
   parts of ≅ △s are
   ≅.)

Ⓑ **9–12.** Use the figure at the right. $\overline{BA}$ and $\overline{BC}$ are tangent to ⊙X.

**9.** Find AB.  8

**10.** If m∠ABC = 72,
     find m∠AXC.  108

**11.** If m∠AXC = 110,
     find m∠ABC.  70

**12.** Find BC.  8

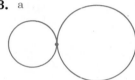

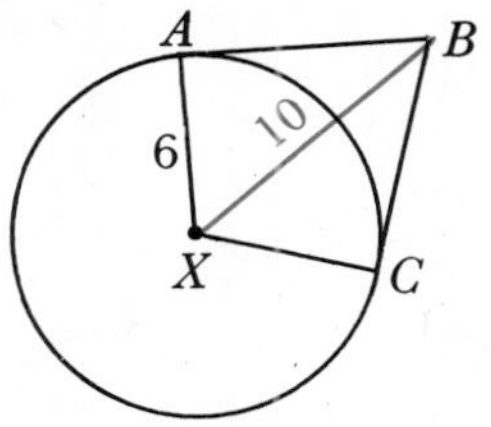

**13–16.** Draw two circles which can have exactly the given number of tangents—no more, no less. Draw the tangents also.

**13.** 1 common external tangent        **14.** 2 common external tangents

**15.** 3 common tangents        **16.** 4 common tangents

**17–22.** Find:

**17.** NT  5        **18.** m∠N  60

**19.** m∠TAI  30        **20.** m∠AIT  30

**21.** NI  10        **22.** AI  $5\sqrt{3}$

$\overleftrightarrow{RI}$ tangent to ⊙N at A
AN = AT = 5

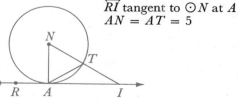

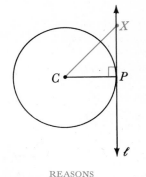

**27.** *1.* $\overline{AB}$ externally tangent to $\odot C$ and $\odot D$; $\overline{AB}$, $\overline{CD}$ not $\parallel$ (Given)
*2.* $\overline{CB} \perp \overline{AB}$, $\overline{DA} \perp \overline{AB}$ (A radius is $\perp$ to tangent at pt. of tangency.)
*3.* $\overline{CB} \parallel \overline{DA}$ (In plane, $\perp$s to same line are $\parallel$.)
*4.* $ABCD$ is trapezoid. (Def. of trapezoid)

**28.** *1.* $\odot A$, $\odot B$ externally tangent at $P$; $\ell$ tangent to $\odot A$ and $\odot B$ at $P$ (Given)
*2.* $\overrightarrow{AP}$ and $\overrightarrow{BP}$ are $\perp$ to $\ell$ at $P$. (A radius is $\perp$ to tangent at pt. of tangency.)
*3.* $A$, $P$, $B$ are collinear. (There is exactly 1 $\perp$ to a line at a given pt.)

**29.** *Given:* $\odot C$, diameter $\overline{AB}$; $\overleftrightarrow{AE}$, $\overleftrightarrow{BF}$ tangent to $\odot C$ at $A$, $B$
*Prove:* $\overleftrightarrow{AE} \parallel \overleftrightarrow{BF}$
*Proof:*
*1.* $\overleftrightarrow{AE}$, $\overleftrightarrow{BF}$ tangent to $\odot C$; diameter $\overline{AB}$ (Given)
*2.* $\overline{AB} \perp \overleftrightarrow{AE}$, $\overline{AB} \perp \overleftrightarrow{BF}$ (A radius is $\perp$ to tangent at pt. of tangency.)
*3.* $\overleftrightarrow{AE} \parallel \overleftrightarrow{BF}$ (In plane, $\perp$s to same line are $\parallel$.)

**30.** *Answer on page 385*

**23–26.** Complete the proof of part **a** of the Tangent Line Theorem.

**Given:** $\odot C$ with radius $\overline{CP}$, $\ell \perp \overline{CP}$ at $P$

**Prove:** Line $\ell$ is tangent to $\odot C$.

[*Plan:* Prove that any point of $\ell$ other than $P$ cannot be on $\odot C$.]

**Proof:**

| STATEMENTS | REASONS |
|---|---|
| *1.* Let $X$ be any point on $\ell$ distinct from $P$. | *1.* **23.** _____ A line contains infinitely many pts. |
| *2.* $\overline{CP} \perp \ell$ | *2.* **24.** _____ Given |
| *3.* $CP < CX$ | *3.* **25.** _____ *At left* |
| *4.* $X$ is in the exterior of $\odot C$. | *4.* **26.** _____ Def. of exterior of $\odot$ |
| *5.* Line $\ell$ is tangent to $\odot C$. | *5.* Def. of tangent line ($\ell$ intersects $\odot C$ at $P$ only.) |

*25.* Shortest seg. from pt. to line is the $\perp$ seg.

**27.** **Given:** $\overline{AB}$ is externally tangent to $\odot C$, and $\odot D$, $\overline{AB}$ is not parallel to $\overline{CD}$.

**Prove:** $ABCD$ is a trapezoid.

**28.** **Given:** $\odot A$ and $\odot B$ externally tangent at $P$, $\ell$ tangent to $\odot A$ and $\odot B$ at $P$.

**Prove:** $A$, $P$, and $B$ are collinear.

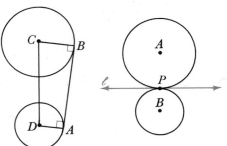

Ex. 27        Ex. 28

© **29.** Prove that the tangents to a circle at the endpoints of a diameter are parallel.

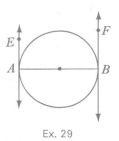

Ex. 29

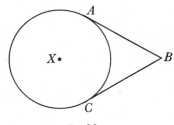

Ex. 30

**30.** Prove that two segments tangent to a circle from an exterior point are congruent.

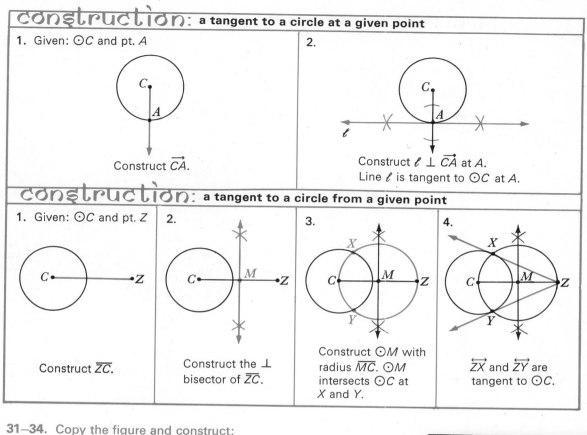

# construction: a tangent to a circle at a given point

**1.** Given: ⊙C and pt. A

Construct $\overrightarrow{CA}$.

**2.**

Construct $\ell \perp \overrightarrow{CA}$ at A.
Line $\ell$ is tangent to ⊙C at A.

# construction: a tangent to a circle from a given point

**1.** Given: ⊙C and pt. Z

Construct $\overline{ZC}$.

**2.**

Construct the ⊥ bisector of $\overline{ZC}$.

**3.**

Construct ⊙M with radius $\overline{MC}$. ⊙M intersects ⊙C at X and Y.

**4.**

$\overleftrightarrow{ZX}$ and $\overleftrightarrow{ZY}$ are tangent to ⊙C.

**31–34.** Copy the figure and construct:

**31.** a tangent to ⊙C at A

**32.** a tangent to ⊙C at B

**33.** a tangent to ⊙C from D

**34.** a tangent to ⊙C from E

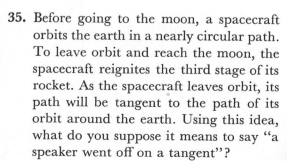

**35.** Before going to the moon, a spacecraft orbits the earth in a nearly circular path. To leave orbit and reach the moon, the spacecraft reignites the third stage of its rocket. As the spacecraft leaves orbit, its path will be tangent to the path of its orbit around the earth. Using this idea, what do you suppose it means to say "a speaker went off on a tangent"?

The speaker abruptly changed from the main topic to another that only touches upon it.

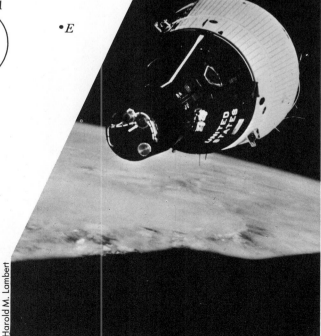

Harold M. Lambert

# 11.4  More About Spheres

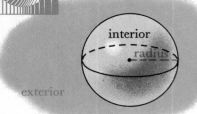

interior
radius
exterior

A sphere separates space into two sets, the interior and the exterior of the sphere. The **interior** of a sphere contains the points in space whose distance from the center of the sphere is less than the radius. The **exterior** of a sphere contains the points in space whose distance from the center of the sphere is greater than the radius.

Look at the photo of the Ping-Pong ball lying on the table. The ball touches the table at exactly one point. Also notice the result of slicing a Ping-Pong ball with a knife. The edge of the cut is a circle.

Consider a sphere and a plane in space. They may have 0, 1, or many points of intersection.

A plane that intersects a sphere at exactly one point is **tangent** to the sphere. The plane is called a *tangent plane* and the point of intersection is called the *point of tangency*.

**0 points of intersection**

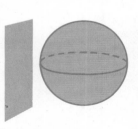

**1 point of intersection**

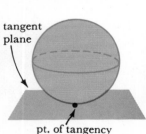

tangent plane

pt. of tangency

**Many points of intersection**

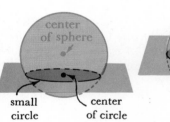

center of sphere

small circle

center of circle

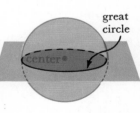

great circle

center

A plane that intersects a sphere at many points intersects the sphere at a circle. If the plane *does not* contain the center of the sphere, the intersection is called a *small circle*. The center of a small circle is the foot of the perpendicular from the center of the sphere to the plane. If the plane contains the center of a sphere, the intersection is called a *great circle*. A sphere and its great circles have the same radius.

The next theorem is about the intersection of a plane and a sphere and is similar to the Tangent Line Theorem.

A plane is perpendicular to a radius at its outer endpoint if and only if it is tangent to the sphere.

**Part a.** If a plane is perpendicular to a radius at its outer endpoint, then it is tangent to the sphere.

Given: Sphere $A$, plane $p \perp \overline{AB}$ at $B$

Prove: Plane $p$ is tangent to sphere $A$.

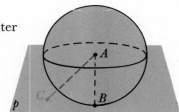

Proof:

| STATEMENTS | REASONS |
|---|---|
| 1. $\overline{AB} \perp p$ at $B$ | 1. Given |
| 2. Choose any point $C$ in $p$ so $B \neq C$. | 2. A plane contains at least 3 pts. |
| 3. $AB < AC$ | 3. The shortest seg. from a pt. to a plane is $\perp$ to the plane. |
| 4. $C$ is in the exterior of sphere $A$. | 4. Def. of ext. of a sphere |
| 5. Plane $p$ is tangent to sphere $A$. | 5. Def. of tangent plane (Plane $p$ intersects sphere $A$ at $B$ only.) |

**Part b.** If a plane is tangent to a sphere, then it is perpendicular to a radius at its outer endpoint.

Given: Plane $p$ tangent to sphere $A$ at $B$        (See figure above.)

Prove: $\overline{AB} \perp p$

You'll be asked to prove part **b** in Exercise 21.

The next theorem is similar to the Chord Theorem for circles.

a. The perpendicular from the center of a sphere to a chord bisects the chord.

b. The segment containing the center of a sphere and bisecting a chord that is not a diameter is perpendicular to the chord.

c. The perpendicular bisecting plane of a chord contains the center of the sphere.

**Chord Theorem for Spheres**

**23.** *1.* Plane $p$ is $\perp$ bisecting plane of chord $\overline{BC}$. (Given)

*2.* $AC = AB$ (Def. of sphere)

*3.* $p$ contains $A$. (Pt. is on $\perp$ bisecting plane of seg. if it is equidistant from endpts. of seg.)

## Part a.

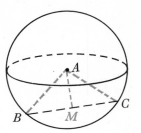

**Given:** Sphere $A$, chord $\overline{BC}$, $\overline{AM} \perp \overline{BC}$

**Prove:** $CM = MB$

**Proof:** Since $\overline{AM} \perp \overline{BC}$, $\angle AMC$ and $\angle AMB$ are right angles. We can draw congruent radii $\overline{AC}$ and $\overline{AB}$ to form right triangles $AMC$ and $AMB$. $\overline{AM} \cong \overline{AM}$, so $\triangle AMC \cong \triangle AMB$ by the HL Theorem, and $MC = MB$ because they are corresponding parts.

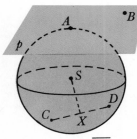

**Part b.** (See figure above.)

**Given:** Sphere $A$, chord $\overline{BC}$, $\overline{AM}$ bisects $\overline{BC}$.

**Prove:** $\overline{AM} \perp \overline{BC}$

**Part c.** (See figure at left.)

**Given:** Sphere $A$, plane $p$ is the perpendicular bisecting plane of chord $\overline{BC}$.

**Prove:** Plane $p$ contains point $A$.

You'll be asked to prove parts **b** and **c** in Exercises 22–23.

## Exercises 11.4

**Assignment Guide**
*Oral:* 1–10
*Written:*
Min. 11–19 odd; Quiz, p. 392
Reg. 11–19 odd; Quiz, p. 392
Max. 11–23 odd; Quiz, p. 392

Ⓐ **1–3.** The radius of sphere $S$ is 9. State whether each point is on the sphere, in its interior, or in its exterior.

**1.** $A$, if $SA = 11$
Exterior

**2.** $B$, if $SB = 7.73$
Interior

**3.** $C$, if $SC = \sqrt{81}$
Sphere

**4–9.** Only point $A$ is on sphere $S$ and in plane $p$. Refer to the figure.

**4.** Name all the points in the interior of sphere $S$.  $S, X$

**5.** Name all the points in the exterior of sphere $S$.  $B$

**6.** Why is plane $p$ a tangent plane?  It intersects sphere $S$ at exactly one pt.

**7.** Name the point of tangency.  $A$

**8.** If $\overline{SX}$ bisects $\overline{CD}$, name 2 perpendicular segments.
$\overline{SX}, \overline{CD}$ (or $\overline{CX}$ or $\overline{XD}$)

**9.** If $\overline{SX} \perp \overline{CD}$, name two segments with the same length.  $\overline{CX}, \overline{XD}$

**Given:** chord $\overline{CD}$

**10.** State the Chord Theorem for Spheres.  *See page 389.*

Ⓑ **11–14.** Points $X$ and $Y$ are on sphere $W$. $M$ is on $\overline{XY}$.

**11.** If $WM = 5$, and $YM = MX = 12$, find the radius of the sphere.  13

**12.** If $WX = 5$, $WM = 3$, and $\overline{WM} \perp \overline{YX}$, find $YM$ and $XM$.
$YM = XM = 4$

**13.** If $WY = 10$, $WM = 8$, and $\overline{WM} \perp \overline{YX}$, find $YX$.
12

**14.** If $XM = YM = 8$, and $WX = 10$, find $WM$.
6

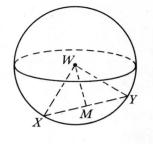

**15.** Can two spheres be tangent to each other? Draw a figure to illustrate your answer.  Yes

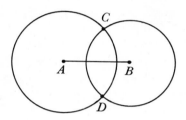

**16.** Circles $A$ and $B$ intersect at $C$ and $D$. Think of rotating the figure around line $AB$. Two intersecting spheres, $A$ and $B$, would be formed. Their intersection would be the path traced by points $C$ and $D$. Describe the intersection.  A circle

**17.** How many great circles can a sphere have?  Infinitely many

**18.** If a sphere has a radius of 10, how many small circles with radius 5 will the sphere have?  Infinitely many

**19–20.** Plane $p$ intersects sphere $A$ at $\odot B$ and $\overline{AB} \perp p$.

**19.** If the radius of sphere $A$ is 5, and $AB = 4$, find the radius of $\odot B$.  3

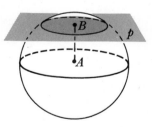

**20.** If $AB = 12$, and the radius of $\odot B$ is 5, find the radius of the sphere.  13

Ⓒ **21.** Prove part **b** of the Tangent Plane Theorem.

**22.** Prove part **b** of the Chord Theorem for Spheres.

**23.** Prove part **c** of the Chord Theorem for Spheres.

⎫
⎬ Use the figures and restatements on pages 389 and 390.
⎭

**24.** Make a model of two planes tangent to a sphere at the endpoints of a diameter. What can you conclude about the planes?
They do not intersect.

**21.** *Proof:* Assume $\overline{AB}$ is not $\perp$ to $p$. Draw $\overleftrightarrow{AC} \perp p$ at $C$. Choose $D$ on ray opp. $\overrightarrow{CB}$, so $\overline{CB} \cong \overline{CD}$. $\triangle ACD \cong \triangle ACB$ by LL Thm. because (1) $\overline{AC} \cong \overline{AC}$; (2) $\angle ACD$, $\angle ACB$ are rt. $\angle$s since $\overline{AC} \perp \overleftrightarrow{BC}$; and (3) $\overline{CB} \cong \overline{CD}$. So, $\overline{AD} \cong \overline{AB}$ because they are corres. parts of $\cong$ $\triangle$s, and $\overline{AD}$ is a radius. So $D$ and $B$ must be on sphere $A$ and plane $p$. But this contradicts the given that $p$ is a tangent plane. So the assumption is false, or $\overline{AB} \perp p$.

**22.** *Proof:* Since $\overline{AM}$ bisects $\overline{BC}$, $\overline{BM} \cong \overline{MC}$. Draw radii $\overline{AB}$ and $\overline{AC}$. Then $\overline{AB} \cong \overline{AC}$ because radii of a sphere are $\cong$. $\overline{AM} \cong \overline{AM}$, so $\triangle AMB \cong \triangle AMC$ by SSS Post. $\angle AMB$ and $\angle AMC$ are $\cong$ (because they are corres. parts) and are supp. (because they are adj. and their non-common sides are opp. rays). So $\angle AMB$, $\angle AMC$ are rt. $\angle$s, and $\overline{AM} \perp \overline{BC}$.

# GREAT CIRCLES OF THE WORLD

Did you know that the shortest air route to Paris from New York passes over Newfoundland? Because the earth's surface is approximately a sphere, the shortest air route between any two points follows the great circle containing those two points.

1. Use a globe to trace the shortest air route
   a. between Chicago, Illinois, and Rome, Italy.
   b. between New Orleans, Louisiana, and New Delhi, India.

2. By a great-circle route which distance is shorter: Los Angeles, California, to Sydney, Australia, or Seattle, Washington, to Tokyo, Japan?

1. a. Over Goose Bay, Newfoundland, and Paris, France
   b. Over Hudson Bay and Arctic Ocean and Omsk, U.S.S.R.

H. Armstrong Roberts

---

**Quick Quiz**
for
Sections
11.1 to 11.4

**1–7.** Name the following in the figure for (a) ⊙A and (b) sphere B.

1. a radius
   a. $\overline{AE}$    b. $\overline{BV}$
2. a tangent (line or plane)
   a. $\overleftrightarrow{MT}$    b. Plane p
3. a secant
   a. $\overleftrightarrow{SY}$    b. $\overleftrightarrow{GR}$
4. a chord
   a. $\overline{WD}$ (or $\overline{SY}$)    b. $\overline{JO}$ (or $\overline{GR}$)
5. perpendicular segments
   a. $\overline{EA} \perp \overline{WD}$    b. $\overline{BV} \perp \overline{JO}$
6. a point in the interior
   a. A    b. B
7. a point in the exterior
   a. M    b. H

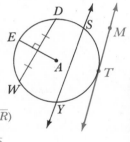

V is on sphere B and in plane p.
$BV \perp p$

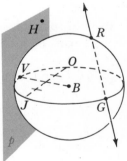

**8–9.** Refer to the figure.

8. Find ZY. 6    9. Find WY. 12

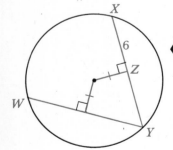

**10–12.** Refer to the figure. ▶

10. Name a great circle.  ⊙D

11. Name a small circle.  ⊙A

12. Find AC.  6

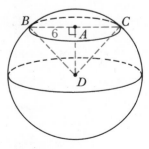

Gene Kuechmann

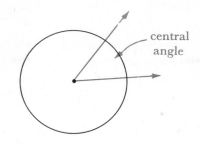
central angle

**Suggested Class Time**

| Course | Min. | Reg. | Max. |
|--------|------|------|------|
| Days | 1 | 1 | 1 |

The hands of a clock form an angle whose vertex is at the center of the face of the clock. Similarly, a **central angle** is an angle whose vertex is at the center of a circle.

| Name | Definition | Figure |
|------|-----------|--------|
| minor arc $AB$ or minor $\overset{\frown}{AB}$ ( $\frown$ is the symbol for arc.) | the points of $\odot C$ in the interior of and on central angle $ACB$ | |
| major arc $AXB$ or major $\overset{\frown}{AXB}$ (A major arc is always named by its endpoints and another point on the arc.) | the points of $\odot C$ in the exterior of and on central angle $ACB$ | minor $\overset{\frown}{AB}$, central angle, major $\overset{\frown}{AXB}$ |
| semicircle $\overset{\frown}{CYD}$ (A semicircle is named by its endpoints and another point on the arc.) | an arc whose endpoints are the endpoints of a diameter | Semicircle $\overset{\frown}{CYD}$, Semicircle $\overset{\frown}{CZD}$ |

All arcs can be measured in arc degrees, and there are 360 arc degrees in a circle.

| Measure | Comments | Figure |
|---------|----------|--------|
| **1** $m\overset{\frown}{AN} = m\angle AGN$ — Read $m\overset{\frown}{AN}$ as "the measure of arc $AN$." | The measure of a minor arc is equal to the measure of the central angle whose sides contain the endpoints of the arc. | |
| **2** $m\overset{\frown}{AEN} = 360 - m\overset{\frown}{AN}$ | The measure of a major arc is equal to 360 (number of degrees in a circle) minus the measure of its corresponding minor arc. | |
| **3** $m\overset{\frown}{NED} = 180$ | The measure of a semicircle is 180. | |

In the same circle or in congruent circles, **congruent arcs** are arcs that have the same measure.

In the same circle or in congruent circles, two chords that are not diameters are congruent if and only if their corresponding minor arcs are congruent.

**Part a.**

Given: $\odot A \cong \odot D$, $\overline{BC} \cong \overline{EF}$

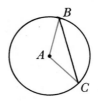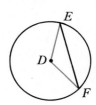

Prove: $\overparen{BC} \cong \overparen{EF}$

[*Plan:* Show $m\angle A = m\angle D$.]

Proof:

| STATEMENTS | REASONS |
|---|---|
| 1. $\overline{BC} \cong \overline{EF}$ | 1. Given |
| 2. Draw radii $\overline{AB}$, $\overline{AC}$, $\overline{DE}$, and $\overline{DF}$. | 2. Two pts. determine a line. |
| 3. $\overline{AB} \cong \overline{AC} \cong \overline{DE} \cong \overline{DF}$ | 3. Radii of $\cong \odot$s are $\cong$. |
| 4. $\triangle ABC \cong \triangle DEF$ | 4. SSS Postulate |
| 5. $m\angle A = m\angle D$ | 5. Corres. parts of $\cong \triangle$s are $\cong$. |
| 6. $m\overparen{BC} = m\angle A$, $m\overparen{EF} = m\angle D$ | 6. Def. of meas. of a minor arc |
| 7. $m\overparen{BC} = m\overparen{EF}$ | 7. Substitution (steps 5 and 6) |
| 8. $\overparen{BC} \cong \overparen{EF}$ | 8. Def. of $\cong$ arcs |

**Part b.**

Given: $\odot A \cong \odot D$, $\overparen{BC} \cong \overparen{EF}$     (See figure above.)

Prove: $\overline{BC} \cong \overline{EF}$

You'll be asked to prove part **b** in Exercise 28.

If $Y$ is on $\overparen{XZ}$, then $m\overparen{XZ} = m\overparen{XY} + m\overparen{YZ}$

*Answers for page 396*

27. *Sketch of Proof:* Draw $\overline{CT}$. $\angle TRC$, $\angle RTC$ are opp. $\cong$ sides of a $\triangle$ and are $\cong$. $\angle RTC \cong \angle TCV$ (Alt. int. $\angle$s) and $\angle TRC \cong \angle VCS$ (Corres. $\angle$s), so $\angle TCV \cong \angle VCS$ ($\angle$s $\cong$ to same $\angle$ are $\cong$). $\overparen{TV}$ and $\overparen{VS}$ are minor arcs of $\cong$ central $\angle$s, so $\overparen{TV} \cong \overparen{VS}$.

28. *1–2.* Same as steps 2–3 at right
  *3.* $\overparen{BC} \cong \overparen{EF}$ (Given)
  *4.* $m\overparen{BC} = m\overparen{EF}$ (Def. of $\cong$ arcs)
  *5.* Same as step 6 at right
  *6.* $m\angle A = m\angle D$ (Subst.)
  *7.* $\triangle ABC \cong \triangle DEF$ (SAS Post.)
  *8.* $\overline{BC} \cong \overline{EF}$ (Corres. parts of $\cong \triangle$s are $\cong$.)

**Example 1:**

Find $m\widehat{XZ}$ if $m\widehat{XY} = 34$, and $m\widehat{YZ} = 91$.

$m\widehat{XZ} = m\widehat{XY} + m\widehat{YZ}$

$\quad\quad = 34 + 91$

$\quad\quad = 125$

**Example 2:**

Find $m\widehat{YZ}$ if $m\widehat{XY} = 34$, and $m\widehat{XZ} = 131$.

$m\widehat{XZ} = m\widehat{XY} + m\widehat{YZ}$

$131 = 34 + m\widehat{YZ}$

$\quad 97 = m\widehat{YZ}$

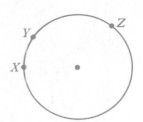

# Exercises 11.5

Ⓐ **1–4.** Name the following:

**1.** a central angle
$\angle RHU$ (or $\angle RHT$)

**2.** a minor arc
$\widehat{RU}$ (or $\widehat{RT}$)

**3.** a major arc
$\widehat{RTU}$ (or $\widehat{RUT}$)

**4.** a semicircle
$\widehat{TRU}$

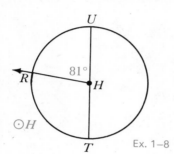

Ex. 1–8

**Assignment Guide**
*Oral:* 1–12
*Written:* Min. 13–24
　　　　　Reg. 13–25 odd
　　　　　Max. 13–27 odd

**5–8.** Find the following:

**5.** $m\widehat{RU}$ 81 　　　 **6.** $m\widehat{RTU}$ 279 　　　 **7.** $m\widehat{TRU}$ 180 　　　 **8.** $m\widehat{RT}$ 99

**9.** The measure of a minor arc is between ___0___ and ___180___.

**10.** The measure of a major arc is between ___180___ and ___360___.

**11–12.** Refer to the figure.

Ex. 11–12

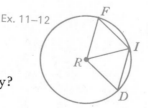

**11.** If $\widehat{FI} \cong \widehat{ID}$, why is $\overline{FI} \cong \overline{ID}$?
In a ⊙, ≅ minor arcs have ≅ chords.

**12.** If $FI = 6$, and $ID = 6$, is $\widehat{FI} \cong \widehat{ID}$? Why?
Yes; in a ⊙, ≅ chords have ≅ minor arcs.

Ⓑ **13–18.** Identify each arc as a minor arc, major arc, or semicircle, and find its measure.

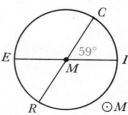

**13.** $\widehat{IR}$
Minor arc, 121

**14.** $\widehat{ER}$
Minor arc, 59

**15.** $\widehat{RIE}$
Major arc, 301

**16.** $\widehat{ERC}$
Major arc, 239

**17.** $\widehat{ERI}$
Semicircle, 180

**18.** $\widehat{RIC}$
Semicircle, 180

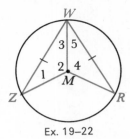

Ex. 19–22

**19–22.** Given $\odot M$ and $m\angle 2 = 116$, find:

**19.** $m\widehat{WZ}$  116  **20.** $m\angle 3$  32

**21.** $m\angle 4$  116  **22.** $m\widehat{ZR}$  128

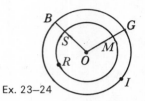

Ex. 23–24

**23–24.** The two circles are concentric, with center $O$.

**23.** Is $m\widehat{BG} = m\widehat{MS}$? Why?
Yes; $m\angle BOG = m\angle SOM$

**24.** If $m\angle O = 104$ find $m\widehat{BIG}$ and $m\widehat{SRM}$.
$m\widehat{BIG} = m\widehat{SRM} = 256$

**25.** *1.* $\overline{CE} \cong \overline{DE}$ (Given)
*2.* $\widehat{EC} \cong \widehat{ED}$ (In a $\odot$, $\cong$ chords have $\cong$ minor arcs.)
*3.* $m\widehat{EC} = m\widehat{ED}$ (Def. of $\cong$ arcs)
*4.* $m\widehat{EC} + m\widehat{CD} = m\widehat{ED} + m\widehat{DC}$ (Add $m\widehat{CD}$ to both sides; $\widehat{DC} = \widehat{CD}$.)
*5.* $m\widehat{ECD} = m\widehat{EC} + m\widehat{CD}$; $m\widehat{EDC} = m\widehat{ED} + m\widehat{DC}$ (Arc. Add. Post.)
*6.* $m\widehat{ECD} = m\widehat{EDC}$ (Subst.)
*7.* $\widehat{ECD} \cong \widehat{EDC}$ (Def. of $\cong$ arcs)

**26.** *Plan:* Use the given, and reverse the order of statements 1–6 above. Then $\triangle CED$ is isos. by def. of isos. $\triangle$.

**27–28.** *Answers on p. 394*

**25.** Given: $\odot G$, $\overline{CE} \cong \overline{DE}$

Prove: $\widehat{ECD} \cong \widehat{EDC}$

**26.** Given: $\odot G$, $m\widehat{ECD} = 220$, $m\widehat{EDC} = 220$

Prove: $\triangle CED$ isosceles

© **27.** Given: $\overline{RS}$ a diameter of $\odot C$, $\overline{RT} \parallel \overline{CV}$

Prove: $\widehat{TV} \cong \widehat{VS}$

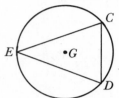

Ex. 25–26

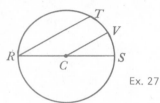

Ex. 27

**28.** Prove part **b** of the Congruent Arcs Theorem. Use the figure and restatement on page 394.

### ◆◆◀ Arcs, Lights, Action ▶◆◆

Some lights used in TV studios, theaters, and movie projectors are called arc lights. In an arc light, electricity leaps from one conductor or electrode to another. Air conducts the electric current and produces a flame in the shape of an arc. The electrodes become very hot which produces the strong, bright light.

Courtesy Mole-Richardson Co.

# CIRCLING THE GLOBE

The earth, approximately a sphere, rotates about one of its diameters. The endpoints of the diameter are the North and South Poles. The diameter itself is called the polar axis. The intersection of the earth and the perpendicular bisecting plane of the polar axis is a great circle called the equator.

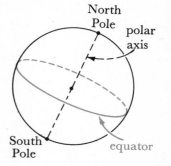

We use latitude and longitude to locate places on the earth. Latitude is the degree measure and direction, north or south of the equator, of a place or point. To find the latitude of a point $A$, think of a plane containing $A$ and the polar axis and intersecting the earth in a great circle. On that great circle the measure of minor $\overarc{AE}$ between $A$ and point $E$ on the equator is the measure of the latitude of point $A$. Since $A$ is north of the equator, the latitude of $A$ is 50° north.

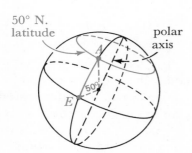

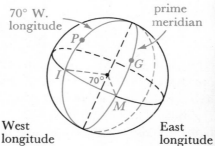

Longitude is the degree measure and direction, east or west of the prime meridian, of a point. The prime meridian is a semicircle containing $G$ (Greenwich, England) and having the North and South Poles as endpoints. To find the longitude of point $P$, find the point $I$ that is the intersection of the equator and the great circle through $P$ and the polar axis. Also find point $M$, the intersection of the prime meridian and the equator. The longitude of point $P$ is $m\overarc{IM}$. In this example, the longitude of $P$ is 70° west.

## Exercises

1–2. In a world atlas find the longitude and latitude of these places to the nearest degree.

1. Rio de Janeiro, Brazil
   43° W, 23° S

2. Seoul, South Korea
   127° E, 38° N

3–4. Identify each place having the following longitude and latitude.

3. longitude 85° east,
   latitude 27° north
   Near Katmandu, Nepal

4. longitude 0°,
   latitude 5° north
   Near Accra, Ghana

# Inscribed Angles and Intercepted Arcs

**Suggested Class Time**

| Course | Min. | Reg. | Max. |
|--------|------|------|------|
| Days   | 2    | 2    | 1    |

An **inscribed angle** of a circle is an angle whose vertex is on the circle and whose sides contain two chords of the circle. Below, $\angle A$, $\angle B$, and $\angle C$ are inscribed angles while $\angle X$ and $\angle Y$ are not. Each inscribed angle is said to be *inscribed in* the arc that contains its vertex. In figures 1 and 2, each of angles $A$, $B$, and $C$ is inscribed in the arc drawn in black.

Inscribed Angles

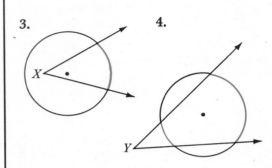

If *both* sides of an angle intersect a circle, the angle **intercepts** an arc. Each of the angles above *intercepts* the arc in red. An **intercepted arc** is in the interior of an angle, except for its endpoints which are on the angle. Notice that more than one angle may intercept an arc. (See figure 2.) Also, an angle may intercept more than one arc. (See figure 4.)

**Inscribed Angle Theorem**

 The measure of an inscribed angle is one half the measure of its intercepted arc.

*Answer for page 402*

**33.** *Given:* $\odot X$, $\angle B$ is inscribed in semicircle $\widehat{ABC}$ and intercepts $\widehat{ADC}$.
*Prove:* $m \angle B = 90$
*Proof:*
1. $\angle B$ intercepts $\widehat{ADC}$. (Given)
2. $m \angle B = \frac{1}{2} m \widehat{ADC}$ (Inscribed $\angle$ Thm.)
3. $m\widehat{ADC} = 180$ (Meas. of semicircle is 180.)
4. $m \angle B = \frac{1}{2} \cdot 180 = 90$ (Subst. and mult.)

**Given:** $\odot C$, $\angle X$ inscribed in $\odot C$ and intercepting $\widehat{YZ}$

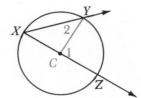

**Prove:** $m\angle X = \frac{1}{2} m\widehat{YZ}$

[*Plan:* To prove this theorem for any $\angle X$, we need to consider 3 cases.]

*Case 1:* The center of $\odot C$ is on $\angle X$. (See figure above.)

**Proof:**

| STATEMENTS | REASONS |
|------------|---------|
| 1. Draw $\overline{CY}$. | 1. Two pts. determine a line. |
| 2. $\overline{CX} \cong \overline{CY}$ | 2. Radii of a $\odot$ are $\cong$. |
| 3. $m\angle X = m\angle 2$ | 3. Isosceles Triangle Thm. (p. 180) |

| 4. $m\angle X + m\angle 2 = m\angle 1$ | 4. Meas. of an ext. $\angle$ of a $\triangle$ = sum of measures of remote int. $\angle$s. |
|---|---|
| 5. $2m\angle X = m\angle 1$ | 5. Substitution and addition |
| 6. $m\angle X = \frac{1}{2}m\angle 1$ | 6. Multiply both sides by $\frac{1}{2}$. |
| 7. $m\angle 1 = m\widehat{YZ}$ | 7. Def. of measure of minor arc |
| 8. $m\angle X = \frac{1}{2}m\widehat{YZ}$ | 8. Substitution ($m\widehat{YZ}$ for $m\angle 1$ in step 6) |

*Case 2:* $C$ is in the interior of $\angle X$.

*Case 3:* $C$ is in the exterior of $\angle X$.

You'll be asked to complete the proof of Case 2 in Exercises 25–30 and to prove Case 3 in Exercise 35.

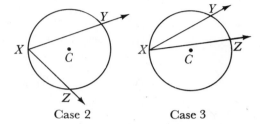

Case 2          Case 3

We can use the Inscribed Angle Theorem to prove the next two theorems. You'll be asked to prove these theorems in Exercises 33–34.

 An angle inscribed in a semicircle is a right angle.  **Semicircle Theorem**

 Two angles inscribed in the same arc are congruent.  **Angles in Same Arc Theorem**

If all the angles of a polygon are inscribed in a circle, then the polygon is *inscribed in* the circle, and the circle is *circumscribed about* the polygon.

Inscribed pentagon
Circumscribed circle

Noninscribed quadrilateral

If each side of a polygon is tangent to a circle, then the polygon is *circumscribed about* the circle, and the circle is *inscribed in* the polygon.

Circumscribed triangle
Inscribed circle

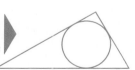

 If a quadrilateral is inscribed in a circle, then its opposite angles are supplementary.  **Inscribed Quadrilateral Theorem**

Given: $ABCD$ inscribed in $\odot R$

Prove: $\angle A$ and $\angle C$ as well as $\angle B$ and $\angle D$ are supplementary.

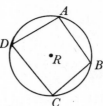

[*Plan:* Let $m\widehat{BCD} = x$. Then $m\widehat{BAD} = 360 - x$. Show $m\angle A + m\angle C = \frac{1}{2}(x + 360 - x) = 180.$]

You'll be asked to prove this theorem in Exercise 36.

# Exercises 11.6 ||||||||||||||||||||||||||||||||||||||||||||||||||||||||||||||||||||||||||||||||||||||||||||||||||||||

**Assignment Guide**
*Oral:* 1–8
*Written:*
Min. (day 1) 9–23 odd; Alg.
Rev., p. 402, odd
(day 2) 10–24 even;
Alg. Rev., p. 402, even
Reg. (day 1) 9–24
(day 2) 25–32; Alg.
Rev., p. 402
Max. 9–23 odd; 25–34
*Constructions:* 38; 40–41

Ⓐ **1–4.** Name the intercepted arc(s) for the angle, if possible.

**1.** $\widehat{BC}$

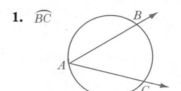

**2.** $\widehat{EF}$

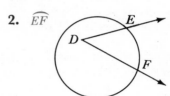

**3.** $\widehat{HK}, \widehat{MN}$

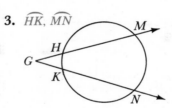

**4.** None

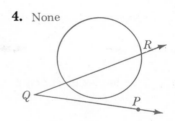

**5–8.** Refer to the figure.

**5.** Name the intercepted arc. $\widehat{XZ}$

**6.** Name the arc in which the angle is inscribed. $\widehat{XYZ}$

*Answer for page 402*
**34.** Given: $\odot X$; $\angle A$, $\angle B$ inscribed in $\widehat{YAZ}$
Prove: $\angle A \cong \angle B$
Proof:
1. $\angle A$, $\angle B$ inscribed in $\widehat{YAZ}$ (Given)
2. $m\angle A = \frac{1}{2}m\widehat{YZ}$, $m\angle B = \frac{1}{2}m\widehat{YZ}$ (Inscribed $\angle$ Thm.)
3. $m\angle A = m\angle B$ (Subst.)
4. $\angle A \cong \angle B$ (Def. of $\cong \angle$s)

**7.** If $m\widehat{XZ} = 72$, find $m\angle Y$.  36

**8.** If $m\angle Y = 41$, find $m\widehat{XZ}$.  82

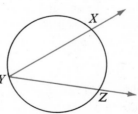

Ex. 5–8

Ⓑ **9–12.** Given $\odot T$, $m\widehat{EA} = 87$. find:

**9.** $m\angle ETA$  87    **10.** $m\angle H$  $43\frac{1}{2}$

**11.** $m\angle AEH$  90    **12.** $m\angle A$  $46\frac{1}{2}$

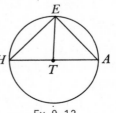

Ex. 9–12

**13–18.** $m\widehat{AB} = 94$, $m\angle DAC = 27$.

**13.** Find $m\angle ADB$. 47      **14.** Find $m\angle ACB$.
                                                  47

**15.** Find $m\widehat{DC}$. 54      **16.** Find $m\angle CBD$.
                                                  27

**17.** $\angle DAB$ and $\angle \underline{\phantom{DCB}}$ are supplementary.
                   DCB

**18.** $\angle ABC$ and $\angle \underline{\phantom{ADC}}$ are supplementary.
                   ADC

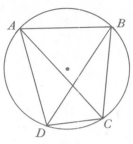

Ex. 13–18

*Ex. 19–24*

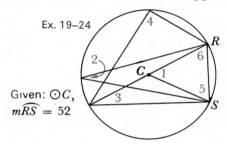

Given: $\odot C$,
$m\widehat{RS} = 52$

**19–24.** Refer to the figure. Find:

**19.** $m\angle 1$      **20.** $m\angle 2$
   52                        26

**21.** $m\angle 3$      **22.** $m\angle 4$
   26                        90

**23.** $m\angle 5$      **24.** $m\angle 6$
   64                        64

**25–30.** Give a reason for each statement.

Given: $\odot C$, $\angle YXZ$ inscribed in $\odot C$
      and intercepting $\widehat{YZ}$, point
      $C$ in the interior of $\angle YXZ$

Prove: $m\angle YXZ = \frac{1}{2}m\widehat{YZ}$

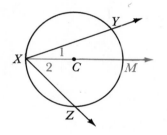

**Answers for page 402**

**35.** *Sketch of Proof:* Draw $\overleftrightarrow{XC}$ intersecting $\odot C$ at $M$. By Arc Add. Post. and subtr., $m\widehat{YZ} = m\widehat{YM} - m\widehat{ZM}$. By $\angle$ Add. Post. and subtr., $m\angle YXZ = m\angle YXM - m\angle ZXM$. Since $m\angle YXM = \frac{1}{2}m\widehat{YM}$ and $m\angle ZXM = \frac{1}{2}m\widehat{ZM}$ (Inscribed $\angle$ Thm., Case 1), $m\angle YXZ = \frac{1}{2}m\widehat{YZ}$ by subst., Distrib. Prop., and subst.

**36.** *Proof:* Let $m\widehat{BCD} = x$. Then $m\widehat{BAD} = 360 - x$ since a $\odot$ has 360 arc degrees. By Inscribed $\angle$ Thm. and subst., $m\angle A = \frac{1}{2}x$ and $m\angle C = \frac{1}{2}(360 - x)$. Then $m\angle A + m\angle C = \frac{1}{2}x + \frac{1}{2}(360 - x) = \frac{1}{2}(x + 360 - x) = 180$ by add. and Distrib. Prop. Sum of $\angle$s of quad. is 360, so $m\angle B + m\angle D = 180$ by subst. and subtr.

**Proof:**

| STATEMENTS | REASONS |
|---|---|
| *1.* $m\angle 1 = \frac{1}{2}m\widehat{YM}$ | *1.* **25.** Inscribed $\angle$ Thm., Case 1 |
| *2.* $m\angle 2 = \frac{1}{2}m\widehat{MZ}$ | *2.* **26.** Same as Ex. 25 |
| *3.* $m\angle YXZ = m\angle 1 + m\angle 2$ | *3.* **27.** $\angle$ Add. Post. (p. 53) |
| *4.* $m\angle YXZ = \frac{1}{2}m\widehat{YM} + \frac{1}{2}m\widehat{MZ}$ | *4.* **28.** Subst. (steps 1–3) |
| *5.* $m\angle YXZ = \frac{1}{2}(m\widehat{YM} + m\widehat{MZ})$ | *5.* Distributive Prop. |
| *6.* $m\widehat{YM} + m\widehat{MZ} = m\widehat{YZ}$ | *6.* **29.** Arc Add. Post. (p. 394) |
| *7.* $m\angle YXZ = \frac{1}{2}m\widehat{YZ}$ | *7.* **30.** Subst. (steps 5 and 6) |

**31.** Draw a circle with an inscribed hexagon.
*Join any 6 pts. on the ⊙.*

**32.** Construct a circle and inscribe a quadrilateral in it.
*Join any 4 pts. on the ⊙.*

**33.** Prove the Semicircle Theorem, page 399. *Answer on page 398*

**34.** Prove the Angles in Same Arc Theorem, page 399.
*Answer on page 400*

© **35.** Prove Case 3 of the Inscribed Angle Theorem. ⎫ Use the figures
35–36. *Answers on p. 401* ⎬ on pages 399
**36.** Prove the Inscribed Quadrilateral Theorem. ⎭ and 400.

**37.** Given: Semicircle $\widehat{ACD}$, $\overline{CB} \perp \overline{AD}$ at $B$

Prove: $\overline{BC}$ is the geometric mean of $\overline{AB}$ and $\overline{BD}$.

**38.** Why does the construction on page 347 work?
*See Ex. 37.*

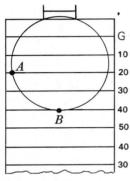

Ex. 39

**39.** Does a field goal kicker have to aim more carefully from point A on the 20 yd. line near the side of the field or from point B on the 40 yd. line at the center of the field? Why?

**37.** *Sketch of Proof:* Draw $\overline{AC}$ and $\overline{CD}$. ∠ inscribed in a semicircle is a rt. ∠, so $ACD$ is a rt. △. $\overline{CB}$ is the alt. to the hypotenuse and is the geometric mean of the segs. of the hypotenuse.

**39.** No; if segs. from $A$ and $B$ are drawn to each upright of the goal, ∠$A$ and ∠$B$ intercept the same arc.

**construction: triangle circumscribed about a circle**

1. Given: ⊙$C$

Choose points $X$, $Y$, and $Z$ so $m\widehat{XYZ} > 180$ and no 2 points are the endpoints of a diameter.

2.

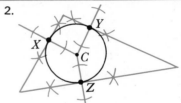

Construct tangents at $X$, $Y$, and $Z$. The tangents will intersect to form a triangle.

**40.** Circumscribe a triangle about a circle with radius 3 cm.

**41.** Circumscribe a triangle about a circle with radius 4 cm.

---

*Algebra Review*

**Review this skill:**
● adding and subtracting rational expressions

Add or subtract. Express each answer in simplest form.

**1.** $\frac{2}{9} + \frac{4}{9}$ $\frac{2}{3}$

**2.** $1 - \frac{1}{5}$ $\frac{4}{5}$

**3.** $\frac{1}{3} + \frac{3}{8}$ $\frac{17}{24}$

**4.** $\frac{7}{9} - \frac{2}{3}$ $\frac{1}{9}$

**5.** $\frac{2}{x} + \frac{5}{x}$ $\frac{7}{x}$

**6.** $\frac{2a}{4b} - \frac{a}{4b}$ $\frac{a}{4b}$

**7.** $\frac{5}{y} + \frac{6y}{2}$ $\frac{3y^2 + 5}{y}$

**8.** $\frac{2s}{3d} - \frac{5}{d}$ $\frac{2s - 15}{3d}$

**9.** $\frac{9w}{10z^2} + \frac{4w^2}{6wz^2}$ $\frac{47w}{30z^2}$

**10.** $\frac{8a}{3b} - \frac{2}{ab^3}$ $\frac{8a^2b^2 - 6}{3ab^3}$

# Angles Formed by Secants, Tangents, and Chords

 **11.7**

We will now use the Inscribed Angle Theorem to prove some theorems about angles formed by chords, secants, and tangents.

NOTE: In the case of chords, an angle is formed when each chord is extended. For example,

**Suggested Class Time**

| Course | Min. | Reg. | Max. |
|--------|------|------|------|
| Days | 2 | 2 | 1 |

chords $\overline{AC}$ and $\overline{BD}$
intersecting at $X$       form $\angle AXD$       as well as $\angle BXC$

*Answer for page 407*

37. *Sketch of Proof:* Draw $\overline{BC}$. Meas. of ext. $\angle$ of a $\triangle$ = sum of measures of remote int. $\angle$s, so $m\angle AXB = m\angle C + m\angle B$. Then $m\angle AXB = \frac{1}{2}m\widehat{AB} + \frac{1}{2}m\widehat{CD}$ by Inscribed $\angle$ Thm. and subst.

The measure of an angle formed by two chords intersecting in the interior of a circle is equal to one half the sum of the measures of the arcs intercepted by the angle and its vertical angle.

 **Intersecting Chords Theorem**

Given: $\odot P$, chords $\overline{BD}$ and $\overline{AC}$ intersect at $X$.

Prove: $m\angle AXB = \frac{1}{2}(m\widehat{AB} + m\widehat{CD})$

[*Plan:* Draw $\overline{BC}$, making $m\angle AXB = m\angle C + m\angle B$, and use the Inscribed Angle Theorem.]

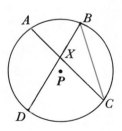

The proof is asked for in Exercise 37.

The measure of an angle formed by a tangent and a chord is one half the measure of the intercepted arc.

 **Tangent and Chord Theorem**

For a tangent and chord to form an angle, an endpoint of the chord must be the point of tangency. When this occurs, there are two cases possible. In each case *two* angles are actually formed.

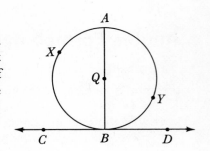

*Case 1:* The chord is a diameter. In this case, $\angle ABC$ and $\angle ABD$ are right angles. (Why?) The arc that each of these angles intercepts is a semicircle (measure 180). So, $m\angle ABC = \frac{1}{2}m\overset{\frown}{AXB}$ and $m\angle ABD = \frac{1}{2}m\overset{\frown}{AYB}$.

*Case 2:* The chord is *not* a diameter.

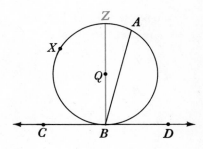

Given: $\odot Q$, chord $\overline{AB}$, $\overleftrightarrow{BC}$ is tangent to $\odot Q$ at $B$.

Prove: $m\angle ABC = \frac{1}{2}m\overset{\frown}{AZB}$,
$\quad\quad m\angle ABD = \frac{1}{2}m\overset{\frown}{AB}$

Proof:

| STATEMENTS | REASONS |
|---|---|
| 1. Draw $\overleftrightarrow{QB} \perp \overleftrightarrow{BC}$ intersecting $\odot Q$ at $Z$. | 1. A radius is $\perp$ to a tangent at the pt. of tangency. |
| 2. $m\angle ZBC = \frac{1}{2}m\overset{\frown}{ZXB}$, $\quad m\angle ZBD = \frac{1}{2}m\overset{\frown}{ZAB}$ | 2. Case 1 above |
| 3. $m\angle ABZ = \frac{1}{2}m\overset{\frown}{AZ}$ | 3. Inscribed Angle Thm. |
| 4. $m\angle ABC = m\angle ABZ + m\angle ZBC$, $\quad m\angle ABD = m\angle ZBD - m\angle ABZ$ | 4. Angle Addition Post. (p. 53) |
| 5. $m\angle ABC = \frac{1}{2}m\overset{\frown}{AZ} + \frac{1}{2}m\overset{\frown}{ZXB}$, $\quad m\angle ABD = \frac{1}{2}m\overset{\frown}{ZAB} - \frac{1}{2}m\overset{\frown}{AZ}$ | 5. Substitution (from steps 2 and 3 into step 4) |
| 6. $m\angle ABC = \frac{1}{2}(m\overset{\frown}{AZ} + m\overset{\frown}{ZXB})$, $\quad m\angle ABD = \frac{1}{2}(m\overset{\frown}{ZAB} - m\overset{\frown}{AZ})$ | 6. Distributive Property |
| 7. $m\overset{\frown}{AZB} = m\overset{\frown}{AZ} + m\overset{\frown}{ZXB}$, $\quad m\overset{\frown}{AB} = m\overset{\frown}{ZAB} - m\overset{\frown}{AZ}$ | 7. Arc Addition Post. |
| 8. $m\angle ABC = \frac{1}{2}m\overset{\frown}{AZB}$, $\quad m\angle ABD = \frac{1}{2}m\overset{\frown}{AB}$ | 8. Substitution |

**Secant and Tangent Theorem**

 The measure of the angle formed by two secants, a tangent and a secant, or two tangents intersecting in the exterior of a circle is one half the difference of the measures of the intercepted arcs.

*Case 1:* The angle is formed by two secants.

**Given:** $\odot C$, secants $\overleftrightarrow{RS}$ and $\overleftrightarrow{RT}$

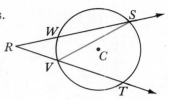

**Prove:** $m\angle R = \frac{1}{2}(m\widehat{ST} - m\widehat{WV})$

**Proof:**

| STATEMENTS | REASONS |
|---|---|
| 1. $\odot C$, secants $\overleftrightarrow{RS}$ and $\overleftrightarrow{RT}$ | 1. Given |
| 2. Draw $\overline{SV}$. | 2. Two pts. determine a line. |
| 3. $m\angle VSR + m\angle R = m\angle SVT$ | 3. Meas. of ext. $\angle$ of a $\triangle$ = sum of measures of remote int. $\angle$s. |
| 4. $m\angle R = m\angle SVT - m\angle VSR$ | 4. Subtr. $m\angle VSR$ from both sides. |
| 5. $m\angle SVT = \frac{1}{2}m\widehat{ST}$, $m\angle VSR = \frac{1}{2}m\widehat{WV}$ | 5. Inscribed Angle Theorem |
| 6. $m\angle R = \frac{1}{2}m\widehat{ST} - \frac{1}{2}m\widehat{WV}$ | 6. Substitution |
| 7. $m\angle R = \frac{1}{2}(m\widehat{ST} - m\widehat{WV})$ | 7. Distributive Prop. |

*Case 2:* The angle is formed by a secant and a tangent.

**Given:** $\overleftrightarrow{XY}$ tangent to $\odot C$ at $Y$, secant $\overleftrightarrow{XW}$

**Prove:** $m\angle X = \frac{1}{2}(m\widehat{YW} - m\widehat{YZ})$

[*Plan:* Draw $\overline{YW}$, and show that $m\angle X = m\angle WYV - m\angle YWX$.]

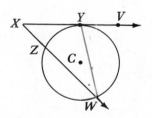

*Case 3:* The angle is formed by two tangents.

**Given:** $\overleftrightarrow{MN}$ tangent to $\odot C$ at $N$, $\overleftrightarrow{MP}$ tangent to $\odot C$ at $P$

**Prove:** $m\angle NMP = \frac{1}{2}(m\widehat{NDP} - m\widehat{NP})$

[*Plan:* Draw $\overleftrightarrow{MC}$ and use Case 2.]

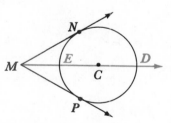

You'll be asked to prove Cases 2 and 3 in Exercises 38–39.

When deciding which theorem to use to find the measure of an angle formed by chords, secants, or tangents, it helps to look at the location of the vertex. Is it on the circle, in the interior of the circle, or in the exterior of the circle?

*Answers for page 407*

**38.** *Sketch of Proof:* Draw $\overline{YW}$. $m\angle X = m\angle WYV - m\angle YWX$ (Meas. of ext. $\angle$ of $\triangle$ = sum of measures of remote int. $\angle$s; subtr.). Use Tangent and Chord Thm., Inscribed $\angle$ Thm., and subst. to show $m\angle X = \frac{1}{2}m\widehat{YW} - \frac{1}{2}m\widehat{YZ}$.

**39.** *Sketch of Proof:* Draw $\overline{MC}$, then $m\angle NMP = m\angle NMC + m\angle CMP$ ($\angle$ Add. Post.). By Case 2, subst., and Distrib. Prop., $m\angle NMP = \frac{1}{2}(m\widehat{ND} + m\widehat{DP}) - \frac{1}{2}(m\widehat{NE} + m\widehat{EP})$. Then, $m\angle NMP = \frac{1}{2}m\widehat{NDP} - \frac{1}{2}m\widehat{NP}$ by Arc Add. Post. and subst.

| Example 1: | Example 2: | Example 3: |
|---|---|---|
| 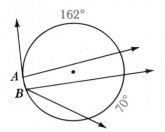 | 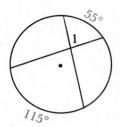 | 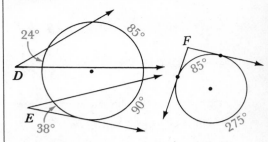 |
| The vertex is *on the circle*, so use the Tangent and Chord or the Inscribed Angle Theorem. | The vertex is *in the interior of the circle*, so use the Intersecting Chords Theorem. | The vertex is *in the exterior of the circle*, so use the Secant and Tangent Theorem. |
| $m\angle A = \frac{1}{2} \cdot 162 = 81$ <br> $m\angle B = \frac{1}{2} \cdot 70 = 35$ | $m\angle 1 = \frac{1}{2}(55 + 115)$ <br> $= \frac{1}{2}(170)$ <br> $= 85$ | $m\angle D = \frac{1}{2}(85 - 24) = \frac{1}{2} \cdot 61 = 30\frac{1}{2}$ <br> $m\angle E = \frac{1}{2}(90 - 38) = \frac{1}{2} \cdot 52 = 26$ <br> $m\angle F = \frac{1}{2}(275 - 85) = \frac{1}{2} \cdot 190 = 95$ |

# Exercises 11.7

(A) **1–10.** Use the appropriate figure to find $m\angle 1$.

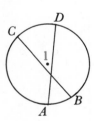

Ex. 1–2

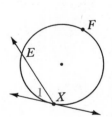

Ex. 3–4

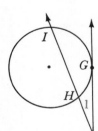

Ex. 5–6

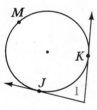

Ex. 7–8

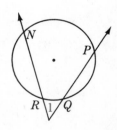

Ex. 9–10

**Assignment Guide**
*Oral:* 1–10
*Written:*
Min. (day 1) 11–27 odd
    (day 2) 12–28 even
Reg. (day 1) 11–27 odd
    (day 2) 12–28 even
Max. 11–39 odd

1. $m\widehat{AB} = 36$, $m\widehat{DC} = 64$   50

2. $m\widehat{AB} = 40$, $m\widehat{DC} = 50$   45

3. $m\widehat{XE} = 102$   51

4. $m\widehat{EFX} = 280$   40

5. $m\widehat{GI} = 88$, $m\widehat{GH} = 48$   20

6. $m\widehat{GH} = 50$, $m\widehat{GI} = 90$   20

7. $m\widehat{JK} = 100$   80

8. $m\widehat{JMK} = 260$   80

9. $m\widehat{NP} = 128$, $m\widehat{RQ} = 30$   49

10. $m\widehat{NP} = 123$, $m\widehat{RQ} = 23$   50

Ⓑ **11–16.** $\overleftrightarrow{DF}$ is tangent to $\odot P$ at $D$. Find:

**11.** $m\angle AGC$   $63\frac{1}{2}$   **12.** $m\angle FDA$   $124$

**13.** $m\angle BCD$   $29\frac{1}{2}$   **14.** $m\angle CDF$   $90$

**15.** $m\angle FDE$   $54$   **16.** $m\angle AGB$   $116\frac{1}{2}$

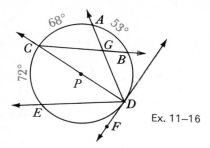

Ex. 11–16

**17–24.** $\overleftrightarrow{DN}$ and $\overleftrightarrow{DR}$ are tangent to $\odot C$. Find:

**17.** $m\angle MNS$   $102\frac{1}{2}$   **18.** $m\angle RDS$   $7\frac{1}{2}$

**19.** $m\angle SDV$   $27\frac{1}{2}$   **20.** $m\angle VTS$   $67\frac{1}{2}$

**21.** $m\angle NDV$   $35$   **22.** $m\angle NDR$   $70$

**23.** $m\angle STX$   $112\frac{1}{2}$   **24.** $m\angle SDM$   $62\frac{1}{2}$

Ex. 17–24

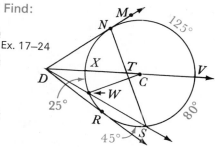

**25–28.** Use the appropriate figure.

**25.**

Find $m\widehat{AB}$.   $15$

**26.**

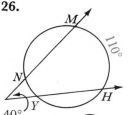

Find $m\widehat{NY}$.   $30$

**27.**

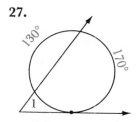

Find $m\angle 1$.   $55$

**28.**

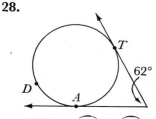

Find $m\widehat{TDA}$, $m\widehat{TA}$.

$242$; $118$

Ⓒ **29–36.** $\overleftrightarrow{TM}$ and $\overleftrightarrow{TC}$ are tangent to $\odot G$. Find:

**29.** $m\angle CMT$   $54$   **30.** $m\widehat{MHC}$   $108$

**31.** $m\widehat{MH}$   $70$   **32.** $m\widehat{SCM}$   $236$

**33.** $m\widehat{MNC}$   $252$   **34.** $m\widehat{SM}$   $124$

**35.** $m\widehat{NS}$   $22$   **36.** $m\angle HNC$   $19$

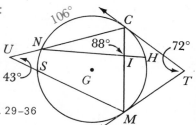

Ex. 29–36

**37.** *Answer on page 403*

**38–39.** *Answers on p. 405*

**37.** Prove the Intersecting Chords Theorem.

**38.** Prove Case 2 of the Secant and Tangent Theorem.

**39.** Prove Case 3 of the Secant and Tangent Theorem.

} Use the figures and restatements on pages 403 and 405.

**40.** Construct a circle. Mark off 36 arcs of 10°. Label the points $M_1$, $M_2$, $M_3$, $\cdots$, $M_{36}$. Draw $\overline{M_1 M_9}$, $\overline{M_3 M_{10}}$, $\overline{M_5 M_{11}}$, $\overline{M_7 M_{12}}$, $\cdots$, $\overline{M_{35} M_8}$. Notice the curve that appears. The mathematical name for the curve is *cardioid*.

# 11.8 Circles and Lengths of Segments

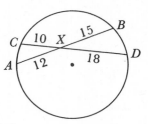

Look at the circle at the left. Chords $\overline{AB}$ and $\overline{CD}$ intersect at $X$. In millimeters, the measures of the segments are $AX = 12$ mm, $BX = 15$ mm, $CX = 10$ mm, and $DX = 18$ mm. Notice that

$$AX \cdot BX = CX \cdot DX$$
$$12 \cdot 15 = 10 \cdot 18$$
$$180 = 180$$

Is this relationship between the lengths of the segments always true? Consider the next theorem.

**Suggested Class Time**

| Course | Min. | Reg. | Max. |
|--------|------|------|------|
| Days   | 1    | 1    | 1    |

**Segments of Chords Theorem**

If two chords intersect in the interior of a circle, the product of the lengths of the segments of one chord is equal to the product of the lengths of the segments of the other chord.

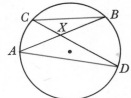

**Given:** Chords $\overline{AB}$ and $\overline{CD}$ intersect at $X$.

**Prove:** $AX \cdot BX = CX \cdot DX$

**Proof:**

| STATEMENTS | REASONS |
|------------|---------|
| 1. Chords $\overline{AB}$ and $\overline{CD}$ intersect at $X$. | 1. Given |
| 2. Draw $\overline{BC}$ and $\overline{AD}$. | 2. Two pts. determine a line. |
| 3. $\angle A \cong \angle C$, $\angle D \cong \angle B$ | 3. Two $\angle$s inscribed in the same arc are $\cong$. |
| 4. $\triangle AXD \sim \triangle CXB$ | 4. AA Similarity Theorem |
| 5. $\dfrac{AX}{CX} = \dfrac{DX}{BX}$ | 5. Corres. sides of $\sim \triangle$s are proportional. |
| 6. $AX \cdot BX = CX \cdot DX$ | 6. Cross multiply. |

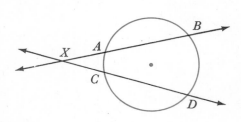

Consider two secants that intersect at a point $X$. $\overline{XB}$ and $\overline{XD}$ are called **secant segments** because part of each segment is in the exterior of the circle. $\overline{XA}$ is the *external part* of secant segment $\overline{XB}$, and $\overline{XC}$ is the external part of $\overline{XD}$. We now prove the Segments of Secants Theorem, which is closely related to the Segments of Chords Theorem.

If two secants intersect at a point in the exterior of a circle, the length of one secant segment times the length of its external part is equal to the length of the other secant segment times the length of its external part.

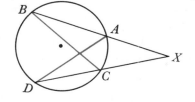

Given: Secant segments $\overline{XB}$ and $\overline{XD}$

Prove: $XB \cdot XA = XD \cdot XC$

Proof:

| STATEMENTS | REASONS |
|---|---|
| 1. Secant segments $\overline{XB}$ and $\overline{XD}$ | 1. Given |
| 2. Draw $\overline{CB}$ and $\overline{AD}$. | 2. Two pts. determine a line. |
| 3. $\angle B \cong \angle D$ | 3. Two $\angle$s inscribed in the same arc are $\cong$. |
| 4. $\angle X \cong \angle X$ | 4. An $\angle$ is $\cong$ to itself. |
| 5. $\triangle CXB \sim \triangle AXD$ | 5. AA Similarity Theorem |
| 6. $\dfrac{XB}{XD} = \dfrac{XC}{XA}$ | 6. Corres. sides of $\sim$ $\triangle$s are proportional. |
| 7. $XB \cdot XA = XD \cdot XC$ | 7. Cross multiply. |

Notice how similar the proofs of the Segments of Chords and the Segments of Secants Theorems are.

A **tangent segment** is a segment that is tangent to a circle at one of its endpoints. $\overline{XC}$ is a tangent segment.

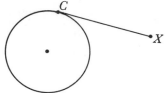

If a tangent segment and a secant segment intersect in the exterior of a circle, the length of the tangent segment squared is equal to the product of the lengths of the secant segment and its external part.

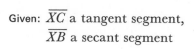

Given: $\overline{XC}$ a tangent segment,
$\overline{XB}$ a secant segment

Prove: $(XC)^2 = XB \cdot XA$

[*Plan:* Draw $\overline{CA}$ and $\overline{CB}$, and show that $\triangle ACX \sim \triangle CBX$.]

You'll be asked to prove the Tangent-Secant Segments Theorem in Exercise 23.

*Answer for page 410*

23. *Sketch of Proof:* Draw $\overline{CA}$, $\overline{CB}$. $\angle X \cong \angle X$, and $\angle B \cong \angle ACX$ since $m\angle B = \frac{1}{2}m\widehat{CA}$ (Inscribed $\angle$ Thm.) and $m\angle ACX = \frac{1}{2}m\widehat{CA}$ (Tangent and Chord Thm.). So $\triangle ACX \sim \triangle CBX$ by AA Sim. Thm., and $\dfrac{XC}{XB} = \dfrac{XA}{XC}$.

When finding the lengths of segments, study the figure to decide which theorem to use, as in the examples below.

**Example 1:**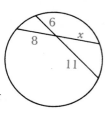

Find $x$.

$8x = 6 \cdot 11$

$8x = 66$

$x = \frac{66}{8} = 8\frac{1}{4}$

**Example 2:**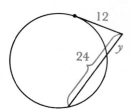

Find $y$.

$12^2 = 24 \cdot y$

$144 = 24 \cdot y$

$6 = y$

## Exercises 11.8

**Assignment Guide**
*Oral:* 1–8
*Written:* Min. 9–16
　　　Reg. 9–16;
　　　　17–21 odd
　　Max. 9–23 odd

Ⓐ **1–8.** State the equation you would use to find $x$.

**1.** $2x = 3 \cdot 6$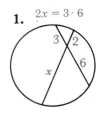

**2.** $12x = 9 \cdot 4$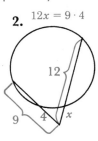

**3.** $x^2 = 8 \cdot 2$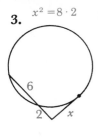

**4.** $6^2 = 3x$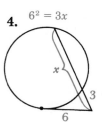

**5.** $2x = 3 \cdot 4$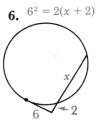

**6.** $6^2 = 2(x + 2)$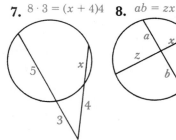

**7.** $8 \cdot 3 = (x + 4)4$

**8.** $ab = zx$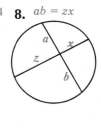

**9.** $x = 9$　**10.** $x = 3$
**11.** $x = 4$　**12.** $x = 12$
**13.** $x = 6$　**14.** $x = 16$
**15.** $x = 2$　**16.** $x = \dfrac{ab}{z}$

Ⓑ **9–16.** Solve for $x$ in Exercises 1–8.

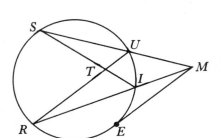

**17–22.** Refer to the figure.

**17.** $ST = 6$, $TI = 5$, $RT = 10$, find $RU$. 13

**18.** $SM = 21$, $RI = 14$, $RM = 22$, find $UM$. $8\frac{8}{21}$

**19.** $ME = 6$, $UM = 4$, find $SM$. 9

**20.** $SI = 8$, $RT = 8$, $TU = 2$, find $ST$. 4

**21.** $MS = 12$, $UM = 2\sqrt{3}$, $MI = 3$, find $RM$. $8\sqrt{3}$

**22.** $IR = 6\sqrt{3}$, $MI = 3\sqrt{3}$, find $ME$. 9

Ⓒ **23.** Prove the Tangent-Secant Segments Theorem. Use the figure and restatement on page 409. *Answer on page 409*

# Locus    11.9

Susan is looking for a summer job. Since she wants to walk to work, she wants to find a job a mile or less from her home. Looking through the want ads of the newspaper, she circles all the jobs that satisfy that condition.

In geometry, sometimes we want to find all the points satisfying a given condition. A **locus of points** (plural, **loci**) is a geometric figure containing all the points, and only those points, that satisfy a given condition.

**Example 1:** In a plane, what is the locus of points 2 cm from point $X$?

◀ NOTE: "In a plane" means that *all* points, those given and those in the locus, are in the same plane.

1.
2.

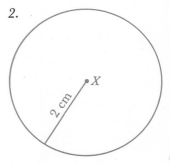

*1.* Make a rough drawing and find some points whose distance from $X$ is 2 cm. (Keep finding points until you can describe the geometric figure.)

*2.* The locus is a circle with center $X$ and radius 2 cm.

Each solution to a locus problem should have
   (1) a neat drawing of the figure satisfying the given condition and
   (2) a statement clearly describing the locus.

## Exercises 11.9

Ⓐ **1–2.** In a plane, the locus of points 7 cm from point $Z$ is a circle with center $Z$ and radius 7 cm.

**1.** If $ZX = 7$ cm, is $X$ in the locus?   Yes

**2.** If $ZW = 9$ cm, is $W$ in the locus?   No

Ⓑ **3–19.** Draw and describe each locus as clearly as possible.

**3.** in a plane, the locus of points 2 cm from a line $\ell$
                    2 ∥ lines each 2 cm from /

**4.** in a plane, the locus of points equidistant from two points $X$ and $Y$
                    The ⊥ bisector of $\overline{XY}$

**5.** in space, the locus of points 5 cm from a given point $X$

*Sphere $X$, with radius 5 cm*

**6.** in space, the locus of points equidistant from points $C$ and $D$

*The $\perp$ bisecting plane of $\overline{CD}$*

**7.** in a plane, the locus of points equidistant from the sides of $\angle XYZ$

*The ray that bisects $\angle XYZ$*

**8.** in space, the locus of points 9 m from a given point $Z$

*Sphere $Z$, with radius 9 m*

**9.** in a plane, the locus of points equidistant from points $A$ and $B$

*The $\perp$ bisector of $\overline{AB}$*

**10.** in a plane, the locus of points whose distance from the center of circle $W$, with radius 3 cm, is 5 cm

*A $\odot$ with radius 5 cm and center $W$*

**11.** in a plane, the locus of points whose distance from point $Z$ is less than or equal to 6 cm

*$\odot Z$, with radius 6 cm, and its interior*

**12.** in a plane, the locus of points 8 cm from line $p$

*2 $\parallel$ lines each 8 cm from $p$*

**13.** in a plane, the locus of points equidistant from lines $\ell$ and $k$ where $\ell \parallel k$

*A line $\parallel$ to and equidistant from $\ell$ and $k$*

**14.** in a plane, the locus of points whose distance from the center of circle $C$, with radius 8 cm, is 2 cm

*A $\odot$ with radius 2 cm and center $C$*

**15.** in a plane, the locus of points whose distance from a point $R$ is greater than 9 cm

*The exterior of $\odot R$, with radius 9 cm*

**16.** in space, the locus of points whose distance from a point $P$ is less than 56 mm

*The interior of sphere $P$, with radius 56 mm*

**17.** in a plane, the locus of points equidistant from $\overleftrightarrow{XZ}$ and $\overleftrightarrow{XW}$

*The bisectors of the 4 $\angle$s formed by $\overleftrightarrow{XZ}$ and $\overleftrightarrow{XW}$*

**18.** in a plane, the locus of points equidistant from two given points $X$ and $Y$ and at a distance of $XY$ from a point $X$

*2 pts. on the $\perp$ bisector of $\overline{XY}$, each a distance of $XY$ from $X$*

**19.** in space, the locus of points at a distance of 5 cm from point $X$ and 3 cm from point $Y$ when

    **a.** $XY = 8$ cm         **b.** $XY = 4$ cm

**19. a.** A pt. $C$ on $\overline{XY}$ such that $XC = 5$ cm and $CY = 3$ cm

    **b.** $\odot Y$, with radius 3, in the plane $\perp$ to $\overline{XY}$ at $Y$

**20.** Anywhere on or between 2 concentric $\odot$s, with radii 30 km and 50 km and center at the "home office"

**20.** A company that manufactures machine tools needs to build a warehouse. A cost study determined that the warehouse should be at least 30 km and no more than 50 km from the home office of the company. Describe the best location for the warehouse.

# Transformations: Turns

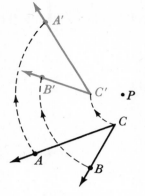

A turn in a plane is described by a center and an arc which gives the direction and magnitude of the turn. At the left the direction of the turn is clockwise and the magnitude is 80. That means that $m\widehat{AA'} = m\widehat{BB'} = m\widehat{CC'} = 80$. The center of the turn, point $P$, is the center of the concentric circles containing arcs $\widehat{AA'}$, $\widehat{BB'}$, $\widehat{CC'}$.

**Suggested Class Time**

| Course | Min. | Reg. | Max. |
|--------|------|------|------|
| Days   | 0    | 0    | 1    |

To turn $\triangle XYZ$ counterclockwise $150°$ with $P$ as the center of the turn, follow these steps. Find the turn image of each vertex separately.

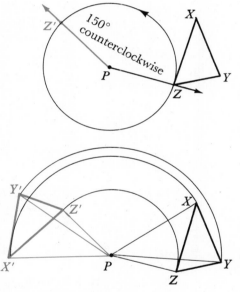

1.  To find the turn image of $Z$, draw $\overrightarrow{PZ}$. Then draw an angle with $\overrightarrow{PZ}$ as a side and measure $150°$. The direction from $\overrightarrow{PZ}$ to the other side of the angle must be counterclockwise.

2.  Draw $\odot P$ with radius $\overline{PZ}$. $Z'$ is the intersection of the new side of the angle and the circle.

3.  Follow steps 1 and 2 to find the turn image of points $X$ and $Y$. Notice that $\widehat{XX'}$, $\widehat{YY'}$, $\widehat{ZZ'}$ are arcs of concentric circles with center $P$, and have equal measure.

By measuring, we find that $XZ = X'Z'$ and $m\angle Z = m\angle Z'$. This suggests that turns preserve distance and angle measure. If a point is between points $X$ and $Z$ its image will be between $X'$ and $Z'$. Notice that the orientation of $\triangle XYZ$ and $\triangle X'Y'Z'$ is clockwise.

Turns preserve:
1. angle measure
2. betweenness
3. collinearity
4. distance
5. orientation

# Exercises 11.10 ||||||||||||||||||||||||||||||||||||||||||||||||||||||||||||||||||||||||||||

**Assignment Guide**
*Oral:* Max. 1–4
*Written:* Max. 5–16

Ⓐ **1.** What is the *direction* of a turn?
    Clockwise or counterclockwise

**2.** What is the *magnitude* of a turn?
    Meas. of an arc

**3–4.** Refer to the figure. *A'* is the turn image of *A* around center *O*.

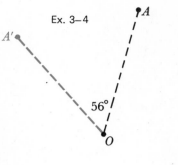

Ex. 3–4

**3.** What is the direction of the turn?
    Counterclockwise

**4.** What is the magnitude of the turn?
    56

Ⓑ **5–6.** $\overline{X'Y'}$ is the turn image of $\overline{XY}$.

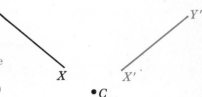

**5.** Name the center and direction of this turn.   Center *C*, direction clockwise

**6.** Find the magnitude of this turn.   100

**7–10.** *A'B'C'D'* is the turn image of *ABCD*. True or False?

**7.** If the orientation of *ABCD* is clockwise, then the orientation of *A'B'C'D'* is counterclockwise.   F

**8.** $m\angle DAB \neq m\angle D'A'B'$   F

**9.** *BC* = 9 and *B'C'* = 7 only if the turn is clockwise.   F

**10.** $m\overset{\frown}{AA'} = m\overset{\frown}{BB'}$ if $\overset{\frown}{AA'}$, $\overset{\frown}{BB'}$, and the turn have center *P*.   T

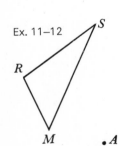

Ex. 11–12

**11–12.** Copy the figure.

**11.** Turn △*MSR* 110° clockwise around center *A*.

**12.** Turn △*MSR* 70° counterclockwise around center *A*.

Ⓒ **13–16.** Copy △*MSR* and point *A* used in Exercises 11–12.

**13.** Draw a line $\ell$ through *A*. Draw *k* intersecting line $\ell$ at *A*.

**14.** Reflect △*MSR* over $\ell$. Label the image △*M'S'R'*.

**15.** Reflect △*M'S'R'* over *k*. Label the image △*M"S"R"*.

**16.** How do △*MSR* and △*M"S"R"* appear to be related?
    △*M"S"R"* is the turn image of △*MSR* around center *A*.

# ■ Chapter 11 Review ■

**Suggested Class Time**

| Course | Min. | Reg. | Max. |
|--------|------|------|------|
| Days | 1 | 1 | 1 |

**1.** Define *radius* of a circle.   See page 376.

**11.1**

**2.** Define *diameter* of a sphere.     **3.** Define *secant* of a circle.
      See page 376.                          See page 376.

**4–8.** Refer to the figure.

**11.2**

**4.** Name a point in the exterior of ⊙*C*.  V

**Assignment Guide**
*Oral:* 1–8
*Written:* Min. 9–33 odd
              Reg. 9–33 odd
              Max. 9–37 odd

**5.** If $\overline{CW}$ bisects chord $\overline{ZY}$, name 2
perpendicular segments.  $\overline{CW}, \overline{ZY}$

**6.** If $\overline{CS} \perp \overline{RT}$, $\overline{CX} \perp \overline{ZY}$, and $CS = CX$,
why is $\overline{RT} \cong \overline{ZY}$?      In a ⊙, chords
                        equidistant from the center are ≅.

**7.** If $\overline{RT} \cong \overline{ZY}$, when is $CS = CX$?
            When $CS \perp \overline{RT}$ and $\overline{CX} \perp \overline{ZY}$

**8.** If $\overline{CW} \perp \overleftrightarrow{WV}$, is $\overleftrightarrow{VW}$ tangent to ⊙*C*? Why?
      Yes; line ⊥ to radius at outer endpt. is tangent to ⊙.

**9.** Draw two concentric circles.

**11.3**

**10.** Draw two externally tangent circles, and
then draw all their common tangents.

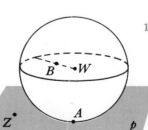

⊙*C*

**11–13.** Sphere *W* is tangent to plane *p* at *A*.

**11.4**

**11.** Name two points in the interior
of the sphere.   *B, W*

**12.** Plane tangent to sphere
is ⊥ to a radius at
outer endpt.

**12.** Why is $\overline{WA} \perp p$?          *Z* is in *p*.

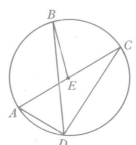

**13.** If $ZA = 8$, and $WZ = 10$, find
the radius of the sphere.   6

**14–18.** Given ⊙*E*, $m\angle BEC = 72$.

**11.5**

**14.** Name two central angles.   ∠*BEC*, ∠*BEA*

**15.** Is $\overparen{BC}$ a minor arc? Why?
      Yes; the pts. are on central ∠ *BEC* or in its int.

**16.** Find $m\overparen{AB}$.  108

**17.** Name two semicircles.   $\overparen{ABC}, \overparen{ADC}$

**18.** Is $\overparen{ADB}$ a major arc? Find $m\overparen{ADB}$.   Yes; 252

**11.6**

**19–22.** Given $\odot S$.

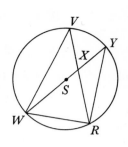

**19.** Any 2 of $\angle WVR$, $\angle WYR$, $\angle YRV$, $\angle YRW$, $\angle VRW$, $\angle RWY$, $\angle RWV$, $\angle YWV$

**19.** Name 2 inscribed angles.

**20.** Name the arc that $\angle RXW$ intercepts.
$\overset{\frown}{RW}$

**21.** Why is $m\angle WVR = m\angle RYW$?
Both are inscribed in same arc.

**22.** Find $m\angle WRY$. 90

**11.7**

**23–31.** $\overrightarrow{RS}$ is tangent to $\odot T$,
$\overline{YJ}$ and $\overline{YN}$ are tangent to $\odot U$.

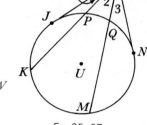

**23.** $m\angle ZXV = \dfrac{1}{2}\ (m\overset{\frown}{ZV} + \overset{\frown}{mRW})$

**24.** $m\angle SRV = \tfrac{1}{2}m\overset{\frown}{RV}$

**25.** $m\angle Y_1 = \tfrac{1}{2}(m\overset{\frown}{KJ} - m\overset{\frown}{JP})$

**26.** $m\angle Y_2 = \tfrac{1}{2}(m\overset{\frown}{KM} - m\overset{\frown}{PQ})$

**27.** $m\angle Y_{123} = \tfrac{1}{2}(m\overset{\frown}{NMJ} - m\overset{\frown}{NJ})$

Ex. 23–24;
28–29

Ex. 25–27;
30–31

**11.8**

**28.** Is $\overline{RS}$ a tangent segment? Yes

**29.** If $ZX = 3$, $XW = 8$, and $XV = 4$, then $XR = $ ___6___

**30.** If $YJ = 9$, and $YP = 3$, then $YK = $ ___27___

**31.** If $YQ = 4$, $YP = 7$, and $PK = 17$, then $QM = $ ___38___

**11.9**

**32.** Define *locus of points*.   See page 411.

**33.** In a plane, what is the locus of points whose distance from the point $C$ is less than or equal to 4.5 cm?
$\odot C$, with radius 4.5 cm, and its interior

**34.** In space, what is the locus of points equidistant from the endpoints of $\overline{AB}$?
The $\perp$ bisecting plane of $\overline{AB}$

**11.10**

**35–38.** $\triangle CDY$ is the turn image of $\triangle ABT$ around center $Z$.

**35.** State the direction of the turn.
Counterclockwise

**36.** Find the magnitude of the turn.
110

**37.** Find $m\overset{\frown}{BD}$.   **38.** Find $m\angle AZC$.
110                      110

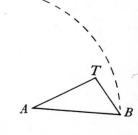

1. Name a radius of ⊙P.   $\overline{PT}$

2. Name a secant of sphere R.

3. Name a chord of sphere R.   $\overleftrightarrow{AN}$

4. Name a tangent of ⊙P.   $\overline{HF}$ (or $\overleftrightarrow{AN}$)

5. Name a point in the interior of ⊙P.   P   $\overleftrightarrow{HO}$

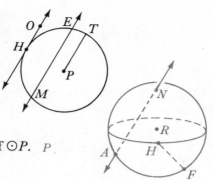

**Assignment Guide**
*Written:* Min. 1–22
            Reg. 1–22
            Max. 1–23

**6–9.** True or False?

6. If a segment bisects a chord, it is perpendicular to the chord.  F

7. Congruent chords of a circle are equidistant from the center of the circle.  T

8. All radii of a circle are congruent.  T

9. Any two small circles of a sphere are congruent.  F

**10–15.** If $m\angle BAD = 46$ and $m\angle FHE = 72$, find:

10. $m\widehat{BD}$     92     11. $m\angle BGD$     92

12. $m\widehat{FE}$     52     13. $m\widehat{DAF}$     220

14. $m\angle CAD$   90     15. $BH$     $6\frac{2}{3}$

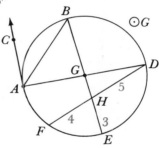

**16–21.** $\overline{PM}$ tangent to ⊙W at N, $\overline{PK}$ tangent to ⊙W at K. Find:

16. $m\angle P$     62     17. $m\angle M$     34

18. $m\angle X$     41     19. $VK$     15

20. $RK$     22     21. $MN$     12

22. In a plane, what is the locus of points equidistant from two intersecting lines?
   Bisectors of the 4 ∠s formed by the 2 lines

23. Copy $\triangle RTU$ and turn it 130° clockwise around center C.

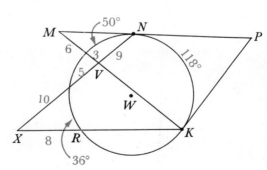

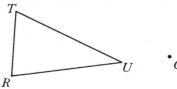

# 12 REGULAR POLYGONS AND CIRCLES

Photos courtesy Valmont Industries Inc.

The center-pivot irrigation system shown at the left contains a long length of pipeline attached to a water source at one end. The pipeline rotates around the water source, propelled by water pressure or electricity. As it rotates, water pumped through the pipeline irrigates a circular area as shown above.

In this chapter we will develop the formula for the area of a circle.

# Inscribed Regular Polygons

You already know that a *regular polygon* is a convex polygon that is both equilateral and equiangular. The figures below review what is meant by *inscribed* and *circumscribed* regular polygons.

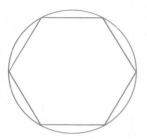

inscribed polygon
circumscribed circle

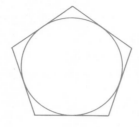

inscribed circle
circumscribed polygon

Courtesy Illinois Institute of Technology

For regular polygons inscribed in a circle, the following terms are often used:

The **center** of a regular polygon is the center of its circumscribed circle.

A **radius** of a regular polygon is a segment that joins its center to a vertex.

An **apothem** of a regular polygon is a perpendicular segment from its center to one of its sides.

A **central angle** of a regular polygon is an angle determined by two radii drawn to the endpoints of a side.

A regular polygon of $n$ sides inscribed in a circle would cut off $n$ congruent arcs, each having degree measure $\frac{360}{n}$. Since each of these arcs is intercepted by a central angle of the regular polygon, we could prove the following theorem:

The degree measure of a central angle of a regular polygon of $n$ sides is $\frac{360}{n}$.

**Theorem**

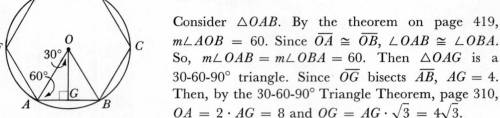

**Example:** Regular hexagon $ABCDEF$ with sides of length 8 is inscribed in $\odot O$. Find the lengths of the apothem $\overline{OG}$ and the radius $\overline{OA}$.

Consider $\triangle OAB$. By the theorem on page 419, $m\angle AOB = 60$. Since $\overline{OA} \cong \overline{OB}$, $\angle OAB \cong \angle OBA$. So, $m\angle OAB = m\angle OBA = 60$. Then $\triangle OAG$ is a 30-60-90° triangle. Since $\overline{OG}$ bisects $\overline{AB}$, $AG = 4$. Then, by the 30-60-90° Triangle Theorem, page 310, $OA = 2 \cdot AG = 8$ and $OG = AG \cdot \sqrt{3} = 4\sqrt{3}$.

**Area Theorem for a Regular Polygon**

The area ($A$) of a regular polygon is equal to one half of the length ($a$) of its apothem times its perimeter ($p$).

$$A = \tfrac{1}{2}ap$$

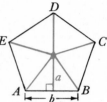

**Given:** Regular polygon $ABCDE$ with apothem of length $a$, perimeter $p$, and area $A$

**Prove:** $A = \tfrac{1}{2}ap$

**Sketch of proof:** Draw radii dividing the polygon into congruent triangles. Each triangle has an area equal to $\tfrac{1}{2}ab$ (where $b$ is the length of one side of the polygon). If the polygon has $n$ sides, then the total area is $n(\tfrac{1}{2}ab)$. So,

$$A = \tfrac{1}{2}a(nb)$$
$$= \tfrac{1}{2}ap$$

◀ From Section 5.2, we know $p = nb$.

# *Exercises 12.1*

**Assignment Guide**
*Oral:* 1–6
*Written:*
Min. (day 1) 7–27 odd
(day 2) 35–38; Alg. Rev., p. 423, odd
Reg. (day 1) 7–31 odd
(day 2) 35–38; Alg. Rev., p. 423, odd
Max. 7–37 odd
*Constructions:* 39–45

Ⓐ **1–6.** Refer to the figure where $O$ is the center of the circle and $ABCD$ is an inscribed square.

**1.** $\overline{OA}$ is a(n) (<u>radius</u>, apothem) of $ABCD$.

**2.** $\overline{OR}$ is a(n) (radius, <u>apothem</u>) of $ABCD$.

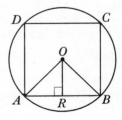

**3.** The center of $ABCD$ is ___$O$___.

**4.** $\angle AOB$ is a <u>Central</u> angle.

**5.** $ABCD$ is (circumscribed about, <u>inscribed in</u>) circle $O$.

**6.** Circle $O$ is (<u>circumscribed about</u>, inscribed in) $ABCD$.

Ⓑ **7–10.** Find the number of degrees in the central angle of a regular polygon having

**7.** 3 sides  120          **8.** 5 sides  72          **9.** 6 sides  60          **10.** 36 sides  10

**11–24.** Regular hexagon *MONKEY* with sides of length 20 is inscribed in circle *P*. Square *LAMB* with sides of length 4 is inscribed in circle *R*.

**11.** What is $m\angle MPO$?  60

Ex. 11–18

**12.** Is $m\angle PMO = m\angle POM$?  Yes

**13.** What is $m\angle PMO$?  60

**14.** What is $m\angle MGP$?  90

**15.** What is $m\angle MPG$?  30

Ex. 19–24

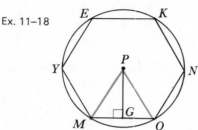

**16.** What is the length of $\overline{MG}$? Of $\overline{PG}$? Of $\overline{PM}$?          $10;\ 10\sqrt{3};\ 20$

**17.** What is the perimeter of *MONKEY*?  120

**18.** What is the area of *MONKEY*?  $600\sqrt{3}$

**19.** What is $m\angle LRA$?  90          **20.** Is $m\angle RLA = m\angle RAL$?  Yes

**21.** What is $m\angle RLA$?  45          **22.** What is $m\angle LRT$?  45

**23.** What is the length of $\overline{LT}$? Of $\overline{RT}$? Of $\overline{LR}$?  $2;\ 2;\ 2\sqrt{2}$          **24.** What is the perimeter of *LAMB*? The area?  $16;\ 16$

**25–28.** Find the length of the apothem for each inscribed regular hexagon or square. HINT: Draw radii and consider special right triangles.

**25.** $7\sqrt{3}$

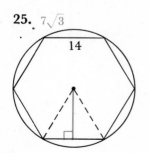

14

**26.** 12

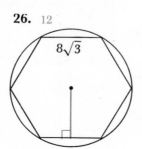

$8\sqrt{3}$

**27.** 9

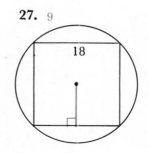

18

**28.** $25\sqrt{2}$

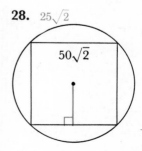

$50\sqrt{2}$

**29–32.** Find the length of the radius for each inscribed regular polygon.

**29.** inscribed regular hexagon with side of length $10\sqrt{3}$

$10\sqrt{3}$

**30.** inscribed regular hexagon with side of length $12\sqrt{3}$

$12\sqrt{3}$

**31.** inscribed square with side of length $16\sqrt{2}$

$16$

**32.** inscribed square with side of length $60$

$30\sqrt{2}$

**33.** If a regular hexagon has a radius of 26 and has a circle inscribed in it, what is the radius of the inscribed circle? NOTE: The midpoint of each side of the hexagon is a point of tangency.

$13\sqrt{3}$

**34.** If a regular hexagon has an inscribed circle of radius $2\sqrt{3}$, what is the radius of the regular hexagon?

$4$

**35–38.** Find the area of each regular polygon having the given perimeter and apothem of length *a*.

**35.** $p = 48$, $a = 4\sqrt{3}$   $96\sqrt{3}$   **36.** $p = 28$, $a = 3\frac{1}{2}$   $49$

**37.** $p = 24\sqrt{3}$, $a = 4$   $48\sqrt{3}$   **38.** $p = 60$, $a = 5\sqrt{3}$   $150\sqrt{3}$

---

## construction: a circle circumscribed about any regular polygon

| 1. Construct the ⊥ bis. of one side. | 2. Construct the ⊥ bis. of another side. | 3. Use the pt. where the ⊥ bis. meet as the center *O*. With *OR* as radius, circumscribe the circle. |
|---|---|---|

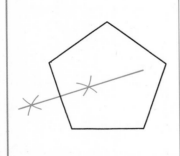
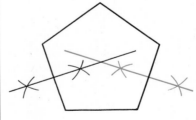
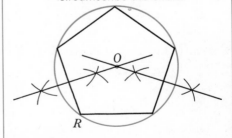

---

**39–40.** Copy each figure. Then circumscribe a circle about the polygon.

**39.**

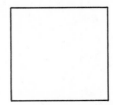

**40.**

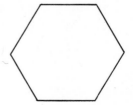

## construction: a circle inscribed in any regular polygon

| 1. Construct an angle bisector. | 2. Construct another angle bisector. | 3. Construct a ⊥ from $P$ to one side. | 4. With $P$ as center and radius $PA$, inscribe the circle. |
|---|---|---|---|
| 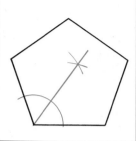 | 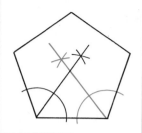 | 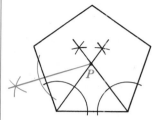 | 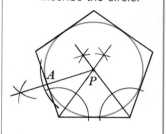 |

**41–42.** Copy each figure in Exercises 39–40. Then inscribe a circle in each polygon.

© **43.** Inscribe a square in a circle. (HINT: Draw any diameter, and then construct another diameter perpendicular to it.) Next bisect each side in order to inscribe a regular octagon in the circle.

**44.** Inscribe a circle in the regular octagon you constructed in Exercise 43.

**45.** Inscribe a regular hexagon in a circle. (See page 169.) Then bisect the sides in order to inscribe a regular 12-sided polygon (dodecagon).

---

**1–12.** Factor each trinomial.

**1.** $x^2 - 3x - 4$
$(x - 4)(x + 1)$

**2.** $x^2 + 5x + 6$
$(x + 3)(x + 2)$

**3.** $x^2 - 6x + 9$
$(x - 3)^2$

**4.** $x^2 + 10x + 25$
$(x + 5)^2$

**5.** $x^2 - 2x - 15$
$(x - 5)(x + 3)$

**6.** $x^2 + 4x - 5$
$(x + 5)(x - 1)$

**7.** $2x^2 + 3x - 2$
$(2x - 1)(x + 2)$

**8.** $3x^2 + 10x + 3$
$(3x + 1)(x + 3)$

**9.** $5x^2 + 7x + 2$
$(5x + 2)(x + 1)$

**10.** $6x^2 + 5x + 1$
$(3x + 1)(2x + 1)$

**11.** $x^2 - 49$
$(x + 7)(x - 7)$

**12.** $25x^2 - 64$
$(5x + 8)(5x - 8)$

**13–20.** Solve each equation by factoring.

**13.** $x^2 - 5x - 6 = 0$    $6, -1$

**14.** $x^2 + 6x + 5 = 0$    $-1, -5$

**15.** $x^2 + 6x + 8 = 0$    $-2, -4$

**16.** $x^2 - 7x + 12 = 0$    $4, 3$

**17.** $2x^2 - 3x = -1$    $\frac{1}{2}, 1$

**18.** $3x^2 + 5x = -2$    $-\frac{2}{3}, -1$

**19.** $4x^2 + 7x = 2$    $-2, \frac{1}{4}$

**20.** $5x^2 + 17x = -6$    $-3, -\frac{2}{5}$

*Algebra Review*

**Review these skills:**

- *factoring trinomials*
- *solving quadratics by factoring*

# 12.2 Circumference

The distance around a polygon is its *perimeter*, while the distance around a circle is its *circumference*. To find the perimeter of a polygon, we add the lengths of the sides, which are segments. However, this method does not work in finding the circumference of a circle. A circle does not contain any segments. Yet notice the polygons below.

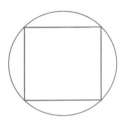 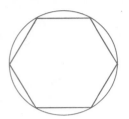  

As the number of sides increases, the polygons get closer and closer to the circle. To approximate the circumference of a circle, we could find the perimeter of an inscribed polygon with a large number of sides.

We will use this idea in defining circumference. Suppose we let $p$ be the perimeter of an inscribed regular polygon with $n$ sides and let $C$ be the circumference of the circle. By choosing $n$ large enough, we can find $p$ as close to $C$ as we want. We say

$$p \text{ approaches } C \text{ as a limit}$$
$$\text{or}$$
$$p \rightarrow C$$

The **circumference** of a circle is the limit of the perimeters of the inscribed regular polygons.

The next theorem is needed to define the number $\pi$.

**Theorem** The ratio of the circumference to the diameter is the same for all circles.

Given: $\odot O$ with radius $r$
and circumference $C$,
$\odot O'$ with radius $r'$
and circumference $C'$

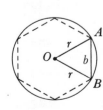 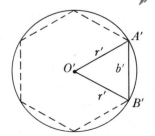

Prove: $\dfrac{C}{2r} = \dfrac{C'}{2r'}$

**Sketch of Proof:** Inscribe regular polygons with $n$ sides having lengths of $b$ and $b'$. In each circle, choose one side and draw radii to the endpoints. The two central angles are congruent because each has measure $\frac{360}{n}$. Also, the sides are proportional: $\frac{r}{r'} = \frac{r}{r'}$. Therefore, by the SAS Similarity Theorem,

$$\triangle AOB \sim \triangle A'O'B'$$

Then,

| $\dfrac{b}{b'} = \dfrac{r}{r'}$ | $\dfrac{nb}{nb'} = \dfrac{r}{r'}$ | $\dfrac{p}{p'} = \dfrac{r}{r'}$ | $\dfrac{p}{r} = \dfrac{p'}{r'}$ |
|---|---|---|---|
| Corresponding sides are proportional. | Multiply left side by $\dfrac{n}{n}$ or 1. | Substitute. ($p = nb$ and $p' = nb'$) | Switch means. |

In the above equations, $p$ and $p'$ are the perimeters of two polygons having $n$ sides. We know by definition that

$$p \to C \quad \text{and} \quad p' \to C' \qquad \text{as } n \text{ increases}$$

Therefore,

$$\frac{p}{r} \to \frac{C}{r} \quad \text{and} \quad \frac{p'}{r'} \to \frac{C'}{r'}$$

Since $\frac{p}{r}$ and $\frac{p'}{r'}$ are equal, their limits are equal. Then

$$\frac{C}{r} = \frac{C'}{r'} \quad \blacktriangleright \text{Multiply both sides by } \tfrac{1}{2}. \blacktriangleright \quad \frac{C}{2r} = \frac{C'}{2r'}$$

The ratio $\frac{C}{2r}$ is denoted by $\pi$. Since this ratio is the same for all circles, we have

$$\frac{C}{2r} = \pi \quad \text{or} \quad C = 2\pi r$$

The circumference ($C$) of a circle is $2\pi$ times its radius ($r$).

$$C = 2\pi r$$

**Circumference Theorem**

The number $\pi$ is irrational. Therefore, it has a nonterminating, nonrepeating decimal expansion. But it can be approximated as closely as we want by rational numbers. Some approximations are

| 3 | 3.14 | $3\frac{1}{7}$ or $\frac{22}{7}$ | 3.1416 | $\frac{355}{113}$ | 3.14159265358979 |
|---|---|---|---|---|---|

# Exercises 12.2

**Assignment Guide**
*Oral:* 1–6
*Written:* Min. 7–19 odd
Reg. 7–21 odd
Max. 7–23 odd

Ⓐ **1.** The distance around a circle is called the $\underset{\text{Circumference}}{\underline{\qquad}}$.

**2.** The circumference of a circle is the $\underset{\text{Limit}}{\underline{\qquad}}$ of the perimeters of the inscribed regular polygons.

**3.** True or False? The number $\pi$ is not rational.   T

**4.** For any circle, the ratio $\frac{C}{2r}$ (where $C$ is the circumference and $r$ is the radius) is denoted by $\underset{\pi}{\underline{\qquad}}$.

**5.** If the radius of a circle is 10, its circumference is $\underset{20}{\underline{\qquad}} \times \pi$.

**6.** If the radius of a circle is 7, the circumference is about $\underset{14}{\underline{\qquad}} \times \frac{22}{7}$ or $\underset{44}{\underline{\qquad}}$.

Ⓑ **7–12.** Use the given measure of a circle to find each missing number. Leave answers in terms of $\pi$.

| | diameter | radius | circumference |
|---|---|---|---|
| **7.** | 18 | 9 | $18\pi$ |
| **8.** | 24 | 12 | $24\pi$ |
| **9.** | 18 | 9 | $18\pi$ |
| **10.** | $20\pi$ | $10\pi$ | $20\pi^2$ |
| **11.** | $14\pi$ | $7\pi$ | $14\pi^2$ |
| **12.** | $50\sqrt{2}$ | $25\sqrt{2}$ | $50\pi\sqrt{2}$ |

**13–24.** Use 3.14 for $\pi$. Find each answer to the nearest tenth.

**13.** The diameter of a wheel is 66 centimeters. How far does the wheel roll in one complete turn?   207.2 cm

**14.** One car manufacturer uses a circular test track. If the radius of the track is 1.17 kilometers, how far does a car travel in going once around the track?   7.3 km

**15.** The world's largest Ferris wheel in Vienna, Austria, has a diameter of 60 meters. What is the circumference of the wheel?   188.4 m

426

**16.** Many modern tires are belted. See the diagram. How long a belt is needed to encircle a tire with the dimensions shown at the right?

201.0 cm

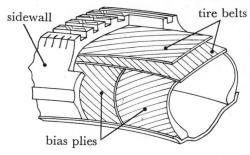

sidewall

tire belts

bias plies

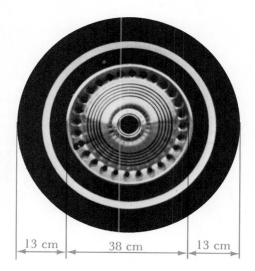

13 cm     38 cm     13 cm

**17.** A strip of sheet metal 9.2 meters long is bent to form a circular outline for a flower bed. What is the diameter of the bed?    2.9 m

**18.** A log has a circumference of 123 centimeters. What is the diameter of the log?

39.2 cm

**19.** The length of a side of a square is 14. Find the circumference of its inscribed circle. Of its circumscribed circle.    $44.0; (44.0)\sqrt{2} \approx 62.2$

**20.** The length of a side of an equilateral triangle is $28\sqrt{3}$. Find the circumference of its inscribed circle. Of its circumscribed circle.

87.9; 175.8

**21.** A track for track-and-field events has ends that are semicircular. (See figure.) How far does a runner travel in going once around the track?    254.2 m

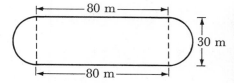

80 m

30 m

80 m

**22.** The distance (in centimeters) that a bicycle travels with each revolution of the pedals is given by the following formula:

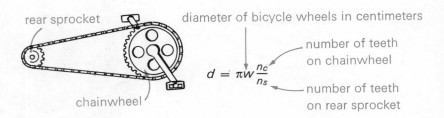

rear sprocket

chainwheel

diameter of bicycle wheels in centimeters

number of teeth on chainwheel

number of teeth on rear sprocket

$$d = \pi w \frac{n_c}{n_s}$$

How far will a bicycle with wheels 68.6 cm in diameter travel for each revolution of the pedals if the chainwheel has 50 teeth and the rear sprocket has 28 teeth?

384.7 cm

**23.** The earth is approximately 149 000 000 kilometers from the sun. How far does the earth travel each year in its almost circular orbit about the sun? What is a close estimate of its speed in kilometers per hour? HINT: Speed = distance ÷ time.

935 720 000 km;
106 817.4 km/h

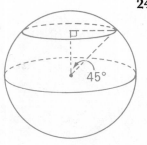

45°

**24.** The radius of the earth is approximately 6336 kilometers. How far does an object at the equator travel during one complete rotation of the earth? What is the object's speed in kilometers per hour? How far does an object at latitude 45°N travel in one rotation? (Use 1.4 for $\sqrt{2}$.) What is the object's speed in kilometers per hour?

39 790.1 km; 1657.9 km/h;
28 421.5 km; 1184.2 km/h

◆◆◆◆◆◆◆◆ **Would You Believe?** ◆◆◆◆◆◆◆◆

In ancient Greece it was known that regular polygons of 3, 4, 5, 6, and 15 sides could be constructed by using only a compass and a straightedge. It wasn't until 1796 that someone discovered that a regular polygon of 17 sides could be constructed with only a compass and a straightedge. Then in 1832 it was found that a regular polygon of 257 sides could be constructed. A Professor Hermes of Lingen is said to have given 10 years of his life to the problem of constructing a regular polygon of 65,537 sides!

# Area of a Circle

A circular region contains both the circle and its interior. For convenience, we usually refer to the area of a circle rather than to the area of a circular region.

Each regular polygon below is inscribed in a circle with radius $r$.

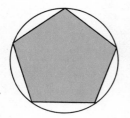 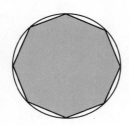 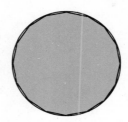

Notice how the area of each polygon gets closer and closer to the area of the circle as $n$, the number of sides of the polygon, increases. We already know that the formula for the area $A_n$ of a regular polygon with $n$ sides is

$$A_n = \tfrac{1}{2}ap \qquad (a \text{ is length of the apothem;}$$
$$p \text{ is the perimeter.})$$

If $A$ is the area of the circle, then

$$A_n \to A \qquad\qquad \text{as } n \text{ increases}$$

The area of a circle is the limit of the areas of the inscribed regular polygons.

To find the formula for the area of a circle, let's consider the following: The length $a$ of the apothem is always less than $r$. But as $n$ increases, the difference between $a$ and $r$ becomes smaller. So,

$$a \to r$$

From Section 12.2, we have $\qquad p \to C$

Therefore, $\qquad\qquad\qquad \tfrac{1}{2}ap \to \tfrac{1}{2}rC$

Since, $A_n = \tfrac{1}{2}ap$, $\qquad\qquad A_n \to \tfrac{1}{2}rC$

But, above, $\qquad\qquad\qquad A_n \to A$

Therefore, $\qquad\qquad\qquad A = \tfrac{1}{2}rC$

Since $C = 2\pi r$, $\qquad\qquad A = \tfrac{1}{2}r \cdot 2\pi r$

$$A = \pi r^2$$

**Area Theorem for a Circle**

The area ($A$) of a circle is $\pi$ times its radius ($r$) squared.

$$A = \pi r^2$$

**Examples:**

1. Find the area of a circle with radius 28. Use $\frac{22}{7}$ for $\pi$.

$A = \pi r^2$

$A = \frac{22}{7} \cdot 28 \cdot 28$

$A = 2464$

2. Find the radius of a circle with area $144\pi$.

$A = \pi r^2$

$144\pi = \pi r^2$

$r^2 = 144$

$r = \pm 12$  But the radius must be positive. So $r = 12$.

## Exercises 12.3 ▮▮▮▮▮▮▮▮▮▮▮▮▮▮▮▮▮▮▮▮▮▮▮▮▮▮▮▮▮▮▮▮▮▮▮▮▮▮▮▮▮▮▮▮▮▮▮▮▮▮

**Assignment Guide**
*Oral:* 1–4
*Written:* Min. 5–19 odd
　　　Reg. 5–19 odd
　　　Max. 5–21 odd

Ⓐ 1. The area of a circle is the limit of the areas of the ___Inscribed___ regular polygons.

2. The formula for the area $A$ of a circle with radius $r$ is ___$A = \pi r^2$___.

3. A circle has a regular pentagon and a regular hexagon inscribed in it. Which polygon has an area closer to the area of the circle? Hexagon

4. If the radius of a circle is 1, its area is ___$\pi$___.

Ⓑ **5–12.** Use the given measure of a circle to find each missing number. Use $\frac{22}{7}$ for $\pi$.

|     | radius | diameter | circumference | area |
|-----|--------|----------|---------------|------|
| 5.  | 7 | 14 | 44 | 154 |
| 6.  | 35 | 70 | 220 | 3850 |
| 7.  | 14 | 28 | 88 | 616 |
| 8.  | 42 | 84 | 264 | 5544 |
| 9.  | 28 | 56 | $56\pi$ | 2464 |
| 10. | 42 | 84 | $84\pi$ | 5544 |
| 11. | 12 | 24 | $75\frac{3}{7}$ | $144\pi$ |
| 12. | 9 | 18 | $56\frac{4}{7}$ | $81\pi$ |

**13–16.** Find each shaded area. Use $\frac{22}{7}$ for $\pi$. All angles are right angles.

**13.** 672

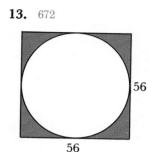

56
56

**14.** 448

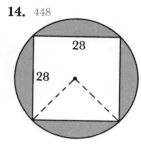

28
28

**15.** 84

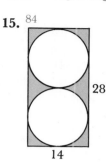

28
14

**16.** 1078

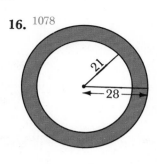

21
28

**17–21.** Use 3.14 for $\pi$.

**17.** The center-pivot method of irrigation mentioned on page 418 involves a pipeline that is rotated about a fixed point, thus forming a circular area of irrigated land. If the pipeline extends 92 meters from the center, what is the area of ground irrigated by the pipeline?

26 576.96 m²

**18.** The largest pizza ever baked was made at Pizza Pete's in Chicago. (Source: *The Guinness Book of World Records.*) It had a diameter of 21 feet. What was its area? An ordinary small pizza has a diameter of 12 inches. How many small pizzas would you have to consume to eat as much pizza as the world's largest pizza contained?

346.185 ft²; 441

**19.** A circular tabletop is cut from a square sheet of plywood that is 142 centimeters on a side. How much plywood is wasted if the largest possible circle is cut out?

4335.26 cm²

**20.** Aluminum lids for cans are stamped out of rectangular sheets of aluminum that are 32 cm by 24 cm. The diameter of each lid is 8 cm. How much aluminum is wasted from each sheet?

165.12 cm²

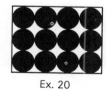

Ex. 20

© **21.** A carpenter cuts a brace from a piece of plywood as shown by the design at the right. The curved portion is made from two circular arcs, each of which is a quarter circle. Find the area of the piece wasted by the cutout.    768

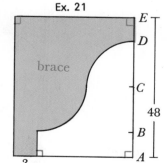

Ex. 21

brace

E
D
C
48
B
A
3

$BC = CD = 2AB = 2DE$

# 12.4   Lengths of Arcs and Areas of Sectors

**Suggested Class Time**

| Course | Min. | Reg. | Max. |
|--------|------|------|------|
| Days   | 1    | 1    | 1    |

As you learned in Chapter 11, an arc is part of a circle. The degree measure of an arc is determined by a central angle. Sometimes we need to find the length of an arc. We already know that the circumference of an entire circle is $2\pi r$, where $r$ is the radius. Notice how we can find the lengths of the two arcs below.

**Example 1:**

**a.**

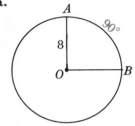

**b.**

De Wys, Inc.

$$\text{length } \widehat{AB} = \frac{m\widehat{AB}}{360} \cdot 2\pi r \qquad \text{length } \widehat{CED} = \frac{m\widehat{CED}}{360} \cdot 2\pi r$$

$$= \frac{90}{360} \cdot 2\pi(8) \qquad\qquad = \frac{240}{360} \cdot 2\pi(5)$$

$$= \frac{1}{4} \cdot 2\pi(8) \qquad\qquad = \frac{2}{3} \cdot 2\pi(5)$$

$$\doteq 4\pi \qquad\qquad\qquad = \frac{20}{3}\pi$$

In Example 1a, $m\widehat{AB} = 90$. Since the entire circle has a degree measure of 360, the length of $\widehat{AB}$ is $\frac{90}{360}$ or $\frac{1}{4}$ of the entire circumference. Likewise, in Example 1b, the length of $\widehat{CED}$ is $\frac{240}{360}$ or $\frac{2}{3}$ of the entire circumference. We can generalize these examples as follows:

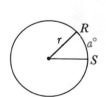

Consider $\widehat{RS}$, with degree measure $a$, where $r$ is the radius of the circle. We know the circumference of the circle is $2\pi r$. Since $m\widehat{RS} = a$, the length of $\widehat{RS}$ is $\frac{a}{360}$ of $2\pi r$. Therefore, we can conclude the next theorem.

**Length of an Arc Theorem**

The length of an arc $RS$ with measure $a°$ is given by the formula

$$\text{length } \widehat{RS} = \frac{a}{360} \cdot 2\pi r, \quad \text{where } r \text{ is the radius of the circle.}$$

In the figures below, the shaded portions are called sectors. A **sector** of a circle is a region bounded by an arc of the circle and the two radii to the endpoints of the arc. Two sectors are shown below.

**Example 2:**

a.

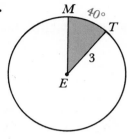

b.

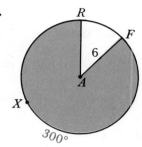

area shaded sector $= \dfrac{m\overarc{MT}}{360} \cdot \pi r^2$    area shaded sector $= \dfrac{m\overarc{RXF}}{360} \cdot \pi r^2$

$\qquad\qquad = \frac{40}{360} \cdot \pi(3)^2 \qquad\qquad\qquad\qquad\qquad = \frac{300}{360} \cdot \pi(6)^2$

$\qquad\qquad = \frac{1}{9} \cdot \pi \cdot 9 \qquad\qquad\qquad\qquad\qquad\quad = \frac{5}{6} \cdot \pi \cdot 36$

$\qquad\qquad = \pi \qquad\qquad\qquad\qquad\qquad\qquad\qquad = 30\pi$

In the preceding examples, we know the area of the entire circle is $\pi r^2$. In Example 2a, $m\overarc{MT} = 40$. So the area of the sector is $\frac{40}{360}$ or $\frac{1}{9}$ of the entire area. These examples suggest the following theorem:

The area of a sector whose arc has measure $a°$ is given by the formula

area sector $= \dfrac{a}{360} \cdot \pi r^2$,   where $r$ is the radius of the circle.

**Area Theorem for a Sector**

**Example 3:**

a. What is the radius of a circle if the length of a 40° arc $(\overarc{RS})$ is $18\pi$?

b. In a circle with radius 6, a sector has area $4\pi$. What is the degree measure of the arc of the sector?

length $\overarc{RS} = \dfrac{a}{360} \cdot 2\pi r$ $\qquad\qquad$ area sector $= \dfrac{a}{360} \cdot \pi r^2$

$\qquad 18\pi = \frac{40}{360} \cdot 2\pi r \qquad\qquad\qquad\qquad 4\pi = \dfrac{a}{360} \cdot \pi(6)^2$

$\qquad 18\pi = \frac{1}{9} \cdot 2\pi r$

$\qquad 18\pi = \frac{2}{9}\pi r \qquad\qquad\qquad\qquad\qquad\quad 4\pi = \dfrac{a}{360} \cdot \pi(36)$

$\qquad\quad 81 = r \qquad\qquad\qquad\qquad\qquad\qquad\quad 40 = a$

The two preceding theorems can be used to prove the next theorem. The proof is outlined in Exercise 37.

**Corollary to Area Theorem for a Sector** The area of a sector of a circle is one half the arc length times the radius.

## Exercises 12.4

NOTE: Leave answers in terms of $\pi$ unless told otherwise.

 1. The formula for finding the length of an arc is $\underline{\frac{a}{360} \cdot 2\pi r}$.

2. The formula for finding the area of a sector is $\underline{\frac{a}{360} \cdot \pi r^2}$.

**Assignment Guide**
*Oral:* 1–10
*Written:* Min. 11–27 odd
        Reg. 11–33 odd
        Max. 11–37 odd

3. If an arc has a degree measure of 180, what fractional part of the entire circle is the arc? $\frac{1}{2}$

4. If a sector has an arc with degree measure 90, what fractional part of the entire area of the circle is the area of the sector? $\frac{1}{4}$

**5–8.** *O* is the center of the circle. *TO* = 6, and $m\widehat{TP}$ = 120.

Ex. 5–8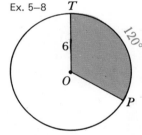

5. What is the circumference of circle *O*? $12\pi$

6. What is the length of $\widehat{TP}$? $4\pi$

7. What is the area of circle *O*? $36\pi$

8. What is the area of the shaded sector? $12\pi$

Ex. 9–10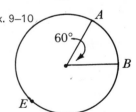

9. What is the degree measure of $\widehat{AB}$? $60$

10. What is the degree measure of $\widehat{AEB}$? $300$

ⓑ **11–14.** The radius of a circle is 24. Find the length of each arc having the given degree measure.

**11.** 60   $8\pi$      **12.** 45   $6\pi$      **13.** 150   $20\pi$      **14.** 270   $36\pi$

**15.** What is the radius of a circle if the length of a 90° arc is $17\pi$?   34

**16.** What is the radius of a circle if the length of a 30° arc is $8\pi$?   48

**17–20.** All four arcs have $P$ as center and degree measure 60. Using the proper radius, find each arc length.

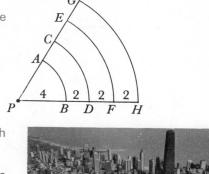

**17.** length $\overset{\frown}{AB}$   $\frac{4}{3}\pi$    **18.** length $\overset{\frown}{CD}$   $2\pi$

**19.** length $\overset{\frown}{EF}$   $\frac{8}{3}\pi$    **20.** length $\overset{\frown}{GH}$   $\frac{10}{3}\pi$

**21–24.** The radius of a circle is 16. Find the area of each sector whose arc has the given degree measure.

**21.** 180   $128\pi$    **22.** 36   $25.6\pi$    **23.** 135   $96\pi$    **24.** 40   $28\frac{4}{9}\pi$

**25.** In a circle with radius 4, a sector has area $3\pi$. What is the length of the arc of the sector?   $\frac{3}{2}\pi$

**26.** In a circle with radius 18, a sector has area $15\pi$. What is the length of the arc of the sector?   $\frac{5}{3}\pi$

**27.** The largest four-faced clock in the world is on the Allen-Bradley Building in Milwaukee, Wisconsin. It has a 6.10-meter (20-foot) minute hand. How many meters does the tip of the minute hand travel in 1 minute? Use 3.14 for $\pi$.    About 0.638 m

**28.** In designing skyscrapers, engineers must allow for the swaying motion of the building. The Sears Tower in Chicago has a height of 443.2 meters (1454 feet). If the top of the building moves along an arc of $\frac{1}{2}°$, how many meters is that? Use 3.14 for $\pi$.    About 3.866 m

Courtesy Sears, Roebuck and Co.

**29–30.** The shaded region in the figure is called a segment of the circle. Its area can be found by subtracting the area of $\triangle AOB$ from the area of the sector with $\overset{\frown}{AB}$. Find the area of each segment if

**29.** $r = 8$, $m\overset{\frown}{AB} = 90$    **30.** $r = 5$, $m\overset{\frown}{AB} = 60$
     $16\pi - 32$                $\frac{25}{6}\pi - \frac{25}{4}\sqrt{3}$

**31–34.** Use the theorem on page 434 to find the area of each sector. The arc length and radius of the circle are given in each case.

**31.** length $\overset{\frown}{RS} = 180$, $r = 4$   360    **32.** length $\overset{\frown}{RS} = 25\pi$, $r = 6$   $75\pi$

**33.** length $\overset{\frown}{RS} = 42\pi$, $r = 7$   $147\pi$    **34.** length $\overset{\frown}{RS} = 120$, $r = 10$   600

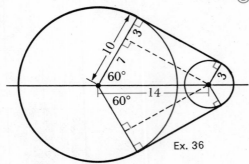

Ex. 36

**35.** A cow is tied with a rope to one corner of a barn that is 12 meters long and 10 meters wide. If the rope is 15 meters long, what is the grazing area available for the cow?

556.565 m²

**36.** A continuous belt fits around two wheels as shown. The wheels have radii of 10 cm and 3 cm. The distance between their centers is 14 cm. Find the length of the belt.

$\frac{2}{3}(2)(3.14)(10) + \frac{1}{3}(2)(3.14)(3) + 2(7\sqrt{3}) \approx 72.4$ cm

**37.** Copy and complete the proof.

Given: $\odot O$ with radius $r$ and $\widehat{RS}$ having degree measure $a$

Prove: Area shaded sector $= \frac{1}{2}(\text{length } \widehat{RS})r$

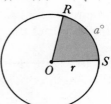

Proof:

| STATEMENTS | REASONS |
|---|---|
| *1.* Area shaded sector $= \dfrac{a}{360} \cdot \pi r^2$ | *1.* <u>Area Thm. for Sector</u> |
| *2.* Area shaded sector $= \dfrac{a}{360} \cdot \pi r \cdot \underline{\quad}$ | *2.* Def. of exponent |
| *3.* Area shaded sector $= \dfrac{a}{360} \cdot (\underline{\quad} \cdot 2)\pi r \cdot r$ | *3.* Inv. and Ident. Props. of Mult. |
| *4.* Area shaded sector $= \frac{1}{2}\left(\dfrac{a}{360} \cdot 2\pi r\right) \cdot r$ | *4.* <u>Assoc.</u> and <u>Commutative</u> Props. of Mult. |
| *5.* Area shaded sector $= \frac{1}{2}(\text{length } \widehat{RS}) \cdot r$ | *5.* <u>Length</u> of Arc Thm. and subst. |

# Transformations: Point Symmetry        12.5

The figures below all have something in common. If you turn this page upside down, the figures still look the same. In other words, each figure coincides with itself after it is turned 180°.

  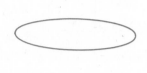    

Such figures are said to have point symmetry. In order to define point symmetry, we need the following definition:

The **reflection image** of a point $R$ over a point $P$ is the point $R'$ such that $P$ is the midpoint of $\overline{RR'}$.

We say that $R$ and $R'$ are symmetric about $P$. Now we can give a better definition of point symmetry.

A set of points has **point symmetry** if and only if there is a point $P$ such that the reflection image over $P$ of each point in the set is also a point in the set. $P$ is called the *center of symmetry*.

Point symmetry is a special case of a more general type of symmetry called *turn symmetry*. If a figure can be turned less than 360° so that it coincides with itself, the figure has turn symmetry.

For example, consider an equilateral triangle. It does not have point symmetry. If vertex $A$ of the first triangle shown at the right is reflected over $O$, its image is not a point on the triangle. Neither is there any other point over which every point of the triangle can be reflected back onto the triangle. Nevertheless, the triangle does have turn symmetry because it can be turned 120° about $O$ so that it coincides with itself.

  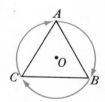

# Exercises 12.5

Ⓐ 1. The reflection image of a point $Q$ over point $P$ is the point $Q'$ such that $P$ is the ___Midpt.___ of $\overline{QQ'}$.

**Assignment Guide**
*Oral:* Max. 1–6
*Written:* Max. 7–21 odd

2. A set of points has ___Point___ symmetry if and only if there is a point $P$ such that the reflection image over $P$ of each point in the set is also a point in the set.

3–6. Refer to the circle having center $O$.

3. The reflection image of $R$ over $O$ is ___$T$___.

4. The reflection image of $S$ over $O$ is ___$W$___.

5. Does a circle have point symmetry?  Yes

6. Does a circle have turn symmetry?  Yes

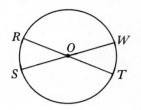

Ⓑ 7–14. Which figures have point symmetry?

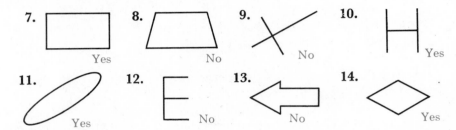

7. Yes   8. No   9. No   10. Yes

11. Yes   12. No   13. No   14. Yes

15–18. Which regular polygons below have point symmetry? Which have turn symmetry?

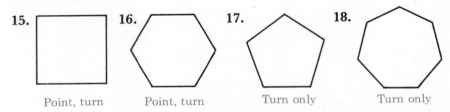

15. Point, turn   16. Point, turn   17. Turn only   18. Turn only

19–20. Copy each figure below. Then draw its reflection image over point $P$.

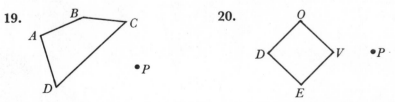

19.   20.

Ⓒ 21. Does each regular polygon have point symmetry? Does each regular polygon have turn symmetry? If a regular polygon has $n$ sides, what is the smallest angle through which it can be turned in order to coincide with itself.

No; yes; $\angle$ of meas. $\dfrac{360}{n}$

# CIRCLE GRAPHS

**Circle graphs** like the one below often appear in newspapers or magazines. In a circle graph, the area of the circle represents 100% (the whole amount). Each sector represents a certain percent of the entire amount. You can quickly compare different amounts by looking at the sizes of their sectors.

In making a circle graph, you need to remember that a circle measures 360°. Suppose you want to draw a sector that shows 25% of the entire amount. Then you must find 25% (or $\frac{1}{4}$) of 360°. Therefore, you would need to draw a sector with an arc of 90°. More generally, to represent $x$% of the entire amount, draw a sector with an arc that measures $x$% of 360°.

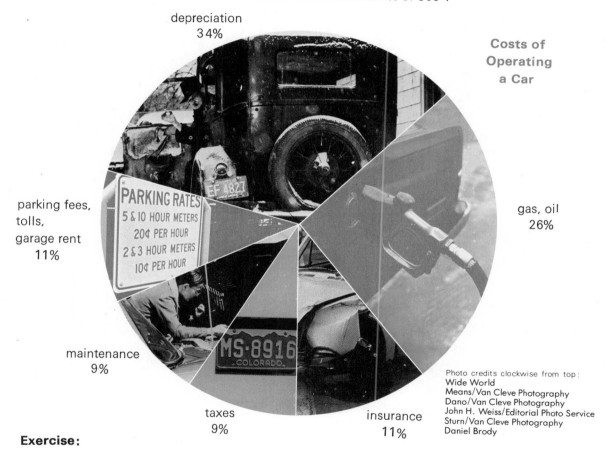

depreciation
34%

Costs of Operating a Car

PARKING RATES
5 & 10 HOUR METERS
20¢ PER HOUR
2 & 3 HOUR METERS
10¢ PER HOUR

parking fees, tolls, garage rent
11%

gas, oil
26%

maintenance
9%

taxes
9%

insurance
11%

Photo credits clockwise from top:
Wide World
Means/Van Cleve Photography
Dano/Van Cleve Photography
John H. Weiss/Editorial Photo Service
Sturn/Van Cleve Photography
Daniel Brody

**Exercise:**

Draw a circle graph to represent the sources of money for the federal government in a recent year: Individual Income Taxes, 30%; Corporation Income Taxes, 14%; Social Insurance Receipts, 26%; Excise Taxes, 9%; Borrowing, 15%; Miscellaneous, 6%.

| Suggested Class Time | | | |
|---|---|---|---|
| Course | Min. | Reg. | Max. |
| Days | 1 | 1 | 1 |

**12.1**

**Assignment Guide**
*Written:* Min. 1–12
Reg. 1–12
Max. 1–16

**1–3.** Refer to the inscribed regular hexagon.

**1.** Find $OA$.    10

**2.** Find $OR$.    $5\sqrt{3}$

**3.** Find the area of the hexagon.    $150\sqrt{3}$

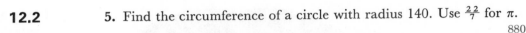

Ex. 1–3

Ex. 4

**4.** Copy the regular pentagon and circumscribe a circle about it.    *See page 422.*

**12.2**

**5.** Find the circumference of a circle with radius 140. Use $\frac{22}{7}$ for $\pi$.
880

**6.** A circle has circumference 628. Find its diameter. Use 3.14 for $\pi$.
200

**12.3**

**7–10.** Use the given measure of a circle to find each missing number. Leave answers in terms of $\pi$.

| | radius | diameter | circumference | area |
|---|---|---|---|---|
| **7.** | 8 | 16 | $16\pi$ | $64\pi$ |
| **8.** | 11 | 22 | $22\pi$ | $121\pi$ |
| **9.** | 16 | 32 | $32\pi$ | $256\pi$ |
| **10.** | 8 | 16 | $16\pi$ | $64\pi$ |

**12.4**

**11–12.** Leave answers in terms of $\pi$.

**11.** Find the length of a 30° arc in a circle with radius 7.    $\frac{7}{6}\pi$

**12.** A circle has radius 10. Find the area of a sector with a 150° arc.
$41\frac{2}{3}\pi$

**12.5**

**13–16.** Which figures have point symmetry?

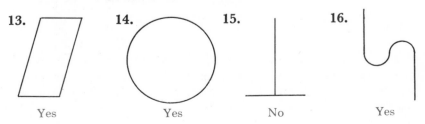

**13.**

Yes

**14.**

Yes

**15.**

No

**16.**

Yes

**1–2.** Equilateral $\triangle RST$ is inscribed in a circle with center $O$.

1. Find $OA$.  8

2. Find $OR$.  16

**Assignment Guide**
*Written:* Min. 1–10
Reg. 1–10
Max. 1–14

Ex. 1–2

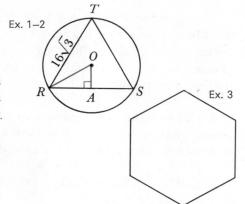

3. Copy the regular hexagon and inscribe a circle in the hexagon.  *See page 423.*

Ex. 3

4. If a regular polygon has perimeter 84 and an apothem of length 6, what is its area?  252

5. Find the circumference of a circle with radius 77. Use $\frac{22}{7}$ for $\pi$.  484

6. Find the diameter of a circle having circumference 1256. Use 3.14 for $\pi$.  400

7. Find the area of a circle with radius $3\frac{1}{2}$. Use $\frac{22}{7}$ for $\pi$.  $38\frac{1}{2}$

8. Find the radius of a circle with area $36\pi$.  6

**9–10.** Leave answers in terms of $\pi$.

9. Find the length of a $100°$ arc in a circle with radius 7.  $\frac{35}{9}\pi$

10. A circle has radius 8. Find the area of a sector with a $10°$ arc.  $\frac{16}{9}\pi$

**11–14.** Which figures have point symmetry?

11.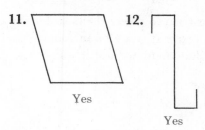
Yes

12.
Yes

13.
No

14.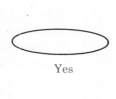
Yes

# MINI-CHAPTER: OTHER GEOMETRIES

The geometry you have been studying in this book is called **Euclidean geometry.** Euclid was a Greek mathematician who lived around 300 B.C. His writings appeared in a written work called *The Elements*. Except for religious scriptures, no written work has been studied more widely.

Euclid was the first person to organize geometry into a deductive system. That is, certain basic assumptions (postulates) were stated and the rest of the development was proved from these postulates.

Probably the most famous postulate in Euclidean geometry is Euclid's Parallel Postulate.

If a straight line falling on two straight lines makes the interior angles on the same side together less than two right angles, the two straight lines, if produced indefinitely, meet on that side on which the angles are together less than two right angles.

As you can see, the Parallel Postulate is very cumbersome and wordy. For years, mathematicians were bothered by its complex form. All the other postulates assumed by Euclid were fairly simple. So mathematicians felt it should be possible to do one of two things.

1. Prove Euclid's Parallel Postulate as a theorem. (That is, deduce it from the other postulates.)

2. Replace it with an equivalent statement which is simpler and more basic. (An equivalent statement is one that can be deduced from Euclid's Postulate, and vice versa.)

It seems that most mathematicians tried to prove the postulate as a theorem. In the process of trying to prove it, they often found other statements that are equivalent. The statement we use in this book is one such statement.

Through a point *P* not on line $\ell$, there is **exactly one** line parallel to $\ell$.

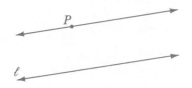

As it turns out, Euclid's Parallel Postulate cannot be proved from his other postulates. It is independent of the other postulates. It took mathematicians hundreds of years to realize this. Three persons are usually credited with making this discovery. Each of them worked independently. A Russian mathematician named Nikolai Lobachevski was the first to publish his own theories. However, János Bolyai, a Hungarian mathematician, reached this conclusion at about the same time. And later Karl Gauss, the great German mathematician, claimed to have made the discovery many years before. But he had never bothered to publish his findings. At any rate, the work of these people was to have far-reaching results.

Until that time, the geometry of Euclid was thought to be the only one possible. With the discovery that Euclid's Parallel Postulate was independent of the other postulates, the way was paved for other kinds of geometry called non-Euclidean. By replacing Euclid's Parallel Postulate with another postulate, entirely different deductions could be made.

Two other possibilities for the Parallel Postulate are

A. For any line $\ell$ and any point $P$ not on $\ell$, there is **more than one** line that contains $P$ and is parallel to $\ell$.

B. For any line $\ell$ and any point $P$ not on $\ell$, there is **no** line that contains $P$ and is parallel to $\ell$.

As you know, *point, line,* and *plane* are undefined terms in geometry. Yet, we often use models for these terms. With our usual models for line and plane, Postulates A and B do not make sense. But since line and plane are undefined, we can use any model that works. As it turns out, models do exist for which Postulates A and B are meaningful.

For Postulate A, let circle $O$ and its interior be the model for "plane" and let the chords be models for "lines." Remember that *parallel* means nonintersecting.

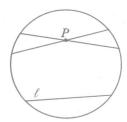

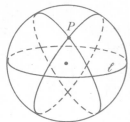

For Postulate B, another model is necessary. Suppose "plane" means sphere and "line" means a great circle on the sphere. (The plane of a great circle passes through the center of a sphere. For example, on the earth, the equator and all circles through the poles are great circles.)

The type of geometry that assumes Postulate A is usually called Lobachevskian (or hyperbolic) geometry. The type of geometry that assumes Postulate B is called Riemannian (or elliptic) geometry. (Georg Riemann, a German mathematician, discovered the non-Euclidean geometry named after him.) The two models just given are not the only possible ones for these geometries.

When non-Euclidean geometry was first developed, no one thought it had any useful applications. But Albert Einstein used concepts from Riemannian geometry in developing his famous theory of relativity.

The following chart shows how different results occur, according to which Parallel Postulate is accepted.

| Euclidean | Lobachevskian | Riemannian |
| --- | --- | --- |
| There is one and only one line through a given point parallel to a given line. | There is more than one line through a given point parallel to a given line. | There is no line through a given point parallel to a given line. |
| The sum of the measures of the angles of a triangle is 180. | The sum of the measures of the angles of a triangle is less than 180. | The sum of the measures of the angles of a triangle is more than 180. |
| Two parallel lines are everywhere equidistant. | Two parallel lines are not equidistant. They approach each other in one direction and diverge in the opposite direction. | There are no parallel lines. Each line intersects every other line. |

The chart above shows only a few of the differences among the three kinds of geometry. It might be pointed out, however, that many theorems are the same, no matter what kind of geometry is being used. This is to be expected since all the postulates are the same, except for the Parallel Postulate. Only those theorems that depend on the Parallel Postulate are different.

# PARALLEL LINES AND PLANES 13

Courtesy Harvard University News Office

Two *planes* are **parallel** if and only if they do not intersect. Also a *line* and a *plane* are **parallel** if and only if they do not intersect. Notice the models of parallel planes and of a line parallel to a plane above.

# Some Theorems on Parallel Lines and Planes

**13.1**

**Suggested Class Time**

| Course | Min. | Reg. | Max. |
|--------|------|------|------|
| Days | 1 | 1 | 1 |

Earlier, we used the symbol ∥ for parallel lines. Now, we also use it for parallel planes. If planes $A$ and $B$ are parallel, we write $A \parallel B$ or $B \parallel A$. If line $\ell$ and plane $C$ are parallel, we write $\ell \parallel C$ or $C \parallel \ell$.

It's reasonable to expect parallel planes to have properties like those of parallel lines. But when we talk about parallel lines and planes together in space, we have to be careful. For example,

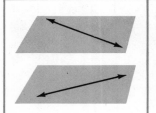

Lines in parallel planes are not always parallel. They might be skew lines.

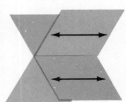

Parallel lines may be in intersecting planes.

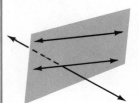

A line in space may intersect only one of two parallel lines.

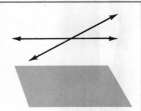

Intersecting lines may both be parallel to the same plane.

In space, lines can intersect, be parallel, or be skew. But planes either intersect, or they are parallel.

Since the intersection of two planes is a line, the intersection of two parallel planes by a third plane will be two lines. In fact,

**Theorem**

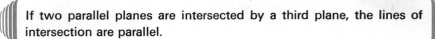

If two parallel planes are intersected by a third plane, the lines of intersection are parallel.

**Given:** Planes $A$ and $B$ are parallel, plane $C$ intersects $A$ and $B$ at lines $\ell$ and $m$.

**Prove:** $\ell \parallel m$

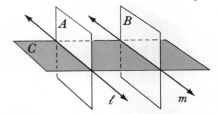

**Proof:**

| STATEMENTS | REASONS |
|------------|---------|
| 1. $\ell$ and $m$ are coplanar. | 1. Given $\ell$ and $m$ both in plane $C$ |
| 2. $\ell$ and $m$ do not intersect. | 2. Given $\ell$ in plane $A$, $m$ in plane $B$, and $A \parallel B$ |
| 3. $\ell \parallel m$ | 3. Definition of parallel lines |

You can illustrate the next theorem by holding a pencil perpendicular to your desk. Then place a book on the other end of the pencil, and hold the book parallel to the desk.

 If a line is perpendicular to one of two parallel planes, it is perpendicular to the other.  **Theorem**

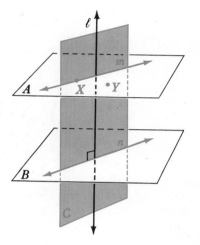

In the figure, planes $A$ and $B$ are parallel, and line $\ell$ is perpendicular to plane $B$. We could prove $\ell \perp A$ by showing that there are two intersecting lines in $A$ perpendicular to $\ell$ (Basic Theorem for Perpendiculars, page 270).

Pick a point $X$ in $A$ but not on $\ell$. Point $X$ and line $\ell$ determine plane $C$, which intersects $A$ and $B$ at lines $m$ and $n$. If a plane intersects two parallel planes, the lines of intersection are parallel; therefore, $m \parallel n$. Since $m \parallel n$ and $\ell \perp n$ (why?), $\ell \perp m$ (why?).

By choosing another point $Y$ in $A$ and repeating the process, we can show there exists a second line in $A$ perpendicular to $\ell$. And $\ell \perp A$ by the Basic Theorem for Perpendiculars.

The next two theorems give conditions to look for when determining if two planes are parallel.

 Two planes perpendicular to the same line are parallel.  **Theorem**

**Given:** Line $\ell \perp$ plane $P$ at point $X$, line $\ell \perp$ plane $Q$ at point $Y$.

**Prove:** $P \parallel Q$

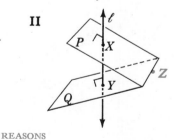

**Proof:**

| STATEMENTS | REASONS |
|---|---|
| 1. Assume $P$ is not parallel to $Q$. | 1. Assume opposite for indirect proof. |
| 2. There is a point $Z$ in both $P$ and $Q$. (See figure II.) | 2. Two planes intersect at a line. (Let $Z$ be any point on that line.) |
| 3. But, there is only one plane through $Z$ perpendicular to $\ell$. | 3. Perpendicular Line and Plane Postulates, part **a** (p. 273) |
| 4. So, $P \parallel Q$. | 4. Principle of Indirect Reasoning |

**Theorem**  Two planes parallel to a third plane are parallel.

Given: Plane $A \parallel$ plane $C$,
   plane $B \parallel$ plane $C$.

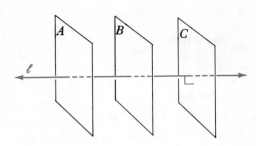

Prove: $A \parallel B$

| Proof: STATEMENTS | REASONS |
|---|---|
| 1. $A \parallel C$ and $B \parallel C$ | 1. Given |
| 2. Let line $\ell$ be perpendicular to plane $C$. | 2. There is a line $\perp$ to $C$ at any point of $C$. |
| 3. $\ell \perp A$ and $\ell \perp B$ | 3. A line $\perp$ to one of two $\parallel$ planes is $\perp$ to the other. |
| 4. $A \parallel B$ | 4. Two planes $\perp$ to the same line are $\parallel$. |

NOTE: If planes $A, B,$ and $C$ are parallel, we can write $A \parallel B \parallel C$.

# *Exercises 13.1*

**Assignment Guide**
*Oral:* 1–10
*Written:* Min. 11–22
   Reg. 11–23
   Max. 11–29 odd

Ⓐ **1–10.** True or False? (Use the figure.)

1. $A \parallel B$   T   **2.** $A \parallel C$   T

3. $m \perp \ell$   T   **4.** $m \perp B$   F

5. $n \perp \ell$   T   **6.** $m \parallel n$   F

7. $m \parallel B$   T   **8.** $n \parallel C$   T

9. $\ell \parallel C$   F   **10.** $\ell \perp C$   T

Given: $\ell \perp A, \ell \perp B,$
$m$ is in $A$ and intersects $\ell$,
$n$ is in $B$ and intersects $\ell$,
$B \parallel C$

Ⓑ **11–18.** True or False? Draw a sketch to illustrate each true statement. Sketch a counterexample for each false statement.

11. If a line is perpendicular to one of two parallel planes, it is perpendicular to the other.   T

12. If two lines are parallel to the same plane, they may be perpendicular to each other.   T

**13.** If two planes are parallel to the same line, they are parallel to each other.     F (The planes might intersect, with their line of intersection ∥ to the given line.)

**14.** If two lines are parallel, every plane containing only one of them is parallel to the other.     T

**15.** If two planes are parallel, any line in one plane is parallel to any line in the other plane.     F (The lines might be skew.)

**16.** If two planes are perpendicular to the same line and are intersected by a third plane, the lines of intersection are parallel.     T

**17.** If two intersecting lines are each parallel to a plane, the plane determined by the lines is parallel to the given plane.     T

**18.** If two planes are intersected by a third plane, the lines of intersection are always parallel.     F (Consider two walls and the floor.)

**19–22.** Use a theorem of this section to answer each exercise.

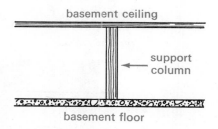

basement ceiling

support column

basement floor

**19.** The basement ceiling and floor are level. (They are parallel planes.) The support column has been placed perpendicular to the floor. Is it also perpendicular to the ceiling? Why?

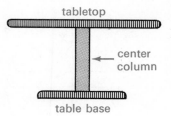

tabletop

center column

table base

**20.** The tabletop has been made perpendicular to the center column, and so has the table base. Are the top and base parallel? Why?

**19.** Yes. If a line is ⊥ to 1 of 2 ∥ planes, it is ⊥ to the other.
**20.** Yes. Two planes ⊥ to the same line are ∥.

**21.** The treads of two steps are parallel. Is the front edge of the top step parallel to the back edge of the bottom step? Why?

treads — front edge — back edge

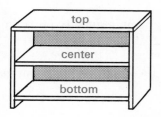

top

center

bottom

**22.** The top and center shelves of the bookcase have been made parallel to the bottom shelf. Are the top and center shelves parallel? Why?

**21.** Yes. If 2 ∥ planes are intersected by a 3rd plane, the lines of intersection are ∥.
**22.** Yes; Two planes ∥ to a 3rd plane are ∥.

**23.** 1. $\ell \perp A$, $\ell \perp B$ (Given)
 2. $A \parallel B$ (Two planes $\perp$ to same line are $\parallel$.)
 3. $C$ intersects $A$ and $B$ at $m$ and $n$. (Given)
 4. $m \parallel n$ (3rd plane intersects 2 $\parallel$ planes at 2 $\parallel$ lines.)

**24.** 1. $m$, $n$ are in $C$, $\ell \perp m$, $\ell \perp n$ (Given)
 2. $\ell \perp C$ (Basic Thm. for $\perp$s)
 3. $\ell \perp D$ (Given)
 4. $C \parallel D$ (2 planes $\perp$ to same line are $\parallel$.)

**23.** **Given:** $\ell \perp A$, $\ell \perp B$, $C$ intersects $A$ and $B$ at $m$ and $n$.

**Prove:** $m \parallel n$

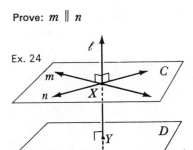

Ex. 24

**24.** **Given:** $\ell$ intersects planes $C$ and $D$ at points $X$ and $Y$, $m$ and $n$ are in $C$, $\ell \perp m$, $\ell \perp n$, and $\ell \perp D$

**Prove:** $C \parallel D$

© **25.** **Given:** $E \parallel F$, $F \parallel G$, $\ell \perp E$

**Prove:** $\ell \perp G$

**25.** 1. $E \parallel F$, $F \parallel G$ (Given)
 2. $E \parallel G$ (2 planes $\parallel$ to 3rd plane are $\parallel$.)
 3. $\ell \perp E$ (Given)
 4. $\ell \perp G$ (Line $\perp$ to 1 of 2 $\parallel$ planes is $\perp$ to the other.)

**26.** 1. $\ell \perp P$, $\ell \perp Q$ (Given)
 2. $P \parallel Q$ (2 planes $\perp$ to same line are $\parallel$.)
 3. $m \perp Q$ (Given)
 4. $m \perp P$ (Line $\perp$ to 1 of 2 $\parallel$ planes is $\perp$ to the other.)

**27.** *Sketch of Proof:* Since $\overleftrightarrow{XY} \perp a$, $\overleftrightarrow{XY} \perp b$ also. So $\overleftrightarrow{XY}$ is $\perp$ to $\overline{YR}$ and $\overline{YS}$ in $b$, and $\triangle XYR$ and $\triangle XYS$ are rt. $\triangle$s. But $\overline{YR} \cong \overline{YS}$ and $\overline{XY} \cong \overline{XY}$, so $\triangle XYR \cong \triangle XYS$ by the LL Thm. Then $\overline{XR} \cong \overline{XS}$ because they are corres. parts.

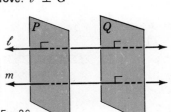

**26.** **Given:** $\ell \perp P$, $\ell \perp Q$, $m \perp Q$

**Prove:** $m \perp P$

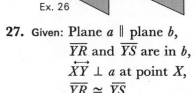

Ex. 26

**27.** **Given:** Plane $a \parallel$ plane $b$, $\overline{YR}$ and $\overline{YS}$ are in $b$, $\overleftrightarrow{XY} \perp a$ at point $X$, $\overline{YR} \cong \overline{YS}$

**Prove:** $\overline{XR} \cong \overline{XS}$

**HINT:** What two triangles are congruent?

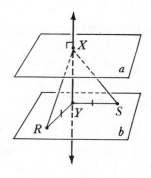

**28–29.** These statements about parallel planes are very much like some theorems about parallel lines in a plane. Complete each statement.

**28.** If three parallel planes intercept congruent segments on a line that intersects them, then they _____.
Intercept $\cong$ segs. on every line that intersects them

**29.** If point $P$ is not in plane $r$, there is exactly one plane that contains $P$ and is ____Parallel____ to $r$.

450    CHAPTER 13    PARALLEL LINES AND PLANES

# More Theorems on Parallel Lines and Planes

Sometimes the way in which lines are related to a plane is a clue to how they are related to each other. If two lampposts are perpendicular to the roadway, does it look as if the posts are parallel?

Two lines perpendicular to the same plane are parallel.

**Theorem**

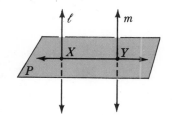

Given: Line $\ell \perp$ plane $P$ at point $X$,
line $m \perp$ plane $P$ at point $Y$.

Prove: $\ell \parallel m$

**Proof:**

| STATEMENTS | REASONS |
|------------|---------|
| 1. $\ell \perp P$ at $X$, $m \perp P$ at $Y$. | 1. Given |
| 2. $\ell$ and $m$ are coplanar. | 2. Two lines $\perp$ to the same plane are coplanar. |
| 3. $\overleftrightarrow{XY}$ is in the same plane as $\ell$ and $m$. | 3. If two points are in a plane, so is the line through them. |
| 4. $\ell \perp \overleftrightarrow{XY}$ and $m \perp \overleftrightarrow{XY}$ | 4. Def. of line $\perp$ to plane |
| 5. $\ell \parallel m$ | 5. In a plane, two lines $\perp$ to the same line are $\parallel$. |

The end zone of a football field illustrates the next two theorems.

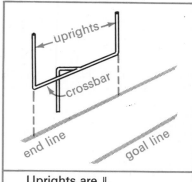

Uprights are $\parallel$.
One upright $\perp$ field.
So, other upright $\perp$ field.

Crossbar $\parallel$ end line.
End line $\parallel$ goal line.
So, crossbar $\parallel$ goal line.

Photo Trends

**Theorem**  If a plane is perpendicular to one of two parallel lines, it is perpendicular to the other.

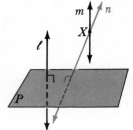

Given: Line $\ell \parallel$ line $m$, $\ell \perp$ plane $P$, point $X$ is on $m$.

Prove: $P \perp m$

**Proof:**

| STATEMENTS | REASONS |
|---|---|
| 1. Let $n$ be a line through $X$ such that $P \perp n$. | 1. Through a given pt., there is exactly one line $\perp$ to a given plane. |
| 2. $\ell \perp P$ | 2. Given |
| 3. $\ell \parallel n$ | 3. Two lines $\perp$ to the same plane are $\parallel$. |
| 4. $\ell \parallel m$ | 4. Given |
| 5. $m = n$ | 5. Parallel Postulate (p. 125) |
| 6. $P \perp m$ | 6. Substitute $m$ for $n$ (steps 1 and 5). |

**Theorem**  Two lines parallel to a third line are parallel.

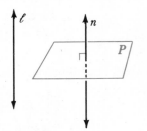

Given: $\ell \parallel n$, $m \parallel n$

Prove: $\ell \parallel m$

NOTE: Three lines do not necessarily have to be co-planar to be parallel.

**Proof:**

| STATEMENTS | REASONS |
|---|---|
| 1. Let $P$ be a plane $\perp$ to $n$ at any point of $n$. | 1. Through a given pt., there is exactly one plane $\perp$ to a given line. |
| 2. $\ell \parallel n$ | 2. Given |
| 3. $\ell \perp P$ | 3. A plane $\perp$ to one of two $\parallel$ lines is $\perp$ to the other. |
| 4. $m \parallel n$ | 4. Why? |
| 5. $m \perp P$ | 5. Why? |
| 6. $\ell \parallel m$ | 6. Why? |

In Chapter 8 we defined the *distance from a point to a plane* as the length of the perpendicular segment from the point to the plane. We now consider *distance between parallel planes*.

**Parallel planes are everywhere equidistant.**

**Theorem**

In terms of the figure, the theorem says that if planes *a* and *b* are parallel, then all points in *a* are equidistant from *b*, and vice versa.

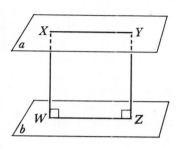

Given: $a \parallel b$, points $X$ and $Y$ are in $a$, $\overline{XW}$ and $\overline{YZ}$ are perpendicular segments from $X$ and $Y$ to $b$.

Prove: $XW = YZ$

**Proof:**

| STATEMENTS | REASONS |
|---|---|
| 1. $a \parallel b$, $\overline{XW} \perp b$, $\overline{YZ} \perp b$ | 1. Given |
| 2. $\overleftrightarrow{XW} \parallel \overleftrightarrow{YZ}$ | 2. Two lines $\perp$ to the same plane are $\parallel$. |
| 3. $\overleftrightarrow{XW}$ and $\overleftrightarrow{YZ}$ are in a plane. | 3. Two $\parallel$ lines are coplanar. |
| 4. $\overleftrightarrow{XY} \parallel \overleftrightarrow{WZ}$ | 4. Intersection of two $\parallel$ planes by third plane is two $\parallel$ lines. |
| 5. $XYZW$ is a parallelogram. | 5. Def. of parallelogram |
| 6. $XW = YZ$ | 6. Opp. sides of a $\square$ are $\cong$. |

NOTE: What special kind of parallelogram is $XYZW$ above? Why?

**Assignment Guide**
*Oral:* 1–8
*Written:*
Min. 9–16
Reg. (day 1) 9–15 odd; 17–28
    (day 2) 29–30; 36–39
Max. (day 1) 9–15 odd; 17–29
    (day 2) 31–39 odd

# Exercises 13.2

Ⓐ 1–3. Using the words *line*(s) and *plane*(s), complete each statement in two different ways.

1. Two _____ perpendicular to the same _____ are parallel.

2. If a _____ is perpendicular to one of two parallel _____, it is perpendicular to the other.

3. Two _____ parallel to a third _____ are parallel.

1. Lines, plane;
   Planes, line

2. Line, planes;
   Plane, lines

3. Lines, line;
   Planes, plane

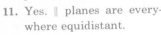

Given:

$p \parallel q$,
$\overline{AD} \perp q$,
$\overline{BE} \perp p$,
$\overline{CF} \perp q$

**4–8.** Complete each statement as a conclusion from the given.

**4.** $\overline{AD} \perp$ ___$p$___    **5.** $\overline{BE} \perp$ ___$q$___

**6.** $\overline{CF} \perp$ ___$p$___    **7.** $\overline{AD} \parallel$ ___$\overline{BE}$___ $\parallel$ ___$\overline{CF}$___

**8.** $AD =$ ___$BE$___ $=$ ___$CF$___

Ⓑ **9–12.** Refer to the figure. Use a theorem to answer each question, and state the theorem.

9. Yes. Plane ⊥ to 1 of 2 ‖ lines is ⊥ to the other.

10. Yes. Two lines ⊥ to same plane are ‖.

11. Yes. ‖ planes are everywhere equidistant.

**9.** If $\ell \parallel m$ and $a \perp \ell$, is $a \perp m$?

**10.** If $\ell \perp a$ and $m \perp a$, is $\ell \parallel m$?

**11.** If $a \parallel b$, $\ell \perp b$, and $m \perp b$, is $XY = ZW$?

**12.** If $\ell \parallel m$, $\ell \perp a$, and $m \perp b$, is $a \parallel b$? (Two theorems needed.)
Yes. Plane ⊥ to 1 of 2 ‖ lines is ⊥ to the other. 2 planes ⊥ to same line are ‖.

**13–16.** True or False? Draw a sketch to illustrate each true statement. Sketch a counterexample for each false statement.

**13.** If a plane is perpendicular to one of two parallel lines, it is perpendicular to the other.    T

**14.** If points $X$ and $Y$ are both in one of two parallel planes, the distances from $X$ and $Y$ to the other plane are equal.    T

**15.** If three lines are parallel, they are in the same plane.    F (Consider $\triangle ABC$ in plane $p$ and lines ⊥ to $p$ at $A$, $B$, and $C$.)

**16.** If a line is in a plane, a perpendicular to the line is perpendicular to the plane.    F (The ⊥ may be in the plane or at any ∠ to the plane.)

Given: $\overleftrightarrow{AB} \perp e$, $\overleftrightarrow{AB} \perp f$, $\overleftrightarrow{BH}$ and $\overleftrightarrow{AB}$ determine a plane intersecting $e$ at $\overleftrightarrow{CA}$, $\overleftrightarrow{BK}$ and $\overleftrightarrow{AB}$ determine a plane intersecting $e$ at $\overleftrightarrow{AD}$, $AC = BH$, $AD = BK$

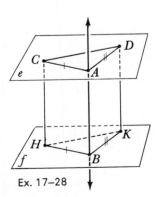

Ex. 17–28

**17–28.** This is a sequence of statements as in a proof. Give a reason for each statement.

**17.** $e \parallel f$    2 planes ⊥ to the same line are ‖.

**18.** $\overline{AC} \parallel \overline{BH}$ and $\overline{AD} \parallel \overline{BK}$
    3rd plane intersects 2 ‖ planes at 2 ‖ lines.

**19.** $\overline{AC} \cong \overline{BH}$ and $\overline{AD} \cong \overline{BK}$
    Definition of ≅ segs.

**20.** $BACH$ and $BADK$ are parallelograms.
    Quadrilateral is ▱ if 2 sides are ‖ and ≅.

454    CHAPTER 13    PARALLEL LINES AND PLANES

**21.** $\overleftrightarrow{CH} \parallel \overleftrightarrow{AB}$ and $\overleftrightarrow{AB} \parallel \overleftrightarrow{DK}$    Opp. sides of ▱ are ∥.

**22.** $\overleftrightarrow{CH} \parallel \overleftrightarrow{DK}$    2 lines ∥ to a 3rd line are ∥.

**23.** $\overline{CH} \cong \overline{AB}$ and $\overline{AB} \cong \overline{DK}$    Opp. sides of ▱ are ≅.

**24.** $\overline{CH} \cong \overline{DK}$    Segs. ≅ to same seg. are ≅.

**25.** CHKD is a parallelogram.    _Same as Ex. 20_

**26.** $\overline{CD} \cong \overline{HK}$    Opp. sides of ▱ are ≅.

**27.** $\triangle CAD \cong \triangle HBK$    SSS Post.

**28.** $\angle CAD \cong \angle HBK$    Corres. parts of ≅ △s are ≅.

**29.** **Given:** $A \parallel B$,
   $C$ intersects $A$ and $B$ at $\ell$ and $m$,
   $m \parallel n$

**Prove:** $\ell \parallel n$

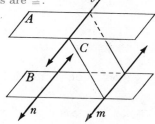

**30.** **Given:** $W$ and $X$ are in $s$, $Z$ and $Y$ are in $t$,
   $\overleftrightarrow{WZ} \perp s$, $\overleftrightarrow{XY} \perp s$, $\overleftrightarrow{WZ} \perp t$

**Prove:** $\overleftrightarrow{XY} \perp t$

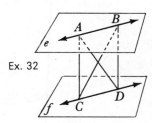

Ex. 30

**31.** **Given:** $C \parallel D$, $\ell \perp C$,
   $m \perp D$, $\ell \parallel n$

**Prove:** $m \parallel n$

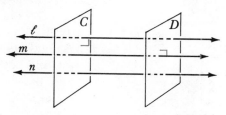

Ex. 32

**32.** **Given:** $e \parallel f$, $\overleftrightarrow{AB}$ is in $e$, $\overleftrightarrow{CD}$ is in $f$,
   $\overline{AC} \perp e$, $\overline{BD} \perp e$

**Prove:** $\overline{AD}$ and $\overline{BC}$ bisect each other.

**HINT:** Diagonals of a ▱ bisect.

**29.** 1. $A \parallel B$; $C$ intersects $A$ and $B$ at $\ell$ and $m$. (Given)
2. $\ell \parallel m$ (3rd plane intersects 2 ∥ planes at 2 ∥ lines.)
3. $m \parallel n$ (Given)
4. $\ell \parallel n$ (2 lines ∥ to same line are ∥.)

**30.** 1. $\overleftrightarrow{WZ} \perp s$, $\overleftrightarrow{XY} \perp s$ (Given)
2. $\overleftrightarrow{WZ} \parallel \overleftrightarrow{XY}$ (2 lines ⊥ to the same plane are ∥.)
3. $\overleftrightarrow{WZ} \perp t$ (Given)
4. $\overleftrightarrow{XY} \perp t$ (Plane ⊥ to 1 of 2 ∥ lines is ⊥ to the other.)

**31.** 1. $C \parallel D$, $\ell \perp C$ (Given)
2. $\ell \perp D$ (Line ⊥ to 1 of 2 ∥ planes is ⊥ to the other.)
3. $m \perp D$ (Given)
4. $m \parallel \ell$ (2 lines ⊥ to same plane are ∥.)
5. $\ell \parallel n$ (Given)
6. $m \parallel n$ (2 lines ∥ to same line are ∥.)

**32.** 1. $e \parallel f$, $\overline{AC} \perp e$, $\overline{BD} \perp e$ (Given)
2. $\overline{AC} \cong \overline{BD}$ (∥ planes are everywhere equidistant.)
3. $\overline{AC} \parallel \overline{BD}$ (2 lines ⊥ to same line are ∥.)
4. ABCD is a ▱. (Quad. is a ▱ if 2 sides are ∥ and ≅.)
5. $\overline{AD}$, $\overline{BC}$ bisect each other. (Diags. of a ▱ bisect each other.)

© **33.** **Given:** Planes $m$ and $n$ intersect at $\overleftrightarrow{XY}$; $m$ and $n$ intersect planes $a$ and $b$ at $\overleftrightarrow{XU}$, $\overleftrightarrow{YV}$, $\overleftrightarrow{XW}$, and $\overleftrightarrow{YZ}$; $a \parallel b$; $XW = YZ$; $XU = YV$

**Prove:** $\angle WXU \cong \angle ZYV$

**HINT:** Show $\overleftrightarrow{XY} \parallel \overleftrightarrow{UV} \parallel \overleftrightarrow{WZ}$ and $UVZW$ is a ▱.

_Statements 1–12 are like those in Ex. 17–28, except for lettering._

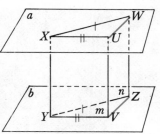

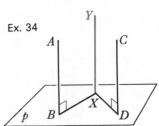

Ex. 34

**34.** Given: $\overline{XB}$ and $\overline{XD}$ in plane $p$, $\overline{AB} \perp \overline{XB}$,
$\overline{CD} \perp \overline{XD}$, $\overline{AB} \parallel \overline{CD}$

Prove: $\overline{AB} \perp p$, $\overline{CD} \perp p$

HINT: Introduce $\overleftrightarrow{YX} \parallel \overline{AB}$, and show $\overleftrightarrow{YX} \perp p$.

**34.** *1.* $\overline{AB} \parallel \overline{CD}$ (Given)
*2.* Let $\overleftrightarrow{YX}$ be $\parallel \overline{AB}$
  ($\parallel$ Post.)
*3.* $\overleftrightarrow{YX} \parallel \overline{CD}$ (2 lines $\parallel$
  to same line are $\parallel$.)
*4.* $\overleftrightarrow{YX}$, $\overline{AB}$ are coplanar.
  $\overleftrightarrow{YX}$, $\overline{CD}$ are coplanar.
  (2 $\parallel$ lines determine
  a plane.)
*5.* $\overline{AB} \perp \overline{XB}$, $\overline{CD} \perp \overline{XD}$
  (Given)
*6.* $\overleftrightarrow{YX} \perp \overline{XB}$, $\overleftrightarrow{YX} \perp \overline{XD}$
  (In a plane, a line
  $\perp$ to 1 of 2 $\parallel$ lines
  is $\perp$ to the other.)
*7.* $\overleftrightarrow{YX} \perp p$ (Basic Thm.
  for $\perp$s)
*8.* $\overline{AB} \perp p$, $\overline{CD} \perp p$ (A
  plane $\perp$ to 1 of 2
  $\parallel$ lines is $\perp$ to the
  other.)

**35.** The 2 lines at which $a$
  intersects the 2 planes
  $\parallel$ to $b$ at a distance
  $PQ$ above and below $b$
  ($P$ is on 1 of the lines.)

**35.** Given: Planes $a$ and $b$ intersect at
  line $\ell$, point $P$ is in $a$,
  $\overline{PQ}$ is the perpendicular
  segment from $P$ to $b$.

Describe the locus of points in $a$
that are a distance of $PQ$ from $b$.

HINT: The points are on both sides of $\ell$.

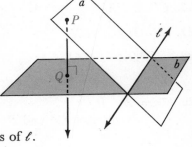

**36–39.** Use a theorem of this section to
answer each exercise.

**36.** Two legs on one end of a table are
made perpendicular to the tabletop.
Are the legs parallel? Why? Yes. 2 lines
  $\perp$ to the same
  plane are $\parallel$.

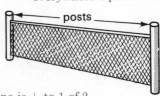

legs →

tabletop

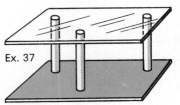

Ex. 37

**37.** An end table is made by fastening the
top and base with three rods. The top
and base are parallel. Are the rods
equal in length? Yes. $\parallel$ planes are
  everywhere equidistant.

**38.** The net on a tennis court is held by
two parallel posts. One post is perpendicular to the court. Is the other
post perpendicular to the court? Why?
  Yes. If a plane is $\perp$ to 1 of 2
  $\parallel$ lines, it is $\perp$ to the other.

← posts →

**39.** Three airplanes are flying in V-
formation. Each outside airplane
keeps its path parallel to the straight
path of the middle airplane. Are the
paths of the two outside airplanes
parallel? Why? Yes. 2 lines $\parallel$ to the
  same line are $\parallel$.

# Dihedral Angles

**13.3**

When two lines in a plane intersect at a point, four angles are formed. Two planes in space intersecting at a line also form four figures. Each figure is called a dihedral angle.

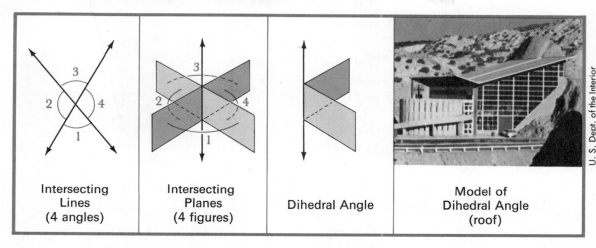

| Intersecting Lines (4 angles) | Intersecting Planes (4 figures) | Dihedral Angle | Model of Dihedral Angle (roof) |

U. S. Dept. of the Interior National Park Service

A **dihedral angle** is formed by a line and two noncoplanar half planes that have the line as their common edge. The line and either half plane is a *face* (or *side*) of the dihedral angle. The line is the *edge* of the dihedral angle. How is the definition of *angle* (in a plane) similar to the definition of *dihedral angle*?

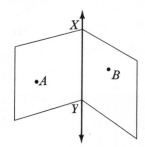

A dihedral angle with edge $\overleftrightarrow{XY}$, point $A$ in one face, and point $B$ in the other face is named

$$\angle A\text{-}\overleftrightarrow{XY}\text{-}B, \text{ or}$$

$$\angle \overleftrightarrow{XY} \text{ if}$$

there is no question as to which dihedral angle has $\overleftrightarrow{XY}$ as its edge.

A **plane angle** of a dihedral angle is the intersection of the dihedral angle and a plane perpendicular to the edge of the dihedral angle. If $p \perp \overleftrightarrow{XY}$ at $Q$, then $\angle RQS$ is a plane angle of $\angle A\text{-}\overleftrightarrow{XY}\text{-}B$. Also, $\overrightarrow{QR} \perp \overleftrightarrow{XY}$, and $\overrightarrow{QS} \perp \overleftrightarrow{XY}$. Why? We will take the definition of *plane angle* to mean that the sides of the plane angle are perpendicular to the edge of the dihedral angle.

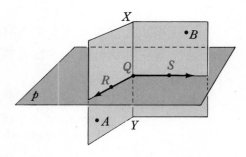

At each point of a line there is exactly one plane perpendicular to the line. Therefore, each dihedral angle has infinitely many plane angles. But we can show that all the plane angles are congruent.

**Theorem**  The plane angles of a dihedral angle are congruent.

Given: ∠RPS and ∠TQU are plane
      angles of ∠A-$\overleftrightarrow{XY}$-B,
      $\overline{RP} \cong \overline{TQ}$, $\overline{SP} \cong \overline{UQ}$

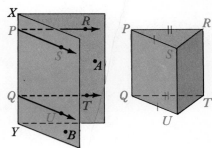

Prove: ∠RPS ≅ ∠TQU

| Proof:    STATEMENTS | REASONS |
|---|---|
| 1. $\overline{RP} \perp \overleftrightarrow{XY}$, $\overline{TQ} \perp \overleftrightarrow{XY}$, $\overline{SP} \perp \overleftrightarrow{XY}$, $\overline{UQ} \perp \overleftrightarrow{XY}$ | 1. Given ∠s RPS and TQU are plane angles, def. of plane angles |
| 2. $\overline{RP} \parallel \overline{TQ}$, $\overline{SP} \parallel \overline{UQ}$ | 2. In a plane, two lines ⊥ to the same line are ∥. |
| 3. $\overline{RP} \cong \overline{TQ}$, $\overline{SP} \cong \overline{UQ}$ | 3. Given |
| 4. RPQT and SPQU are ▱s. | 4. Pair of opp. sides are ∥ and ≅. |
| 5. $\overline{RT} \parallel \overline{PQ} \parallel \overline{SU}$ | 5. Opp. sides of a ▱ are ∥, and 2 lines ∥ to the same line are ∥. |
| 6. $\overline{RT} \cong \overline{PQ}$, $\overline{PQ} \cong \overline{SU}$ | 6. Opp. sides of a ▱ are ≅. |
| 7. $\overline{RT} \cong \overline{SU}$ | 7. Segs. ≅ to the same seg. are ≅. |
| 8. RSUT is a ▱. | 8. Same as reason 4 |
| 9. $\overline{RS} \cong \overline{TU}$ | 9. Same as reason 6 |
| 10. △RPS ≅ △TQU | 10. SSS Postulate |
| 11. ∠RPS ≅ ∠TQU | 11. Corres. parts of ≅ △s are ≅. |

Now we can say that the **measure** of a dihedral angle is the measure of any of its plane angles. And a **right dihedral angle** is a dihedral angle whose plane angles are right angles. The definitions of *acute* and *obtuse dihedral angles* are left for you to furnish in the exercises.

Ⓐ **1–2.** Name the following:

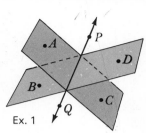

Ex. 1

◀ **1.** four dihedral angles

**2.** two dihedral angles ▶
(Give two names for
each angle.)

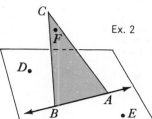

Ex. 2

**Assignment Guide**
*Oral:* 1–10
*Written:* Min. 11–23 odd
      Reg. 11–31 odd
      Max. 11–35 odd

**3.** Find models of three dihedral angles in your classroom.
*Answers will vary.*

1. $\angle A\text{-}\overleftrightarrow{PQ}\text{-}B$, $\angle B\text{-}\overleftrightarrow{PQ}\text{-}C$,
$\angle C\text{-}\overleftrightarrow{PQ}\text{-}D$, $\angle D\text{-}\overleftrightarrow{PQ}\text{-}A$

2. $\angle C\text{-}\overleftrightarrow{AB}\text{-}D$ (or $\angle F\text{-}\overleftrightarrow{AB}\text{-}D$),
$\angle C\text{-}\overleftrightarrow{AB}\text{-}E$ (or $\angle F\text{-}\overleftrightarrow{AB}\text{-}E$)

**4–10.** $\angle ARB$ is a plane angle of $\angle \overleftrightarrow{XY}$.

**4.** $\overleftrightarrow{XY}$ is the ___Edge___ of $\angle \overleftrightarrow{XY}$.

**5.** Point $B$ is on a _____ of $\angle \overleftrightarrow{XY}$.
      Face (or side)

**6.** $\overrightarrow{RA}$ and $\overrightarrow{RB}$ are ___⊥___ to $\overleftrightarrow{XY}$.

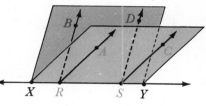

**7.** If $\angle CSD$ is a plane angle of $\angle \overleftrightarrow{XY}$, then $\angle CSD$ ___≅___ $\angle ARB$.

**8.** If $m\angle ARB = 45$, then $m\angle \overleftrightarrow{XY} =$ ___45___. **9.** $m\angle ARS =$ ___90___

**10.** If $\angle ARB$ is a right angle, then $\angle \overleftrightarrow{XY}$ is a ___Right___ dihedral angle.

Ⓑ **11–12.** Name the following:

**11.** five dihedral angles
$\angle R\text{-}\overleftrightarrow{ST}\text{-}Y$, $\angle R\text{-}\overleftrightarrow{ST}\text{-}U$, $\angle R\text{-}\overleftrightarrow{ST}\text{-}X$,
$\angle U\text{-}\overleftrightarrow{ST}\text{-}X$, $\angle U\text{-}\overleftrightarrow{ST}\text{-}Y$

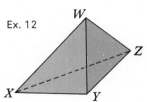

Ex. 11

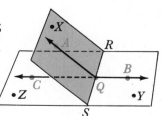

Ex. 12

**12.** six dihedral angles
$\angle \overleftrightarrow{XW}$, $\angle \overleftrightarrow{XY}$, $\angle \overleftrightarrow{XZ}$, $\angle \overleftrightarrow{WY}$,
$\angle \overleftrightarrow{WZ}$, $\angle \overleftrightarrow{YZ}$ (or $\angle Y\text{-}\overleftrightarrow{XW}\text{-}Z$, etc.)

**13–16.** Give a reason for each statement.

**13.** $m\angle AQB = m\angle X\text{-}\overleftrightarrow{RS}\text{-}Y$
Def. of meas. of dihedral $\angle$

**14.** $\overrightarrow{QA} \perp \overleftrightarrow{RS}$ and $\overrightarrow{QB} \perp \overleftrightarrow{RS}$
Def. of plane $\angle$

**15.** If $\overrightarrow{QC} \perp \overleftrightarrow{RS}$ and $\overrightarrow{QA} \perp \overleftrightarrow{RS}$, then

**(a)** $\overrightarrow{QC}$ and $\overrightarrow{QA}$ are in a plane $\perp$ to $\overleftrightarrow{RS}$ at $Q$.

**(b)** $\angle CQA$ is a plane angle of $\angle Z\text{-}\overleftrightarrow{RS}\text{-}X$.

   **a.** Basic Thm. for $\perp$s      **b.** Def. of plane $\angle$

**16.** $\angle X\text{-}\overleftrightarrow{RS}\text{-}Y$ is a right dihedral angle if $m\angle AQB = 90$.
      Def. of rt. dihedral $\angle$

**Given:** $\angle AQB$ is a plane
      angle of $\angle X\text{-}\overleftrightarrow{RS}\text{-}Y$.

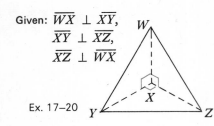

Given: $\overline{WX} \perp \overline{XY}$,
$\overline{XY} \perp \overline{XZ}$,
$\overline{XZ} \perp \overline{WX}$

Ex. 17–20

**17–20.** Name the following:

**17.** a plane angle of $\angle W\text{-}\overleftrightarrow{XY}\text{-}Z$   $\angle WXZ$

**18.** the dihedral angle for which $\angle YXZ$ is a plane angle $\angle \overleftrightarrow{WX}$

**19.** the dihedral angle for which $\angle WXY$ is a plane angle $\angle \overleftrightarrow{XZ}$

**20.** a dihedral angle whose measure is 90

Any one of $\angle \overleftrightarrow{XY}$, $\angle \overleftrightarrow{XZ}$, or $\angle \overleftrightarrow{WX}$

**25.** 1. $\angle ABC$, $\angle DEF$ are plane $\angle$s of $\angle A\text{-}\overleftrightarrow{XY}\text{-}F$. (Given)
2. $\angle ABC \cong \angle DEF$ (Plane $\angle$s of a dihedral $\angle$ are $\cong$.)
3. $\overline{AB} \cong \overline{DE}$, $\overline{BC} \cong \overline{EF}$ (Given)
4. $\triangle ABC \cong \triangle DEF$ (SAS Post.)
5. $\overline{AC} \cong \overline{DF}$ (Corres. parts of $\cong \triangle$s are $\cong$.)

**26.** *Sketch of Proof:* Since the measures of the dihedral $\angle$s and their plane $\angle$s are equal, $m\angle FDE + m\angle DEF = 120$. But the sum of the measures of the $\angle$s of $\triangle DEF$ is 180. So $m\angle EFD = 60$, and therefore $m\angle \overleftrightarrow{FC} = 60$.

**35.** *Plan:* Use a plane $\perp$ to the common edge of the vertical dihedral $\angle$s. Show that the $\perp$ plane and the given planes intersect at lines that form $\cong$ vertical $\angle$s. These $\angle$s are plane $\angle$s of the given dihedral $\angle$s.

**21–24.** Find the measure of each dihedral angle.

Given: $\overrightarrow{QA}$, $\overrightarrow{QD}$, and $\overleftrightarrow{XY}$ are $\perp$ to $\overleftrightarrow{BC}$ at $Q$, $m\angle AQX = 125$, $m\angle DQX = 55$

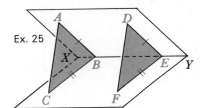

**21.** $\angle D\text{-}\overleftrightarrow{BC}\text{-}X$   55    **22.** $\angle A\text{-}\overleftrightarrow{BC}\text{-}D$   70

**23.** $\angle A\text{-}\overleftrightarrow{BC}\text{-}Y$   55    **24.** $\angle Y\text{-}\overleftrightarrow{BC}\text{-}D$
                        125

Ex. 25

**25.** Given: $\angle ABC$ and $\angle DEF$ are plane angles of $\angle A\text{-}\overleftrightarrow{XY}\text{-}F$, $\overline{AB} \cong \overline{DE}$, $\overline{BC} \cong \overline{EF}$

Prove: $\overline{AC} \cong \overline{DF}$

**26.** Given: $\angle FDE$ is a plane angle of $\angle \overleftrightarrow{DA}$, $\angle DEF$ is a plane angle of $\angle \overleftrightarrow{EB}$, $\angle EFD$ is a plane angle of $\angle \overleftrightarrow{FC}$, $m\angle \overleftrightarrow{DA} = 50$, $m\angle \overleftrightarrow{EB} = 70$

Prove: $m\angle \overleftrightarrow{FC} = 60$

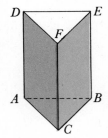

**27–34.** Using the definitions in Chapter 2 as a guide, define these terms. (*Example:* **Congruent dihedral angles** are dihedral angles that have the same measure.) Also draw a sketch for each definition.

See page given.

**27.** acute dihedral angle   *p. 60*    **28.** obtuse dihedral angle   *p. 60*

**29.** complementary dihedral angles **30.** supplementary dihedral angles
               *p. 60*                         *p. 56*

**31.** interior of a dihedral angle    **32.** exterior of a dihedral angle
               *p. 49*                         *p. 49*

**33.** adjacent dihedral angles    **34.** vertical dihedral angles
               *p. 53*                         *p. 68*

**35.** Prove this theorem: Vertical dihedral angles are congruent.

# DIHEDRAL ANGLES IN OBJECTS

Pictured below are objects whose sides form congruent dihedral angles. In each case shown, if a cross section of the object is taken so that the edges of the dihedral angles are perpendicular to the "plane" of the slice, the plane angles of the dihedral angles form regular polygons. For example,

the cross section of the prism shows that the plane angles (∠A, ∠B, and ∠C) form an equilateral triangle. Each angle measures 60°. Why? Therefore, we know that the sides of the prism form dihedral angles with a measure of 60°. Why?

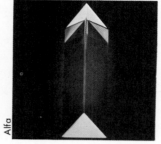

Alfa

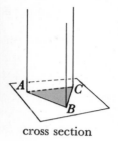

cross section

Determine the kind of regular polygon formed by plane angles of each remaining object. Then find the measure of the congruent dihedral angles. (Finding the measures of interior angles of convex polygons is covered in Section 5.3.)

Dr. E. R. Degginger

**Crystal**  Square; 90

Wide World Photos

**The Pentagon**  Pentagon; 108

Dr. E. R. Degginger

**Beehive Cells**  Hexagon; 120

Bill Miller

**Fountain**  Octagon; 135

# Perpendicular Planes

## Suggested Class Time

| Course | Min. | Reg. | Max. |
|--------|------|------|------|
| Days   | 1    | 1    | 1    |

**Perpendicular planes** are planes that contain a right dihedral angle. In the figure, $\angle A\text{-}\overleftrightarrow{BC}\text{-}D$ is a right dihedral angle, so planes $p$ and $q$ are perpendicular. One model of perpendicular planes is the door and the floor of a room.

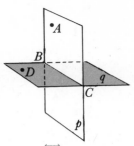

$\angle A\text{-}\overleftrightarrow{BC}\text{-}D$ is a rt. dihedral angle and $p \perp q$.

We saw that lines sometimes indicate when two planes are parallel. Lines can also tell us when planes are perpendicular. For example,

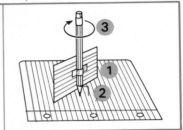

**1** Tape pencil (model line) to index card (model plane).

**2** Hold pencil perpendicular to paper (another model plane).

**3** Rotate pencil slowly so index card takes different positions.

How many different planes that contain the pencil seem to be perpendicular to the paper? The theorem below gives the answer.

**Theorem**

If a line is perpendicular to a given plane, then every plane containing the line is perpendicular to the given plane.

**Given:** $\overleftrightarrow{RS} \perp$ plane $p$ at point $R$, plane $q$ contains $\overleftrightarrow{RS}$ and intersects $p$ at $\overleftrightarrow{XY}$.

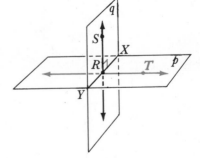

**Prove:** $q \perp p$

**Proof:**

| STATEMENTS | REASONS |
|------------|---------|
| 1. $\overleftrightarrow{RS} \perp \overleftrightarrow{XY}$ | 1. Given $\overleftrightarrow{RS} \perp p$ and def. of line $\perp$ to plane |
| 2. There is a line $\overleftrightarrow{RT}$ in $p$ such that $\overleftrightarrow{RT} \perp \overleftrightarrow{XY}$ at $R$. | 2. In a plane, there is exactly one line $\perp$ to a line at a given pt. |

| | |
|---|---|
| **3.** The plane containing $\overleftrightarrow{RS}$ and $\overleftrightarrow{RT}$ is perpendicular to $\overleftrightarrow{XY}$. | **3.** Basic Theorem for Perpendiculars (p. 270) |
| **4.** $\angle SRT$ is a plane angle of $\angle S\text{-}\overleftrightarrow{XY}\text{-}T$. | **4.** Def. of plane angle |
| **5.** $\overleftrightarrow{RS} \perp \overleftrightarrow{RT}$ | **5.** Def. of line $\perp$ to plane |
| **6.** $\angle SRT$ is a rt. $\angle$. | **6.** Def. of $\perp$ lines |
| **7.** $\angle S\text{-}\overleftrightarrow{XY}\text{-}T$ is a rt. dihedral $\angle$. | **7.** Def. of rt. dihedral $\angle$ |
| **8.** $p \perp q$ | **8.** Def. of $\perp$ planes |

The next theorem gives us a way to determine if a line is perpendicular to a plane. After reading the theorem, make a model using an index card and a piece of paper as planes and a pencil as the line.

 If two planes are perpendicular, a line in one of them perpendicular to their line of intersection is perpendicular to the other.  **Theorem**

Given: Planes $p$ and $q$ are perpendicular and intersect at $\overleftrightarrow{XY}$, $\overleftrightarrow{JK}$ is in $q$, $\overleftrightarrow{JK} \perp \overleftrightarrow{XY}$ at point $J$.

Prove: $\overleftrightarrow{JK} \perp p$

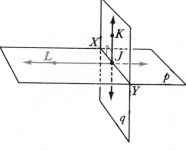

Proof:

| STATEMENTS | REASONS |
|---|---|
| **1.** There is a line $\overleftrightarrow{JL}$ in plane $p$ such that $\overleftrightarrow{JL} \perp \overleftrightarrow{XY}$ at $J$. | **1.** In a plane, there is exactly one line $\perp$ to a line at a given pt. |
| **2.** The plane containing $\overleftrightarrow{JK}$ and $\overleftrightarrow{JL}$ is perpendicular to $\overleftrightarrow{XY}$. | **2.** Given $\overleftrightarrow{JK} \perp \overleftrightarrow{XY}$ and Basic Theorem for Perpendiculars |
| **3.** $\angle KJL$ is a plane angle of $\angle K\text{-}\overleftrightarrow{XY}\text{-}L$. | **3.** Given $p$ and $q$ intersect at $\overleftrightarrow{XY}$ and def. of a plane angle |
| **4.** $\angle K\text{-}\overleftrightarrow{XY}\text{-}L$ is a right dihedral $\angle$. | **4.** Given $p \perp q$ and def. of $\perp$ planes |
| **5.** $\angle KJL$ is a right $\angle$. | **5.** Def. of rt. dihedral $\angle$ |
| **6.** $\overleftrightarrow{JK} \perp \overleftrightarrow{JL}$ | **6.** Def. of $\perp$ lines |
| **7.** $\overleftrightarrow{JK} \perp p$ | **7.** Basic Theorem for Perpendiculars ($\overleftrightarrow{JK} \perp \overleftrightarrow{JL}$ and given $\overleftrightarrow{JK} \perp \overleftrightarrow{XY}$) |

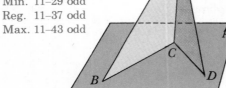

Like lines, planes can also be named by points contained in them. In the figure, $B$, $C$, and $D$ are three noncollinear points in plane $p$. Another name for plane $p$ is **plane BCD.** Plane $ABC$ and plane $ACD$ are also represented. We can also talk about plane $ABD$, even though it is not drawn in the figure. Remember, the three points you use in naming a plane cannot all be on the same line.

Assignment Guide
*Oral:* 1–10
*Written:* Min. 11–29 odd
Reg. 11–37 odd
Max. 11–43 odd

# Exercises 13.4

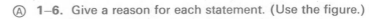

Ⓐ **1–6.** Give a reason for each statement. (Use the figure.)

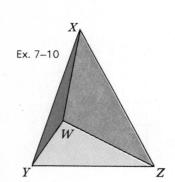

Ex. 1–6

**1.** If $p \perp q$, then $\angle A\text{-}\overleftrightarrow{XY}\text{-}D$ is a right dihedral angle.

**2.** If $\angle C\text{-}\overleftrightarrow{XY}\text{-}B$ is a right dihedral angle, then $p \perp q$.

**3.** If $\overleftrightarrow{AB} \perp q$, then $p \perp q$.     **4.** If $\overleftrightarrow{CD} \perp p$, then $q \perp p$.

**5.** If $p \perp q$ and $\overleftrightarrow{CD} \perp \overleftrightarrow{XY}$, then $\overleftrightarrow{CD} \perp p$.

**6.** If $p \perp q$ and $\overleftrightarrow{AB} \perp \overleftrightarrow{XY}$, then $\overleftrightarrow{AB} \perp q$.

1–2. Def. of $\perp$ planes
3–4. Theorem on page 462
5–6. Theorem on page 463

**7–10.** Name the following. (Use the figure.)

Ex. 7–10

**7.** a right dihedral angle, if plane $XYW \perp$ plane $XWZ$     $\angle\overleftrightarrow{XW}$

**8.** two perpendicular planes, if $\angle Y\text{-}\overleftrightarrow{ZW}\text{-}X$ is a right dihedral angle
Plane $WYZ$, plane $WXZ$

**9.** two planes perpendicular to plane $YZW$, if $\overline{XW} \perp$ plane $YZW$
Plane $XWY$, plane $XWZ$

**10.** a plane perpendicular to $\overline{XW}$, if plane $XYW \perp$ plane $YZW$
and $\overline{XW} \perp \overline{YW}$
Plane $YZW$

Ⓑ **11–14.** Give a reason for each statement. (Use the figure for Exercises 7–10.)

**11.** If $\angle Y\text{-}\overleftrightarrow{WX}\text{-}Z$ is a rt. dihedral angle, then plane $WXY \perp$ plane $WXZ$.
Def. of $\perp$ planes

**12.** If plane $WXZ \perp$ plane $WYZ$, then $\angle Y\text{-}\overleftrightarrow{WZ}\text{-}X$ is a rt. dihedral angle.
Def. of $\perp$ planes

**13.** If plane $WXY \perp$ plane $WYZ$ and $\overline{WX} \perp \overline{WY}$, then $\overline{WX} \perp$ plane $WYZ$.
Theorem on page 463

**14.** If $\overline{WX} \perp$ plane $WYZ$, then plane $WXZ \perp$ plane $WYZ$.
Theorem on page 462

464     CHAPTER 13     PARALLEL LINES AND PLANES

**15–22.** True or False? Draw a sketch to illustrate each true statement. Sketch a counterexample for each false statement.

**15.** If a line is perpendicular to a plane, then there is exactly one plane that contains the line and is perpendicular to the given plane.
F (2 walls ⊥ to the floor intersect at a line ⊥ to the floor.)

**16.** If a line is in a plane, there is exactly one plane that contains the line and is perpendicular to the given plane.
T

**17.** If two planes are perpendicular, then every line in one plane perpendicular to their line of intersection is perpendicular to the other plane.
T

**18.** If two planes are perpendicular, then every line in one plane intersecting the other plane is perpendicular to the other plane.
F (Consider 2 intersecting walls and either diagonal of 1 of them.)

**19.** If two planes are both perpendicular to a third plane, then they are parallel.
F (Consider 2 intersecting walls and the floor.)

**20.** If two planes are both perpendicular to the same plane and their lines of intersection with that plane are parallel, then the two planes are parallel.
T

**21.** If a line is parallel to a plane, no plane containing the line can be perpendicular to the given plane.
F (The intersection of the ceiling and a wall is a line ∥ to the floor, but the wall is ⊥ to the floor.)

**22.** If two planes intersect and each is perpendicular to a third plane, their line of intersection is perpendicular to the third plane.
T

**23–36.** Find the measure of each angle. (Use the figures.)

**23.** $\angle Q\text{-}\overleftrightarrow{PS}\text{-}R$   90
**24.** $\angle Q\text{-}\overleftrightarrow{RS}\text{-}P$   90

**25.** $\angle QSR$   90
**26.** $\angle QSP$   90

**27.** $\angle QPS$   45
**28.** $\angle RPS$   45

**29.** $\angle PQR$   60
**30.** $\angle PRQ$   60

Ex. 23–30

Given: $\overline{PS} \cong \overline{QS} \cong \overline{RS}$,
plane $PQS$ ⊥ plane $PSR$,
plane $PSR$ ⊥ plane $QRS$,
plane $QRS$ ⊥ plane $PQS$.

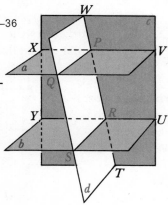

Ex. 31–36

Given:
Planes $a$ and $b$ are parallel and both are perpendicular to plane $c$; plane $d$ intersects planes $a$, $b$, and $c$; $\overleftrightarrow{PQ}$ ⊥ $c$; $\overleftrightarrow{RS}$ ⊥ $c$

**31.** $\angle WPV$, if $m\angle PRU = 120$   120
**32.** $\angle WPX$, if $m\angle PRY = 60$   60
**33.** $\angle R\text{-}\overleftrightarrow{PQ}\text{-}V$, if $m\angle T\text{-}\overleftrightarrow{RS}\text{-}U = 75$   75
**34.** $\angle R\text{-}\overleftrightarrow{PQ}\text{-}X$, if $m\angle T\text{-}\overleftrightarrow{RS}\text{-}Y = 130$   130
**35.** $\angle P\text{-}\overleftrightarrow{RS}\text{-}Y$, if $m\angle V\text{-}\overleftrightarrow{PQ}\text{-}R = 50$   50
**36.** $\angle U\text{-}\overleftrightarrow{RS}\text{-}T$, if $m\angle W\text{-}\overleftrightarrow{PQ}\text{-}X = 80$   80

**37.** *1.* $\overline{AD} \perp$ plane $BDC$
(Given)

*2.* Plane $ADC \perp$
plane $BDC$
(Plane containing
line $\perp$ to given
plane is $\perp$ to
given plane.)

*3.* $\angle A\text{-}\overrightarrow{DC}\text{-}B$ is a rt.
dihedral $\angle$. (Def.
of $\perp$ planes)

**38.** *1.* $p \perp q$, $\overline{AB} \perp \overleftrightarrow{XY}$
(Given)

*2.* $\overline{AB} \perp q$ (If 2 planes
are $\perp$, a line in
1 $\perp$ to line of
intersection is
$\perp$ to the other.)

*3.* $\overline{AB} \perp \overline{BC}$ (Def. of
$\perp$ line and plane)

*4.* $\angle ABC$ is a rt. $\angle$.
(Def. of $\perp$ segs.)

*5.* $\triangle ABC$ is a rt. $\triangle$.
(Def. of rt. $\triangle$)

**39.** *1.* Pln. $PQS \perp$ pln. $PQR$,
pln. $RQS \perp$ pln. $PQR$,
$\overline{PQ} \perp \overline{RQ}$ (Given)

*2.* $\overline{RQ} \perp$ plane $PQS$,
$\overline{PQ} \perp$ plane $RQS$ (If 2
planes are $\perp$, a line
in 1 $\perp$ to line of intersection is $\perp$ to
the other.)

*3.* $\overline{RQ} \perp \overline{SQ}$, $\overline{PQ} \perp \overline{SQ}$
(Def. of $\perp$ line, plane)

*4.* $\overline{SQ} \perp$ plane $PQR$
(Basic Thm. for $\perp$s)

**40.** *Sketch of Proof:* Since
$\overline{XY} \perp$ plane $YWZ$, planes
$XYZ$ and $YWZ$ are also
$\perp$. And since $\angle WZY$ is
a rt. $\angle$, $\overline{WZ}$ is $\perp$ to
the intersection of the
two planes. Therefore
$\overline{WZ} \perp$ plane $XYZ$ and, by
definition, $\overline{WZ} \perp \overline{XZ}$.

Ex. 37

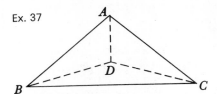

**37. Given:** $\overline{AD} \perp$ plane $BDC$.

**Prove:** $\angle A\text{-}\overrightarrow{DC}\text{-}B$ is a right
dihedral angle.

Ex. 38

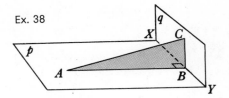

**38. Given:** Plane $p \perp$ plane $q$,
$\overline{AB} \perp \overleftrightarrow{XY}$

**Prove:** $\triangle ABC$ is a right triangle.

Ex. 39

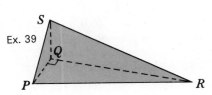

© **39. Given:** Plane $PQS \perp$ plane $PQR$,
plane $RQS \perp$ plane $PQR$,
$\overline{PQ} \perp \overline{RQ}$

**Prove:** $\overline{SQ} \perp$ plane $PQR$.

**HINT:** $\overline{PQ}$ is the intersection of
two $\perp$ planes, and so is $\overline{RQ}$.

Ex. 40

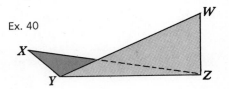

**40. Given:** $\overline{XY} \perp$ plane $YWZ$ at
point $Y$, $\angle WZY$
is a right angle.

**Prove:** $\overline{WZ} \perp \overline{XZ}$

**HINT:** Start by showing
plane $XYZ \perp$ plane $YWZ$.

**41–43.** Use a theorem or definition of this section to answer each exercise.

**41.** The side and base of a bookend
form a right dihedral angle. Are
the side and base perpendicular?
Why?      Yes. Def. of $\perp$ planes

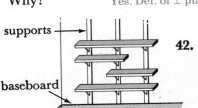

supports →

baseboard

**42.** The shelf supports attached to the
wall are perpendicular to the baseboard. Are the supports perpendicular to the floor? Why?

Yes. Theorem on page 463

**43.** A revolving door turns on a post
that is perpendicular to the floor.
Are the three panels each perpendicular to the floor? Why?

Yes. Theorem on page 462

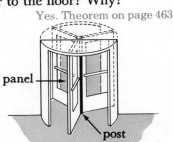

panel →

post

# Transformations: Slides and Turns in Space

Recall that a slide in a plane can be described by its *magnitude* and *direction*. The same information is needed to describe a **slide in space.** In the diagram at the right, the heavy arrow gives both the magnitude and direction.

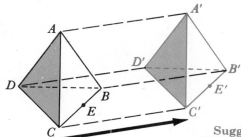

| Suggested Class Time | | | |
|---|---|---|---|
| Course | Min. | Reg. | Max. |
| Days | 0 | 0 | 1 |

Like slides in a plane, slides in space preserve distance, collinearity, betweenness, and angle measure. Also, slides in space preserve coplanarity. Since *A, B, E,* and *C* are coplanar, their images *A', B', E',* and *C'* are coplanar.

In a plane, we turn a figure about a point. But in space, we turn a figure about a line, called the *axis of turn.* To describe a **turn in space,** we need an axis of turn and a magnitude. The magnitude is the measure of a dihedral angle such that one face contains points of the original figure, and the other face contains the images of those points.

Turns in space preserve distance, collinearity, betweenness, angle measure, and coplanarity.

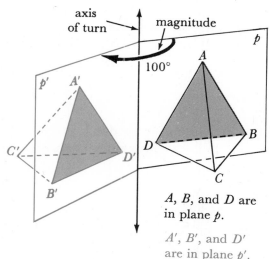

*A, B,* and *D* are in plane *p*.

*A', B',* and *D'* are in plane *p'*.

---

## Exercises 13.5

(A) **1–4.** Complete each statement.

**Assignment Guide**
*Oral:* Max. 1–10
*Written:* Max. 11–24

**1.** An arrow can show the _____ and _____ of a slide in space.
    Magnitude; direction

**2.** The length of the arrow gives the _____ of the slide.
    Magnitude

**3.** A turn in space is described by an _____ and a _____.
    Axis of turn; magnitude

**4.** The _____ of a turn in space is the measure of a dihedral angle.
    Magnitude

**5–10.** True or False? In space,

**5.** Slides preserve length.  T

**6.** Turns preserve length.  T

**7.** Turns change angle measure.  F

**8.** Slides change coplanarity.  F

**9.** Segments joining two points to their slide images are parallel.  T

**10.** If $A'$ and $B'$ are the turn images of $A$ and $B$ around axis $\overleftrightarrow{XY}$, then $\angle A\text{-}\overleftrightarrow{XY}\text{-}A' \cong \angle B\text{-}\overleftrightarrow{XY}\text{-}B'$.  T

Ⓑ **11–14.** Tell if the model described is for a slide or a turn in space.

**11.** an elevator going up
Slide

**12.** the turning wheel of a windmill
Turn

**13.** a car turning a corner
Turn

**14.** a car riding on a level straight road
Slide

**15.** What is the direction of the slide in Exercise 11?  Up

**16.** If an elevator goes up six floors, what is the magnitude of the slide (1 unit = 1 floor)?  6

**17.** What is the axis of turn for the turn in Exercise 12?
The axle of the wheel

**18.** If a windmill wheel turns clockwise (as you look at it), what is the magnitude of a quarter turn?  90

Ex. 19–22

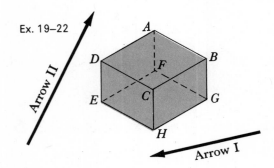

Arrow II

Arrow I

**19–20.** Copy and draw the image of a slide in space having the magnitude and direction given by

**19.** arrow I.

**20.** arrow II.

**21–22.** What is the axis of turn if the turn image of *BGHC* is

**21.** *DEHC*?  $\overleftrightarrow{CH}$

**22.** *BGFA*?  $\overleftrightarrow{BG}$

*Answers for page 469*

**13.** A plane containing a line ⊥ to a given plane is ⊥ to the given plane.

**14.** If 2 planes are ⊥, a line in 1 of them ⊥ to their line of intersection is ⊥ to the other.

Ⓒ **23.** A slide in a plane is equivalent to successive reflections over parallel lines. (See Ex. 19–22, p. 159.) What would a slide in space be equivalent to?   · Successive reflections over parallel planes

**24.** A turn in a plane is equivalent to successive reflections over intersecting lines. (See Ex. 13–16, p. 414.) What would a turn in space be equivalent to? What would be its axis of turn?
Successive reflections over intersecting planes; the intersection of the planes

# ■ Chapter 13 Review ■

**Suggested Class Time**

| Course | Min. | Reg. | Max. |
|--------|------|------|------|
| Days   | 1    | 1    | 1    |

**1–7.** Give a reason for each statement. (Use the figures.)

**1.** If $G \parallel H$ and $\ell \perp G$, then $\ell \perp H$.
Line $\perp$ to 1 of 2 $\parallel$ planes is $\perp$ to the other.

**2.** If $H \perp k$ and $I \perp k$, then $H \parallel I$.
2 planes $\perp$ to the same line are $\parallel$.

**3.** If $G \parallel H$ and $H \parallel I$, then $G \parallel I$.
2 planes $\parallel$ to the same plane are $\parallel$.

**4.** If $\overleftrightarrow{AB} \parallel \overleftrightarrow{CD}$ and $\overleftrightarrow{CD} \parallel \overleftrightarrow{EF}$, then $\overleftrightarrow{AB} \parallel \overleftrightarrow{EF}$.
2 lines $\parallel$ to the same line are $\parallel$.

**5.** If $\overleftrightarrow{CD} \parallel \overleftrightarrow{EF}$ and $p \perp \overleftrightarrow{CD}$, then $p \perp \overleftrightarrow{EF}$.
Plane $\perp$ to 1 of 2 $\parallel$ lines is $\perp$ to the other.

**6.** If $\overleftrightarrow{AB} \perp p$ and $\overleftrightarrow{CD} \perp p$, then $\overleftrightarrow{AB} \parallel \overleftrightarrow{CD}$.
2 lines $\perp$ to the same plane are $\parallel$.

**7.** If $p \parallel q$, $\overleftrightarrow{AB} \perp q$, and $\overleftrightarrow{CD} \perp q$, then $AB = CD$.
$\parallel$ planes are everywhere equidistant.

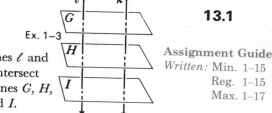

**13.1**

Ex. 1–3

Given: Lines $\ell$ and $k$ intersect planes $G$, $H$, and $I$.

**Assignment Guide**
*Written:* Min. 1–15
Reg. 1–15
Max. 1–17

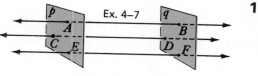

**13.2**

Ex. 4–7

Given: $\overleftrightarrow{AB}$, $\overleftrightarrow{CD}$, and $\overleftrightarrow{EF}$ intersect planes $p$ and $q$ at pts. $A$, $B$, $C$, $D$, $E$, and $F$.

**8–11.** Complete each statement. (Use the figure.)

**8.** $\angle R\text{-}\overleftrightarrow{AB}\text{-}U$ is a <u>Dihedral</u> angle.

**9.** $\overleftrightarrow{AB}$ is the <u>Edge</u> of $\angle R\text{-}\overleftrightarrow{AB}\text{-}U$.

**10.** Point $U$ is on a _____ of $\angle R\text{-}\overleftrightarrow{AB}\text{-}U$.
Face (or side)

**11.** If $\angle RXU$ is a <u>Plane</u> angle of $\angle R\text{-}\overleftrightarrow{AB}\text{-}U$, then $m\angle R\text{-}\overleftrightarrow{AB}\text{-}U = m\angle RXU$.

**13.3**

Given: Planes $p$ and $q$ intersect at $\overleftrightarrow{AB}$, $\overleftrightarrow{TU}$ is in $p$, $\overleftrightarrow{RS}$ is in $q$.

Ex. 8–11

**12–15.** Give a reason for each statement. (Use the figure.)

**12.** If $a \perp b$, then $\angle R\text{-}\overleftrightarrow{XY}\text{-}P$ is a right dihedral angle.   Def. of $\perp$ planes

**13.** If $\overleftrightarrow{RS} \perp a$, then $b \perp a$.
13–14. *Answers on p. 468*

**14.** If $a \perp b$ and $\overrightarrow{PQ} \perp \overleftrightarrow{XY}$, then $\overrightarrow{PQ} \perp b$.

**15.** If $\angle Q\text{-}\overleftrightarrow{XY}\text{-}R$ is a right dihedral angle, then $a \perp b$.
Def. of $\perp$ planes

**13.4**

Given: Planes $a$ and $b$ intersect at $\overleftrightarrow{XY}$, $\overrightarrow{PQ}$ is in $a$, $\overleftrightarrow{RS}$ is in $b$.

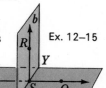

Ex. 12–15

**16.** If $ABCD$ is the slide image in space of $EFGH$, the magnitude of the slide is ($EF$, <u>$AE$</u>, $\angle BAE$).

**17.** If $ABFE$ is the turn image in space of $CBFG$, the axis of turn is ($\angle ABC$, point $B$, $\overleftrightarrow{BF}$).

**13.5**

Ex. 16–17

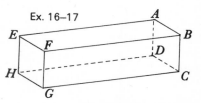

# Chapter 13
## Test

**Assignment Guide**
*Written:* Min. 1–13
      Reg. 1–14
      Max. 1–16

5. Any 3 of $\angle\overleftrightarrow{AB}$, $\angle\overleftrightarrow{AC}$, $\angle\overleftrightarrow{BC}$, $\angle\overleftrightarrow{AD}$, $\angle\overleftrightarrow{BE}$, $\angle\overleftrightarrow{CF}$, $\angle\overleftrightarrow{DE}$, $\angle\overleftrightarrow{DF}$, $\angle\overleftrightarrow{EF}$

14. 1. $\overline{AD} \perp \overline{AB}$, $\overline{AD} \perp \overline{AC}$ (Given)
  2. $\overline{AD} \perp$ plane $ABC$ (Basic Thm. for $\perp$s)
  3. $\overline{AD} \perp$ plane $DEF$ (Given)
  4. Pln. $ABC \parallel$ pln. $DEF$ (2 planes $\perp$ to same line are $\parallel$.)

15. 1. $\overline{AB} \perp$ plane $BCD$ (Given)
  2. Pln. $ABC \perp$ pln. $BCD$ (Plane containing line $\perp$ to given plane is $\perp$ to given plane.)
  3. $\angle A\text{-}\overleftrightarrow{BC}\text{-}D$ is a rt. dihedral $\angle$. (Def. of $\perp$ planes)

**1–4.** Write a definition for each term.

**1.** *parallel planes* See page 445.

**2.** *perpendicular planes* See page 462.

**3.** *dihedral angle* See page 457.

**4.** *plane angle* See page 457.

**5.** Name three dihedral angles.

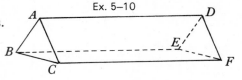

Ex. 5–10

**6–10** Give a reason for each statement. (Use figure at right.)

**6.** If $\overline{BE} \perp$ plane $DEF$, then $\angle DEF$ is a plane angle of $\angle A\text{-}\overleftrightarrow{BE}\text{-}F$.
    Def. of plane $\angle$

**7.** If $\overline{AD} \perp$ plane $ABC$ and $\overline{AD} \perp$ plane $DEF$, then plane $ABC \parallel$ plane $DEF$.
    2 planes $\perp$ to same line are $\parallel$.

**8.** If $BA \perp$ plane $ACF$, then plane $ABC \perp$ plane $ACF$.
    A plane containing a line $\perp$ to a given plane is $\perp$ to the given plane.

**9.** If $\overline{BE} \perp$ plane $DEF$ and $\overline{CF} \perp$ plane $DEF$, then $\overline{BE} \parallel \overline{CF}$.
    2 lines $\perp$ to same plane are $\parallel$.

**10.** If $\overline{AD} \parallel \overline{CF}$ and $\overline{CF} \parallel \overline{BE}$, then $\overline{AD} \parallel \overline{BE}$.
    2 lines $\parallel$ to same line are $\parallel$.

**11–13.** True or False? Draw a sketch to illustrate each true statement. Sketch a counterexample for each false statement.

**11.** If two lines are parallel to the same plane, then they are parallel to each other.
    F (They might be intersecting lines in a plane $\parallel$ to the given plane.)

**12.** If a plane is perpendicular to the edge of a dihedral angle, then it is perpendicular to each face of the dihedral angle.
    T

**13.** If two planes are perpendicular to the same plane, then they are parallel.
    F (Consider 2 intersecting walls and the floor.)

**14.** Given: $\overline{AD} \perp \overline{AB}$, $\overline{AD} \perp \overline{AC}$, $\overline{AD} \perp$ plane $DEF$.

Prove: Plane $ABC \parallel$ plane $DEF$.

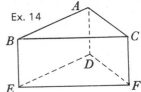

Ex. 14

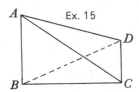

Ex. 15

**15.** Given: $\overline{AB} \perp$ plane $BCD$.

Prove: $\angle A\text{-}\overleftrightarrow{BC}\text{-}D$ is a right dihedral angle.

**16.** A (slide, <u>turn</u>) in space is done about an axis of (slide, <u>turn</u>).

Courtesy General Dynamics Corp.

14 SOLIDS

A **solid figure,** or **solid,** cannot be contained in a plane since it has three dimensions. There are two common ways to think of a solid:

**1.** as a surface, or shell, that encloses a part of space (*models:* an empty box and a Ping-Pong ball)

**2.** as the figure formed by a surface **and** the part of space that it encloses (*models:* a brick and a pool ball)

We think of a solid in the first way when we consider the area of the surface. And we use the second way when we consider its volume—the measure of the amount of space it encloses.

# 14.1 Polyhedrons

In a plane, a polygon is formed by joining segments at their endpoints. A polygon and its interior form a polygonal region. The 3-dimensional counterpart of a polygon is a *polyhedron*.

POLYGONAL REGION

POLYHEDRONS

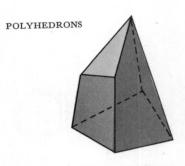

A **polyhedron** is formed by joining polygonal regions (called *faces*) at their sides (called *edges*). The faces intersect at the edges only, with each face intersecting exactly one other face at each edge. The vertices of the polygons bounding the faces are the *vertices* of the polyhedron.

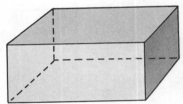

Just as a polygon separates a plane into two parts, a polyhedron separates space into two parts—the *exterior* and the *interior* of the polyhedron. If its interior is a convex set, then the polyhedron is *convex*. We will discuss only convex polyhedrons.

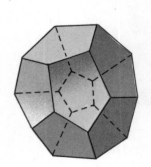

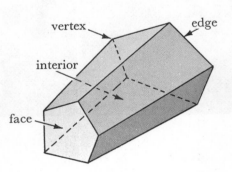

vertex — edge

interior

face

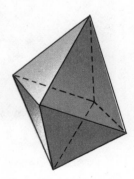

Since each face of a polyhedron is in a plane, a polyhedron is often described as a solid figure bounded by planes. Each of its edges is in the intersection of two planes, which means that each edge of the solid is in the edge of a *dihedral angle*. Two faces with a common edge determine a dihedral angle of the polyhedron. In the figure, one dihedral angle is $\angle B\text{-}\overleftrightarrow{AC}\text{-}D$.

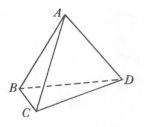

Ⓐ 1. The 3-dimensional counterpart of a polygon is a $\underline{\text{Polyhedron}}$.

2. Each $\underline{\text{Face}}$ of a polyhedron is a polygonal region.

3. A polyhedron separates space into $\underline{\text{2}}$ parts.

4. A polyhedron is convex if its $\underline{\text{Interior}}$ is a convex set.

5. A polyhedron is a solid figure bounded by $\underline{\text{Planes}}$.

6. Two faces with a common edge determine a $\underline{\phantom{xxxx}}$ of a polyhedron.
   $\overset{\text{Dihedral angle}}{}$

Ⓑ **7–12.** Name the following for the given solid:

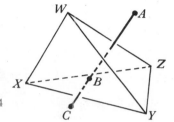

7. vertices  $W, X, Y, Z$

8. edges  $\overline{WX}, \overline{WY},$ $\overline{WZ}, \overline{XY}, \overline{YZ}, \overline{ZX}$

9. an interior point  $B$

10. an exterior point $A$ (or $C$)

11. dihedral angles
   $\angle \overleftrightarrow{WX}, \angle \overleftrightarrow{WY}, \angle \overleftrightarrow{WZ}, \angle \overleftrightarrow{XY}, \angle \overleftrightarrow{YZ}, \angle \overleftrightarrow{ZX}$

12. number of faces  4

**13–16.** Is each polyhedron convex or not?

13. Convex

14. Not convex

15. Not convex

16. Convex

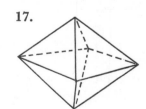
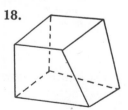
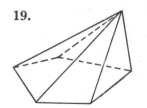
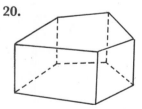

**17–20.** Find the number of (**a**) vertices, (**b**) faces, (**c**) edges, and (**d**) dihedral angles of each polyhedron.

17.
18.
19.
20.

Ⓒ 21. The least number of sides a polygon can have is three. What is the least number of faces a polyhedron can have? Sketch the solid.
   4; See figure at bottom of page 472.

22. Sketch a solid that has six faces, all triangular regions.

23. Sketch a solid that has six faces, all square regions.

| | a | b | c | d |
|---|---|---|---|---|
| 17. | 6 | 8 | 12 | 12 |
| 18. | 8 | 6 | 12 | 12 |
| 19. | 6 | 6 | 10 | 10 |
| 20. | 10 | 7 | 15 | 15 |

## 14.2 Right Prisms

**Suggested Class Time**

| Course | Min. | Reg. | Max. |
|--------|------|------|------|
| Days   | 1    | 1    | 1    |

A **right prism** (see figure below) has two faces bounded by congruent convex polygons in parallel planes and all other faces bounded by rectangles. The faces in the parallel planes are called *bases*, and the rectangular faces are called *lateral faces*. The edges of the lateral faces that are not also edges of a base are called *lateral edges*.

An *altitude* of a right prism is any perpendicular segment from the plane of one base to the plane of the other. Therefore, all altitudes are congruent. The *height* of a right prism is the length of an altitude.

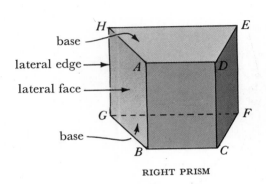

RIGHT PRISM

In the figure, $\overline{AB}$ is a side of rectangles $ABCD$ and $ABGH$. So $\overline{AB}$ is perpendicular to $\overline{BC}$ and $\overline{BG}$ and to the plane containing base $BCFG$. Similarly, $\overline{AB}$ is perpendicular to the plane containing the other base. Therefore, $\overline{AB}$ is an altitude of the prism. In fact, all lateral edges of a right prism are altitudes, and the length of any one of them is the height.

A prism is classified by the number of sides each base has. For example,

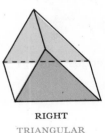

RIGHT
TRIANGULAR
PRISM

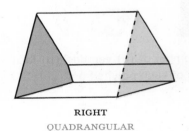

RIGHT
QUADRANGULAR
PRISM

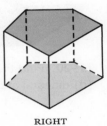

RIGHT
PENTAGONAL
PRISM

The bases of a **right rectangular prism** are bounded by rectangles, and any of its faces could be called a base. Cardboard boxes, bricks, and many buildings have shapes the same as right rectangular prisms. A **cube** is a right rectangular prism whose edges are all congruent (all faces are bounded by squares).

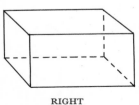

RIGHT
RECTANGULAR
PRISM

**Volume** is the measure of the amount of space taken up by a solid, just as area is the measure of the amount of surface covered by a polygonal region.

To measure the volume of a solid, we must have a unit of volume. The most convenient unit is the *cubic unit*. For example, if we measure distance in centimeters and area in square centimeters, then we measure volume in cubic centimeters. NOTE: cm³ means cubic centimeters, m³ means cubic meters, and so on.

Suppose a right rectangular prism has dimensions (length and width of its base and its height) that are 5 cm, 3 cm, and 4 cm.

$$\overline{\phantom{xxxx}}$$

1 unit
of length

1 square unit
of area

1 cubic unit
of volume

Notice that the number of cubic centimeters needed to "cover" the base is $5 \cdot 3$, and it would take 4 such layers to "fill" the prism. So, its volume is

$$(5 \cdot 3) \cdot 4 = 60 \text{ cm}^3$$

We state this as a postulate.

1 cm
1 cm
1 cm

cubic
centimeter
(cm³)

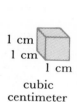

4 cm

3 cm

5 cm

**Example 1:** Find the volume of the right rectangular prism with the given dimensions.

    **a.** length $= 3.7$ m, width $= 2.1$ m, height $= 4$ m

$$V = Bh$$
$$= (3.7 \cdot 2.1) \cdot 4$$
$$= 7.77 \cdot 4 = 31.08 \text{ m}^3$$

    **b.** $\ell = 4$ cm, $w = 2$ cm, $h = 52$ mm

$$V = Bh$$
$$= (4 \cdot 2) \cdot 5.2 \blacktriangleleft 52 \text{ mm} = 5.2 \text{ cm}$$
$$= 41.6 \text{ cm}^3$$

**Example 2:** A right rectangular prism has a volume of 600 cm³ and a height of 3 cm. Find its base area.

$$V = Bh \qquad 600 = B \cdot 3 \qquad B = 200 \text{ cm}^2$$

# Exercises 14.2 ||||||||||||||||||||||||||||||||||||||||||||||||||||||||||||||||||||||||||||||||||||||||||||||||||||||||||

**Assignment Guide**
*Oral:* 1–10
*Written:*
Min. 11–25 odd; 29–30
Reg. 11–27 odd; 29–34
Max. 11–27 odd; 29–36

Ⓐ **1–6.** Refer to the given figure.

1. The solid is a right _____ prism. *[Triangular]*

2. Regions __ABC__ and __DEF__ are bases.

3. Region *BCFE* is a _____ of the prism. *[Lateral face]*

4. __AD__, __BE__, and __CF__ are lateral edges.

5. Lateral edges are also _____ of the prism. *[Altitudes]*

6. *BE* is the __Height__ of the prism.

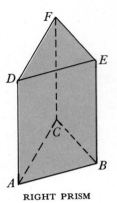

**RIGHT PRISM**

**7–10.** True or False?

7. The bases of a right prism are always bounded by rectangles.  F

8. Any perpendicular segment from the plane of one base of a right prism to the plane of the other is a lateral edge.   F

9. Any face of a right rectangular prism can be a base.  T

10. All faces of a cube are triangular regions.   F

Ⓑ **11–14.** Find the volume of a cube whose edges have the given length.

| 11. 5.1 cm | 12. 2.5 cm | 13. $e$ m | 14. $e$ units |
|---|---|---|---|
| 132.651 cm$^3$ | 15.625 cm$^3$ | $e^3$ m$^3$ | $e^3$ cubic units |

**15–20.** Find the volume of a right rectangular prism with the given dimensions.

15. 1.3 cm, 1.3 cm, 4 cm
    6.76 cm$^3$

16. 10 m, 3 m, 1 m    30 m$^3$

17. 5 cm, 15 mm, 12 mm
    9 cm$^3$ or 9000 mm$^3$

18. 8 cm, 25 mm, 4.5 cm
    90 cm$^3$ or 90 000 mm$^3$

19. $\ell$ mm, $w$ mm, $h$ mm
    $\ell wh$ mm$^3$

20. $\ell$ units, $w$ units, $h$ units
    $\ell wh$ cubic units

**21–26.** Find the following if $V$ = volume, $B$ = base area, and $h$ = height of a right rectangular prism:

21. $V$, if $B = 16$ cm$^2$, $h = 8$ cm
    128 cm$^3$

22. $V$, if $B = 3.6$ cm$^2$, $h = 7$ cm
    25.2 cm$^3$

23. $B$, if $V = 24$ m$^3$, $h = 6$ m
    4 m$^2$

24. $B$, if $V = 85$ mm$^3$, $h = 5$ mm
    17 mm$^2$

25. $h$, if $V = 144$ cm$^3$, $B = 9$ cm$^2$
    16 cm

26. $h$, if $V = 96$ m$^3$, $B = 2$ m$^2$
    48 m

**27–28.** Find the volume of each right rectangular prism.

**27.**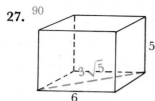
90

**28.**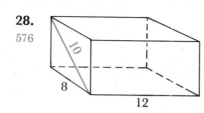
576

**29.** How many cubic centimeters are there in one cubic meter?    1 000 000

**30.** How many cubic millimeters are there in one cubic centimeter?   1000

**31–32.** Determine what happens to the volume of a cube when

**31.** The edge is doubled.
Volume is multiplied by 8.

**32.** The edge is halved.
Volume is divided by 8.

© **33.** Find the volume of the cube.
216

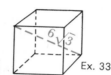
Ex. 33

Ex. 34

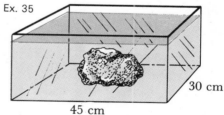
9 ft

4 in.

15 ft

**34.** How many cubic feet of concrete are needed to fill the rectangular form for a patio?    45

Ex. 35

**35.** When the rock was put into the rectangular fish tank, the level of the water rose 1.25 cm. What is the volume of the rock?
1687.5 cm³

30 cm

45 cm

**36.** During a 1.5-cm rainfall, how many liters of water fell on a lawn that is 22 m long and 16 m wide? (1 liter = 1000 cm³)    5280

**37.** At the right is a pattern for a model of a right prism whose base is bounded by a trapezoid. Make a larger pattern like this one. Then make the model.

**38.** Make a pattern for a model of a cube whose edges are 5 cm long. Then make the model.

**39.** Make a pattern for a model of a right triangular prism whose base edges are all 5 cm long and whose height is 10 cm. Make the model.

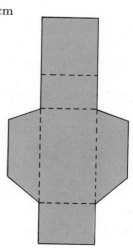

# 14.3 More About Right Prisms

Two right triangular prisms are **congruent** if and only if a base of one is congruent to a base of the other, and their heights are equal.

**Volume Postulate for Congruent Right Triangular Prisms**

If two right triangular prisms are congruent, then their volumes are equal.

**Volume Addition Postulate**

If two solids with no common interior points form a third solid, then its volume is the sum of the volumes of the two solids.

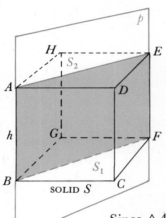

In the figure, solid $S$ is a right rectangular prism. Therefore, its lateral edges are perpendicular to the same plane, and they are parallel. So $\overline{AB} \parallel \overline{EF}$, and both are in plane $p$. Plane $p$ separates $S$ into solids $S_1$ and $S_2$, which we can show are congruent right triangular prisms.

Since $\overline{AB} \parallel \overline{EF}$ and $\overline{AB} \cong \overline{EF}$, $ABFE$ is a parallelogram. $\overline{AB} \perp \overline{BF}$ (why?), so $ABFE$ is a rectangle. By the definition of a right prism, $ABCD$ and $DCFE$ are also rectangles. Therefore, $\overline{AE} \cong \overline{BF}$, $\overline{AD} \cong \overline{BC}$, and $\overline{DE} \cong \overline{CF}$, giving us $\triangle ADE \cong \triangle BCF$ by the SSS Postulate.

Since $\triangle ADE$ and $\triangle BCF$ are in parallel planes (why?), $S_1$ is a right triangular prism. $S_2$ is a right triangular prism by the same reasoning. $S_1$ and $S_2$ are congruent because $AB$, or $h$, is the height of both, and their bases, $\triangle BCF$ and $\triangle FGB$, are congruent ($\overline{BF}$ is a diagonal of rectangle $BCFG$). Now we can find the volume of $S_1$.

| | |
|---|---|
| volume $S_1$ + volume $S_2$ = volume $S$ | Volume Addition Post. |
| volume $S_1$ + volume $S_1$ = volume $S$ | Vol. Post. for $\cong$ Rt. Triangular Prisms (Substitute vol. $S_1$ for vol. $S_2$.) |
| 2 (volume $S_1$) = volume $S$ | Addition |
| volume $S_1$ = $\frac{1}{2}$(volume $S$) | Multiply both sides by $\frac{1}{2}$. |
| volume $S_1$ = $\frac{1}{2}$(area $\square BCFG$)$h$ | Vol. Post. for Rectangular Prism |
| volume $S_1$ = $\frac{1}{2}$(area $\triangle BCF$ + area $\triangle FGB$)$h$ | Area Addition Post. |
| volume $S_1$ = $\frac{1}{2}$(area $\triangle BCF$ + area $\triangle BCF$)$h$ | Area of $\cong$ $\triangle$s Post. |
| volume $S_1$ = (area $\triangle BCF$)$h$ | Addition and multiplication |

The volume of $S_1$ is equal to the area of its base times its height. In fact,

The volume ($V$) of any right triangular prism is equal to the area ($B$) of its base times its height ($h$).

$$V = Bh$$

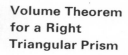

**Volume Theorem for a Right Triangular Prism**

A convex polygon can be separated into triangles by drawing segments from one vertex to each nonconsecutive vertex. All planes that contain the same lateral edge and one other nonconsecutive lateral edge of a right prism separate the prism into right triangular prisms.

In the figure, right prism $S$ with height $h$ and base area $B$ has been separated into right triangular prisms $S_1$, $S_2$, and $S_3$ whose base areas are $B_1$, $B_2$, and $B_3$. So,

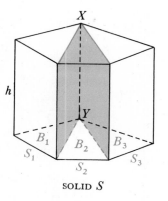

SOLID $S$

volume $S$ = volume $S_1$ + volume $S_2$ + volume $S_3$    Volume Addition Post.

    $= B_1h + B_2h + B_3h$    Vol. Thm. for Rt. Triangular Prism

    $= (B_1 + B_2 + B_3)h$    Distributive Property

    $= Bh$    Area Addition Post.

Since a right prism with any number of base edges can be separated into right triangular prisms, we can state the next theorem.

The volume ($V$) of any right prism is equal to the area ($B$) of its base times its height ($h$).

$$V = Bh$$

**Volume Theorem for a Right Prism**

## Exercises 14.3

Ⓐ **1–6.** True or False?

**Assignment Guide**
*Oral:* 1–6
*Written:*
Min. 7–10; 11–15 odd
Reg. 7–10; 11–17 odd
Max. 7–15 odd; 17–20

**1.** All lateral edges of a right prism are parallel.  T

**2.** All lateral edges of a right prism do not necessarily have equal lengths.  F

**3.** Right triangular prisms are congruent if their heights are equal and their bases are congruent.  T

**4.** Right triangular prisms are congruent if they have equal volumes.  F

**5.** Any right rectangular prism can be separated into two triangular prisms.  T

**6.** The volume of a right hexagonal prism is equal to the area of its base times its height.  T

Ⓑ **7–16.** Find the volume of each right prism.

**7.** 42

**8.** 240

**9.** 360

**10.** 360

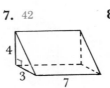
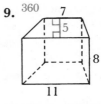
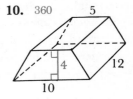

**11.** BASE: right triangle with legs of 5 cm and 7 cm; HEIGHT: 3.2 cm

56 cm³

**12.** BASE: isosceles right triangle with hypotenuse of $16\sqrt{2}$ mm; HEIGHT: 8.4 mm

1075.2 mm³

**13.** BASE: parallelogram with base of 5 m and corresponding height of 5.6 m; HEIGHT: 3 m

84 m³

**14.** BASE: rhombus with diagonals of 11.5 cm and 9.6 cm; HEIGHT: 15 cm

828 cm³

**15.** BASE: trapezoid with bases of 6 cm and 10 cm and height of 11 cm; HEIGHT: 75 mm

660 cm³ or 660 000 mm³

**16.** BASE: trapezoid with bases of 13.7 mm and 18.3 mm and height of 10 mm; HEIGHT: 2.5 cm

4 cm³ or 4000 mm³

Ⓒ **17.** The base of a right hexagonal prism is bounded by a regular hexagon with sides of length 6. If the prism has height 7, what is its volume?

$378\sqrt{3}$

**18.** Find the volume of the building.
3150 m³

Ex. 18

**19.** How many cubic yards of dirt were removed when the swimming pool was built?

$550\frac{25}{27}$

**20.** How many gallons of water will it take to fill the pool in Ex. 19? (1 ft³ = $7\frac{1}{2}$ gallons)

111,562.5

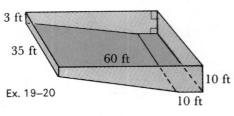

Ex. 19–20

# Right Circular Cylinders

A **right circular cylinder** (see figure below) has two bases that are congruent circular regions in parallel planes. The segment joining the centers of the bases, called the *axis*, is perpendicular to the planes of the bases. The *lateral surface* of the cylinder is formed by all segments that are parallel to the axis and have one endpoint on each circle bounding the bases.

**Suggested Class Time**

| Course | Min. | Reg. | Max. |
|--------|------|------|------|
| Days   | 2    | 2    | 1    |

An *altitude* is any perpendicular segment from the plane of one base to the plane of the other. (The axis and all segments of the lateral surface are altitudes. Why?) The *height* is the length of an altitude. The radius of a base is the *radius* of the cylinder. Tin cans and many other containers are models of cylinders.

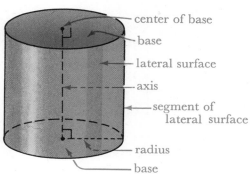

A right prism is *inscribed* in a right circular cylinder if the bases of the prism are inscribed in the bases of the cylinder. We can use inscribed **regular prisms** (right prisms whose bases are regular polygonal regions) to estimate the volume of a cylinder.

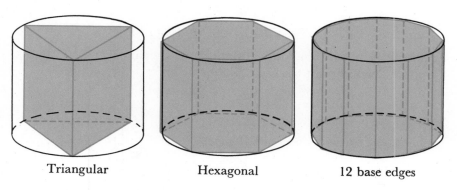

Triangular   Hexagonal   12 base edges

We can see that the volume of the regular triangular prism is less than the volume of the cylinder. If the number of base edges of the prism is doubled to obtain a regular hexagonal prism, its volume will be greater than the volume of the triangular prism but still less than the volume of the cylinder.

If we continue the process of doubling the base edges to obtain regular prisms, the volume of each new prism will be closer to the actual volume of the cylinder. Even the shape of the prism with many base edges is very close to the shape of the cylinder.

The process of increasing the number of base edges of the inscribed regular prisms is the 3-dimensional counterpart of the method used for finding the area of a circular region. (See Section 12.3.) And, just as the area of a circular region is the limit of the areas of its inscribed regular polygonal regions, the volume of the cylinder is the limit of the volumes of its inscribed regular prisms.

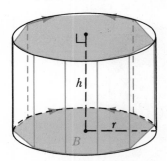

Cylinder and Inscribed
Regular Prism (with
many base edges)

For a right circular cylinder with height $h$ and radius $r$,

$$\text{volume cylinder} = \text{limit } Bh$$

where $h$ is the height and $B$ is the base area of its inscribed prisms. Since the limit of $B$ is the area of the base of the cylinder, limit $Bh = \pi r^2 h$. So,

$$\text{volume cylinder} = \pi r^2 h$$

Volume Theorem
for a Right
Circular Cylinder

The volume (*V*) of any right circular cylinder (with radius *r*) is equal to the area ($\pi r^2$) of its base times its height (*h*).

$$V = \pi r^2 h$$

**Assignment Guide**
*Oral:* 1–10
*Written:*
Min. (day 1) 11–18
    (day 2) 21–23;
    Quiz, p. 485
Reg. (day 1) 11–23 odd
    (day 2) 18–24 even;
    Quiz, p. 485
Max. 11–25 odd; Quiz, p. 485

**Example:** Find the volume of a right circular cylinder with height 6 cm and radius 2 cm.

$$V = \pi r^2 h$$
$$= \pi(2^2)(6)$$
$$= 24\pi \text{ cm}^3$$

# Exercises 14.4

NOTE: Leave answers in terms of $\pi$ unless told otherwise.

Ⓐ **1.** If point $A$ is the center of one base of a right circular cylinder and point $B$ is the center of the other base, then $\overline{AB}$ is the __Axis__.

**2.** The bases of a right circular cylinder are in __Parallel__ planes.

**3.** A segment of the lateral surface of a right circular cylinder is __Parallel__ to the axis.

**4.** The formula for the volume of a cylinder is _____.  $V = \pi r^2 h$

**5–10.** True or False? Use the given figure.

**5.** $\overline{CD}$ is an altitude.    F      **6.** $\overline{AD}$ is a radius.   F

**7.** $AB = CE$        T      **8.** height $= BC$    T

**9.** $\overline{BC} \parallel \overline{AD}$        T      **10.** $\overline{AB} \perp \overline{BC}$     T

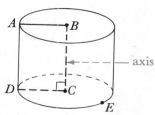

RIGHT CIRCULAR CYLINDER

Ⓑ **11–16.** Copy and complete the table for a right circular cylinder.

|  | Radius | Height | Volume |
|---|---|---|---|
| **11.** | 5 cm | 12 cm | ?  $300\pi$ cm³ |
| **12.** | 10 mm | 45 mm | ?  $4500\pi$ mm³ |
| **13.** | 2.5 m | ?  8 m | $50\pi$ m³ |
| **14.** | 1.2 mm | ?  25 mm | $36\pi$ mm³ |
| **15.** | ?  7 cm | 4 cm | $196\pi$ cm³ |
| **16.** | ?  11 mm | 8 mm | $968\pi$ mm³ |

Courtesy Renaissance Center Partnership

**17–20.** Find the volume of each right circular cylinder.

**17.** a cylinder of height 8 whose base has a circumference of $6\pi$   $72\pi$

**18.** a cylinder of height 3 whose base has a circumference of $8\pi$   $48\pi$

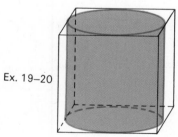

Ex. 19–20

**19.** a cylinder inscribed in a cube whose edge has a length of 7
$85\frac{3}{4}\pi$

**20.** a cylinder inscribed in a cube whose edge has a length of 9
$182\frac{1}{4}\pi$

**21.** The "wheels" of cheese are right circular cylinders. Which wheel has more cheese?

The one with radius 7

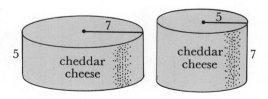

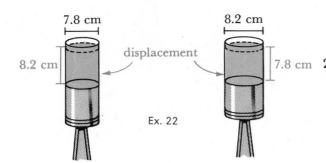

Ex. 22

**22.** The cylindrical pistons in an automobile engine move up and down, displacing a certain volume. Which piston has the greater displacement?

The one with diameter 8.2 cm

**23.** How many cm³ of copper are there in 20 m of copper wire that is 1.5 mm in diameter? Use $\pi = 3.14$.

35.325 cm³

**24.** How many cm³ of water are used if a center-pivot irrigation system with radius 92 m covers the ground with 1.2 cm of water? Use $\pi = 3.14$. (See p. 418 and Ex. 17, p. 431.)

318 923 520 cm³

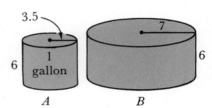

A          B

© **25.** Containers *A* and *B* are cylindrical. If container *A* holds 1 gallon, how many gallons would container *B* hold?  4

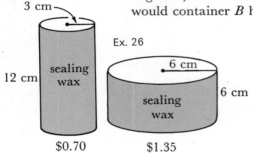

Ex. 26

sealing wax

$0.70          $1.35

**26.** The cakes of sealing wax are cylindrical. Which is the better buy? Why? The wider one; twice the volume for less than twice the cost

**27.** A cube whose edge has a length of 8 is inscribed in a cylinder. Find the volume of the cylinder.   $256\pi$

**28.** $V = \pi(2\frac{3}{4})^2(30 \times 12)$
$\quad = 8548\frac{13}{20}$ in.³
$8548\frac{13}{20} \div 231 = 37\frac{11}{1540}$
or about 37 gallons
NOTE: The outside diameter is not relevant.

**28.** The outside diameter of a pipe is 6 in. If its inside diameter is $5\frac{1}{2}$ in., how many gallons of water would 30 ft of pipe hold? Use 1 gallon = 231 cubic inches, and $\pi = 3.14$.

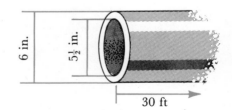

30 ft

**29.** $V = \pi(2)^2(12) - \pi(1.98)^2(11.96)$
$\quad = 3.49173024$ or
about 3.49 ft³

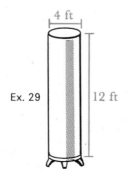

Ex. 29      12 ft

**29.** How many cubic feet of steel does it take to make a cylindrical tank 4 ft wide and 12 ft high if the shell of the tank is 0.24 in. thick? Use $\pi = 3.14$. HINT: The top and bottom are part of the shell.

# GEOMETRIC PATTERNS

Make a kaleidoscope. Use three small rectangular mirrors of equal size and bits of colorful material (paper, plastic, or beads).

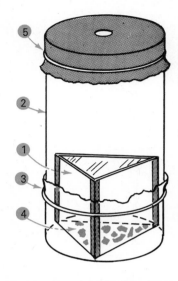

① Tape mirrors together (front of mirrors to the inside) to form a regular triangular prism.

② Use heavy paper to make a cylinder around the mirrors (so the prism is enclosed in the cylinder).

③ Fasten cellophane over end of cylinder with a rubber band.

④ Put colorful material into prism.

⑤ Fasten paper over other end of cylinder with a rubber band, and make a small hole in the center of the paper.

---

1. A polyhedron separates _Space_ into two parts.

2. The lateral faces of a right prism are always bounded by _Rectangles_

3. The volume of a right prism with base area $B$ and height $h$ is _$Bh$_.

4. The volume of a right circular cylinder with radius $r$ and height $h$ is _$\pi r^2 h$_.

Quick Quiz

for Sections 14.1 to 14.4

**5–6.** Find the volume of each right rectangular prism with the given dimensions.

5. 2.4 cm, 3.7 cm, 5 cm

   44.4 cm$^3$

6. 200 mm, 35 cm, 2 m

   0.14 m$^3$, 140 000 cm$^3$, or 140 000 000 mm$^3$

**7–8.** Find the volume of each right prism with the given base and height.

7. BASE: right triangle with legs of 4.5 cm and 8 cm; HEIGHT: 3.6 cm

   64.8 cm$^3$

8. BASE: rhombus with diagonals of 3 m and 1.2 m; HEIGHT: 4 m

   7.2 m$^3$

**9–10.** Find the volume of each circular cylinder (in terms of $\pi$).

9. radius 6 cm, height 0.5 cm

   18$\pi$ cm$^3$

10. radius 1.4 cm, height 9.6 cm

    18.816$\pi$ cm$^3$

# 14.5 Oblique Prisms and Circular Cylinders

**Suggested Class Time**

| Course | Min. | Reg. | Max. |
|--------|------|------|------|
| Days   | 1    | 1    | 1    |

**Oblique prisms** and **oblique circular cylinders** are very much like right prisms and right circular cylinders. The same definitions apply. However, the lateral edges of an oblique prism are *not* perpendicular to the planes of the bases. Therefore, the lateral faces can be bounded by any parallelogram. Similarly, the axis of an oblique cylinder is *not* perpendicular to the planes of its bases.

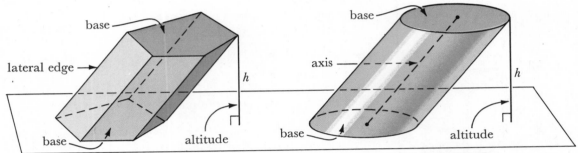

OBLIQUE PENTAGONAL PRISM          OBLIQUE CIRCULAR CYLINDER

A *cross section* of a prism or a circular cylinder (right or oblique) is the intersection of the solid with a plane parallel to the planes of bases.

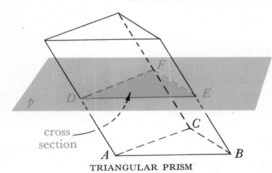

cross section

TRIANGULAR PRISM

Plane $p$ is parallel to the planes of the bases of the triangular prism in the figure. Therefore, $\triangle DEF$ and its interior form a cross section of the prism. $\overline{AB} \parallel \overline{DE}$ and, by the definition of a prism, $\overline{AD} \parallel \overline{BE}$. So $ABED$ is a parallelogram, and $\overline{AB} \cong \overline{DE}$. We can show $\overline{BC} \cong \overline{EF}$ and $\overline{AC} \cong \overline{DF}$ by the same reasoning, and $\triangle ABC \cong \triangle DEF$ by the SSS Postulate. In fact,

**Theorem** ⦀ All cross sections of a triangular prism are congruent to its bases. ⦀

If we separate the prism at the right into triangular prisms, its cross section and base are separated into triangular regions. The cross section of each triangular prism is congruent to its base. Since congruent triangles have equal areas, $C_1 = B_1$, $C_2 = B_2$, and $C_3 = B_3$.

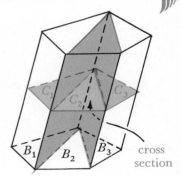

cross section

Therefore,     $C_1 + C_2 + C_3 = B_1 + B_2 + B_3$

area cross section = area base

 All cross sections of a prism have the same area as the base.  **Prism Cross Section Theorem**

There is a similar theorem for cross sections of a circular cylinder.

 All cross sections of a circular cylinder have the same area as the base. **Cylinder Cross Section Theorem**

The cross section of a circular cylinder is a circular region with its center on the axis of the cylinder. $\overline{BC} \parallel \overline{AD}$ by the definition of a cylinder. So $\overline{BC}$ and $\overline{AD}$ are in a plane that intersects the cross section and base. $\overline{AB} \parallel \overline{CD}$ (why?), and $ABCD$ is a parallelogram. Since $\overline{AB} \cong \overline{CD}$, the cross section and base are congruent, and they have equal areas.

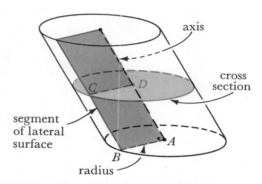

Alfa

Figure 1 is a right rectangular prism represented by a deck of very thin cards. If we "slant" an identical deck of cards, we have an oblique prism, figure 2, whose base and height are exactly like the base and height of figure 1. The volume of figure 1 is equal to the sum of the volumes of its cards. Since figure 2 is made up of exact copies of the cards, it has the same volume. Figure 3 is another deck that has been "twisted." It also represents a solid with the same volume.

Think of the cards as cross sections (no longer having volume, just area). Then any plane parallel to the bottom cards of the decks will intersect each figure at identical cards with equal areas.

An Italian mathematician, Bonaventura Cavalieri (1598–1647), was the first to make these observations about solids and their volumes.

**Cavalieri's Postulate**

If two solids with bases in the same plane have equal heights, and if the cross sections of both solids made by any plane parallel to the plane of the bases have equal areas, then the solids have equal volumes.

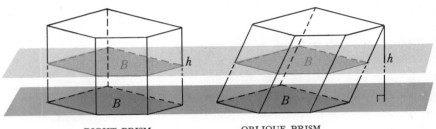

RIGHT PRISM      OBLIQUE PRISM

The bases of the prisms above are in the same plane. Both prisms have base area $B$ and height $h$. By the Prism Cross Section Theorem, all cross sections of each prism have area $B$. So the cross sections formed by any plane parallel to the plane of the bases will have area $B$. Therefore, by Cavalieri's Postulate,

volume oblique prism = volume right prism

In general,

**Volume Theorem for a Prism**

The volume ($V$) of any prism is equal to the area ($B$) of its base times its height ($h$)

$$V = Bh$$

The same is true for circular cylinders with equal base areas and heights.

The cylinders in the figure have equal radii and heights. Why are their volumes equal?

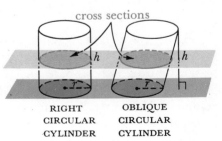

cross sections

RIGHT CIRCULAR CYLINDER      OBLIQUE CIRCULAR CYLINDER

**Volume Theorem for a Circular Cylinder**

The volume ($V$) of any circular cylinder (with radius $r$) is equal to the area ($\pi r^2$) of its base times its height ($h$).

$$V = \pi r^2 h$$

Ⓐ **1–12.** Use the given figures.

NOTE: For cylinders, leave answers in terms of π unless told otherwise.

**1.** The prism is called an oblique $\overset{\text{Triangular}}{\underline{\hspace{1.5cm}}}$ prism.

**2.** *BEDA* is a (parallelogram, square, rectangle).

**3.** $\overline{BE}$ is a(n) $\underline{\hspace{2cm}}$ of the prism.   Lateral edge

**4.** $\overline{AD} \parallel \underline{\;\overline{BE}\;} \parallel \underline{\;\overline{CF}\;}$   **5.** $\overline{DG} \underline{\;\perp\;}$ plane *ABC*

**6.** *DG* is the $\underline{\;\text{Height}\;}$ of the prism.

**7.** $\underline{\;\overline{UV}\;}$ is a segment of the lateral surface of the cylinder.

**8.** $\overline{ST}$ is the $\underline{\;\text{Axis}\;}$ of the cylinder.

**9.** $\overline{UT}$ is a(n) $\underline{\text{Radius}}$ of the cylinder.

**10.** *VY* is the $\underline{\;\text{Height}\;}$ of the cylinder.

**11.** $\overline{VU} \parallel \underline{\;\overline{ST}\;}$   **12.** Plane *VSW* $\underline{\;\parallel\;}$ plane *UTY*

Ex. 1–6

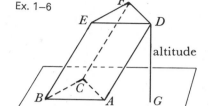

OBLIQUE PRISM

Ex. 7–12

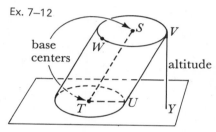

OBLIQUE CIRCULAR CYLINDER

Ⓑ **13–20.** True or False?

**13.** The bases of an oblique prism are not bounded by congruent polygons.   F

**14.** All lateral faces of an oblique prism are bounded by rectangles.   F

**15.** A lateral edge of an oblique prism is an altitude.   F

**16.** The bases of a circular cylinder are bounded by congruent circles.   T

**17.** The axis of an oblique cylinder is perpendicular to the planes of the bases.   F

**18.** The height of an oblique cylinder is the length of any segment of the lateral surface.   F

**19.** Any cross section of a circular cylinder has the same area as either base.   T

**20.** Some cross sections of a prism do not have the same area as either base.   F

**Assignment Guide**
*Oral:* 1–12
*Written:*
Min. 13–25 odd
Reg. 13–25 odd; 27–29
Max. 13–25 odd; 27–32

**21–26.** Sketch each solid. Then find its volume.

**21.** oblique prism of height 10 cm whose base is bounded by a rectangle with length 6 cm and width 2 cm                  120 cm³

**22.** oblique prism of height 7 m whose base is bounded by an equilateral triangle with a perimeter of 18 m            $63\sqrt{3}$ m³

**23.** oblique cylinder of height 9 and radius 3    $81\pi$

**24.** oblique cylinder of height 8.5 whose base has a diameter of 5
                                                                    $53.125\pi$

**25.** oblique cylinder of height 16 whose base has a circumference of $\pi$
                                                                    $4\pi$

**26.** oblique cylinder of height 3.6 whose base has a circumference of $4\pi$
                                                                    $14.4\pi$

© **27–29.** Determine what happens to the volume of a cylinder when

**27.** The radius is doubled.              **28.** The height is doubled.
     Volume multiplied by 4                    Volume multiplied by 2
**29.** Both the radius and the height are doubled.
                                    Volume multiplied by 8

**30–32.** To apply Cavalieri's Postulate, the bases of two solids do not have to be congruent, nor do they have to be bounded by the same kind of figure. Use Cavalieri's Postulate to answer each exercise.

**30.** Why do both prisms have the same volume?
     Both have base area 24, height 5.

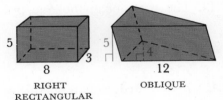

RIGHT
RECTANGULAR                     OBLIQUE

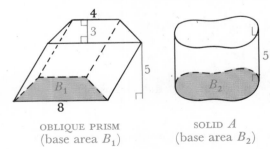

OBLIQUE PRISM               SOLID $A$
(base area $B_1$)          (base area $B_2$)

**31.** The areas of all cross sections of solid $A$ are equal to $B_2$. If $B_1 = B_2$, why is it possible to find the volume of solid $A$? Find its volume.
     Cavalieri's Post.; 90

**32.** $ABCD$, $RSTU$, and $VWXY$ are squares. Does Cavalieri's Postulate apply to the prism and solid $Q$? Why, or why not?
     No; Cross sections of solid $Q$ and of prism do not have equal areas.

OBLIQUE PRISM               SOLID $Q$

# Pyramids and Cones

Courtesy Northrop Corp.

Keith Krieger

A **pyramid** has one face, called the *base*, bounded by any convex polygon. All other faces, called *lateral faces*, are bounded by triangles with a common vertex and bases that are the edges of the base of the pyramid. The common vertex of the lateral faces is the *vertex* of the pyramid. The *altitude* of the pyramid is the perpendicular segment from its vertex to the plane of its base, and the *height* is the length of the altitude.

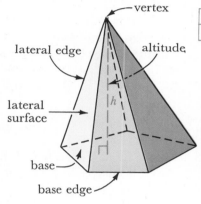

vertex

lateral edge

altitude

lateral surface

$h$

base

base edge

| Suggested Class Time | | | |
|---|---|---|---|
| Course | Min. | Reg. | Max. |
| Days | 1 | 1 | 1 |

A pyramid is a **regular pyramid** if and only if its base is bounded by a regular polygon and its lateral faces are bounded by congruent isosceles triangles. A pyramid is named by the number of base edges it has. For example,

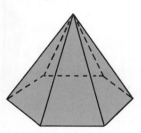

REGULAR HEXAGONAL PYRAMID

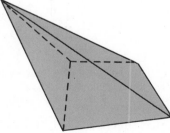

QUADRANGULAR PYRAMID

If two triangular pyramids have congruent bases and equal heights, then they have equal volumes.

**Volume Postulate for Triangular Pyramids**

Any triangular prism can be separated into three pyramids. In the figure below, planes $XEZ$ and $DEZ$ separate the prism into pyramids $S_1$, $S_2$, and $S_3$.

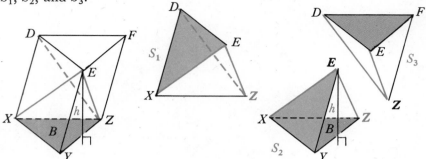

For $S_1$ and $S_2$, $\triangle XDE \cong \triangle EYX$ because $XYED$ is a parallelogram by the definition of a prism, and $\overline{XE}$ is its diagonal (a diagonal separates a parallelogram into two congruent triangles). Since $\triangle XDE$ and $\triangle EYX$ are in the same plane, the perpendicular from point $Z$ to the plane of each base is the same segment. Therefore, $S_1$ and $S_2$ have congruent bases and equal heights. And, by the Volume Postulate for Triangular Pyramids,

$$\text{volume } S_1 = \text{volume } S_2$$

For $S_3$ and $S_2$, $\triangle DEF \cong \triangle XYZ$ because they are the bases of a prism. The perpendicular from point $Z$ to plane $DEF$ has the same length as the perpendicular from point $E$ to plane $XYZ$. Why? And, by the Volume Postulate for Triangular Pyramids,

$$\text{volume } S_3 = \text{volume } S_2$$

By the Volume Addition Postulate and substitution,

$$\text{volume } S_1 + \text{volume } S_2 + \text{volume } S_3 = \text{volume prism}$$
$$\text{volume } S_2 + \text{volume } S_2 + \text{volume } S_2 = \text{volume prism}$$
$$3(\text{volume } S_2) = \text{volume prism}$$
$$\text{volume } S_2 = \tfrac{1}{3}(\text{volume prism})$$
$$\text{volume } S_2 = \tfrac{1}{3}Bh$$

Notice that the base and altitude of the prism are the base and altitude of pyramid $S_2$.

| Volume Theorem for a Triangular Pyramid | The volume ($V$) of any triangular pyramid is equal to one third the area ($B$) of its base times it height ($h$). $$V = \tfrac{1}{3}Bh$$ |
| --- | --- |

Any pyramid can be separated into triangular pyramids. In the figure at right, pyramid $S$ with base area $B$ is separated into three pyramids. Pyramids $S_1$, $S_2$, and $S_3$ all have the same height $h$. Why?

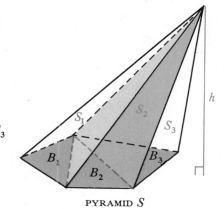

PYRAMID $S$

$$\text{volume } S = \text{volume } S_1 + \text{volume } S_2 + \text{volume } S_3$$
$$= \tfrac{1}{3}B_1h + \tfrac{1}{3}B_2h + \tfrac{1}{3}B_3h$$
$$= \tfrac{1}{3}(B_1 + B_2 + B_3)h$$
$$= \tfrac{1}{3}Bh$$

The volume ($V$) of any pyramid is equal to one third the area ($B$) of its base times its height ($h$).

$$V = \tfrac{1}{3}Bh$$

**Volume Theorem for a Pyramid**

A **circular cone** has one face, called the *base*, that is bounded by a circle and a *vertex* that is a point not in the plane of the base. All segments joining the vertex and a point on the circle bounding the base form the *lateral surface*. The segment joining the vertex to the center of the base is the *axis*.

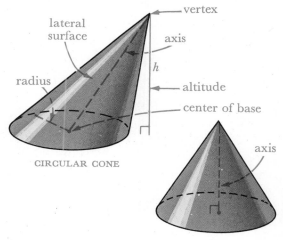

CIRCULAR CONE

The *altitude* of the cone is the perpendicular segment from the vertex to the plane of the base, and the *height* is the length of the altitude. Any radius of the base is a *radius* of the cone. A **right circular cone** is a cone whose axis is perpendicular to the plane of the base.

RIGHT CIRCULAR CONE

To find the volume of a circular cone, we will use a method similar to the one used for a right circular cylinder. A pyramid is inscribed in a cone if its base is inscribed in the base of the cone and its vertex is the same as the vertex of the cone.

INSCRIBED PYRAMIDS

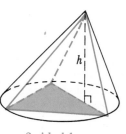
3-sided base

6-sided base

many-sided base

493

As the number of base edges of the inscribed pyramid increases, the shape of the pyramid begins to resemble the shape of the cone, and the volume of the pyramid is close to the volume of the cone. In fact, the volume of the cone is the limit of the volumes of its inscribed pyramids. If $B$ is the area of the pyramid base, and $h$ is the height, then

$$\text{volume cone} = \text{limit volumes of pyramids}$$
$$= \text{limit } \tfrac{1}{3}Bh$$

The limit of $B$ is the area of the circular base of the cone, which is $\pi r^2$, so

$$\text{volume cone} = \tfrac{1}{3}\pi r^2 h$$

In general,

**Volume Theorem for a Circular Cone**

The volume ($V$) of any circular cone (with radius $r$) is equal to one third the area ($\pi r^2$) of its base times its height ($h$).

$$V = \tfrac{1}{3}\pi r^2 h$$

## Exercises 14.6

NOTE: For cones, leave answers in terms of $\pi$ unless told otherwise.

Assignment Guide
*Oral:* 1–8
*Written:*
Min. 9–20
Reg. 9–20; 25–26
Max. 9–27 odd; 30–33

Ⓐ **1–8.** Use the given figures.

**1.** Point $A$ is the <u>Vertex</u> of the pyramid.

**2.** $AX$ is the <u>Height</u> of the pyramid.

**3.** <u>BCDE</u> is the base of the pyramid.

**4.** If the pyramid is a regular pyramid, then $\triangle ABC$ is <u>Isosceles</u>.

**5.** $\overline{RS}$ is the <u>Axis</u> of the circular cone.

**6.** $\overline{ST}$ is a(n) <u>Radius</u> of the cone.

**7.** $\overline{RQ}$ is the <u>Altitude</u> of the cone.

**8.** The volume of the cone is _____.
$\tfrac{1}{3}\pi r^2 h$ or $\tfrac{1}{3}\pi (ST)^2(RQ)$

Ex. 1–4

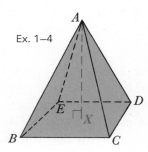

Ex. 5–8

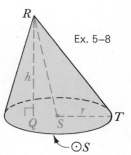

Ⓑ **9–14.** True or False?

**9.** All lateral edges of a regular pyramid are congruent. T

**10.** The height of a triangular pyramid is always less than the length of any lateral edge.     F (One lateral edge could be ⊥ to the base.)

**11.** The axis of a right circular cone is also the altitude.   T

**12.** Any rhombus can be the base of a regular pyramid.   F

**13.** If $\overline{PQ}$, $\overline{PR}$, $\overline{PS}$, and $\overline{PT}$ are the lateral edges of a pyramid, then points $Q$, $R$, $S$, and $T$ are coplanar.   T

**14.** If $\overline{AB}$ is the axis of a right circular cone with radius $\overline{BC}$, then $\triangle ABC$ is a right triangle.   T

**15–20.** Find the volume of each solid.

**15.** 300 cm³

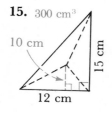

**16.** 5 m³

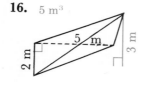

**17.** 64π cm³ or 64 000π mm³

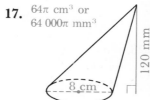

**18.**

32π cm³ or 32 000π mm³

**19.** 225

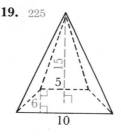

**20.** 36

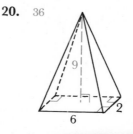

**21–24.** Find the following:

**21.** the volume of a pyramid whose height is 25 and whose base is a rhombus with diagonals of 5 and 6

          125

**22.** the height of a right circular cone whose volume is 12.5π and whose base circumference is 10π   1.5

**23.** the base area of a regular hexagonal pyramid whose volume is 4.5 and whose height is 0.5   27

**24.** the circumference of the base of a right circular cone whose volume is 96π and whose height is 8

          12π

**25.** The Transamerica Pyramid Building is in San Francisco. Without its first four levels and "wings," the rest of the building is a pyramid with a square base measuring 149' on a side and a height of 800'. Find the volume of the pyramid.

          5,920,266⅔ ft³

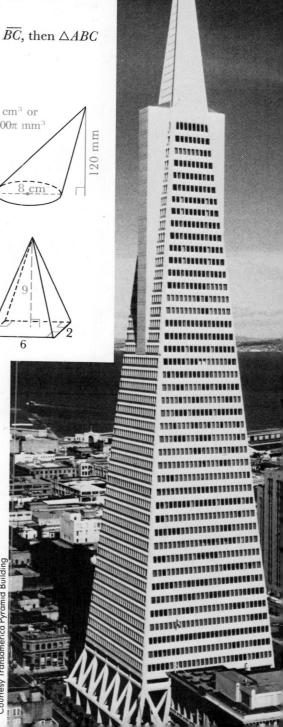

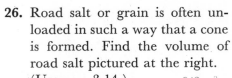

**26.** Road salt or grain is often un-loaded in such a way that a cone is formed. Find the volume of road salt pictured at the right. (Use $\pi = 3.14$.)   942 m³

Ex. 27

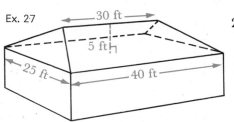

**27.** To install an attic fan, the volume of the attic in the building shown must be found. Find it. HINT: Together, the two ends would form a pyramid with a rectangular base of $25 \times 10$ feet.

$2291\frac{2}{3}$ ft³

Ex. 29

**28.** Find the volume of the sand hopper pictured at the right. (Use $\pi = 3.14$.)   2411.52 ft³

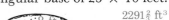

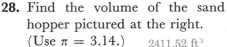

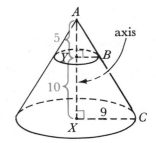

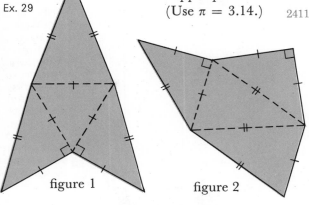

figure 1          figure 2

© **29.** Trace two copies of figure 1 and one of figure 2. Make a model of a pyramid with each copy and fit them together to form a right triangular prism.

**30.** Find $YB$, the radius of the cross section of the cone at the right. HINT: $\overline{AC}$ is a segment of the lateral surface of the cone and contains point $B$.   3

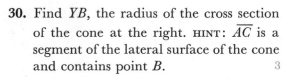

**31.** Find the volume of the solid that is bounded by the base and cross section of the cone in Exercise 30.   $390\pi$

Ex. 32–33

**32–33.** The figure at the left is a right circular cone and a right circular cylinder with the same base and axis.

**32.** What is the volume of the solid bounded by the lateral surface of the cone and the lateral surface and upper base of the cylinder?

$\frac{4}{3}\pi r^3$

**33.** Sketch a cross section of the solid described in Exercise 32.

*See Ex. 28, page 507*

# Surface Area

**Suggested Class Time**

| Course | Min. | Reg. | Max. |
|--------|------|------|------|
| Days | 1 | 1 | 1 |

The **lateral area** (**L.A.**) of a prism or pyramid is the measure of the lateral faces; of a cylinder or cone, it is the measure of the lateral surface. The **surface area** (**S.A.**) of a solid is the measure of its total surface—including the lateral area and the base area.

For the right triangular prism below, the lateral area is the sum of the areas of its lateral faces. So,

L.A. = area $PQTS$ + area $QRUT$ + area $RPSU$.

The prism has height $h$, and its lateral edges are altitudes. Therefore, $PS = QT = RU = h$. Since the lateral faces are rectangular regions,

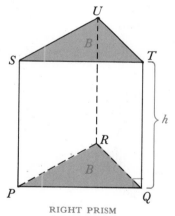

RIGHT PRISM

$$\text{L.A.} = (PQ)h + (QR)h + (RP)h$$
$$= (PQ + QR + RP)h$$

Notice that $PQ + QR + RP = p$, where $p$ is the perimeter of $\triangle PQR$, the base of the prism. So,

$$\text{L.A.} = ph$$

The surface area of the prism is the sum of the areas of all its faces. The bases are congruent, and each has area $B$.

$$\text{S.A.} = \text{L.A.} + 2B$$

In general,

> For any right prism, lateral area (L.A.) is equal to the perimeter ($p$) of its base times its height ($h$), and surface area (S.A.) is equal to its lateral area plus twice the area ($B$) of its base.
>
> L.A. = $ph$ and S.A. = L.A. + 2B

**L.A. and S.A. Theorem for a Right Prism**

The lateral area of the regular pyramid below is the sum of the areas of its lateral faces.

$$\text{L.A.} = \text{area } \triangle AXY + \text{area } \triangle AYZ + \text{area } \triangle AZX$$

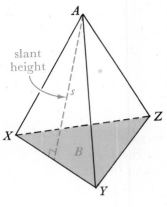

slant height

REGULAR PYRAMID

The *slant height* of a regular pyramid is the height of the triangle bounding any lateral face. The slant height ($s$) of the pyramid in the figure is the height of isosceles $\triangle AXY$. $\triangle AYZ$ and $\triangle AZX$ also have heights of $s$. Why? Therefore,

$$\text{L.A.} = \tfrac{1}{2}(XY)s + \tfrac{1}{2}(YZ)s + \tfrac{1}{2}(ZX)s$$
$$= \tfrac{1}{2}(XY + YZ + ZX)s$$

But $XY + YZ + ZX = p$, the perimeter of the pyramid's base. So,

$$\text{L.A.} = \tfrac{1}{2}ps$$

The area of $\triangle XYZ$ is $B$, so the surface area of the pyramid is

$$\text{S.A.} = \text{L.A.} + B$$

In general,

**L.A. and S.A. Theorem for a Regular Pyramid**

For any regular pyramid, lateral area (L.A.) is equal to one half the perimeter ($p$) of its base times its slant height ($s$), and surface area (S.A.) is equal to its lateral area plus the area ($B$) of its base.

$$\text{L.A.} = \tfrac{1}{2}ps \qquad \text{and} \qquad \text{S.A.} = \text{L.A.} + B$$

RIGHT CIRCULAR CYLINDER

RECTANGULAR REGION

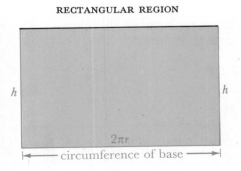

circumference of base

To find the lateral area of a right circular cylinder, imagine "peeling" the lateral surface off the cylinder at left. The "unrolled" surface is a rectangular region. Its length is the same as the circumference of the cylinder base, and its width is the same as the height of the cylinder. The area of the rectangular region is the same as the lateral area of the cylinder. So for the cylinder,

$$\text{L.A.} = (\text{circumference of base})h$$

If the base has radius $r$, then its circumference is $2\pi r$, and

$$\text{L.A.} = 2\pi rh$$

The surface area of the cylinder is its lateral area plus the area of both bases. Each base has an area of $\pi r^2$, so

$$\text{S.A.} = \text{L.A.} + 2\pi r^2 = 2\pi rh + 2\pi r^2 = 2\pi r(h + r)$$

For any right circular cylinder, lateral area (L.A.) is equal to the circumference ($2\pi r$) of its base times its height ($h$), and surface area (S.A.) is equal to its lateral area plus twice the area ($\pi r^2$) of its base.

$$\text{L.A.} = 2\pi rh \qquad \text{and} \qquad \text{S.A.} = \text{L.A.} + 2\pi r^2 = 2\pi r(h + r)$$

L.A. and S.A. Theorem for a Right Circular Cylinder

The *slant height* of a right circular cone is the length of any segment from the vertex to any point of the circle bounding the base. If the lateral surface of the right circular cone in the figure is "peeled off," it is a sector of a circle with radius $s$ (the slant height of the cone). The arc length of the sector is $2\pi r$ (the circumference of the base of the cone). The area of a sector is half the arc length times the radius (see Section 12.4). So, for the cone,

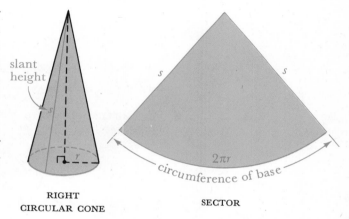

RIGHT CIRCULAR CONE

SECTOR

L.A. = area of sector

    $= \frac{1}{2}(\text{circumference of cone base})s$

    $= \frac{1}{2}(2\pi r)s$

    $= \pi rs$

The surface area of the cone is the sum of its lateral area and the area of its base, which is $\pi r^2$. So,

$$\text{S.A.} = \text{L.A.} + \pi r^2 = \pi rs + \pi r^2 = \pi r(s + r)$$

For any right circular cone, lateral area (L.A.) is equal to one half the circumference ($2\pi r$) of its base times its slant height ($s$), and surface area (S.A.) is equal to its lateral area plus the area ($\pi r^2$) of its base.

$$\text{L.A.} = \pi rs \qquad \text{and} \qquad \text{S.A.} = \text{L.A.} + \pi r^2 = \pi r(s + r)$$

L.A. and S.A. Theorem for a Right Circular Cone

# Exercises 14.7

NOTE: For cylinders and cylinders and cones, leave answers in terms of $\pi$ unless told otherwise.

**Assignment Guide**
*Oral:* 1–8
*Written:*
Min. 9–21 odd; Alg. Rev., p. 502, odd
Reg. 9–25 odd; Alg. Rev., p. 502, odd
Max. 9–21 odd; 23–29; 32

Ⓐ 1. The sum of the areas of the lateral faces of a regular pyramid is called the ——— of the pyramid. Lateral area

2. The surface area of a solid is its $\underline{\text{Lateral}}$ area plus its $\underline{\text{Base}}$ area.

3. The length of a segment from the vertex of a right circular cone to a point of the circle bounding the base is called the $\underline{\text{Slant height}}$.

4. The slant height of a regular pyramid is the $\underline{\text{Height}}$ of one of its lateral faces.

5. The lateral area of a right prism of height $h$ and base perimeter $p$ is $\underline{ph}$.

6. The lateral area of a regular pyramid with slant height $s$ and base perimeter $p$ is $\underline{\frac{1}{2}ps}$.

7. The surface area of a right circular cone of radius $r$ and slant height $s$ is L.A. $+ \underline{\pi r^2} = \underline{\pi r(s + r)}$.

8. The surface area of a right circular cylinder with radius $r$ and height $h$ is L.A. $+ \underline{2\pi r^2} = \underline{2\pi r(h + r)}$.

Ⓑ **9–12.** Find **(a)** the lateral area and **(b)** the surface area of each solid.

9. **a.** 60 cm²; **b.** 72 cm²
10. **a.** 630 mm²; **b.** 1071 mm²
11. **a.** 48π m²; **b.** 66π m²
12. **a.** 27π cm²; **b.** 36π cm²

9.

5 cm
5 cm
3 cm    4 cm

right prism

10.

15 mm
21 mm

regular pyramid

11.

8 m
3 m

right circular cylinder

12.

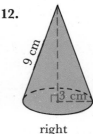

9 cm
3 cm

right circular cone

**13–22.** Sketch each solid. Then find **(a)** its lateral area and **(b)** its surface area.

13. right square prism with lateral edge of length 8 and base edge of length 10                    **a.** 320; **b.** 520

14. right rectangular prism whose height is $5\frac{2}{3}$ and whose base has length 6 and width $2\frac{1}{2}$                    **a.** $96\frac{1}{3}$; **b.** $126\frac{1}{3}$

**15.** cube with edge of length 3

**a. 36; b. 54**

**16.** cube whose volume is $e^3$

**a.** $4e^2$; **b.** $6e^2$

**17.** regular square pyramid with slant height of 2.5 and base edge of length 1.5

**a. 7.5; b. 9.75**

**18.** regular triangular pyramid with slant height of 12 and base edge of length 8

**a. 144; b.** $144 + 16\sqrt{3}$

**19.** right circular cylinder of height 11 and radius 2    **a.** $44\pi$; **b.** $52\pi$

**20.** right circular cylinder of height 8.5 and base circumference of $5\pi$

**a.** $42.5\pi$; **b.** $55\pi$

**21.** right circular cone with slant height of 9 and radius of $2\frac{1}{3}$

**a.** $21\pi$;    **b.** $26\frac{4}{9}\pi$

**22.** right circular cone with slant height of 20 and base diameter of 10

**a.** $100\pi$;    **b.** $125\pi$

**23–26.** Solve each problem. Assume there is no waste or overlap.

**23.** How many square centimeters of cardboard are needed to make a box 30 cm long, 20 cm wide, and 15 cm high?

2700 cm²

**24.** How many square centimeters of tin are needed to make a cylindrical tin can with a radius of 7 cm and a height of 10 cm? (Use $\frac{22}{7}$ for $\pi$.)    748 cm²

**25.** How much roofing paper is needed to cover the garage roof shown?    440 ft²

**26.** How much tin is needed to make the funnel? (Use $\frac{22}{7}$ for $\pi$.)    220 cm²

Ex. 25

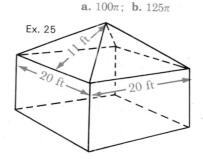

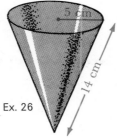

Ex. 26

Ex. 27

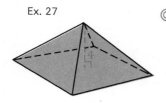

© **27.** The altitude of any regular pyramid contains the center of the polygon bounding the base. (See Section 12.1.) Find the surface area of the regular square pyramid in the figure if its base area is 64 square units.

$64 + 64\sqrt{2}$ square units

**28.** The formulas for the lateral areas of right prisms and regular pyramids cannot be used for finding the lateral areas of oblique prisms and nonregular pyramids. Why?

**28.** The height of an oblique prism is not the height of every lateral face. The faces of a nonregular pyramid are not congruent, so the pyramid has no slant height.

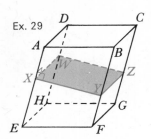

Ex. 29

29. $WXYZ \perp \overline{AE}$, so it is $\perp$ to all lateral edges of the prism; then the sides of $WXYZ$ are altitudes of the ▱s bounding the lateral faces. But $AE = BF = CG = DH$, so the area of each face is its height times $AE$, and the sum of the areas is the sum of the heights (the perimeter of $WXYZ$) times $AE$.

**29.** The intersection of the oblique prism in the figure and a plane perpendicular to $\overline{AE}$ is region $WXYZ$. Why is the lateral area of the prism equal to the perimeter of $WXYZ$ times $AE$?

**30.** Construct two 15 cm × 10 cm rectangular regions and make a model of a right circular cylinder (without bases) of height 15 cm and one of height 10 cm. Which cylinder has the greater lateral area? The greater surface area (if each had bases)?

*Lateral areas are equal; the one with height 10 cm*

**31.** Construct a semicircular region of radius 8 cm and make a model of a right circular cone (without a base). What would be the radius of the circle needed to fit this cone with a base? 4 cm

**32.** Find both the surface area and volume for each right rectangular prism. (Does it seem that the cube is the right rectangular prism that encloses the greatest volume for a given surface area?) Yes

| | a. | b. | c. | d. | e. | f. |
|---|---|---|---|---|---|---|
| S.A. | 216 | 216 | 216 | 216 | 216 | 216 |
| V | 144 | 180 | 201.6 | 214.2 | 215.28 | 216 |

a. 6, 12, 2
b. 6, 10, 3
c. 6, 8.4, 4
d. 6, 6.8, 5.25
e. 6, 6.5, 5.52
f. 6, 6, 6

---

## *Algebra Review*

**Review this skill:**

● *solving quadratic equations using the quadratic formula*

Solve by using the quadratic formula, shown at the right. Express irrational roots in simplest radical form.

If $ax^2 + bx + c = 0$,

$$x = \frac{-b \pm \sqrt{b^2 - 4ac}}{2a}.$$

**1.** $x^2 + 3x + 2 = 0$   $-1, -2$

**2.** $x^2 - 4x + 3 = 0$   $3, 1$

**3.** $5t^2 + 2t - 3 = 0$   $-1, \frac{3}{5}$

**4.** $y^2 + 6y = 2$   $-3 \pm \sqrt{11}$

**5.** $x^2 + 1 = 4x$   $2 \pm \sqrt{3}$

**6.** $3s^2 + 6s + 1 = 0$   $\frac{-3 \pm \sqrt{6}}{3}$

**7.** $2p^2 = 4p - 1$   $\frac{2 \pm \sqrt{2}}{2}$

**8.** $2n^2 = 3 - 6n$   $\frac{-3 \pm \sqrt{15}}{2}$

**9.** $x^2 = 5x + 4$   $\frac{5 \pm \sqrt{41}}{2}$

**10.** $2w^2 + 4w - 8 = 0$   $-1 \pm \sqrt{5}$

**11.** $y^2 + 2\sqrt{3}y + 3 = 0$   $-\sqrt{3}$

**12.** $t^2 - 2t + \frac{2}{3} = 0$   $1 \pm \frac{\sqrt{3}}{3}$

## GEOMETRIC BIOLOGY

Biologists have found that for warm-blooded animals the metabolic rate (and, therefore, the amount of food that must be eaten in a given time) is related to the ratio of surface area to volume. The higher the ratio, the higher the metabolic rate.

Estimate the size of a rabbit by a right rectangular prism of length 0.4 m, width 0.12 m, and height 0.14 m. Estimate the size of a person by a right rectangular prism of length 0.34 m, width 0.25 m, and height 1.7 m. Find the ratio of surface area to volume for each. Which has the higher metabolic rate?  *Answer below*

Harold M. Lambert

Leonard Lee Rue III
Van Cleve Photography

Estimate the size of a lion by a right circular cylinder with radius 0.4 m and height 2.3 m. Estimate the size of a hippopotamus by a right circular cylinder with radius 0.75 m and height 2.7 m. Find the ratio of surface area to volume for each. Which has the higher metabolic rate?

Lion: $\frac{2.16\pi}{0.368\pi} \approx 5.87$; Hippo: $\frac{5.175\pi}{1.51875\pi} \approx 3.41$; Lion

eonard Lee Rue III/Van Cleve Photography

Leonard Lee Rue III/Van Cleve Photography

Rabbit: $\frac{0.2416}{0.00672} \approx 35.95$; Person: $\frac{2.176}{0.1445} \approx 15.06$; Rabbit

# 14.8 Spheres

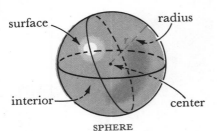

SPHERE

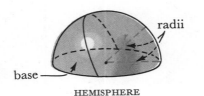

HEMISPHERE

In Chapter 11, a sphere was defined as all points in space that are a given distance (the radius) from a given point (the center). When we refer to the volume of a sphere, we mean, of course, the volume of a solid formed by the sphere and its interior.

Any plane containing the center separates a sphere into two solids of equal volume called **hemispheres.** The *base* of each hemisphere is bounded by a great circle.

In the figure below, a right circular cone is inscribed in a hemisphere that is inscribed in a right circular cylinder. All three solids have the same base. The heights of the cone and cylinder are equal to the radius of the hemisphere.

The volume of the hemisphere appears to be somewhere between the volumes of the cone and cylinder. Although we will not prove it, the average of the volumes of the cone and cylinder is equal to the volume of the hemisphere.

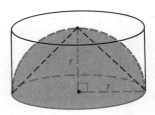

$$\text{volume cone} = \tfrac{1}{3}\pi r^2 r = \tfrac{1}{3}\pi r^3$$

$$\text{volume cylinder} = \pi r^2 r = \pi r^3$$

$$\text{volume hemisphere} = \tfrac{1}{2}(\tfrac{1}{3}\pi r^3 + \pi r^3) = \tfrac{2}{3}\pi r^3$$

Since the volume of the hemisphere is half the volume of a sphere with the same radius,

$$\text{volume sphere} = 2(\tfrac{2}{3}\pi r^3)$$

$$= \tfrac{4}{3}\pi r^3$$

**Volume Theorem for a Sphere**

The volume (*V*) of any sphere is $\frac{4}{3}\pi$ times its radius (*r*) cubed.

$$V = \tfrac{4}{3}\pi r^3$$

Imagine the surface of a sphere to be made up of many small regions as in the figure at right. Let $n$ be the number of regions.

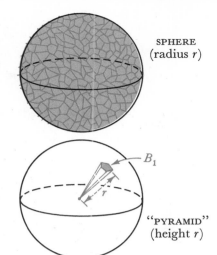

SPHERE
(radius $r$)

The segments from the center of the sphere to the boundary of each region separate the sphere into $n$ small "pyramids" with slightly curved bases. Each pyramid has height $r$, the radius of the sphere. If $B_1$ is the area of the base of one pyramid, the volume of that pyramid is $\frac{1}{3}B_1 r$. The sum of the volumes of all $n$ pyramids is the volume of the sphere. So,

"PYRAMID"
(height $r$)

$$\tfrac{1}{3}B_1 r + \tfrac{1}{3}B_2 r + \cdots + \tfrac{1}{3}B_n r = \text{volume sphere} = \tfrac{4}{3}\pi r^3$$

$$\tfrac{1}{3}r(B_1 + B_2 + \cdots + B_n) = \tfrac{4}{3}\pi r^3$$

Since the sum of the areas of the pyramid bases is the surface area of the sphere, $B_1 + B_2 + \cdots + B_n = \text{surface area sphere}$. And

$$\tfrac{1}{3}r(\text{surface area sphere}) = \tfrac{4}{3}\pi r^3$$

$$\text{surface area sphere} = 4\pi r^2$$

This is not a proof of the formula for surface area. However, the formula can be proved using more advanced mathematics.

Assignment Guide
*Oral:* 1–6
*Written:* Min. 7–14
       Reg. 7–23 odd
       Max. 7–27 odd

The surface area (S.A.) of any sphere is $4\pi$ times its radius ($r$) squared.

$$\text{S.A.} = 4\pi r^2$$

**Surface Area
Theorem
for a Sphere**

## Exercises 14.8

Ⓐ **1–6.** Refer to the given figure.

NOTE: Leave answers in terms of $\pi$ unless told otherwise.

1. The radius of the sphere is ___$r$___.

2. The surface area of the sphere is ___$4\pi r^2$___.

3. The volume of the sphere is ___$\frac{4}{3}\pi r^3$___.

4. If $r = 2$, the surface area of the sphere is ___$16\pi$___.

5. If $r = 3$, the volume of the sphere is ___$36\pi$___.

6. The volume of a hemisphere of radius $r$ is ___$\frac{2}{3}\pi r^3$___.

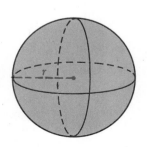

**7.** $288\pi$ cm$^3$; $144\pi$ cm$^2$

**8.** $4.5\pi$ m$^3$; $9\pi$ m$^2$

**9.** $121.5\pi$ mm$^3$; $81\pi$ mm$^2$

**10.** $\frac{1}{6}d^3\pi$ cubic units; $d^2\pi$ square units

**7.** 6 cm     **8.** 1.5 m     **9.** 4.5 mm     **10.** $\frac{1}{2}d$ units

**11.** Find the volume of a sphere with surface area $100\pi$ square units.

$166\frac{2}{3}$ cubic units

**12.** Find the volume of a sphere with surface area $144\pi$ square units.

$288\pi$ cubic units

**13.** Find the surface area of a sphere with volume $288\pi$ cubic units.

$144\pi$ square units

**14.** Find the surface area of a sphere with volume $36\pi$ cubic units.

$36\pi$ square units

**15.** What is the volume of a sphere formed by spinning a semicircular region around its diameter, which is 18 cm in length?     $972\pi$ cm$^3$

**16.** What is the surface area of a solid formed by spinning the sector in the figure around one radius?     $147\pi$ m$^2$

7 m

**17.** If the radius of a sphere is doubled, what happens to the surface area and volume of the sphere?     S.A. multiplied by 4; $V$ multiplied by 8

**18.** What is the ratio of the volume of a sphere of radius 6 to the volume of a sphere of radius 9?     8:27

**19.** What is the ratio of the area of a great circle of a sphere to the surface area of the sphere?     1:4

Ex. 20

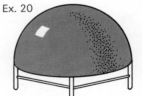

**20.** A water tank is the shape of a hemisphere. If it took 5 gallons of paint to cover its base, how much paint will it take to cover its curved surface?     10 gallons

**21.** What is the volume of the smallest right circular cylinder that can hold a sphere of diameter 14 cm?     $686\pi$ cm$^3$

**22.** What is the volume of the smallest box that will hold a soccer ball whose diameter is 22 cm?     10 648 cm$^3$

**23.** Find the radius, surface area, and volume of a sphere whose surface area is $x$ square units and whose volume is $x$ cubic units.

3 units; $36\pi$ sq. units; $36\pi$ cu. units

**24.** Find the radius, surface area, and volume of a sphere whose surface area is $x$ square units and whose volume is $y$ cubic units such that $x > y$.     $r < 3$ units; S.A. $< 36\pi$ sq. units; $V < 36\pi$ cu. units

© **25.** The diameter of the earth is about 12 800 km. About 70% of the earth's surface is covered by water. How many square kilometers of land are there? (Use $\pi = 3.14$.)

154 337 280 km$^2$

**26.** A steel ball bearing has a radius of 1 cm. How much steel is needed to make 1000 such ball bearings? (Use $\pi = 3.14$.)

About 4186.67 cm$^3$

**27.** The ship pictured on page 471 is being equipped with spherical tanks that will carry liquefied natural gas. The inside diameter of each tank is 120 ft. How many ft$^3$ will each tank hold? (Use $\pi = 3.14$.)

904,320 ft$^3$

**28–30.** In the figure below, solid $S$ contains all points of the right circular cylinder (height $2r$, radius $r$) that are not points of the right circular cones (each with height $r$, radius $r$, vertex $X$). The sphere has radius $r$. A plane parallel to the base of the cylinder intersects solid $S$ at a distance of $h$ from the vertex of the cones and the sphere at a distance of $h$ from its center.

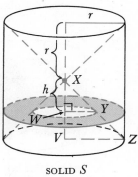

SOLID $S$

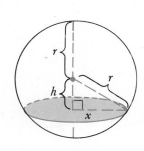

SPHERE

**28.** $\triangle XWY \sim \triangle XVZ$, so $\dfrac{WY}{VZ} = \dfrac{XW}{XV}$.

That is, $\dfrac{WY}{r} = \dfrac{h}{r}$, so $WY = h$.

$A = \pi(r^2 - h^2)$

**30.** Volumes are equal.

$V =$ volume of cylinder $-$
$\qquad\qquad$ volume of cones
$\quad = \pi r^2 \cdot 2r - 2(\frac{1}{3}\pi r^2 \cdot r)$
$\quad = 2\pi r^3 - \frac{2}{3}\pi r^3 = \frac{4}{3}\pi r^3$

**28.** Why does the cross section of solid $S$ have an inside radius of $h$? (See Ex. 30, p. 496.) Find the area of this cross section.

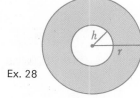

Ex. 28

**29.** Why is the cross section of the sphere a circular region? Find the area of the cross section in terms of $h$ and $r$.

*See page 388; $A = \pi(r^2 - h^2)$*

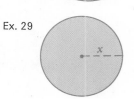

Ex. 29

**30.** What do the results of Ex. 28 and 29 and Cavalieri's Postulate imply about the volumes of solid $S$ and the sphere? Using solid $S$, find this volume.

# 14.9 Transformations: Plane Symmetry

**Suggested Class Time**

| Course | Min. | Reg. | Max. |
|--------|------|------|------|
| Days   | 0    | 0    | 1    |

The 3-dimensional counterpart of line symmetry (see section 5.10) is **plane symmetry.** If a figure can be separated into two "congruent halves" by a plane, the figure has plane symmetry (also called *reflection symmetry with respect to a plane*). A figure that has plane symmetry can be reflected over a plane so that the figure is its own reflection image. The reflecting plane is called a **symmetry plane** of the figure.

**A regular triangular prism has four symmetry planes.**

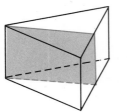 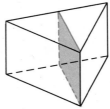 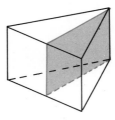 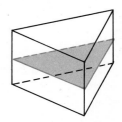

Three symmetry planes contain a symmetry line of each base.

The fourth symmetry plane bisects each lateral edge.

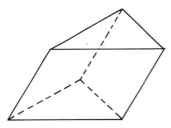 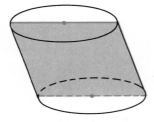 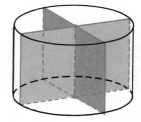

This oblique triangular prism has no symmetry planes.

An oblique circular cylinder has exactly one symmetry plane.

A right circular cylinder has **infinitely many symmetry planes** (each plane that contains its axis and the perpendicular bisecting plane of its axis).

## Exercises 14.9

**Assignment Guide**
*Oral:* Max. 1–4
*Written:* Max. 5–14

Ⓐ **1.** If a figure can be separated into two "congruent halves" by a plane, the figure has <u>Plane symmetry</u>

**2.** A figure that has plane symmetry can be reflected over a plane so that the figure is its own <u>Reflection image</u>

**3.** A regular triangular prism has <u>Four</u> symmetry plane(s).

**4.** A figure (must have at least one, <u>may have no</u>) symmetry plane(s).

Ⓑ **5–18.** Determine how many symmetry planes each type of solid has. (Draw sketches or use models if necessary.)

**5.** a right rectangular prism, no faces square   *Three*

**6.** a regular square pyramid   *Four*

**7.** a rectangular pyramid, base not a square, lateral faces isosceles   *Two*

**8.** a right square prism, not a cube   *Five*

**9.** a regular pentagonal prism, lateral faces not square   *Six*

**10.** a regular hexagonal prism, lateral faces not square   *Seven*

**11.** a right circular cone   *Infinitely many*

**12.** a nonright circular cone   *One*

**13.** a triangular pyramid, all faces scalene   *None*

**14.** a sphere   *Infinitely many*

Ⓒ **15.** a cube   *Nine*

**16.** a triangular pyramid, all faces equilateral   *Six*

## SYMMETRY IN NATURE

Many plants and animals have plane symmetry (called bilateral symmetry in biology). The leaf has bilateral symmetry because it can be separated into two identical parts by a plane. The reflection of one half of the leaf over the plane is the other half. Which of the plants and animals below have bilateral symmetry?
Butterfly, Silkworm cocoon, Cat

Dr. E. R. Degginger

GEOMETRY AROUND YOU

Camerique
Cactus

Leonard Lee Rue III Van Cleve Photography
Butterfly

Grant Heilman
Silkworm cocoon

Field Museum of Natural History
Lobster

Dr. E. R. Degginger
Cat

# ■ Chapter 14 Review ■

**14.1**

**Assignment Guide**
*Oral:* 1–10
*Written:* 11–41 odd

**1–4.** Give the number of each for the given polyhedron.

1. vertices  Four  **2.** edges  Six

3. faces  Four  **4.** dihedral angles  Six

5. Is the polyhedron for Ex. 1–4 convex?  Yes

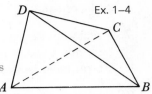

Ex. 1–4

**14.2**

**6–10.** True or False? Use the given figure.

6. Plane *ABC* ∥ plane *DEF*.  T

7. $\overline{AD} \parallel \overline{BE} \parallel \overline{CF}$  T  **8.** △*ABC* ≅ △*DEF*  T

9. The prism is right rectangular.  F

10. $\overline{AC}$ and $\overline{DF}$ are altitudes of the prism.  F

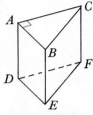

RIGHT PRISM

11. If a box is 10 × 12 × 8 cm, what is its volume?  960 cm³

**14.3**

12. If *AB* = 5, *AC* = 6, and *AD* = 10, find the volume of the prism shown above.  150

13. Find the volume of a right hexagonal prism with a base area of 1.85 m² and a height of 0.23 m.  0.4255 m³

**14.4**

**14–18.** Refer to the given cylinder.

14. Circles *X* and *Y* bound the __Bases__ of the cylinder and are in __Parallel__ planes.

15. $\overline{XY}$ is the __Axis__ of the cylinder.

16. *YZ* is the __Radius__ of the cylinder.

17. *XY* is the __Height__ of the cylinder.

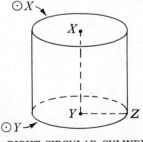

RIGHT CIRCULAR CYLINDER

18. If *XY* = 10 m and *YZ* = 4 m, find the volume in terms of π.  160π m³

**14.5**

**19–23.** True or False?

19. The bases of an oblique prism are bounded by congruent polygons.  T

20. A lateral edge of an oblique prism can also be an altitude.  F

21. The height of an oblique circular cylinder is the length of the axis.  F

**22.** All segments of the lateral surface of an oblique circular cylinder are parallel to the axis.  T

**23.** The area of a cross section of a cylinder (made by a plane parallel to a base) is equal to the area of the base.  T

**24–25.** Find the volume of each solid. (Use $\pi = 3.14$.)

**24.** an oblique prism with a square base 6 cm on a side and a height of 5 cm

180 cm$^3$

**25.** an oblique circular cylinder with height 25 mm and radius 10 mm

7850 mm$^3$

**26–29.** Name each part for the given pyramid.

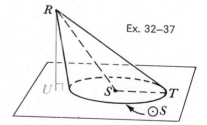

Ex. 26–29

**14.6**

**26.** vertex  $A$    **27.** lateral edges  $\overline{AB}, \overline{AC}, \overline{AD}, \overline{AE}, \overline{AF}$

**28.** base    **29.** altitude  $\overline{AX}$

  $BCDEF$

**30.** What kinds of polygons bound (**a**) the base and (**b**) the lateral faces of a regular pyramid?

**a.** Regular polygon; **b.** $\cong$ isosceles $\triangle$s

**31.** Find the volume of a pyramid whose height is 12 cm and whose base area is 200 cm².

800 cm$^3$

**32–37.** Refer to the given circular cone.

Ex. 32–37

**32.** $\overline{RS}$ is the ___Axis___.    **33.** $R$ is the ___Vertex___.

**34.** $ST$ is the ___Radius___.    **35.** $RU$ is the ___Height___.

**36.** If $\overline{RS}$ and the plane of the base are ___⊥___, then the cone is a right circular cone.

**37.** Find the volume in terms of $\pi$ if $RU = 12$ cm and $ST = 8$ cm.

256$\pi$ cm$^3$

**38–40.** Find the lateral area and surface area of each solid.

**14.7**

**38.** regular square pyramid with base edges of length 2 and slant height of 19   76; 80

**39.** right circular cylinder of height 16 and radius 4

128$\pi$; 160$\pi$

NOTE: Leave answers
39–41 in terms of $\pi$.

**40.** right circular cone of slant height 10 and radius 6

60$\pi$; 96$\pi$

**41.** Find the volume and surface area of a sphere with radius 3 cm.

**14.8**

36$\pi$ cm$^3$; 36$\pi$ cm$^2$

**42.** The symmetry planes of a right circular cone contain its (<u>axis</u>, base, lateral surface).

**14.9**

**Assignment Guide**
*Written:* Min. 1–18
Reg. 1–18
Max. 1–19

1. Each face of a polyhedron is bounded by a _____. Polygon

2. A solid whose lateral faces are bounded by rectangles is a _____. Right prism

3. A circular cylinder whose axis is perpendicular to the planes of both bases is a _____. Right circular cylinder

4. A solid with one base whose lateral faces are bounded by congruent isosceles triangles is a _____. Regular pyramid

5. A solid that has one vertex and a circular base is a _____. Cone

6. The measure of the amount of space enclosed by a solid is its _____. Volume

7. The measure of the total surface of a solid is its _____. Surface area

**8–13.** Find the surface area and volume of each solid.

NOTE: Leave answers 10–13 in terms of $\pi$.

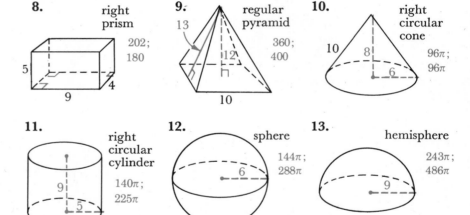

8. right prism — 202; 180 (9, 5, 4)

9. regular pyramid — 360; 400 (13, 12, 10)

10. right circular cone — $96\pi$; $96\pi$ (10, 8, 6)

11. right circular cylinder — $140\pi$; $225\pi$ (9, 5)

12. sphere — $144\pi$; $288\pi$ (6)

13. hemisphere — $243\pi$; $486\pi$ (9)

14. Find the lateral area, surface area, and volume of a cube whose edge is 5 cm long.     100 cm²; 150 cm²; 125 cm³

15. Find the surface area of a right circular cylinder whose volume is $128\pi$ cubic units and whose radius is 4 units. (Leave in terms of $\pi$.)
$96\pi$ square units

16. What is the radius of a sphere whose surface area is $324\pi$ cm²?
9 cm

17. What is the slant height of a regular square pyramid whose surface area is 182 cm² and whose base edge is 7 cm long?     9.5 cm

18. Find the height of a circular cone with volume $256\pi$ and radius 8.
12

19. A right circular cylinder has (no, exactly one, many) symmetry planes.

*Answer for page 513*

3. For a regular $n$-gon with $n \geq 6$, each $\angle$ has measure $\geq 120$. So the sum of 3 such $\angle$s is $\geq 360$. But the sum of $\angle$ measures at the vertex of a regular solid is $< 360$.

# MINI-CHAPTER: PLATONIC SOLIDS

A **regular polyhedron** is a convex polyhedron whose faces are bounded by congruent convex polygons and whose dihedral angles are congruent. Regular polyhedrons are sometimes referred to as "Platonic solids" after the Greek philosopher Plato. There are only five such solids, and Plato felt they represented fire, earth, air, water, and the universe.

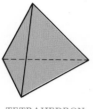
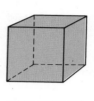
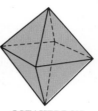
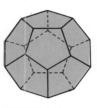
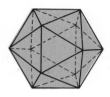

| TETRAHEDRON (fire) | HEXAHEDRON (earth) | OCTAHEDRON (air) | DODECAHEDRON (universe) | ICOSAHEDRON (water) |

Each solid is named by the number of its faces. The prefix *tetra-* means four, so a tetrahedron has four faces. Which solids have 6, 8, 12, and 20 faces?

Notice that the same number of faces intersect at each vertex of any one solid. Three is the least number of faces at one vertex that will form a convex 3-dimensional corner, as in a tetrahedron. Six equilateral triangles with the same vertex are in the same plane and cannot be "folded" to form a convex 3-dimensional corner. So, *the sum of the measures of the angles of the faces at one vertex of a regular solid must be less than 360.*

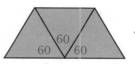

Can be folded to form 3 faces of a tetrahedron. Sum of angle measures is less than 360.

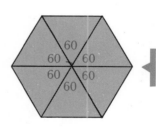

Cannot be folded. Sum of angle measures is 360.

Use the method above to show why

1. The tetrahedron, octahedron, and icosahedron are the only regular polyhedrons with faces bounded by triangles. (How many faces are at each vertex of each solid?)

2. The hexahedron is the only regular polyhedron with faces bounded by squares, and the dodecahedron is the only regular polyhedron with faces bounded by pentagons. (How many faces are at each vertex of each solid?)

3. No regular polyhedron could have faces bounded by regular polygons with more than five sides.
*Answer on page 512*

|  | *m* for ea. face ∠ | faces at ea. vertex | sum of *m* at ea. vertex |
|---|---|---|---|
| **1.** Tetrahedron | 60 | 3 | 180 |
| Octahedron | 60 | 4 | 240 |
| Icosahedron | 60 | 5 | 300 |
| *Not possible* | 60 | 6 | 360 |
| **2.** Hexahedron | 90 | 3 | 270 |
| *Not possible* | 90 | 4 | 360 |
| Dodecahedron | 108 | 3 | 324 |
| *Not possible* | 108 | 4 | 432 |

Copy and complete the chart below. Use the formulas below and your answers from Exercises 1–3 on page 513.

$$\frac{\text{no. of vertices}}{\text{of a solid}} = \frac{(\text{no. of vertices of each face}) \cdot (\text{no. of faces})}{(\text{no. of faces at each vertex})}$$

$$\frac{\text{no. of edges}}{\text{of a solid}} = \frac{(\text{no. of sides of each face}) \cdot (\text{no. of faces})}{2}$$

NOTE: 2 is the number of faces that meet at each edge of the solid.

| Regular solid | No. of faces | Type of faces | No. faces at each vertex | Total no. vertices | Total no. edges |
|---|---|---|---|---|---|
| Tetrahedron | 4 | triangular regions | 3 | $\frac{3 \cdot 4}{3} = 4$ | $\frac{3 \cdot 4}{2} = 6$ |
| Hexahedron | 6 | square regions | 3 | $\frac{4 \cdot 6}{3} = 8$ | $\frac{4 \cdot 6}{2} = 12$ |
| Octahedron | 8 | triangular regions | 4 | $\frac{3 \cdot 8}{4} = 6$ | $\frac{3 \cdot 8}{2} = 12$ |
| Dodecahedron | 12 | pentagonal regions | 3 | $\frac{5 \cdot 12}{3} = 20$ | $\frac{5 \cdot 12}{2} = 30$ |
| Icosahedron | 20 | triangular regions | 5 | $\frac{3 \cdot 20}{5} = 12$ | $\frac{3 \cdot 20}{2} = 30$ |

Enlarge the patterns below and make models of the Platonic solids. (Cut along the solid lines and fold along the dashed lines.)

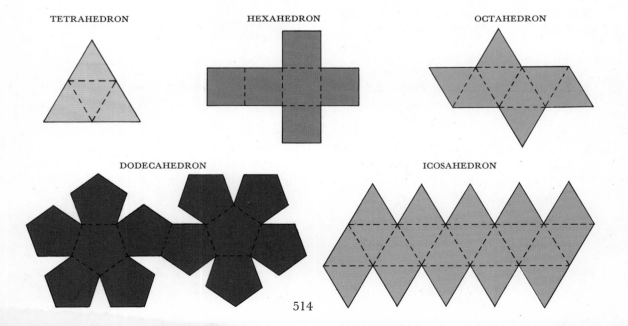

TETRAHEDRON

HEXAHEDRON

OCTAHEDRON

DODECAHEDRON

ICOSAHEDRON

# COORDINATE GEOMETRY

As the photos here suggest, graphs have many uses. In this chapter, graphs will be used to study geometry.

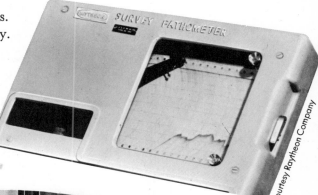

Oceanology

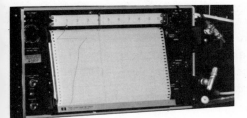

Pollution control

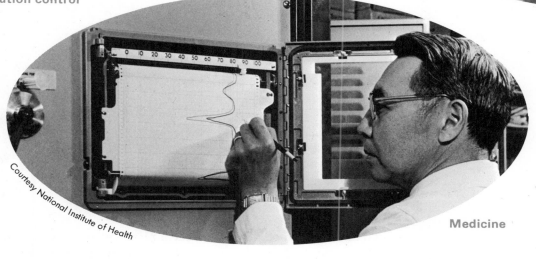

Medicine

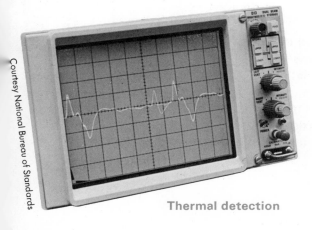

Thermal detection

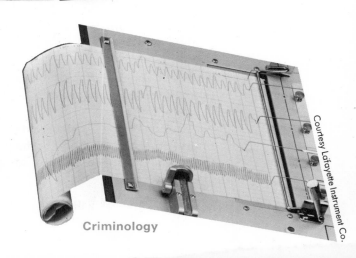

Criminology

# 15.1 The Coordinate Plane

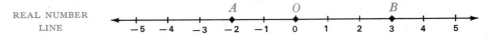

Suggested Class Time

| Course | Min. | Reg. | Max. |
|--------|------|------|------|
| Days | 1 | 1 | 1 |

On a real number line, every point is matched with exactly one real number, and every real number is matched with exactly one point.

REAL NUMBER LINE

Point $A$ has coordinate $-2$.

3 is the coordinate of point $B$.

Point $O$ is the zero point of the line.

There is a similar system for points in a plane. Let line $x$ be a real number line. There is a line $y$ perpendicular to line $x$ at its zero point. By the Ruler Postulate, the points of line $y$ can be matched with the real numbers so that its point of intersection with line $x$ has coordinate 0.

COORDINATE PLANE

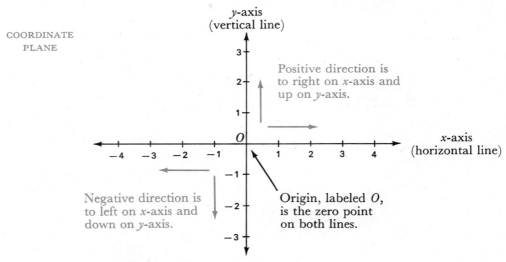

The **axes** (plural of *axis*) determine a plane called the **coordinate plane.** A point on a number line has one coordinate, and a point in the coordinate plane has a pair of coordinates.

FIRST COORDINATE: the coordinate of the foot of the perpendicular from $R$ to the $x$-axis (also called the $x$-*coordinate* or *abscissa*)

SECOND COORDINATE: the coordinate of the foot of the perpendicular from $R$ to the $y$-axis (also called the $y$-*coordinate* or *ordinate*)

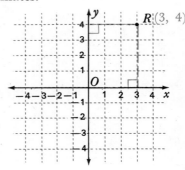

The coordinates of $R$ are the **ordered pair** (3, 4). The coordinates of a point are an *ordered* pair because the *x-coordinate* is always named *first*. We can write $R(3, 4)$ to show that point $R$ is at (3, 4). And we say that $R$ is the *graph* of the ordered pair (3, 4).

**Example:** Name the coordinates of each point shown on the graph.

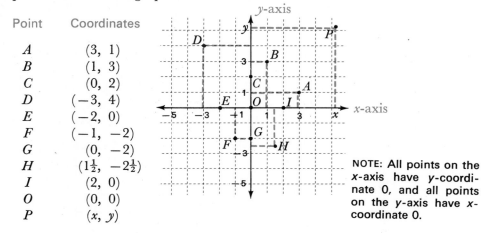

| Point | Coordinates |
|-------|-------------|
| $A$ | (3, 1) |
| $B$ | (1, 3) |
| $C$ | (0, 2) |
| $D$ | (−3, 4) |
| $E$ | (−2, 0) |
| $F$ | (−1, −2) |
| $G$ | (0, −2) |
| $H$ | ($1\frac{1}{2}$, −$2\frac{1}{2}$) |
| $I$ | (2, 0) |
| $O$ | (0, 0) |
| $P$ | ($x$, $y$) |

NOTE: All points on the x-axis have y-coordinate 0, and all points on the y-axis have x-coordinate 0.

In general, for every point $P$ in the coordinate plane, there is exactly one ordered pair $(x, y)$ of real numbers where $x$ is the $x$-coordinate and $y$ is the $y$-coordinate of $P$. Conversely, for every ordered pair $(x, y)$ of real numbers, there is exactly one point $P$ in the coordinate plane whose $x$-coordinate is $x$ and whose $y$-coordinate is $y$.

Any line perpendicular to the $y$-axis is parallel to the $x$-axis (why?) and is a horizontal line. Lines perpendicular to the $x$-axis are vertical lines. An easy way to locate points on a graph is to imagine "traveling" on horizontal and vertical lines. For $(-3, 2)$ and $(2, -3)$, start at the origin $(0, 0)$. Then

Go 3 negative units along $x$-axis ($x = -3$) and 2 positive units parallel to $y$-axis ($y = 2$).

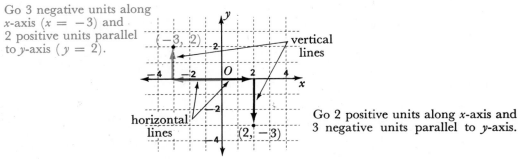

Go 2 positive units along $x$-axis and 3 negative units parallel to $y$-axis.

NOTE: $(-3, 2)$ and $(2, -3)$ are **not** the same point.

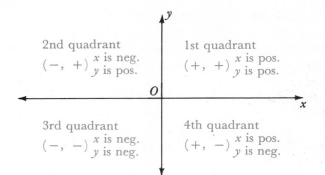

2nd quadrant
$(-, +)$ $x$ is neg.
$y$ is pos.

1st quadrant
$(+, +)$ $x$ is pos.
$y$ is pos.

3rd quadrant
$(-, -)$ $x$ is neg.
$y$ is neg.

4th quadrant
$(+, -)$ $x$ is pos.
$y$ is neg.

The axes separate the plane into four parts called *quadrants*, which are numbered as shown. Points on the axes are not in any of the quadrants. Notice the signs of the coordinates of points in each quadrant.

## Exercises 15.1

**Assignment Guide**
*Oral:* 1–24
*Written:* Min. 25–43 odd
Reg. 25–45 odd
Max. 25–49 odd

Ⓐ **1–8.** Use the figure below to complete each statement.

**1.** The line labeled $x$ is called the _x-axis_ .

**2.** The line labeled $y$ is called the _y-axis_ .

**3.** The axes determine the _____ plane.            Coordinate

**4.** The coordinates of a point are given as a(n) _Ordered_ pair.

**5.** The first coordinate of a point is called the _____.
    *x*-coordinate (or abscissa)

**6.** The second coordinate of a point is called the _____.
    *y*-coordinate (or ordinate)

**7.** The point $(0, 0)$ is called the _Origin_ .

**8.** The axes separate the coordinate plane into four _Quadrants_ .

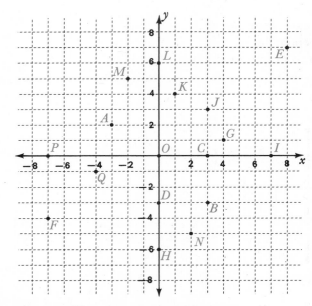

**9–18.** Name the point on the graph whose ordered pair is given.

| | | | |
|---|---|---|---|
| **9.** $(4, 1)$ | $G$ | **10.** $(1, 4)$ | $K$ |
| **11.** $(-2, 5)$ | $M$ | **12.** $(2, -5)$ | $N$ |
| **13.** $(7, 0)$ | $I$ | **14.** $(-7, 0)$ | $P$ |
| **15.** $(0, 6)$ | $L$ | **16.** $(0, -6)$ | $H$ |
| **17.** $(3, 3)$ | $J$ | **18.** $(-4, -1)$ | $Q$ |

**19–24.** Name the coordinates of each point.

**19.** $A$ $(-3, 2)$ **20.** $B$ $(3, -3)$ **21.** $C$ $(3, 0)$

**22.** $D$ $(0, -3)$ **23.** $E$ $(8, 7)$ **24.** $O$ $(0, 0)$

**25–34.** Graph. Use a separate pair of axes for each exercise.

**25.** (1, 0), (3, 0), (5, 0),
(0, 0), (−2, 0), (−4, 0)

**26.** (0, −3), (0, −1), (0, 0),
(0, 2), (0, 4), (0, 6)

**27.** (2, 1), (2, 3), (2, 4),
(2, 0), (2, −1), (2, −2)

**28.** (−3, −5), (−2, −5), (−1, −5),
(0, −5), (1, −5), (2, −5)

**29.** (−3, 2), (−1, 2), (1, 2),
(1, 6), (−1, 6), (−3, 6)

**30.** (−2, 2), (−5, 2), (−5, −2),
(−5, −4), (−2, −4), (−2, −1)

**31.** $(-2\frac{1}{2}, 6)$, $(-2\frac{1}{2}, 4)$, $(-2\frac{1}{2}, 2)$,
$(-2\frac{1}{2}, 0)$, $(-2\frac{1}{2}, -2\frac{1}{2})$, $(2\frac{1}{2}, 0)$

**32.** (−8, 6), (−5, 6), (−2, 6)
(0, 3), (−3, 3), (−6, 3)

**33.** (−2, 2), (0, 0), (2, −2),
(2, −5), (0, −3), (−5, 2)

**34.** (0, −4), (4, 0), (8, 0),
(12, −4), (8, −8), (4, −8)

**35–38.** Use your graphs for Exercises 25–34 to answer each exercise.

**35.** If the $y$-coordinate of a point is ____0____, then it is on the $x$-axis.

**36.** If the $x$-coordinate of a point is ____0____, then it is on the $y$-axis.

**37.** Points with the same __$x$__-coordinate are on the same vertical line.

**38.** Points with the same __$y$__-coordinate are on the same horizontal line.

**39–44.** Join, in the order given, the points on your graphs for Exercises
29–34. Join the last point to the first. What kind of figure is each?

**45.** If (1, 7) and (1, 3) are two vertices of a square that is in the 1st
quadrant, name its other two vertices.                          (5, 3), (5, 7)

**39.** Square
**40.** Rectangle
**41.** Triangle
**42.** Parallelogram
**43.** Trapezoid
**44.** Hexagon

**46.** If (−4, −6), (−7, −1), and (−2, −4) are the vertices of a triangle, which quadrant is the triangle in?                          3rd

Ⓒ **47–49.** Graph $A(-3, 3)$, $B(-3, -3)$, $C(3, -3)$, and $D(3, 3)$.

**47.** What is the perimeter of $ABCD$?     **48.** What is the length of $\overline{AC}$?
                                    24                                      $6\sqrt{2}$

**49.** Name (**a**) four points that appear to be on $\overline{AC}$, (**b**) four points that
appear to be on $\overline{BD}$, and (**c**) one point that appears to be on both
$\overline{AC}$ and $\overline{BD}$.       a. Any 4 pts. where coordinates are opposites between −3 and 3
                    b. Any 4 pts. where coordinates are equal and between −3 and 3
                    c. (0, 0)

# 15.2 Distance Formula

On a number line, the distance between two points is the absolute value of the difference of their coordinates.

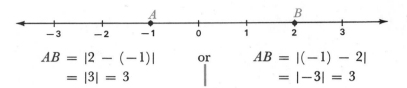

$$AB = |2 - (-1)| \qquad \text{or} \qquad AB = |(-1) - 2|$$
$$= |3| = 3 \qquad\qquad\qquad = |-3| = 3$$

In the coordinate plane, all points on a horizontal line have the same $y$-coordinate. So we can use the method for distance on a number line to find $AB$ for $A(-3, 2)$ and $B(4, 2)$ below.

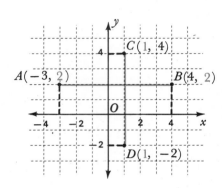

$$AB = |\text{difference of } x\text{-coordinates}|$$
$$= |4 - (-3)|$$
$$= |7| = 7$$

Similarly, all points on a vertical line have the same $x$-coordinate. For $C(1, 4)$ and $D(1, -2)$,

$$CD = |\text{difference of } y\text{-coordinates}|$$
$$= |-2 - 4|$$
$$= |-6| = 6$$

We can use the method above and the Pythagorean Theorem to find the distance between points not on horizontal or vertical lines.

Below, point $P$ is at $(-2, 1)$ and point $Q$ is at $(2, 4)$. The horizontal line through $P$ and the vertical line through $Q$ intersect at point $R$. Since $R$ is on the same vertical line as $Q$, its $x$-coordinate is 2. $R$ is on the same horizontal line as $P$, so its $y$-coordinate is 1. $\triangle PQR$ is a right triangle. Why?

By the method above, $\qquad PR = |2 - (-2)| = 4$
$$QR = |4 - 1| = 3$$

By the Pythagorean Theorem and substitution,

$$(PQ)^2 = (PR)^2 + (QR)^2$$
$$(PQ)^2 = 4^2 + 3^2$$
$$(PQ)^2 = 25$$

And, $\quad \sqrt{(PQ)^2} = \sqrt{25}$
$$PQ = 5$$

A formula for the distance between points in the coordinate plane can be found by letting $P$ and $Q$ be any points at $(x_1, y_1)$ and $(x_2, y_2)$. The *subscripts* $_1$ and $_2$ indicate that $x_1$ and $x_2$ (or $y_1$ and $y_2$) can have different values.

The horizontal and vertical lines through $P$ and $Q$ intersect at point $R(x_2, y_1)$. Why? So,

$$(PQ)^2 = (PR)^2 + (QR)^2$$
$$= |x_2 - x_1|^2 + |y_2 - y_1|^2$$

Since for any number $n$, $|n|^2 = n^2$, even when $n < 0$ (why?), we can write

$$(PQ)^2 = (x_2 - x_1)^2 + (y_2 - y_1)^2$$

By taking the square root of both sides of the equation, we get

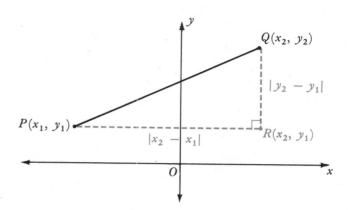

> If $P$ is a point at $(x_1, y_1)$ and $Q$ is another point at $(x_2, y_2)$, then the distance from $P$ to $Q$ is
> $$PQ = \sqrt{(x_2 - x_1)^2 + (y_2 - y_1)^2}$$

**Distance Formula Theorem**

NOTE: Distance is always a positive number. Why?

**Example:** Use the distance formula to find $PQ$ for $P(6, 3)$ and $Q(-3, 0)$.

Let $(x_1, y_1) = (6, 3)$ and $(x_2, y_2) = (-3, 0)$. Then $x_1 = 6, y_1 = 3$, $x_2 = -3$, and $y_2 = 0$.

$$PQ = \sqrt{(x_2 - x_1)^2 + (y_2 - y_1)^2}$$
$$= \sqrt{(-3 - 6)^2 + (0 - 3)^2}$$
$$= \sqrt{(-9)^2 + (-3)^2} \qquad \text{— Simplify radical.}$$
$$= \sqrt{81 + 9} = \sqrt{90} = 3\sqrt{10}$$

## Exercises 15.2

(A) **1.** $\sqrt{(x_2 - x_1)^2 + (y_2 - y_1)^2}$ is the _____ Distance from $P(x_1, x_2)$ to $Q(y_1, y_2)$.

**2.** If $P$ is at $(3, 0)$, $Q$ is at $(2, 5)$, and $x_1 = 3$, then $y_1 = \underline{0}$, $x_2 = \underline{2}$, and $y_2 = \underline{5}$.

**3.** If $P$ is at $(1, 0)$ and $Q$ is at $(4, 0)$, then $PQ = \underline{3}$.

**4.** If $P$ is at $(0, -6)$ and $Q$ is at $(0, -2)$, then $PQ = \underline{4}$.

**5.** If $P$ is at $(3, 2)$ and $Q$ is at $(-1, 2)$, then $PQ = \underline{4}$.

**Assignment Guide**
*Oral:* 1–6
*Written:* Min. 7–16
Reg. 7–25 odd
Max. 7–29 odd

**6.** Can the distance between points $P$ and $Q$ be a negative number?
No

Ⓑ **7.** A vertical line through $A(2, 6)$ and a horizontal line through $B(7, -3)$ intersect at point $C$. Find the coordinates of $C$.    $(2, -3)$

**8.** A horizontal line through $A(2, 6)$ and a vertical line through $B(7, -3)$ intersect at point $C$. Find the coordinates of $C$.    $(7, 6)$

**9–20.** Find the distance between the given points. Simplify radicals.

| | |
|---|---|
| **9.** $(0, 0)$, $(5, 12)$    13 | **10.** $(-2, -4)$, $(0, 0)$    $2\sqrt{5}$ |
| **11.** $(1, 5)$, $(1, -8)$    13 | **12.** $(-2, -1)$, $(7, -1)$    9 |
| **13.** $(3, 4)$, $(7, 2)$    $2\sqrt{5}$ | **14.** $(-3, -6)$, $(-4, -1)$    $\sqrt{26}$ |
| **15.** $(-10, 5)$, $(6, -1)$   $2\sqrt{73}$ | **16.** $(12, -8)$, $(-2, 2)$    $2\sqrt{74}$ |
| **17.** $(11, 8)$, $(35, 15)$    25 | **18.** $(101, -106)$, $(1, -6)$   $100\sqrt{2}$ |
| **19.** $(5, 5)$, $(-5, -5)$   $10\sqrt{2}$ | **20.** $(-8, 8)$, $(8, -8)$    $16\sqrt{2}$ |

**21–28.** Use the distance formula and a graph to answer each exercise.

**21.** Is $\triangle ABC$ isosceles if $A$ is at $(-3, 1)$, $B$ is at $(5, 1)$, and $C$ is at $(1, 5)$?   Yes. $AC = BC = 4\sqrt{2}$

**22.** Is $\triangle PQR$ equilateral if $P$ is at $(3, -4)$, $Q$ is at $(5, -2)$, and $R$ is at $(6, -5)$?    No

**23.** Find the lengths of the diagonals of a quadrilateral with vertices $A(1, -2)$, $B(5, -2)$, $C(6, 1)$, and $D(2, 1)$.   $AC = \sqrt{34}$, $BD = 3\sqrt{2}$

**25.** $AB = \sqrt{13}$, $AC = \sqrt{13}$, and $BC = \sqrt{26}$; $(\sqrt{13})^2 + (\sqrt{13})^2 = (\sqrt{26})^2$

**24.** Are the diagonals of quadrilateral $JKLM$ with vertices $J(3, 1)$, $K(7, -2)$, $L(1, -3)$, and $M(-1, -1)$ equal in length?    No

**25.** Using the Pythagorean Theorem, show that a triangle with vertices $A(-3, 3)$, $B(-5, 6)$, and $C(0, 5)$ is a right triangle.

**26.** $DE = \sqrt{10}$, $DF = 2\sqrt{2}$, $EF = \sqrt{10}$; $(\sqrt{10})^2 + (\sqrt{10})^2 \neq (2\sqrt{2})^2$, $(\sqrt{10})^2 + (2\sqrt{2})^2 \neq (\sqrt{10})^2$

**26.** Using the Pythagorean Theorem, show that a triangle with vertices $D(3, 0)$, $E(4, -3)$, and $F(1, -2)$ is not a right triangle.

Ⓒ **27.** A segment has endpoints $P(3, 4)$ and $Q(6, y)$. Find two possible values for $y$ if $PQ = 5$.    $y = 0$ or $y = 8$

**28.** Can a triangle with vertices $A(0, -2)$, $B(-2, 2)$, and $C(2, 0)$ be inscribed in a circle of radius 2 and center at the origin?    No, $B$ is not on the circle.

**29.** Name the coordinates of four points, each on an axis, that are on a circle of radius 5 and center at the origin.    $(5, 0)$, $(-5, 0)$, $(0, 5)$, $(0, -5)$

# Midpoint Formula

15.3

In the graph below $P(-2, 2)$ and $Q(4, 2)$ are the endpoints of a horizontal segment. $M$ is the midpoint of $\overline{PQ}$, and its $y$-coordinate is 2. Why? Let $x$ be its $x$-coordinate. Since $\overline{PM}$ and $\overline{MQ}$ are horizontal,

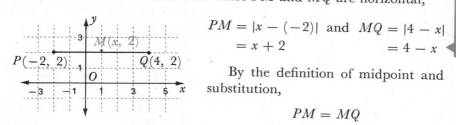

$$PM = |x - (-2)| \quad \text{and} \quad MQ = |4 - x|$$
$$= x + 2 \qquad\qquad\qquad = 4 - x$$

Since $-2 < x < 4$, $x + 2 > 0$ and $4 - x > 0$. So we can eliminate the absolute value signs.

By the definition of midpoint and substitution,

$$PM = MQ$$
$$x + 2 = 4 - x$$
$$2x = 2$$
$$x = 1$$

So, $M$ is at $(1, 2)$.

Let $P$ be at $(x_1, 2)$ and $Q$ at $(x_2, 2)$ with $x_1 < x_2$. Then midpoint $M$ is at $(x, 2)$ and $x_1 < x < x_2$.

$$PM = |x - x_1| \quad \text{and} \quad MQ = |x_2 - x|$$
$$= x - x_1 \qquad\qquad\qquad = x_2 - x$$

$$PM = MQ$$
$$x - x_1 = x_2 - x$$
$$2x = x_1 + x_2$$
$$x = \frac{x_1 + x_2}{2}$$

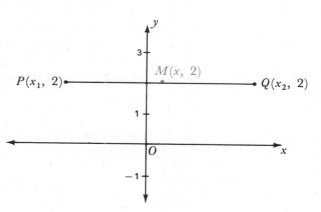

And $M$ is at $\left(\dfrac{x_1 + x_2}{2}, 2\right)$. Notice that the $x$-coordinate of $M$ is the average of the $x$-coordinates of the endpoints. For $P(-2, 2)$ and $Q(4, 2)$ above, the $x$-coordinate of $M$ is 1, which is the average of $-2$ and 4.

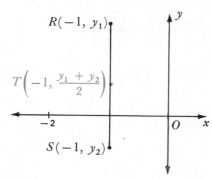

Using that same type of reasoning, we find that the $y$-coordinate of the midpoint of a vertical segment is the average of the $y$-coordinates of the endpoints. For $R(-1, y_1)$ and $S(-1, y_2)$, midpoint $T$ of $\overline{RS}$ is

$$T\left(-1, \frac{y_1 + y_2}{2}\right)$$

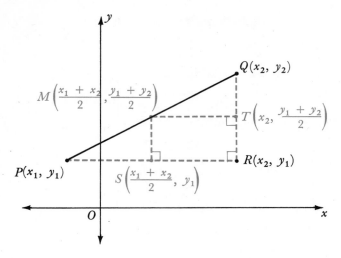

Now we can find the coordinates of the midpoint of $\overline{PQ}$ at left, which is not horizontal or vertical. The horizontal and vertical lines through $P(x_1, y_1)$ and $Q(x_2, y_2)$ give us $R(x_2, y_1)$. Why? $\overline{PR}$ is a horizontal segment, so its midpoint $S$ is at

$$S\left(\frac{x_1 + x_2}{2}, y_1\right)$$

$\overline{QR}$ is a vertical segment, so its midpoint $T$ is at

$$T\left(x_2, \frac{y_1 + y_2}{2}\right)$$

The horizontal segment through $T$ and the vertical segment through $S$ both intersect $\overline{PQ}$ at its midpoint $M$. (If a line parallel to one side of a triangle bisects either of the other two sides, it bisects both of them.) The $x$-coordinate of $M$ is the same as the $x$-coordinate of $S$, and the $y$-coordinate of $M$ is the same as the $y$-coordinate of $T$. Why?

**Midpoint Formula Theorem**

> If point $P$ is at $(x_1,\ y_1)$ and point $Q$ is at $(x_2,\ y_2)$, then the midpoint $M$ of $\overline{PQ}$ is
>
> $$M\left(\frac{x_1 + x_2}{2}, \frac{y_1 + y_2}{2}\right)$$

**Example 1:** Find the coordinates of the midpoint of a segment whose endpoints are at $(-2,\ 6)$ and $(3,\ -2)$.

Midpoint formula: $\left(\dfrac{x_1 + x_2}{2}, \dfrac{y_1 + y_2}{2}\right)$

$$\frac{x_1 + x_2}{2} = \frac{-2 + 3}{2} \qquad \text{and} \qquad \frac{y_1 + y_2}{2} = \frac{6 + (-2)}{2}$$

$$= \tfrac{1}{2} \qquad\qquad\qquad\qquad = 2$$

The midpoint is at $(\tfrac{1}{2},\ 2)$.

**Example 2:** $M(-1, -3)$ is the midpoint of $\overline{PQ}$. If $P$ is at $(-3, 2)$, find the coordinates of $Q$.

1. Let $Q$ have coordinates $(x, y)$. By the midpoint formula, the midpoint of $\overline{PQ}$ is

$$\left(\frac{x-3}{2}, \frac{y+2}{2}\right)$$

2. We are given that $M(-1, -3)$ is the midpoint of $\overline{PQ}$. So

$$\frac{x-3}{2} = -1 \quad \text{and} \quad \frac{y+2}{2} = -3$$

$$x - 3 = -2 \qquad\qquad y + 2 = -6$$

$$x = 1 \qquad\qquad\quad y = -8$$

So $Q$ is at $(1, -8)$.

## Exercises 15.3

Ⓐ **1–12.** What are the coordinates of the midpoint of the segment joining each pair of points?

**1.** $(0, 0)$, $(4, 0)$
$(2, 0)$

**2.** $(0, 0)$, $(-4, 0)$
$(-2, 0)$

**3.** $(0, 0)$, $(0, 6)$
$(0, 3)$

**4.** $(0, 0)$, $(0, -6)$
$(0, -3)$

**5.** $(1, 0)$, $(7, 0)$
$(4, 0)$

**6.** $(0, -1)$, $(0, -5)$
$(0, -3)$

**7.** $(4, 0)$, $(-4, 0)$
$(0, 0)$

**8.** $(0, -3)$, $(0, 3)$
$(0, 0)$

**9.** $(1, 0)$, $(-3, 0)$
$(-1, 0)$

**10.** $(0, 1)$, $(0, -9)$
$(0, -4)$

**11.** $(1, 6)$, $(1, 10)$
$(1, 8)$

**12.** $(3, 1)$, $(7, 1)$
$(5, 1)$

**13.** For $P(x_1, y_1)$ and $Q(x_2, y_2)$, $M\left(\dfrac{x_1 + x_2}{2}, \dfrac{y_1 + y_2}{2}\right)$ is the ____ Midpoint ____ of $\overline{PQ}$.

**14.** If $M$ is the midpoint of $\overline{PQ}$, then $PM$ ____ $\overset{=}{\phantom{x}}$ ____ $MQ$ ____ $\overset{=}{\phantom{x}}$ ____ $\frac{1}{2}PQ$.

Ⓑ **15–26.** Using the midpoint formula, find the coordinates of the midpoint of the segment joining each pair of points.

**15.** $(0, 8)$, $(4, 2)$
$(2, 5)$

**16.** $(3, 10)$, $(1, 0)$ $(2, 5)$

**17.** $(-5, 7)$, $(-7, 5)$
$(-6, 6)$

**18.** $(13, -9)$, $(9, -13)$
$(11, -11)$

**19.** $(7, 3)$, $(8, 4)$ $(7\frac{1}{2}, 3\frac{1}{2})$

**20.** $(-6, -5)$, $(9, -5)$
$(1\frac{1}{2}, -5)$

**21.** $(\frac{2}{3}, \frac{1}{2})$, $(0, 1)$ $(\frac{1}{3}, \frac{3}{4})$

**22.** $(-\frac{5}{8}, \frac{3}{4})$, $(-\frac{3}{8}, \frac{1}{2})$
$(-\frac{1}{2}, \frac{5}{8})$

**23.** $(\sqrt{2}, \sqrt{3})$, $(\sqrt{2}, 3\sqrt{3})$ $(\sqrt{2}, 2\sqrt{3})$

**24.** $(\sqrt{5}, 3\sqrt{7})$, $(\sqrt{5}, \sqrt{7})$
$(\sqrt{5}, 2\sqrt{7})$

**25.** $(a, 0)$, $(b, 0)$
$\left(\dfrac{a+b}{2}, 0\right)$

**26.** $(a, b)$, $(c, d)$ $\left(\dfrac{a+c}{2}, \dfrac{b+d}{2}\right)$

**Assignment Guide**
*Oral:* 1–14
*Written:*
Min. 15–27 odd; 33–37 odd
Reg. 15–37 odd
Max. 15–43 odd

**27.** Find the coordinates of the midpoint of each side of a triangle with vertices at $(3, 5)$, $(6, -4)$, and $(-1, 1)$.

$(4\frac{1}{2}, \frac{1}{2}), (2\frac{1}{2}, -1\frac{1}{2}), (1, 3)$

**28.** Find the coordinates of the midpoint of each side of a quadrilateral with vertices at $(-2, -4)$, $(7, -8)$, $(4, -3)$, and $(-5, 2)$.

$(2\frac{1}{2}, -6), (5\frac{1}{2}, -5\frac{1}{2}), (-\frac{1}{2}, -\frac{1}{2}), (-3\frac{1}{2}, -1)$

**29.** Find the length of each median of a triangle with vertices at $(-1, 6)$, $(-3, -2)$, and $(7, -4)$.

$3\sqrt{10}, 3\sqrt{5}, 3\sqrt{13}$

**30.** Find the perimeter of the figure whose vertices are the midpoints of a quadrilateral with vertices at $(7, 4)$, $(1, 8)$, $(-3, 4)$, and $(3, -2)$.

$10 + 2\sqrt{26}$

**31.** A rectangle has vertices $A(-6, 4)$, $B(-6, -1)$, $C(2, -1)$, and $D(2, 4)$. Show that its diagonals have the same midpoint.

$(-2, 1\frac{1}{2})$ is the midpt. of $\overline{AC}$ and $\overline{BD}$.

**32.** A parallelogram has vertices $P(7, 3)$, $Q(12, 7)$, $R(10, -2)$, and $S(5, -6)$. Show that its diagonals have the same midpoint.

$(8\frac{1}{2}, \frac{1}{2})$ is the midpt. of $\overline{PR}$ and $\overline{QS}$.

**33–38.** One endpoint and the midpoint of a segment are given. Use the midpoint formula to find the coordinates of the second endpoint.

**33.** endpt. $(3, 5)$, midpt. $(-2, 1)$
$(-7, -3)$

**34.** endpt. $(5, 7)$, midpt. $(6, 3\frac{1}{2})$
$(7, 0)$

**35.** endpt. $(4, 7)$, midpt. $(6, 3)$
$(8, -1)$

**36.** endpt. $(-1, 4)$, midpt. $(1, 1)$
$(3, -2)$

**37.** endpt. $(a, 0)$, midpt. $(0, a)$
$(-a, 2a)$

**38.** endpt. $(a, b)$, midpt. $(c, d)$
$(2c - a, 2d - b)$

© **39.** Use the distance formula to show that $Q(1, -1)$ is the midpoint of the segment with endpoints $A(4, 1)$ and $B(-2, -3)$.

39. $AQ$
$= \sqrt{(1 - 4)^2 + (-1 - 1)^2}$
$= \sqrt{9 + 4} = \sqrt{13}$
$QB$
$= \sqrt{(-2 - 1)^2 + [-3 - (-1)]^2}$
$= \sqrt{9 + 4} = \sqrt{13}$
$AB$
$= \sqrt{(-2 - 4)^2 + (-3 - 1)^2}$
$= \sqrt{36 + 16} = \sqrt{52}$
$= 2\sqrt{13}$
$AB = AQ + QB$, $AQ = QB$
So $Q$ is midpt. of $\overline{AB}$.

**40.** Points $A$ and $B$ are the endpoints of a segment that contains point $C$. For the given coordinates of $A$ and $B$, find the coordinates $(x, y)$ of $C$ so that $AC = r \cdot CB$.

**a.** $A(x_1, 0)$, $B(x_2, 0)$

**b.** $A(0, y_1)$, $B(0, y_2)$

**c.** $A(x_1, y_1)$, $B(x_2, y_2)$  HINT: Use your results from parts **a** and **b**.

40. **a.** $\left(\dfrac{x_1 + rx_2}{r + 1}, 0\right)$

**b.** $\left(0, \dfrac{y_1 + ry_2}{r + 1}\right)$

**c.** $\left(\dfrac{x_1 + rx_2}{r + 1}, \dfrac{y_1 + ry_2}{r + 1}\right)$

**41–42.** Use the results from Exercise 40 to find the coordinates of point $C$ on $\overline{AB}$ so that $AC = r \cdot CB$.

**41.** $A(-3, -2)$, $B(6, 4)$, $r = \frac{1}{2}$
$(0, 0)$

**42.** $A(2, 5)$, $B(6, -3)$, $r = 3$
$(5, -1)$

**43.** Find the coordinates of the two points that trisect (separate into three congruent parts) the segment with endpoints $(-1, -4)$ and $(5, 8)$.  $(1, 0)$ and $(3, 4)$

H. Armstrong Roberts

# Slope

**15.4**

The "steepness" or "slope" of a stairway is the ratio of "riser" to "tread." The riser is the *vertical change* (or *rise*) of each step, and the tread is the *horizontal change* (or *run*) of each step. For the stairway shown,

$$\text{slope} = \frac{\text{vertical change}}{\text{horizontal change}} = \frac{5}{9}$$

**Suggested Class Time**

| Course | Min. | Reg. | Max. |
|--------|------|------|------|
| Days   | 1    | 1    | 1    |

The slope of a nonvertical line is defined in a similar way. By looking at the graph of points $A$, $B$, and $C$ on line $\ell$ below, we can find the slope of the line.

From point $A$ to point $B$

$$\frac{\text{vertical change}}{\text{horizontal change}} = \frac{2 \text{ units up}}{3 \text{ units right}} = \frac{+2}{+3} = \frac{2}{3}$$

From point $B$ to point $C$

$$\frac{\text{vertical change}}{\text{horizontal change}} = \frac{4 \text{ units up}}{6 \text{ units right}} = \frac{+4}{+6} = \frac{2}{3}$$

From point $C$ to point $A$

$$\frac{\text{vertical change}}{\text{horizontal change}} = \frac{6 \text{ units down}}{9 \text{ units left}} = \frac{-6}{-9} = \frac{2}{3}$$

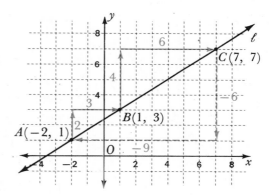

The slope of line $\ell$ is $\frac{2}{3}$. Notice that the slope of $\ell$ is the same no matter which two points are used. Also, segments on the same line have the same slope (slope of $\overline{AB}$ = slope of $\overline{BC}$ = slope of $\overline{CA}$ = $\frac{2}{3}$).

Another way to find the slope is to subtract the coordinates of the points.

From $A$ to $B$:  $\dfrac{\text{vert. change}}{\text{horiz. change}} = \dfrac{\text{difference of } y\text{-coordinates}}{\text{difference of } x\text{-coordinates}} = \dfrac{3-1}{1-(-2)} = \dfrac{2}{3}$

From $C$ to $A$:  $\dfrac{\text{vert. change}}{\text{horiz. change}} = \dfrac{\text{difference of } y\text{-coordinates}}{\text{difference of } x\text{-coordinates}} = \dfrac{1-7}{-2-7} = \dfrac{-6}{-9} = \dfrac{2}{3}$

In general, the **slope of a nonvertical line** is the ratio

$$\frac{\text{difference of } y\text{-coordinates}}{\text{difference of } x\text{-coordinates}}$$ for any two points on the line.

The slope $m$ of a line that contains points at $(x_1,\ y_1)$ and $(x_2,\ y_2)$ when $x_1 \neq x_2$ is $m = \dfrac{y_2 - y_1}{x_2 - x_1}$.

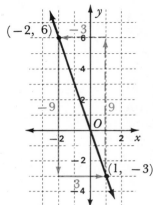

**Example 1:** Find the slope of the line that contains points at $(-2,\ 6)$ and $(1,\ -3)$.

Let $(x_1,\ y_1) = (-2,\ 6)$    or    Let $(x_1,\ y_1) = (1,\ -3)$
and $(x_2,\ y_2) = (1,\ -3)$.          and $(x_2,\ y_2) = (-2, 6)$.

$$m = \frac{y_2 - y_1}{x_2 - x_1} \qquad\qquad m = \frac{y_2 - y_1}{x_2 - x_1}$$

$$= \frac{-3 - 6}{1 - (-2)} \qquad\qquad = \frac{6 - (-3)}{-2 - 1}$$

$$= \frac{-9}{3} = -3 \qquad\qquad = \frac{9}{-3} = -3$$

**Example 2:** Graph the line with slope $\frac{4}{3}$ and point $(-2,\ -3)$.

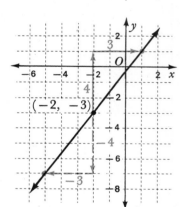

- Graph $(-2,\ -3)$.
- The slope is $\frac{4}{3}$. From $(-2,\ -3)$, go 4 units up and 3 units right to find a second point.
- For a third point, go 4 units down and 3 units left.
- Draw the line.

NOTE: Since two points determine a line, the third point is found as a check. If the three points are not collinear, a mistake has been made.

Not only can the slope of a line be positive or negative, it can be zero. And, some lines have no slope.

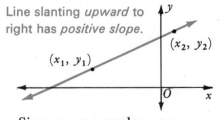

Line slanting *upward* to right has *positive slope*.

Since $x_1 < x_2$ and $y_1 < y_2$,

$$\frac{y_2 - y_1}{x_2 - x_1} = \frac{\text{pos.}}{\text{pos.}} = \text{pos. slope}$$

or $\dfrac{y_1 - y_2}{x_1 - x_2} = \dfrac{\text{neg.}}{\text{neg.}} = \text{pos. slope}$

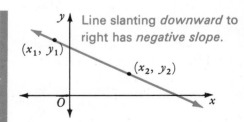

Line slanting *downward* to right has *negative slope*.

Since $x_1 < x_2$ and $y_1 > y_2$,

$$\frac{y_2 - y_1}{x_2 - x_1} = \frac{\text{neg.}}{\text{pos.}} = \text{neg. slope}$$

or $\dfrac{y_1 - y_2}{x_1 - x_2} = \dfrac{\text{pos.}}{\text{neg.}} = \text{neg. slope}$

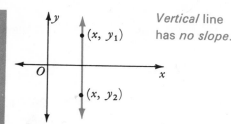

Horizontal line has *zero slope*.

$(x_1, y)$    $(x_2, y)$

Vertical line has *no slope*.

$(x, y_1)$

$(x, y_2)$

Since $y = y$,

$$\frac{y - y}{x_2 - x_1} = \frac{0}{x_2 - x_1} = 0$$

or $\dfrac{y - y}{x_1 - x_2} = \dfrac{0}{x_1 - x_2} = 0$

Since $x = x$,

$$\frac{y_2 - y_1}{x - x} = \frac{y_2 - y_1}{0}, \text{ which is undefined}$$

or $\dfrac{y_1 - y_2}{x - x} = \dfrac{y_1 - y_2}{0}$, which is undefined

## Exercises 15.4

Ⓐ 1. Describe a line whose slope is (**a**) positive, (**b**) negative, (**c**) zero.
   **a.** Slants upward to right; **b.** Slants downward to right; **c.** Horizontal
2. Describe a line that has no   3. The slope of a line is the ratio
   slope.    Vertical    of what two differences?

4. Which equations below show a correct way to find the slope of the line through $(8, 7)$ and $(5, 2)$?

   **a.** $\dfrac{8 - 5}{7 - 2} = \dfrac{3}{5}$   **b.** $\dfrac{7 - 2}{8 - 5} = \dfrac{5}{3}$   **c.** $\dfrac{5 - 8}{2 - 7} = \dfrac{3}{5}$   **d.** $\dfrac{2 - 7}{5 - 8} = \dfrac{5}{3}$

5. Find the slope of the line that contains $(0, 0)$ and the given point.
   **a.** $(4, 7)$ $\frac{7}{4}$  **b.** $(-4, 3)$ $-\frac{3}{4}$  **c.** $(-2, -5)$ $\frac{5}{2}$  **d.** $(3, 0)$ $0$  **e.** $(9, -2)$ $-\frac{2}{9}$

6. If a line with the given slope contains the origin, give the coordinates of any other point on the line.    *Typical answers*
   **a.** $m = \frac{2}{3}$  **b.** $m = -\frac{4}{3}$  **c.** $m = -\frac{1}{5}$    **d.** $m = \frac{7}{2}$  **e.** $m = 0$
   $(3, 2)$      $(-3, 4)$      $(-5, 1)$      $(2, 7)$      $(1, 0)$

Ⓑ **7–22.** Find the slope of a line that contains the given points.

7. $(6, 7), (3, 5)$ $\frac{2}{3}$   8. $(8, 9), (4, 8)$ $\frac{1}{4}$   9. $(3, 1), (15, 4)$ $\frac{1}{4}$

10. $(1, 10), (3, 16)$ $3$  11. $(-5, 2), (-12, 4)$ $-\frac{2}{7}$ 12. $(-3, 5), (2, 3)$ $-\frac{2}{5}$

13. $(-3, -7), (0, -12)$ $-\frac{5}{3}$      14. $(-2, -6); (5, -8)$ $-\frac{2}{7}$

15. $(1.2, 3.5), (2.4, 5.1)$ $\frac{4}{3}$      16. $(6.2, 4.7), (8.2, 5.9)$ $\frac{3}{5}$

17. $(1.5, 2.6), (-0.3, 4.5)$ $-\frac{19}{18}$      18. $(2.7, 1.8), (5.2, -0.6)$ $-\frac{24}{25}$

19. $(12000, 15200), (0, 0)$ $\frac{19}{15}$      20. $(14000, 17300), (0, 0)$ $\frac{173}{140}$

21. $(\frac{1}{2}, \frac{13}{4}); (\frac{9}{4}, \frac{1}{3})$ $-\frac{5}{3}$      22. $(\frac{2}{3}, \frac{11}{4}), (\frac{7}{4}, \frac{3}{2})$ $-\frac{15}{13}$

**Assignment Guide**
*Oral:* 1–6
*Written:* Min. 7–29 odd
       Reg. 7–33 odd
       Max. 7–45 odd

3. Diff. of $y$-coordinates and diff. of $x$-coordinates of 2 points on the line

**23–30.** Graph the line that contains the given point and has the given slope *m.*                     *One more point on each graph is given.*

**23.** $(0, 0)$, $m = \frac{8}{5}$        $(5, 8)$        **24.** $(0, 0)$, $m = \frac{7}{3}$        $(3, 7)$

**25.** $(2, 5)$, $m = -\frac{6}{7}$        $(9, -1)$        **26.** $(3, 4)$, $m = -\frac{5}{6}$        $(9, -1)$

**27.** $(0, 0)$, $m = 1$        $(2, 2)$        **28.** $(0, 0)$, $m = -1$        $(-2, 2)$

**29.** $(-2, 3)$, $m = -\frac{5}{2}$        $(0, -2)$        **30.** $(4, -3)$, $m = -\frac{4}{3}$        $(7, -7)$

**31–34.** Use slope to decide whether the three points are collinear.

**31.** $(0, 3)$, $(4, 1)$, $(6, -3)$        **32.** $(-9, 0)$, $(0, 6)$, $(-6, 2)$
Not collinear        Collinear

**33.** $(6, 0)$, $(3, -2)$, $(0, -4)$        **34.** $(-6, 3)$, $(-5, 0)$, $(-3, -5)$
Collinear        Not collinear

© **35–38.** Find the slope of a line that contains the given points.

**35.** $(a, b)$, $(a + b, a)$  $\frac{a - b}{b}$ if $b \neq 0$   **36.** $(0, e)$, $(e, 0)$   $-1$

**37.** $(c, d)$, $(c + 2, d + 2)$   $1$        **38.** $(e, f)$, $(f, e)$   $-1$

**39–42.** If both points are contained by a line with the given slope *m,* find the missing coordinate.

**39.** $m = \frac{3}{5}$, $(2, 5)$, $(?, 17)$   $22$        **40.** $m = \frac{4}{3}$, $(-3, 7)$, $(-6, ?)$   $3$

**41.** $m = -\frac{2}{3}$, $(5, -1)$, $(-1, ?)$   $3$   **42.** $m = -\frac{5}{2}$, $(12, 3)$, $(?, 13)$   $8$

**43–46.** The grade of a road is its slope expressed as a percent. For example, since $15\% = \frac{15}{100} = \frac{3}{20}$, a grade of 15% means a rise of 3 units for a run of 20 units. Find the grade for each of the following:

| | | rise (vertical change) | run (horizontal change) |
|---|---|---|---|
| **43.** Maximum grade on interstate highway | 7% | 7 meters | 100 meters |
| **44.** Road up Pike's Peak | 10% | 1 meter | 10 meters |
| **45.** A San Francisco street | 25% | 1 meter | 4 meters |
| **46.** General Motors test hill | 45% | 9 meters | 20 meters |

# Equations of Lines    15.5

Given the coordinates of two points on a line, we can graph the line. We can also describe a line algebraically with an equation.

**Suggested Class Time**

| Course | Min. | Reg. | Max. |
|---|---|---|---|
| Days | 2 | 2 | 2 |

The equations for vertical and horizontal lines are easy to find.

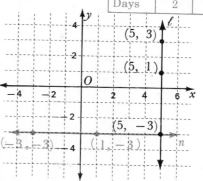

Line $\ell$ contains all points $(x, y)$ whose $x$-coordinates are 5, and is described by the equation

$$x = 5$$

Or we can say line $\ell$ is the graph of equation $x = 5$.

Line $n$ is the graph of the equation $y = -3$ since it contains all points whose $y$-coordinates are $-3$.

For a line that is not horizontal or vertical, we can find an equation if we know the coordinates of one point on the line and the slope of the line. Line $k$ contains point $(2, 3)$ and has slope $\frac{4}{5}$. Let $(x, y)$ be any point on $k$ different from $(2, 3)$. By the slope formula,

$$\frac{y - 3}{x - 2} = \frac{4}{5}$$

The equation has no meaning for $x = 2$ (denominator is zero) and is the equation for $k$ without point $(2, 3)$. Multiplying both sides of the equation by $(x - 2)$, we get the equation for $k$:

$$y - 3 = \tfrac{4}{5}(x - 2)$$

That is, all ordered pairs $(x, y)$ that are solutions of the equation are the coordinates of points on the line, and the coordinates of all points on the line are solutions of the equation. The equation for a line is called a *linear equation*.

The equation $y - 3 = \frac{4}{5}(x - 2)$ is in *point-slope form*. By looking at the equation, we can tell that the line has slope $\frac{4}{5}$ and contains point $(2, 3)$. In general,

 If a line contains point $(x_1, y_1)$ and has slope $m$, then the equation of the line is $y - y_1 = m(x - x_1)$.    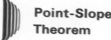 **Point-Slope Theorem**

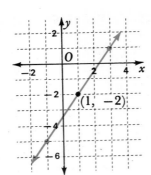

**Example 1:** Graph the line $y + 2 = \frac{3}{2}(x - 1)$.

- Point-slope form: $y - y_1 = m(x - x_1)$

$$y - (-2) = \tfrac{3}{2}(x - 1)$$

$$m = \tfrac{3}{2} \text{ and } (x_1, y_1) = (1, -2)$$

- Plot $(1, -2)$, and use the slope to find one or two other points.

- Draw line.

We can simplify the equation in Example 1.

| | |
|---|---|
| $y + 2 = \frac{3}{2}(x - 1)$ | Given |
| $2(y + 2) = 3(x - 1)$ | Multiply both sides by 2. |
| $2y + 4 = 3x - 3$ | Distributive property |
| $-3x + 2y = -7$ | Add $-4$ and $-3x$ to both sides. |
| $3x - 2y = 7$ | Multiply both sides by $-1$. |

The equation is in the form $ax + by = c$, with $a$ and $b$ not both equal to zero. This is the *standard form* of the equation of a line. (For $3x - 2y = 7$, $a = 3$, $b = -2$, and $c = 7$.)

Given the slope and one point on a line, we can find the equation of the line.

**Example 2:** Point $(-3, 1)$ is on a line with slope 2. Find the equation of the line in standard form.

Use substitution and point-slope form.

$$m = 2, \; (x_1, y_1) = (-3, 1)$$

$$y - y_1 = m(x - x_1)$$
$$y - 1 = 2(x - (-3))$$
$$y - 1 = 2x + 6$$
$$-2x + y = 7 \quad \text{or} \quad 2x - y = -7$$

NOTE: If we multiply both sides of an equation by the same nonzero number, we get an equivalent equation. So, standard form is *not* unique. We usually prefer the coefficients to be integers, and the coefficient of $x$ to be the smallest positive integer possible.

Given two points on a line, we can use the point-slope form to find the equation of the line.

**Example 3:** Points $(7, -1)$ and $(-8, 5)$ are on a line. Find the equation of the line in standard form.

- Use the given points to find the slope of the line.

$$m = \frac{5 - (-1)}{-8 - 7} = \frac{6}{-15} = -\frac{2}{5}$$

- Use the slope and one of the given points and substitute into point-slope form.

$$m = -\tfrac{2}{5}, \text{ let } (x_1, y_1) = (7, -1)$$
$$y - y_1 = m(x - x_1)$$
$$y - (-1) = -\tfrac{2}{5}(x - 7)$$
$$5y + 5 = -2x + 14$$
$$2x + 5y = 9$$

NOTE: We could have let $(x_1, y_1) = (-8, 5)$.

# Exercises 15.5

Ⓐ **1.** The equation of a line is called a $\underline{\text{Linear}}$ equation.

**2.** $y - 4 = \tfrac{2}{3}(x - 1)$ is the $\underline{\text{Point-slope}}$ form of an equation of a line.

**3.** $4x + 3y = 6$ is the $\underline{\text{Standard}}$ form of an equation of a line.

**4.** $y = -2$ is the equation of a line with slope $\underline{\quad 0 \quad}$.

**5–12.** Find **(a)** the slope of the line, if any, and **(b)** the coordinates of a point on the line. *Typical answers for part b*

**5.** $y = 6$    **a.** 0; **b.** (0, 6)

**6.** $x = -2$    **a.** None; **b.** $(-2, 0)$

**7.** $y - 1 = \tfrac{1}{2}(x - 3)$
   **a.** $\tfrac{1}{2}$; **b.** (3, 1)

**8.** $y - 7 = -\tfrac{2}{3}(x + 4)$
   **a.** $-\tfrac{2}{3}$; **b.** $(-4, 7)$

**9.** $y = 3(x + 2)$
   **a.** 3; **b.** $(-2, 0)$

**10.** $y - 4 = -x$
   **a.** $-1$; **b.** (0, 4)

**11.** $y + 5 = \tfrac{4}{5}(x + 3)$
   **a.** $\tfrac{4}{5}$; **b.** $(-3, -5)$

**12.** $y - \tfrac{1}{2} = -\tfrac{2}{7}(x + 8)$
   **a.** $-\tfrac{2}{7}$; **b.** $(-8, \tfrac{1}{2})$

Ⓑ **13–20.** Graph the lines in Exercises 5–12. Use a separate pair of axes for each exercise.

Assignment Guide
*Oral:* 1–12
*Written:*
Min. (day 1) 13–20; 21–33 odd
    (day 2) 35–43 odd;
    Quiz, p. 535
Reg. (day 1) 13–20; 21–33 odd
    (day 2) 35–43 odd;
    Quiz, p. 535
Max. (day 1) 13–20; 21–39 odd
    (day 2) 45–49 odd;
    Quiz, p. 535

21. $y - 4 = \frac{2}{3}(x - 1)$;
    $2x - 3y = -10$
22. $y - 7 = \frac{1}{2}(x - 3)$;
    $x - 2y = -11$
23. $y - 5 = -\frac{1}{4}(x - 4)$;
    $x + 4y = 24$
24. $y - 8 = -\frac{2}{7}(x + 2)$;
    $2x + 7y = 52$
25. $y + 8 = \frac{3}{5}(x + 3)$;
    $3x - 5y = 31$
26. $y + 1 = -5(x + 5)$;
    $5x + y = -26$
27. $y - 0 = 3(x - 4)$;
    $3x - y = 12$
28. $y - 0 = -2(x + 3)$;
    $2x + y = -6$
29. $y + 7 = -\frac{2}{9}(x - 0)$;
    $2x + 9y = -63$
30. $y - 6 = 4(x - 0)$;
    $4x - y = -6$
31. $y + 5 = 0(x - 0)$;
    $0x + y = -5$
32. $y - 1 = 0(x + 2)$;
    $0x + y = 1$

35. $x - 4y = -7$
36. $3x - 2y = -5$
37. $3x + 5y = 19$
38. $2x + 3y = 5$
39. $2x - y = -2$
40. $3x + y = -19$
41. $0x + y = -1$
42. $0x + y = 5$
43. $x + 0y = 4$
44. $x + 0y = -2$

45. Both points were used to find the slope. Then each point was used to write an equation in point-slope form; both equations have standard form $6x + 5y = 13$.

46. $y - 4 = \frac{3}{5}(x - 2)$
    $y - 1 = \frac{3}{5}(x + 3)$
    Both have standard form
    $3x - 5y = -14$.

**21–32.** Find the point-slope form, and then the standard form, of the equation of a line that has the given slope and contains the given point.

| | SLOPE | POINT | | SLOPE | POINT |
|---|---|---|---|---|---|
| **21.** | $\frac{2}{3}$ | $(1, 4)$ | **22.** | $\frac{1}{2}$ | $(3, 7)$ |
| **23.** | $-\frac{1}{4}$ | $(4, 5)$ | **24.** | $-\frac{2}{7}$ | $(-2, 8)$ |
| **25.** | $\frac{3}{5}$ | $(-3, -8)$ | **26.** | $-5$ | $(-5, -1)$ |
| **27.** | $3$ | $(4, 0)$ | **28.** | $-2$ | $(-3, 0)$ |
| **29.** | $-\frac{2}{9}$ | $(0, -7)$ | **30.** | $4$ | $(0, 6)$ |
| **31.** | $0$ | $(0, -5)$ | **32.** | $0$ | $(-2, 1)$ |

**33–34.** A line with no slope contains the given point. Find its equation.

**33.** $(7, -4)$  $x = 7$       **34.** $(3, -2)$  $x = 3$

**35–44.** Find the standard form of the equation of a line that contains the given points.

| | | | | | |
|---|---|---|---|---|---|
| **35.** $(1, 2)$ | $(5, 3)$ | | **36.** $(3, 7)$ | $(1, 4)$ | |
| **37.** $(-2, 5)$ | $(-7, 8)$ | | **38.** $(4, -1)$ | $(7, -3)$ | |
| **39.** $(-5, -8)$ | $(-1, 0)$ | | **40.** $(-3, -10)$ | $(-5, -4)$ | |
| **41.** $(3, -1)$ | $(5, -1)$ | | **42.** $(-7, 5)$ | $(0, 5)$ | |
| **43.** $(4, -6)$ | $(4, -4)$ | | **44.** $(-2, -3)$ | $(-2, 7)$ | |

© **45.** If points $(3, -1)$ and $(-2, 5)$ are on a line, why are $y + 1 = -\frac{6}{5}(x - 3)$ and $y - 5 = -\frac{6}{5}(x + 2)$ both equations of the line?

**46.** Find two equations in point-slope form for the line containing $(2, 4)$ and $(-3, 1)$. Then show that the equations are equivalent.

**47.** Find two equations in point-slope form for the line containing points $(x_1, y_1)$ and $(x_2, y_2)$.

**48.** Find the equation of the line that has slope $-\frac{2}{5}$ and contains the midpoint of the segment with endpoints $(-2, 6)$ and $(3, 10)$.

**49.** Find the equations of the lines that contain the sides of a triangle with vertices at $(0, -3)$, $(5, -1)$, and $(1, -1)$.

**50.** Find the vertices of the triangle whose sides are on the lines $y = -3$, $x = 4$, and $9x + 5y = 66$. HINT: Draw a graph.

$(4, -3), (9, -3), (4, 6)$

1. Graph the ordered pairs using one pair of axes.

$(1, 6)$, $(6, 1)$, $(3, -2)$, $(-2, 3)$, $(0, -8)$
$(5, 0)$, $(-5, 0)$, $(-7, -5)$, $(-7, 5)$, $(-\frac{1}{2}, 4)$

2. Which ordered pairs in Exercise 1 are in the 2nd quadrant?
$(-2, 3)$, $(-7, 5)$, $(-\frac{1}{2}, 4)$

3. Find the distance between $(0, 0)$ and $(3, 4)$.   5

4. Find the distance between $(-2, -5)$ and $(-4, 1)$.   $2\sqrt{10}$

**5–6.** Find the coordinates of the midpoint of the segment with the given endpoints.

5. $(0, 0)$ and $(6, 4)$   $(3, 2)$

6. $(-3, -8)$ and $(4, -3)$
$(\frac{1}{2}, -5\frac{1}{2})$

7. A $\underline{\text{Vertical}}$ line has no slope.

8. A line that has a $\underline{\text{Negative}}$ slope slants downward to the right.

9. Find the slope of the line that contains points $(2, -3)$ and $(5, 9)$.   4

10. The graph of $y - 1 = \frac{1}{2}(x - 3)$ has slope $\underline{\frac{1}{2}}$ and contains point $\underline{(3, 1)}$.

11. Graph $y - 3 = \frac{3}{4}(x - 1)$.

12. Graph $y - 5 = -2(x + 6)$.

*Two points on each graph are given:* 11. $(1, 3)$, $(-3, 0)$   12. $(-6, 5)$, $(-5, 3)$

**13–14.** Find, in standard form, the equation of a line that

13. contains point $(-6, 3)$ and has slope $-\frac{1}{4}$   $x + 4y = 6$

14. contains points $(3, 10)$ and $(-2, 3)$   $7x - 5y = -29$

47. $y - y_1 = \frac{y_2 - y_1}{x_2 - x_1}(x - x_1)$

$y - y_2 = \frac{y_2 - y_1}{x_2 - x_1}(x - x_2)$

48. $y - 8 = -\frac{2}{5}(x - \frac{1}{2})$ or $2x + 5y = 41$

49. $y + 1 = \frac{2}{5}(x - 5)$ or $2x - 5y = 15$; $y = -1$; $y + 1 = 2(x - 9)$ or $2x - y = 3$

## USING GRAPHS

# GEOMETRY AT WORK

Graphing in a coordinate plane is a useful way to record and display many different kinds of information. In applications, the units on one axis usually represent time or distance, while the units on the other axis depend on the information being graphed.

The Santa Fe Railway has a special track geometry car which graphically records changes in track measurements.

A polygraph (lie detector) graphically records changes in breathing, blood pressure, and pulse.

535

# 15.6   More About Equations of Lines

If the equation of a line is in point-slope form, it is easy to draw the graph. But very often equations are in standard form.

The solutions of a linear equation are ordered pairs, and the graph of the solution set is a line. If we find at least two solutions, we can plot the points and draw the line.

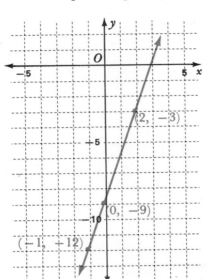

**Example 1:** Graph $3x - y = 9$.

• The replacement set for $x$, and for $y$, is the set of real numbers. To find a solution, let $x$ be any real number, and then solve for $y$.

Let $x = 0$.
$3(0) - y = 9$
$y = -9$ ⟶ $(0, -9)$ is a solution.

Let $x = 2$.
$3(2) - y = 9$
$y = -3$ ⟶ $(2, -3)$ is a solution.

Let $x = -1$.
$3(-1) - y = 9$
$y = -12$ ⟶ $(-1, -12)$ is a solution.

• Plot points and draw line.

Every nonvertical line intersects the $y$-axis at exactly one point. The $x$-coordinate of that point is 0, and the $y$-coordinate is called the **$y$-intercept** of the line. In Example 1, the line intersects the $y$-axis at $(0, -9)$, and $-9$ is the $y$-intercept.

In general, if $b$ is the $y$-intercept of a line, then $(0, b)$ is on the line. Let $(x, y)$ be any other point on the line, and let the line have slope $m$. Then, using the slope formula,

$$\frac{y - b}{x - 0} = m$$

$$\frac{y - b}{x} = m$$

$$y - b = mx$$

$$y = \underset{\text{slope}}{mx} + \underset{y\text{-intercept}}{b}$$

This form of the equation of a line is called *slope-intercept form*.

**Example 2:** For the graph of $y = -3x + 6$, what is the slope and the point of intersection with the $y$-axis?

- Use slope-intercept form: $y = mx + b$

  $y = -3x + 6$ —— $y$-intercept is 6.

- Slope $= -3$, and $(0, 6)$ is the point of intersection.

**Example 3:** Where does $y = \frac{1}{3}x$ intersect the $y$-axis?

- Use slope-intercept form: $y = mx + b$

  $y = \frac{1}{3}x + 0$

- Line intersects $y$-axis at $(0, 0)$.

**Example 4:** Find the slope and $y$-intercept of the graph of $3x - 5y = 15$.

- Solve for $y$: $3x - 5y = 15$

  $-5y = -3x + 15$

  $y = \frac{3}{5}x - 3$ —— Sign must be $+$

  $y = \frac{3}{5}x + (-3)$

- Slope $= \frac{3}{5}$, and $y$-intercept $= -3$.

## Exercises 15.6

Ⓐ 1. Every nonvertical line intersects the $y$-axis at exactly one <u>Point</u>.

2. If a line contains $(0, 5)$, then its $y$-intercept is <u>5</u>.

3. The equation $y = \frac{2}{3}x + 4$ is in _____ form. Slope-intercept

4. For $y = \frac{2}{3}x + 4$, <u>$\frac{2}{3}$</u> is the slope and <u>4</u> is the $y$-intercept.

**5–14.** Find the slope and $y$-intercept of each line.

5. $y = \frac{1}{4}x + 3$      $\frac{1}{4}$; 3

6. $y = \frac{2}{5}x + 1$      $\frac{2}{5}$; 1

7. $y = \frac{3}{7}x + (-4)$   $\frac{3}{7}$; $-4$

8. $y = 4x + (-5)$    4; $-5$

9. $y = -5x - 2$    $-5$; $-2$

10. $y = -\frac{1}{6}x - 8$    $-\frac{1}{6}$; $-8$

11. $y = \frac{4}{5}x$      $\frac{4}{5}$; 0

12. $y = -\frac{9}{7}x$      $-\frac{9}{7}$; 0

13. $y = 2$      0; 2

14. $y = -5$      0; $-5$

Ⓑ **15–24.** Graph each line for Exercises 5–14. Use the $y$-intercept to find one point and the slope to find at least one other point.

**Assignment Guide**
*Oral:* 1–14
*Written:*
Min. (day 1) 15–33 odd
    (day 2) 35–43 odd;
    Alg. Rev., p. 538, odd
Reg. (day 1) 15–33 odd
    (day 2) 35–43 odd;
    Alg. Rev., p. 538
Max. 15–43 odd

**35. a.** $y = -1x + 4$
  **b.** $-1, 4$
**36. a.** $y = 1x + (-3)$
  **b.** $1, -3$
**37. a.** $y = -\frac{2}{3}x + \frac{7}{3}$
  **b.** $-\frac{2}{3}, \frac{7}{3}$
**38. a.** $y = -\frac{1}{5}x + (-2)$
  **b.** $-\frac{1}{5}, -2$
**39. a.** $y = \frac{3}{2}x + (-\frac{15}{2})$
  **b.** $\frac{3}{2}, -\frac{15}{2}$
**40. a.** $y = 1x + \frac{5}{2}$
  **b.** $1, \frac{5}{2}$
**41. a.** $y = -\frac{4}{5}x + (-4)$
  **b.** $-\frac{4}{5}, -4$
**42. a.** $y = -\frac{3}{8}x + 3$
  **b.** $-\frac{3}{8}, 3$
**43. a.** $y = 0x + \frac{1}{3}$
  **b.** $0, \frac{1}{3}$
**44. a.** $y = 0x + (-\frac{2}{5})$
  **b.** $0, -\frac{2}{5}$

**47.** The $x$-intercept of a (nonhorizontal) line is the $x$-coordinate of the point at which the line intersects the $x$-axis.

**25–34.** Find three solutions for each equation and draw its graph.

*Typical answers*

**25.** $x + y = 4$
  $(0, 4), (2, 2), (4, 0)$

**26.** $x - y = 3$
  $(0, -3), (4, 1), (3, 0)$

**27.** $2x + 3y = 7$
  $(-4, 5), (-1, 3), (2, 1)$

**28.** $x + 5y = -10$
  $(0, -2), (-5, -1), (-10, 0)$

**29.** $6x - 4y = 30$
  $(-1, -9), (3, -3), (5, 0)$

**30.** $2x - 2y = -5$
  $(-2\frac{1}{2}, 0), (0, 2\frac{1}{2}), (2\frac{1}{2}, 5)$

**31.** $-4x - 5y = 20$
  $(-5, 0), (0, -4), (5, -8)$

**32.** $-3x - 8y = -24$
  $(0, 3), (8, 0), (-8, 6)$

**33.** $y = \frac{1}{3}$
  $(-2, \frac{1}{3}), (0, \frac{1}{3}), (5, \frac{1}{3})$

**34.** $y = -\frac{2}{5}$
  $(-2, -\frac{2}{5}), (0, -\frac{2}{5}), (5, -\frac{2}{5})$

**35–44.** For each equation in Exercises 25–34, (**a**) find the slope-intercept form and (**b**) find the slope and $y$-intercept of the graph.

© **45.** Find the coordinates of the vertices of a triangle whose sides are on the graphs of $y = \frac{2}{3}x - 4$, $y = -3x - 4$, and $x = 3$.
  $(3, -2), (3, -13), (0, -4)$

**46.** Given points $A(-4, 0)$, $B(4, 0)$, and $C(0, 8)$, find the coordinates of the point on the $y$-axis where the medians of $\triangle ABC$ intersect.
  $(0, \frac{8}{3})$

**47.** Write a definition for the *x-intercept* of a line.

**48.** A line with slope $m$ contains point $(a, 0)$. What might be the *x-intercept form* of the equation of the line? HINT: See Exercise 47.
  $x = \frac{1}{m}y + a$

---

*Algebra Review*

**Review this skill:**

• *solving systems of equations*

**1–3.** Solve by graphing.

**1.** $2x - 3y = 12$
  $3y = 2x + 21$
  No solutions

**2.** $y = \frac{7}{2}x - 5$
  $14x - 4y = 20$
  Many solutions

**3.** $5x - 2y = 3$
  $3y = 2x + 1$
  $(1, 1)$

**4–6.** Solve by substitution.

**4.** $x = 2y$
  $x + 3y = 30$ $(12, 6)$

**5.** $y = x + 3$
  $3x + 2y = 46$ $(8, 11)$

**6.** $2y = 5x$
  $3x + 4y = 39$
  $(3, \frac{15}{2})$

**7–9.** Solve by the multiplication-addition method.

**7.** $7x + 3y = 30$
  $2x - 3y = 42$ $(8, -\frac{26}{3})$

**8.** $2x + 5y = 49$
  $x - y = 7$ $(12, 5)$

**9.** $3x + 4y = 15$
  $4x - 3y = 20$
  $(5, 0)$

## Parallel and Perpendicular Lines

**Suggested Class Time**

| Course | Min. | Reg. | Max. |
|--------|------|------|------|
| Days | 1 | 1 | 1 |

If we know the slopes of two nonvertical lines, we can tell how the lines are related.

In the figure, lines $\ell$ and $n$ intersect at $P(x_1, y_1)$. $Q(x_2, y_2)$ is on $\ell$. Since $\ell$ and $n$ are not the same line, point $R$ on $n$ with $x_2$ as its $x$-coordinate must have $y$-coordinate $y_3$ such that $y_3 \neq y_2$.

$$\text{Slope of } \ell = \frac{y_2 - y_1}{x_2 - x_1}$$

$$\text{Slope of } n = \frac{y_3 - y_1}{x_2 - x_1}$$

And $\frac{y_2 - y_1}{x_2 - x_1} \neq \frac{y_3 - y_1}{x_2 - x_1}$, since $y_3 \neq y_2$. So, intersecting lines have different slopes.

If two nonvertical lines are parallel, they have equal slopes.

$$\text{Slope of } s = \frac{PR}{RQ}$$

$$\text{Slope of } t = \frac{AC}{CB} \quad \text{(Def. of slope)}$$

$\angle 1 \cong \angle 2$ (If lines are ‖, corres. $\angle$s are $\cong$.)

$\angle PRQ \cong \angle ACB$ (Rt. $\angle$s are $\cong$.)

$\triangle PQR \sim \triangle ABC$ (AA Similarity Theorem)

$\frac{PR}{AC} = \frac{RQ}{CB}$ (Corres. sides of $\sim$ $\triangle$s are proportional.)

$\frac{PR}{RQ} = \frac{AC}{CB}$ (Switch means.)

Slope of $s$ = slope of $t$ (Substitution)

We can prove the converse. So,

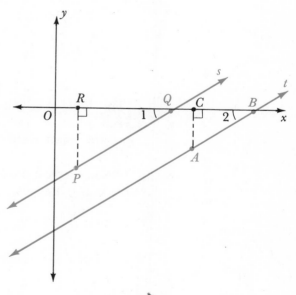

 Two nonvertical lines are parallel if and only if they have equal slopes.  **Theorem**

NOTE: Two lines with no slope are both vertical, so they are parallel.

We can also tell if two lines are perpendicular by their slopes. Below, lines $\ell'_1$ and $\ell'_2$ are perpendicular. By the Parallel Postulate, we can choose $\ell_1$ through the origin parallel to $\ell'_1$ and $\ell_2$ through the origin parallel to $\ell'_2$. Parallel lines have equal slopes, so whatever we prove about the slopes of $\ell_1$ and $\ell_2$ is also true for $\ell'_1$ and $\ell'_2$. Let $m_1 = $ slope of $\ell_1$ and $m_2 = $ slope of $\ell_2$. Then $m_1 = \frac{y_1}{x}$ and $m_2 = \frac{y_2}{x}$.

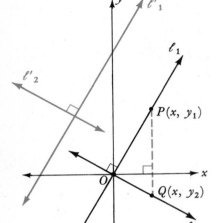

By the Pythagorean Theorem and the distance formula,

$$(PQ)^2 = (PO)^2 + (QO)^2$$

$$(\sqrt{(y_2 - y_1)^2})^2 = (\sqrt{x^2 + (y_1)^2})^2 + (\sqrt{x^2 + (y_2)^2})^2$$

$$(y_2)^2 - 2y_1 y_2 + (y_1)^2 = x^2 + (y_1)^2 + x^2 + (y_2)^2$$

$$-2y_1 y_2 = 2x^2$$

$$y_1 y_2 = -x^2$$

Since $x \neq 0$, we can divide both sides by $x^2$.

$$\frac{y_1 y_2}{x^2} = \frac{-x^2}{x^2}$$

$$\frac{y_1}{x} \cdot \frac{y_2}{x} = -1$$

By substituting $m_1$ and $m_2$ for $\frac{y_1}{x}$ and $\frac{y_2}{x}$,

$$m_1 \cdot m_2 = -1$$

$$m_1 = -\frac{1}{m_2}$$

The slopes of $\ell_1$ and $\ell_2$ (and of $\ell'_1$ and $\ell'_2$) are negative reciprocals of each other. By reversing the process, we could show that if their slopes are negative reciprocals, then the lines are perpendicular.

**Theorem**

Two nonvertical lines are perpendicular if and only if their slopes ($m_1$ and $m_2$) are negative reciprocals of each other.

$$m_1 = -\frac{1}{m_2} \qquad \text{or} \qquad m_1 m_2 = -1$$

NOTE: A line with slope 0 and a line with no slope are perpendicular.

**Example 1:** One line contains points $(5, -8)$ and $(-6, -3)$. Another line contains $(-9, 0)$ and $(2, -5)$. Are the lines parallel?

- Find the slope of each line: $m_1 = -\frac{5}{11}$ and $m_2 = -\frac{5}{11}$

- The lines are parallel because their slopes are equal.

**Example 2:** Determine whether $3x - 5y = 21$ and $5x + 3y = -4$ are equations of perpendicular lines.

- Use slope-intercept form to find the slope of each line.

$$y = \tfrac{3}{5}x - \tfrac{21}{5} \qquad\qquad y = -\tfrac{5}{3}x - \tfrac{4}{3}$$
$$m_1 = \tfrac{3}{5} \qquad\qquad\qquad m_2 = -\tfrac{5}{3}$$

- Check to see if $m_1 \cdot m_2 = -1$.

$\tfrac{3}{5}(-\tfrac{5}{3}) = -1$, so the lines are perpendicular.

## Exercises 15.7

Ⓐ **1.** Nonvertical, parallel lines have __Equal__ slopes.

**2.** If two lines each have no slope, then the lines are __Vertical__ and __∥__.

**3.** Two lines are perpendicular if the product of their slopes is __-1__.

**4.** A line perpendicular to a vertical line has slope __0__.

**5.** Any line parallel to a line with slope $\tfrac{1}{3}$ has slope __$\tfrac{1}{3}$__.

**6.** Any line perpendicular to a line with slope $\tfrac{3}{4}$ has slope __$-\tfrac{4}{3}$__.

**Assignment Guide**
*Oral:* 1–14
*Written:* Min. 15–31 odd
Reg. 15–37 odd
Max. 15–39 odd

**7–14.** Find the slope of a line **(a)** parallel to and **(b)** perpendicular to the given line.

|  | a. | b. |  |  | a. | b. |  |  | a. | b. |
|---|---|---|---|---|---|---|---|---|---|---|
| **7.** $y = \tfrac{2}{3}x$ | $\tfrac{2}{3}$ | $-\tfrac{3}{2}$ | **8.** $y = -\tfrac{4}{5}x$ | | $-\tfrac{4}{5}$ | $\tfrac{5}{4}$ | **9.** $y = 2x$ | | 2 | $-\tfrac{1}{2}$ |

**10.** $y = -4x$ $\;-4\;$ $\;\tfrac{1}{4}\;$ **11.** $y = \tfrac{5}{8}x + 2$ $\;\tfrac{5}{8}\;$ $\;-\tfrac{8}{5}\;$ **12.** $y = -\tfrac{2}{7}x + 8$ $\;-\tfrac{2}{7}\;$ $\;\tfrac{7}{2}$

**13.** $y = -\tfrac{3}{10}x - 7$ a. $-\tfrac{3}{10}$ b. $\tfrac{10}{3}$ **14.** $y = -\tfrac{4}{9}x - \tfrac{2}{3}$ a. $-\tfrac{4}{9}$ b. $\tfrac{9}{4}$

Ⓑ **15–22.** Each pair of points determines a line. Are the two lines in each exercise parallel, perpendicular, or neither?

**15.** $(0, 0)$ and $(4, 5)$;
$(1, 6)$ and $(-3, 1)$ $\qquad\parallel$

**16.** $(0, 0)$ and $(3, 7)$;
$(2, 5)$ and $(-5, 8)$ $\qquad\perp$

**17.** $(-3, 2)$ and $(-4, -3)$;
$(-7, 8)$ and $(3, 6)$ $\qquad\perp$

**18.** $(15, -21)$ and $(-9, -12)$;
$(5, 3)$ and $(-11, 9)$ $\qquad\parallel$

**19.** $(-2, 14)$ and $(-7, -6)$;
$(3, 0)$ and $(-4, 3)$ Neither

**20.** $(-8, 5)$ and $(2, 5)$;
$(3, 10)$ and $(-4, 10)$ $\qquad\parallel$

**21.** $(13, -6)$ and $(13, 2)$;
$(17, 9)$ and $(-4, 9)$ $\qquad\perp$

**22.** $(-1, -6)$ and $(2, 7)$;
$(21, 7)$ and $(8, 9)$ $\quad$ Neither

**23–28.** Determine if the lines are parallel, perpendicular, or neither.

**23.** $2x + y = -4$
$x - 2y = 5$ $\perp$

**24.** $5x - y = -2$
$4x + 3y = 27$
Neither

**25.** $8x - 2y = -7$
$9x - 3y = -11$
Neither

**26.** $3x + 8y = 16$
$16x - 6y = -21$ $\perp$

**27.** $5y - 5x = 0$
$3y - 3x = 19$ $\parallel$

**28.** $2x - 7y = 8$
$2x - 7y = -4$ $\parallel$

**29–32.** Find the standard form of the equation of the line that

**29.** contains $(4, -1)$ and is parallel to the graph of $y = -\frac{2}{5}x + 7$.
$2x + 5y = 3$

**30.** contains $(0, -3)$ and is perpendicular to the graph of $y = 3x - 10$.
$x + 3y = -9$

**31.** is the perpendicular bisector of the segment whose endpoints are $(3, 4)$ and $(-5, 12)$.
$x - y = -9$

**32.** is parallel to the hypotenuse and contains the vertex of the right angle of a triangle with vertices at $(0, 10)$, $(-6, 0)$, and $(0, 0)$.
$5x - 3y = 0$

**33.** Show that a quadrilateral with vertices $A(-5, 4)$, $B(3, 5)$, $C(7, -2)$, and $D(-1, -3)$ is a parallelogram. HINT: Show that opposite sides are parallel.
Slope of $\overline{AB}$ and $\overline{CD}$ is $\frac{1}{8}$; slope of $\overline{BC}$ and $\overline{AD}$ is $-\frac{7}{4}$.

**34.** Show that $\square ABCD$ in Exercise 33 is a rhombus. HINT: Show that its diagonals are perpendicular.
Slope of $\overline{AC}$ is $-\frac{1}{2}$, and slope of $\overline{BD}$ is 2.

**35.** Show that a triangle with vertices at $J(-9, 6)$, $K(12, 8)$, and $L(14, -13)$ is a right triangle.
Slope of $\overline{JK}$ is $\frac{2}{21}$, and slope of $\overline{KL}$ is $-\frac{21}{2}$. So $\overline{JK} \perp \overline{KL}$, and $\triangle JKL$ is a rt. $\triangle$.

**36.** Midpts. of $\overline{AC}$ and $\overline{BC}$ are at $(2, 3)$ and $(7, 2)$, so seg. joining them has slope $-\frac{1}{5}$. $\overline{AB}$ has slope $-\frac{1}{5}$, so the segs. are $\parallel$.

**36.** $\triangle ABC$ has vertices $A(-1, -1)$, $B(9, -3)$, and $C(5, 7)$. Show that the segment joining the midpoints of $\overline{AC}$ and $\overline{BC}$ is parallel to $\overline{AB}$.

**37.** Find the slopes of the altitudes of $\triangle ABC$ in Exercise 36. $5, \frac{2}{5}, -\frac{3}{4}$

**38.** Show that a quadrilateral with vertices at $A(-7, 6)$, $B(-2, 9)$, $C(6, 4)$, and $D(9, -4)$ is a trapezoid. HINT: Show that only two sides are parallel.
Slope of $\overline{BC}$ and $\overline{AD}$ is $-\frac{5}{8}$, so $\overline{BC} \parallel \overline{AD}$. Slope of $\overline{AB}$ is $\frac{3}{5}$, and slope of $\overline{CD}$ is $-\frac{8}{3}$, so $\overline{AB}$ and $\overline{CD}$ are not $\parallel$.

**40.** Slope of first line:
$\frac{d - a}{c}$. Slope of second line: $\frac{c}{a - d}$ or $-\frac{c}{d - a}$.
$\frac{d - a}{c}\left(-\frac{c}{d - a}\right) = -1$,
so the lines are $\perp$.

© **39.** Find the slope of the perpendicular bisector of the segment whose endpoints are $(0, a)$ and $(b, c)$.
$-\frac{b}{c - a}$ or $\frac{b}{a - c}$

**40.** Show that the line containing points at $(0, a)$ and $(c, d)$ is perpendicular to the line containing points at $(d, 0)$ and $(a, c)$.

# Coordinate Proofs 15.8

In this section, we will use the coordinate plane to do proofs. But first, we will look at the placement of geometric figures in the coordinate plane.

Below, $\triangle ABC$ is shown in different positions in the coordinate plane. Notice how much simpler the algebraic expression for $AB$ is in figure 3 than in figures 1 and 2.

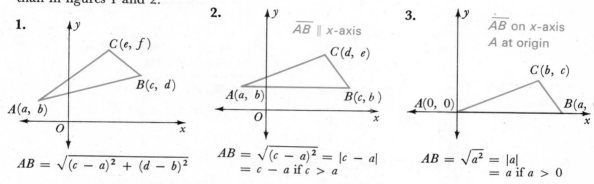

1.
$$AB = \sqrt{(c - a)^2 + (d - b)^2}$$

2. $\overline{AB} \parallel x\text{-axis}$
$$AB = \sqrt{(c - a)^2} = |c - a|$$
$$= c - a \text{ if } c > a$$

3. $\overline{AB}$ on $x$-axis, $A$ at origin
$$AB = \sqrt{a^2} = |a|$$
$$= a \text{ if } a > 0$$

In general, parts of the axes are used as parts of the geometric figure so that the coordinates of the vertices can be expressed with as few variables as possible. This is done so that algebraic expressions needed in proofs will be as simple as possible. Below are just a few examples of how figures might be placed in the coordinate plane. Notice how the definition of each figure was used to assign coordinates.

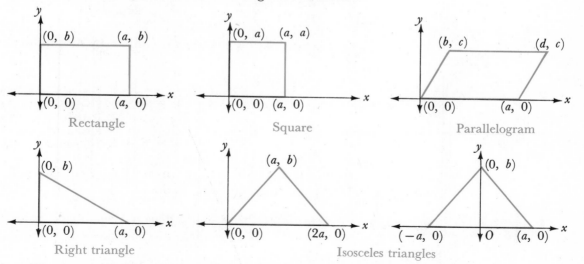

The first example of a coordinate proof shows how the distance and midpoint formulas are used in a proof.

**Example 1:** Prove that the length of the median to the hypotenuse of a right triangle is half the length of the hypotenuse.

Start by stating the *Given* and the *Prove* in terms of a figure in the coordinate plane.

**Given:** Right $\triangle ABC$ with pt. $C$ at $(0, 0)$, legs $\overline{CA}$ and $\overline{CB}$ on the axes, median $\overline{CM}$ to hypotenuse $\overline{AB}$

**Prove:** $CM = \frac{1}{2}AB$

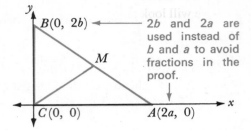

$2b$ and $2a$ are used instead of $b$ and $a$ to avoid fractions in the proof.

9. *Given:* $\square ABCD$, $A$ at $(0, 0)$, $\overline{AB}$ on $x$-axis
   *Prove:*
   $\overline{AB} \cong \overline{DC}$, $\overline{AD} \cong \overline{BC}$
   *Sketch of Proof:* By the distance formula,
   $AB = DC = a$ and
   $AD = BC = \sqrt{b^2 + c^2}$.

10. *Given: Same as Ex. 9*
    *Prove:* $\overline{AC}$ and $\overline{DB}$ bisect each other.
    *Sketch of Proof:* By the midpt. formula, midpts. of $\overline{AC}$ and $\overline{BD}$ are both at $\left(\frac{a+b}{2}, \frac{c}{2}\right)$.

**Proof: 1.** By definition of median, $M$ is the midpoint of $\overline{AB}$. And by the midpoint formula, $M$ is at $(a, b)$.

**2.** By the distance formula, $CM = \sqrt{a^2 + b^2}$

$$AB = \sqrt{(2a)^2 + (2b)^2} = 2\sqrt{a^2 + b^2}$$
$$\tfrac{1}{2}AB = \sqrt{a^2 + b^2}$$

**3.** By substitution, $CM = \frac{1}{2}AB$.

Before doing a proof about parallelograms, we will take a closer look at how coordinates are assigned to the vertices of a parallelogram. For $\square ABCD$ below, $\overline{AB}$ is on the $x$-axis with $A$ at $(0, 0)$. Opposite sides of a parallelogram are parallel, so $\overline{CD}$ is horizontal, and points $C$ and $D$ have the same $y$-coordinate. By the slope formula,

$$\text{slope } \overline{AD} = \frac{c}{b} \qquad \text{and} \qquad \text{slope } \overline{BC} = \frac{c}{d-a}$$

Slope of $\overline{AD}$ = slope of $\overline{BC}$ (why?). By substitution,

$$\frac{c}{b} = \frac{c}{d-a}$$
$$c(d - a) = cb$$
$$d - a = b$$
$$d = a + b$$

Notice that the $x$-coordinate of $C$ is the sum of the $x$-coordinates of $B$ and $D$.

So, the coordinates of $C$ can be written as $(a + b, c)$. This will make proofs about parallelograms easier to do.

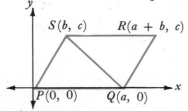

**Example 2:** Prove that a diagonal separates a parallelogram into two congruent triangles.

**Given:** $\square PQRS$ with $P$ at $(0, 0)$ and $\overline{PQ}$ on the $x$-axis

**Prove:** $\triangle PQS \cong \triangle RSQ$

**Proof: 1.** By the distance formula, $PQ = a$, $RS = a$, $PS = \sqrt{b^2 + c^2}$, and $RQ = \sqrt{b^2 + c^2}$. So, $\overline{PQ} \cong \overline{RS}$ and $\overline{PS} \cong \overline{RQ}$.

**2.** Since $\overline{QS} \cong \overline{QS}$, $\triangle PQS \cong \triangle RSQ$ by the SSS Postulate.

**Assignment Guide**
*Oral:* Reg. & Max. 1–8
*Written:*
Reg. 9–15 odd
Max. (day 1) 9–19 odd
(day 2) 12–20 even

# Exercises 15.8

Ⓐ **1–2.** *ABCD* below is a square. Find the coordinates of each vertex if

**1.** $B$ is at $(c, 0)$.  $C(c, c)$
$D(0, c)$

**2.** $B$ is at $(2g, 0)$.  $C(2g, 2g)$
$D(0, 2g)$

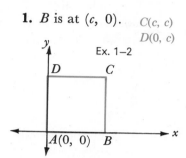
Ex. 1–2

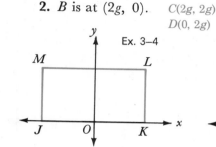
Ex. 3–4

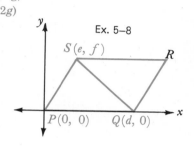
Ex. 5–8

**3–4.** *JKLM* above is a rectangle. The *y*-axis is the perpendicular bisector of $\overline{JK}$. Find the coordinates of each vertex if

**3.** $L$ is at $(h, k)$.  $M(-h, k)$
$J(-h, 0)$
$K(h, 0)$

**4.** $M$ is at $(-a, 4b)$.  $L(a, 4b)$
$J(-a, 0)$
$K(a, 0)$

**5–8.** *PQRS* above is a parallelogram. Find the coordinates of

**5.** vertex $R$  $(d + e, f)$
**6.** midpt. of $\overline{PQ}$  $\left(\dfrac{d}{2}, 0\right)$
**7.** midpt. of $\overline{PS}$  $\left(\dfrac{e}{2}, \dfrac{f}{2}\right)$
**8.** midpt. of $\overline{QS}$  $\left(\dfrac{d + e}{2}, \dfrac{f}{2}\right)$

Ⓑ **9–16.** Write a coordinate proof for each statement. Start by stating the *Given* and the *Prove* in terms of the given figure.

**9.** The opposite sides of a parallelogram are congruent.

**10.** The diagonals of a parallelogram bisect each other.

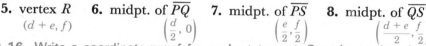
Ex. 9–10
$D(b, c)$  $C(a + b, c)$
$A(0, 0)$  $B(a, 0)$

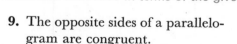
Ex. 11–12
$M(2b, 2c)$  $L(2d, 2c)$
$A$  $B$
$J(0, 0)$  $K(2a, 0)$

**11.** The midline of a trapezoid is parallel to its bases.

**12.** The length of the midline of a trapezoid is half the sum of the lengths of its bases.

**11.** *Given:* Trapezoid *JKLM*, $J$ at $(0, 0)$, $\overline{JK}$ on x-axis, midline $\overline{AB}$
*Prove:*
$\overline{AB} \parallel \overline{JK}$, $\overline{AB} \parallel \overline{ML}$
*Sketch of Proof:* By the midpt. form., $A$, $B$ are at $(b, c)$, $(a + d, c)$. So the slope of $\overline{AB}$ is 0. But the slopes of $\overline{JK}$ and $\overline{ML}$ are also 0.

**12.** *Given:* Same as Ex. 11
*Prove:*
$AB = \frac{1}{2}(JK + ML)$
*Sketch of Proof:* By the midpt. formula, $A(b, c)$ and $B(a + d, c)$ are endpoints of the midline. By the dist. formula, $AB = a + d - b$, $JK = 2a$, $ML = 2d - 2b$.
$a + d - b = $
$\frac{1}{2}(2a + 2d - 2b)$

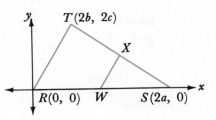

13. *Given:* △RST, R is at (0, 0), $\overline{RS}$ on x-axis, midpts. W and X
*Prove:* $\overline{WX} \parallel \overline{RT}$
*Sketch of Proof:* By the midpt. form., W, X are at $(a, 0)$, $(a + b, c)$.
So slopes of $\overline{WX}$ and $\overline{RT}$ are both $\frac{c}{b}$.

14. *Given:* △ABC, A is at (0, 0), $\overline{AB}$ on x-axis, $AC = BC$, medians $\overline{AS}$ and $\overline{BR}$
*Prove:* $\overline{AS} \cong \overline{BR}$
*Sketch of Proof:* By the midpt. form., R, S are at $(a, 2b)$, $(3a, 2b)$.
By the dist. formula, $AS = BR = \sqrt{9a^2 + 4b^2}$.

15. *Given:* Square DEFG, D at (0, 0), $\overline{DE}$ on x-axis
*Prove:* $\overline{DF}$, $\overline{EG}$ are ⊥ bisectors of each other.
*Sketch of Proof:* Slope of $\overline{GE}$ is $-1$. Slope of $\overline{DF}$ is 1. $1(-1) = -1$, so $\overline{DF} \perp \overline{GE}$. By midpt. formula, midpts. of $\overline{DF}$, $\overline{EG}$ are both at $(a, a)$.

16. *Given:* WXYZ, W is at (0, 0), $\overline{WX}$ on x-axis, midpts. A, B, C, D
*Prove:* $\overline{AC}$, $\overline{BD}$ bisected
*Sketch of Proof:* By midpt. form., midpts. are A(2b, 2c), B(2a, 0), C(2a + 2d, 2e), and D(2b + 2d, 2c + 2e).
Midpts. of $\overline{AC}$, $\overline{BD}$ are at $(a + b + d, c + e)$.

**13.** The segment joining the midpoints of two sides of a triangle is parallel to the third side.

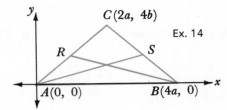

Ex. 14

**15.** The diagonals of a square are perpendicular bisectors of each other.

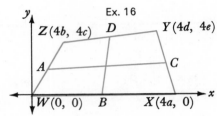

Ex. 16

© **17.** *ABCD* below is an isosceles trapezoid. Find the coordinates of *C*.

© **18.** △EFG below is equilateral. Find the coordinates of G.

© **19.** *RSTU* below is a rhombus. Find the coordinates of *S* and *T*.

**14.** The medians to the legs of an isosceles triangle are congruent.

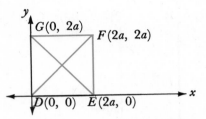

**16.** The segments joining the midpoints of the opposite sides of a quadrilateral bisect each other.

19. $S(\sqrt{a^2 + b^2}, 0)$, $T(a + \sqrt{a^2 + b^2}, b)$

$C(a - b, c)$

$G(a, a\sqrt{3})$

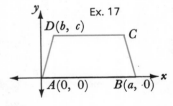

Ex. 17

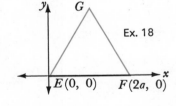

Ex. 18

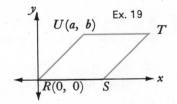

Ex. 19

**20–22.** Prove each statement. Use the results from Exercises 17–19 to assign coordinates for the figure.

**20.** The segments joining, in order, the midpoints of the sides of an isosceles trapezoid form a rhombus.

**21.** The segments joining the midpoints of the sides of an equilateral triangle form an equilateral triangle.

**22.** The diagonals of a rhombus are perpendicular.

546     CHAPTER 15     COORDINATE GEOMETRY

# Locus in the Coordinate Plane

From Chapter 11, we know that a locus is a geometric figure containing all points, and only those points, that meet a given condition. The equation of a line is an algebraic condition, and its graph is the set of points whose coordinates meet that condition. A condition that uses an inequality symbol is called an **inequality.** Consider

$$x \geq 1 \quad \text{"is greater than or equal to"}$$

Its graph contains all points and only those points whose $x$-coordinates are greater than or equal to 1. No condition is given for the $y$-coordinates, so $y$ can be any real number. That is, the graph contains all points in the half plane to the right of line $x = 1$ and all points on the line. Line $x = 1$ is called the *boundary line* and is drawn as a solid line.

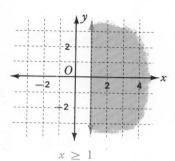

$x \geq 1$

**Suggested Class Time**

| Course | Min. | Reg. | Max. |
|--------|------|------|------|
| Days   | 1    | 1    | 1    |

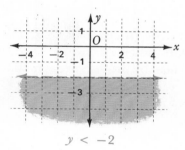

$y < -2$

The graph at the left satisfies the condition $y < -2$. Notice that points on the boundary line $y = -2$ do not satisfy the condition. The line is not part of the graph, and we show this by drawing it as a dashed line.

**Example 1:** Graph $y > 3x - 4$.

1. Graph boundary line $y = 3x - 4$. Draw it as a dashed line.

2. To decide which half plane to shade, pick a point on each side of the boundary line. Then check to see which one satisfies the condition.

| Above: $(0, 0)$ | Below: $(3, -1)$ |
|-----------------|------------------|
| $0 > 3(0) - 4$  | $-1 > 3(3) - 4$  |
| $0 > -4$        | $-1 > 5$         |
| True            | False            |

Shade above the line. As a check, try another point above the line.

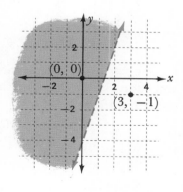

20. *Given:* Trap. $ABCD$, $A$ at $(0, 0)$, $\overline{AB}$ on $x$-axis, $AD = BC$; $M$, $N$, $P$, $Q$, midpts. of $\overline{AB}$, $\overline{BC}$, $\overline{CD}$, $\overline{DA}$, respectively
    *Prove:* $MNPQ$ a rhombus
    [*Plan:* Use the midpoint formula to find coordinates of $M$, $N$, $P$, and $Q$. Use dist. formula to show $\overline{MN} \cong \overline{PQ} \cong \overline{MQ} \cong \overline{NP}$.]

21. *Given:* Equilateral $\triangle$ $EFG$, $E$ at $(0, 0)$, $\overline{EF}$ on $x$-axis; $R$, $S$, $T$ midpts. of $\overline{EF}$, $\overline{FG}$, $\overline{GE}$, respect.
    *Prove:* $\triangle RST$ equilat.
    [*Plan:* Use midpt. form. to find coordinates of $\overline{EF}$, $\overline{FG}$, $\overline{GE}$. Use distance formula to show $\overline{EF} \cong \overline{FG} \cong \overline{GE}$.]

22. *Given:* Rhombus $RSTU$, $R$ at $(0, 0)$, $\overline{RS}$ on $x$-axis
    *Prove:* $\overline{RT} \perp \overline{SU}$
    [*Plan:* Find the slopes of $\overline{RT}$ and $\overline{SU}$; show that the product is $-1$.]

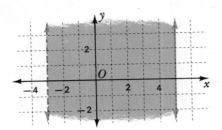

**Example 2:** Describe the graph of $-3 < x \leq 5$. Then draw the graph. NOTE: $-3 < x \leq 5$ means $x > -3$ **and** $x \leq 5$.

1. The graph contains all points whose $x$-coordinates are greater than $-3$ and less than or equal to 5.

2. Boundary lines are $x = -3$ (dashed) and $x = 5$ (solid). Shade between the lines.

**Example 3:** Draw the graph, then write an algebraic condition for the set of all points whose coordinates are both positive.

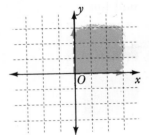

1. The graph is the 1st quadrant.

2. The algebraic condition is $x > 0$ and $y > 0$.

By using the distance formula, we can write an algebraic condition for a circle. Let the center of circle $O$ with radius 4 be at the origin. Let $P(x, y)$ be any point on the circle. Then, by the distance formula,

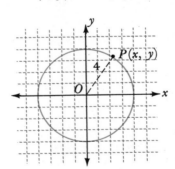

$$OP = 4$$
$$\sqrt{x^2 + y^2} = 4$$
$$x^2 + y^2 = 16$$

This is the equation of circle $O$. That is, the coordinates of all points on circle $O$ satisfy the equation. Also, only the coordinates of points on the circle satisfy the equation.

Suppose circle $A$ has center at $A(2, 3)$ and radius 5. If $P(x, y)$ is any point on the circle, then

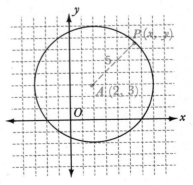

$$AP = 5$$
$$\sqrt{(x - 2)^2 + (y - 3)^2} = 5$$
$$(x - 2)^2 + (y - 3)^2 = 25$$

Notice how the equation tells us where the center of the circle is and what the radius of the circle is. In general,

The equation of a circle with center $(h, k)$ and radius $r$ is

$$(x - h)^2 + (y - k)^2 = r^2$$

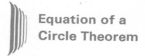

Equation of a Circle Theorem

NOTE: $x^2 + y^2 = r^2$ is the equation of a circle with center at $(0, 0)$.

**Example 4:** Graph $(x + 5)^2 + (y - 1)^2 = 36$.

1. Find center and radius.

$$(x - (-5))^2 + (y - 1)^2 = 6^2$$

⎿ Sign must be −

Center is at $(-5, 1)$, and radius is 6.

2. Plot center. Find points on horizontal and vertical lines through the center that are 6 units from the center.

3. Draw circle.

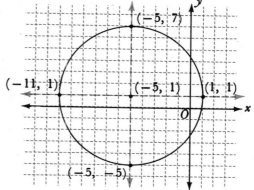

## Exercises 15.9

Ⓐ **1–12.** For each inequality, **(a)** name the boundary line(s) and **(b)** determine if its graph is a solid or a dashed line.

Assignment Guide
*Oral:* 1–24
*Written:* Min. 25–43 odd
　　　　 Reg. 25–47 odd
　　　　 Max. 25–53 odd

**1.** $x > 5$
　**a.** $x = 5$; **b.** Dashed

**2.** $x < -2$
　**a.** $x = -2$; **b.** Dashed

**3.** $y \geq 4$
　**a.** $y = 4$;　**b.** Solid

**4.** $y \geq x$
　**a.** $y = x$; **b.** Solid

**5.** $y < -x$
　**a.** $y = -x$; **b.** Dashed

**6.** $y \geq 3x + 5$
　**a.** $y = 3x + 5$; **b.** Solid

**7.** $y < -\frac{2}{5}x - 4$

**8.** $y \leq \frac{1}{4}x + 1$

**9.** $-3 < y < 1$

**10.** $-10 < y \leq -4$

**11.** $-2 \leq x \leq 2$

**12.** $1 \leq x < 6$

**13–20.** Determine **(a)** the coordinates of the center and **(b)** the radius of each circle.

**13.** $x^2 + y^2 = 2^2$　**a.** $(0, 0)$;　**b.** 2

**14.** $x^2 + y^2 = 100$
　　**a.** $(0, 0)$;　　**b.** 10

**15.** $x^2 + (y - 3)^2 = 9$
　　**a.** $(0, 3)$;　**b.** 3

**16.** $(x + 1)^2 + y^2 = 36$
　　**a.** $(-1, 0)$;　**b.** 6

**17.** $(x - 3)^2 + (y - 8)^2 = 49$
　　**a.** $(3, 8)$;　**b.** 7

**18.** $(x - 4)^2 + (y + 6)^2 = 81$
　　**a.** $(4, -6)$;　**b.** 9

**19.** $(x + 2)^2 + (y - 5)^2 = 25$
　　**a.** $(-2, 5)$; **b.** 5

**20.** $(x + 7)^2 + (y + 5)^2 = 64$
　　**a.** $(-7, -5)$; **b.** 8

**7. a.** $y = -\frac{2}{5}x - 4$
　　**b.** Dashed

**8. a.** $y = \frac{1}{4}x + 1$
　　**b.** Solid

**9. a.** $y = -3$, $y = 1$
　　**b.** Both dashed

**10. a.** $y = -10$, $y = -4$
　　**b.** Dashed, solid

**11. a.** $x = -2$, $x = 2$
　　**b.** Both solid

**12. a.** $x = 1$, $x = 6$
　　**b.** Solid, dashed

SECTION 15.9　　LOCUS IN THE COORDINATE PLANE　　549

**21–24.** Determine which graph below is described by each inequality.

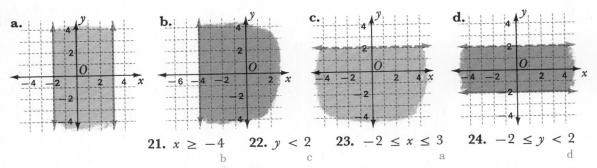

**a.**  **b.**  **c.**  **d.**

**21.** $x \geq -4$    **22.** $y < 2$    **23.** $-2 \leq x \leq 3$    **24.** $-2 \leq y < 2$
   b              c                 a                     d

Ⓑ **25–44.** Draw the graphs for Exercises 1–20. Use a separate pair of axes for each.

**45–50.** Solve each inequality for $y$. Then draw the graph.

**45.** $x + y < 3$
   $y < -x + 3$

**46.** $5x + y > 7$
   $y > -5x + 7$

**47.** $y + 2 > -4$
   $y > -6$

**48.** $3y - 5 \leq 4$
   $y \leq 3$

**49.** $25x + 50y \leq -100$
   $y \leq -\frac{1}{2}x - 2$

**50.** $5y - 3x \geq 10$
   $y \geq \frac{3}{5}x + 2$

**51–63.** Write an algebraic condition for each. Then draw the graph.

**51.** all points with $x$-coordinates less than 6    $x < 6$

**52.** all points with $y$-coordinates greater than or equal to $-4$    $y \geq -4$

**53.** all points whose $x$-coordinates have absolute values less than 5
   $|x| < 5$ or $-5 < x < 5$

**54.** all points whose $y$-coordinates have absolute values less than $8\frac{1}{2}$
   $|y| < 8\frac{1}{2}$ or $-8\frac{1}{2} < y < 8\frac{1}{2}$

**55.** all points in the 3rd quadrant  $x < 0$ and $y < 0$

**56.** all points in the 4th quadrant  $x > 0$ and $y < 0$

**57.** a circle with center (0, 0) and radius 3
   $x^2 + y^2 = 9$

**58.** a circle with center $(-2, 8)$ and radius 5    $(x + 2)^2 + (y - 8)^2 = 25$

**59.** a circle with center $(2, -3)$ that contains point $(-1, -3)$
   $(x - 2)^2 + (y + 3)^2 = 9$

**60.** a circle with center (5, 7) that is tangent to the $x$-axis
   $(x - 5)^2 + (y - 7)^2 = 49$

Ⓒ **61.** a circle inscribed in a square with vertices $(-2, 5)$, $(2, 5)$, $(2, 1)$, and $(-2, 1)$
   $x^2 + (y - 3)^2 = 4$

**62.** the interior of a circle with center $(-2, 5)$ and radius 4
   $(x + 2)^2 + (y - 5)^2 < 16$

**63.** $\triangle ABC$ and its interior, given $A(-3, -2)$, $B(0, 0)$, and $C(2, -3)$
   $y \leq \frac{2}{3}x$ and $y \leq -\frac{3}{2}x$ and $y \geq -\frac{1}{5}x - \frac{13}{5}$

# Transformations and Coordinates

Some transformations are easy to describe with coordinates.

| $(x, y)$ | $(x + 4, y - 2)$ |
|---|---|
| $A(-3, 4)$ | $A'(1, 2)$ |
| $B(0, 0)$ | $B'(4, -2)$ |
| $C(1, 3)$ | $C'(5, 1)$ |
| $D(-1, 1\frac{1}{3})$ | $D'(3, -\frac{2}{3})$ |
| $E(\frac{1}{2}, 1\frac{1}{2})$ | $E'(4\frac{1}{2}, -\frac{1}{2})$ |

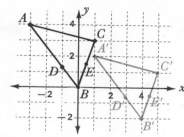

| Suggested Class Time | | | |
|---|---|---|---|
| Course | Min. | Reg. | Max. |
| Days | 0 | 0 | 1 |

Notice that adding 4 to the $x$-coordinate of each point slides a figure 4 units to the right. Adding $-2$ to the $y$-coordinate of each point slides a figure 2 units down.

The magnitude of the slide is the distance between any point and its image, and can be found by the distance formula. In this case,

$$\sqrt{(-3 - 1)^2 + (4 - 2)^2} = \sqrt{16 + 4}$$
$$= \sqrt{20} = 2\sqrt{5} \approx 4.5 \quad \blacktriangleleft \text{magnitude}$$

A slide of magnitude $\sqrt{a^2 + b^2}$ can be described as

$$(x, y) \rightarrow (x + a, y + b)$$

where $a$ and $b$ are any two real numbers, $(x, y)$ is any point in the coordinate plane, and $(x + a, y + b)$ is its image.

| $(x, y)$ | $(3x, 3y)$ |
|---|---|
| $A(-1, 2)$ | $A'(-3, 6)$ |
| $B(2, 0)$ | $B'(6, 0)$ |
| $C(2, 1)$ | $C'(6, 3)$ |
| $D(1, 2)$ | $D'(3, 6)$ |

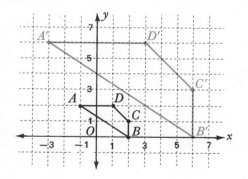

Notice that multiplying both coordinates of each point by 3 gives a size change of magnitude 3, center $(0, 0)$.

A size change of magnitude $k$ and center $(0, 0)$ can be described as

$$(x, y) \rightarrow (kx, ky)$$

where $k$ is any positive real number, $(x, y)$ is any point in the coordinate plane, and $(kx, ky)$ is its image.

Other transformations can be similarly described with coordinates.

# Exercises 15.10 ▮▮▮▮▮▮▮▮▮▮▮▮▮▮▮▮▮▮▮▮▮▮▮▮▮▮▮▮▮▮▮▮▮▮▮▮▮▮▮▮▮▮▮▮▮▮▮▮▮▮▮▮▮▮▮▮▮▮▮▮▮▮

**Assignment Guide**
*Oral:* Max. 1–6
*Written:* Max. 7–29 odd

Ⓐ **1.** Adding 4 to the $x$-coordinate of each point slides a figure __4__ units to the (**right**, left).

**2.** Adding $-2$ to the $y$-coordinate of each point slides a figure __2__ units (up, **down**).

**3.** Adding $-3$ to the __$x$__-coordinate of each point slides a figure 3 units to the left.

**4.** Adding $1\frac{1}{2}$ to the __$y$__-coordinate of each point slides a figure $1\frac{1}{2}$ units up.

**5.** Adding __$-1.6$__ to the $x$-coordinate and __2.3__ to the $y$-coordinate of each point slides a figure 1.6 units left and 2.3 units up.

**6.** Multiplying both coordinates of each point of a figure by __$\frac{1}{2}$__ gives a size change of magnitude $\frac{1}{2}$ and center $(0, 0)$.

Ⓑ **7–18.** Draw the polygon in the coordinate plane. Then use the transformation described to draw the image of the polygon.

| | VERTICES OF POLYGON | TRANSFORMATION |
|---|---|---|
| | **7.** $A(3, 5)$, $B(-2, 7)$, $C(0, 0)$ | $(x, y) \rightarrow (x - 3, y + 8)$ |
| **19.** Slide, magnitude $\sqrt{73}$ | **8.** $E(4, 0)$, $F(0, -4)$, $G(3, -8)$ | $(x, y) \rightarrow (x + 2, y + 10)$ |
| **20.** Slide, magnitude $2\sqrt{26}$ | **9.** $H(2, 9)$, $I(7, 9)$, $J(9, 5)$, $K(2, 3)$ | $(x, y) \rightarrow (x - 10, y - 2)$ |
| **21.** Slide, magnitude $2\sqrt{26}$ | **10.** $L(3, 2)$, $M(8, 4)$, $N(8, 7)$, $Z(6, 7)$ | $(x, y) \rightarrow (x - 9, y + 7)$ |
| **22.** Slide, magnitude $\sqrt{130}$ | **11.** $P(2, 5)$, $Q(5, 2)$, $R(5, -2)$, $S(2, -5)$ | $(x, y) \rightarrow (2x, 2y)$ |
| **23.** Size change, magnitude 2, center $(0, 0)$ | **12.** $A(4, 4)$, $B(6, 0)$, $C(4, -4)$, $D(0, -6)$ | $(x, y) \rightarrow (\frac{1}{2}x, \frac{1}{2}y)$ |
| **24.** Size change, magnitude $\frac{1}{2}$, center $(0, 0)$ | **13.** $K(3, 6)$, $L(6, 9)$, $M(9, 0)$ | $(x, y) \rightarrow (\frac{1}{3}x, \frac{1}{3}y)$ |
| **25.** Size change, magnitude $\frac{1}{3}$, center $(0, 0)$ | **14.** $P(2, 0)$, $Q(6, 0)$, $R(6, -4)$, $S(2, -4)$ | $(x, y) \rightarrow (3x, 3y)$ |
| **26.** Size change, magnitude 3, center $(0, 0)$ | **15.** $W(2, 5)$, $X(5, 2)$, $Y(7, 4)$, $Z(5, 8)$ | $(x, y) \rightarrow (-x, y)$ |
| **27.** Reflection over $y$-axis | **16.** $A(4, 0)$, $B(6, 4)$, $C(1, 1)$ | $(x, y) \rightarrow (y, x)$ |
| **28.** Reflection over line $x = y$ | **17.** $G(3, -1)$, $H(7, 5)$, $I(7, 0)$ | $(x, y) \rightarrow (-y, x)$ |
| **29.** 90° turn counterclockwise around $(0, 0)$ | **18.** $K(7, 1)$, $L(2, 0)$, $M(6, -6)$ | $(x, y) \rightarrow (y, -x)$ |
| **30.** 90° turn clockwise around $(0, 0)$ | | |

Ⓒ **19–30.** Describe each transformation in Exercises 7–18 as a reflection, slide, turn, or size change. If a magnitude, center, or reflecting line is involved, tell what it is.

**Suggested Class Time**

| | Min. | Reg. | Max. |
|---|---|---|---|
| Course | | | |
| Days | 1 | 1 | 1 |

**1.** The $x$-axis and the $y$-axis determine the ———— plane.
Coordinate

**2.** The ———— of a point are given as an ordered pair. Coordinates

**3.** The origin is the point at $\underline{(0, 0)}$.

**4.** A point whose $x$-coordinate is $\underline{0}$ is on the $y$-axis.

**5.** Graph the following ordered pairs using the same pair of axes:
$(5, 7), (7, 5), (0, 1), (-3, 0), (-6, 2), (6, -2), (2, -6), (-6, -2)$

**6.** What is the distance between points $(x_1, y_1)$ and $(x_2, y_2)$?

**7.** A horizontal line through point $(1, 4)$ and a vertical line through point $(-5, -2)$ intersect at point $\underline{(-5, 4)}$.

**8–10.** Find the distance between the given points.

**8.** $(0, 4), (5, 4)$ ₅ 5

**9.** $(3, -2), (3, 7)$ ₉ 9

**10.** $(-7, 5), (2, -8)$ $5\sqrt{10}$

**11.** Is a triangle with vertices $(5, -8), (-5, -1)$, and $(3, 8)$ isosceles? No

**12–13.** Find the midpoint of the segment joining each pair of points.

**12.** $(0, 0), (6, -10)$ $(3, -5)$

**13.** $(-2\sqrt{3}, -7\sqrt{5}), (-10\sqrt{3}, -\sqrt{5})$
$(-6\sqrt{3}, -4\sqrt{5})$

**14.** Find the midpoint of each side of a triangle with vertices $(-5, -4), (-1, 3)$, and $(3, 0)$.
$(-3, -\frac{1}{2}), (1, 1\frac{1}{2}), (-1, -2)$

**15.** If a segment has an endpoint at $(-3, -7)$, and its midpoint is at $(4, -2)$, find the coordinates of its other endpoint.
$(11, 3)$

**16–18.** Find the slope of the line that contains the given points.

**16.** $(0, 0), (3, -7)$ $-\frac{7}{3}$

**17.** $(-4, -9), (7, 2)$ 1

**18.** $(\frac{1}{2}, \frac{5}{12}), (\frac{3}{4}, \frac{7}{8})$ $\frac{11}{6}$

**19.** Graph the line that contains point $(5, -8)$ and has slope $\frac{2}{9}$.

**20.** Are points $(0, 0), (2, 5)$, and $(-4, -10)$ collinear? Yes

**21.** The graph of a linear equation is a $\underline{\text{Line}}$.

**22.** $y - y_1 = m(x - x_1)$ is the $\underline{\text{Point-slope}}$ ———— form of an equation of a line.

**23–24.** Find the standard form of the equation of a line that

**23.** has slope 3 and contains point $(4, -3)$ $3x - y = 15$

**24.** contains points $(2, -16)$ and $(-34, -6)$ $5x + 18y = -278$

**15.1**

**Assignment Guide**
*Written:* Min. 1–33 odd; 37
Reg. 1–41 odd
Max. 1–43 odd

**15.2**

**15.3**

**15.4**

**15.5**

**15.6**

**25.** $y = mx + b$ is the ____ Slope-intercept form of an equation of a line.

**26.** The $y$-intercept of a line that contains point $(0, -7)$ is ___$-7$___.

**27.** Graph $y = -2x - 3$.     **28.** Graph $10x - 7y = 21$.

**15.7**

**29.** If two nonvertical lines are parallel, then their slopes are ___Equal___.

**30.** If two nonvertical lines are perpendicular, then the product of their slopes is ___$-1$___.

**31.** Are the graphs of $9x - 2y = -5$ and $4x + 6y = 9$ parallel, perpendicular, or neither?   Neither

**32–33.** Find the standard form of the equation of a line that

**32.** contains $(11, 3)$ and is perpendicular to a line with slope $-5$
$x - 5y = -4$

**33.** contains $(0, 0)$ and is parallel to the line through $(-3, 5)$ and $(9, 1)$
$x + 3y = 0$

**15.8**

**34.** If three vertices of a rectangle are at $(0, 7b)$, $(0, 0)$, and $(4a, 0)$, find the coordinates of the fourth vertex.     $(4a, 7b)$

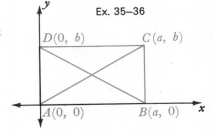
Ex. 35–36

35. *Given:* $\square ABCD$, $A$ at $(0, 0)$, $\overline{AB}$ on $x$-axis
*Prove:* $\overline{AC} \cong \overline{BD}$

$D(0, b)$     $C(a, b)$
$A(0, 0)$     $B(a, 0)$

**35–36.** Consider this statement: The diagonals of a rectangle are congruent.

**35.** State the *Given* and *Prove* in terms of the given figure.

**36.** Write a coordinate proof of the statement.   *Sketch of Proof:* By the distance formula, $AC = DB = \sqrt{a^2 + b^2}$.

**15.9**

**37–39.** Graph each inequality on a separate pair of axes.

**37.** $y < \frac{2}{5}x + 1$     **38.** $8x + 3y \geq -6$     **39.** $-5 \leq y < 4$

**40–42.** Write an algebraic condition for each. Then draw the graph.

**40.** all points with $x$-coordinates greater than $-4$   $x > -4$

**41.** all points in the 2nd quadrant
$x < 0$ and $y > 0$

**42.** a circle with center $(0, 3)$ and radius 5   $x^2 + (y - 3)^2 = 25$

**15.10**

**43–44.** A triangle has vertices at $A(0, 0)$, $B(4, 6)$, and $C(2, -4)$. In the coordinate plane, draw the triangle and its image using the given transformation.

**43.** $(x, y) \rightarrow (x + 2, y - 3)$     **44.** $(x, y) \rightarrow (\frac{1}{2}x, \frac{1}{2}y)$

**1–2.** Given $A(3, 7)$, $B(7, 3)$, $C(-5, 0)$, and $D(-7, 5)$,

**1.** Draw quadrilateral $ABCD$ in the coordinate plane.

**2.** Find the length of each side of quadrilateral $ABCD$. $AB = 4\sqrt{2}$, $BC = 3\sqrt{17}$, $CD = \sqrt{29}$, $DA = 2\sqrt{26}$

**3–4.** The vertices of $\triangle RST$ are $R(6, 3)$, $S(-4, 5)$, and $T(4, 9)$.

**3.** Find the coordinates of the midpoint for each side of $\triangle RST$.
$(1, 4), (0, 7), (5, 6)$

**4.** Find the slope of each side of $\triangle RST$. $-\frac{1}{5}, \frac{1}{2}, -3$

**5.** Show that $E(-3, 5)$, $F(2, 2)$, and $G(5, 1)$ are not collinear.

**6.** Graph $y - 4 = \frac{2}{3}(x - 1)$.

**7.** Graph $3x + 4y = 12$.

**8–12.** Find the standard form of the equation of the line described.

**8.** contains points $(3, -1)$ and $(-2, 5)$ $6x + 5y = 13$

**9.** slope $-\frac{5}{2}$, $y$-intercept $-2$
$5x + 2y = -4$

**10.** slope 3, contains point $(5, -1)$
$3x - y = 16$

**11.** parallel to the graph of $y = 2x$, contains point $(0, 4)$
$2x - y = -4$

**12.** perpendicular to the graph of $y = 2x$, contains point $(-11, 2)$
$x + 2y = -7$

**13.** Prove that the segment joining the midpoints of the diagonals of a trapezoid is parallel to its bases. HINT: Start by stating the *Given* and *Prove* in terms of the given figure.

**14–16.** Graph each on a separate pair of axes.

**14.** $x < 3$

**15.** $-2 \le y \le 4$

**16.** $y > \frac{1}{3}x + 1$

**17.** Write an algebraic condition to describe the graph at the right.
$x \le 1$ and $y < 3$

**18.** Write an algebraic condition to describe all points whose $x$-coordinates have absolute values less than $3\frac{1}{2}$. $|x| < 3\frac{1}{2}$ or $-3\frac{1}{2} < x < 3\frac{1}{2}$

**19–20.** Find the equation of each circle.

**19.** center at the origin, radius 3
$x^2 + y^2 = 9$

**20.** center at $(-2, 3)$, radius 5
$(x + 2)^2 + (y - 3)^2 = 25$

**21–22.** A triangle has vertices at $P(3, 5)$, $Q(-2, 3)$, and $R(-3, 0)$. In the coordinate plane, draw the triangle and its image using the given transformation.

**21.** $(x, y) \rightarrow (x - 2, y + 1)$

**22.** $(x, y) \rightarrow (x, -y)$

Assignment Guide
*Written:* Min. 1–12; 14–16
Reg. 1–20
Max. 1–22

**5.** Slope of $\overline{EF}$: $-\frac{3}{5}$
of $\overline{FG}$: $-\frac{1}{3}$
of $\overline{EG}$: $-\frac{1}{2}$

**13.** *Given:* Trap. $ABCD$, $A$ at $(0, 0)$, $\overline{AB}$ on $x$-axis; $R$, $S$ midpts. of $\overline{AC}$, $\overline{BD}$, respect. *Prove:* $\overline{RS} \parallel \overline{AB} \parallel \overline{DC}$ *Sketch of Proof:* By midpt. form., $R$ and $S$ are at $(d, c)$ and $(a + b, c)$. Slopes of $\overline{RS}$, $\overline{AB}$, and $\overline{DC}$ are all 0.

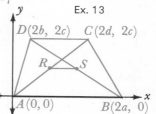

Ex. 13
$D(2b, 2c)$  $C(2d, 2c)$
$R$  $S$
$A(0,0)$  $B(2a, 0)$

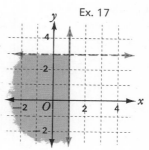

Ex. 17

# ■ Cumulative Review: Chapters 8–15 ■

**Ch. 8**

**3.** Yes; A pt. in the ⊥ bis. plane of a seg. is equi- dist. from the endpts. of the seg.

**1.** State the definition of a line perpendicular to a plane.

*See page 266.*

**2.** State the Basic Theorem for Perpendiculars.

*See page 270.*

**3–7.** Plane *n* is the perpendicular bisecting plane of $\overline{RS}$ at *T*. Points *T*, *W*, and *U* are in *n*. Points *R*, *S*, *Z*, *T*, and *X* are in plane *p*.

**3.** Is $RW = SW$? If so, why?

**4.** Is $\overleftrightarrow{TU} \perp \overleftrightarrow{RS}$? If so, why?   Yes; Def. of ⊥ line and plane

**5.** Is $RT < RW$? If so, why?

**6.** If $\overleftrightarrow{RS} \perp \overleftrightarrow{ZX}$ at *T*, is $\overleftrightarrow{ZX}$ in *n*? If so, why?

**7.** How many planes are perpendicular to $\overleftrightarrow{RS}$ at *R*?   One

Ex. 3–7

**Ch. 9**

**5.** Yes; Shortest seg. to a plane from a pt. not in the plane is the ⊥ seg.

**6.** Yes; If line and plane are ⊥, they intersect at a pt., and the plane contains every line ⊥ to given line at the pt.

**12.** *Sketch of Proof:* By def. of median, $MC = MB$; $AR$ is height of both △s.

Area △ABM
  $= \frac{1}{2}(MB)(AR)$
  $= \frac{1}{2}(MC)(AR)$

Area △AMC
  $= \frac{1}{2}(MC)(AR)$

So the areas are equal.

**8–11.** Find the area of each figure.

**8.** square with a side of length $2\frac{1}{2}$ cm    $6\frac{1}{4}$ cm²

**9.** rhombus with diagonals of lengths $3\frac{1}{2}$ and 5    $8\frac{3}{4}$

**10.** parallelogram with a base 4.2 cm long and a corresponding height of 16 mm

6.72 cm² or 672 mm²

**11.** trapezoid with height 7 and bases of lengths 6 and 10

56

**12.** Given: △ABC, median $\overline{AM}$, altitude $\overline{AR}$

Prove: Area △ABM = area △AMC

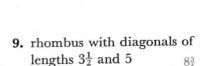

**13.** Simplify:    **a.** $\sqrt{75}$   $5\sqrt{3}$   **b.** $\sqrt{\frac{1}{5}}$   $\frac{\sqrt{5}}{5}$   **c.** $\frac{1}{\sqrt{2}}$   $\frac{\sqrt{2}}{2}$

**14.** If the lengths of the legs of a right triangle are 4 and 6, find the length of the hypotenuse (in simplified radical form).    $2\sqrt{13}$

**15.** In a 30-60-90° triangle, the hypotenuse has length 16. Find the length of each leg.    $8, 8\sqrt{3}$

**16.** Can a right triangle have sides of lengths 16, 18, and 20?   No

**17.** In △ABC, $m\angle B = 90$. Find $AB$ (in simplified radical form) if $AB = BC$ and $AC = 10$.    $5\sqrt{2}$

**18–20.** Let $\dfrac{a}{4} = \dfrac{3}{b}$.

**18.** $ab = \underline{\quad 12 \quad}$  **19.** $\dfrac{a}{3} = \underline{\quad \frac{4}{b} \quad}$  **20.** If $b = 5$, $a = \underline{\quad \frac{12}{5} \quad}$

**21.** Given: Isosceles rt. △s
$XYZ$ and $KLM$
Prove: $\triangle XYZ \sim \triangle KLM$

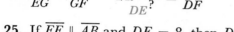

**22.** Given: Trapezoid $RSTU$
with $\overline{RS} \parallel \overline{TU}$
Prove: $\triangle PRS \sim \triangle PTU$

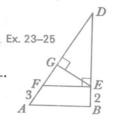

**23–25.** Refer to the figure.

**23.** $\dfrac{DG}{EG} = \dfrac{?\,EG}{GF}$  **24.** $\dfrac{DG}{DE\,?} = \dfrac{DE}{DF}$

Ex. 23–25

**25.** If $\overline{FE} \parallel \overline{AB}$ and $DE = 8$, then $DF = \underline{\quad 12 \quad}$.

**26.** If $a:b:c = 2:5:3$ and $a = 6$, find $b$ and $c$.
$b = 15,\ c = 9$

**21.** *Plan:* Form proportions, use LL Similarity Thm.

**22.** *Plan:* Use Alt. Int. ∠s Theorem and AA Similarity Theorem.

---

**27–32.** $\overleftrightarrow{CA}$ is tangent to $\odot X$ at $A$.

**27.** Name 4 radii.
$\overline{AX},\ \overline{GX},\ \overline{EX},\ \overline{FX}$

**28.** Is $m\widehat{GAF} > 180$? Why?
Yes; $\widehat{GAF}$ is major arc.

Ex. 27–32

**29.** If $AD = 5$, $GD = 3$, $DE = 2$, find $DF$. $\quad 3\frac{1}{3}$

**30.** If $CG = 3$, $GF = 9$, find $CA$. $\quad 6$

**31.** Find $m\angle C$ if $m\widehat{AG} = 62$ and $m\widehat{AF} = 160$. $\quad 49$

**32.** Find $m\angle ADG$ if $m\widehat{AG} = 64$ and $m\widehat{FE} = 62$. $\quad 63$

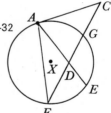

**33.** Given: $\odot C$, diameter $\overline{XZ}$, chords $\overline{YZ}$ and $\overline{WZ}$, $\overline{YZ} \cong \overline{WZ}$
Prove: $\triangle XYZ \cong \triangle XWZ$  *Plan:* Use Semicircle Thm. to show $\triangle XYZ$, $\triangle XWZ$ are rt. △s. Use HL Thm. to prove they are $\cong$.

Ex. 33–34

**34.** Given: $\odot C$, chords $\overline{XY}$ and $\overline{XW}$, diameter $\overline{XZ}$, $\angle 1 \cong \angle 2$
Prove: $\overline{XY} \cong \overline{XW}$  *Plan:* Use Semicircle Thm. to show $\triangle XYZ$, $\triangle XWZ$ are rt. △s. Use HA Thm. to prove they are $\cong$. $\overline{XY}$, $\overline{XW}$ are corres. parts.

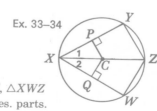

**35–36.** Given: Sphere $M$

Ex. 35–36

**35.** $\underline{\quad \overline{PN} \quad}$ is a chord of the sphere.

**36.** If $T$ is in the interior of sphere $M$, then $TM\ (=, >, \underline{\leq})\ MN$.

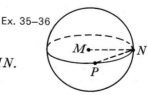

**37.** If a plane and a sphere intersect at exactly one point, they are
<u>Tangent</u>.

**Ch. 12**

**38–39.** Square *ABCD* is inscribed in ⊙ *O*. *AB* = 8.

**38.** Find *OE*.   4

**39.** Find *OA*.

   $4\sqrt{2}$

**40.** A regular polygon has a perimeter of 100 and an apothem of 10. Find its area.   500

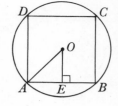

**41–44.** Use the given measure of a circle to find each missing number. Leave answers in terms of π.

| | radius | diameter | circumference | area |
|---|---|---|---|---|
| **41.** | 5 | 10 | $10\pi$ | $25\pi$ |
| **42.** | 9 | 18 | $18\pi$ | $81\pi$ |
| **43.** | 4 | 8 | $8\pi$ | $16\pi$ |
| **44.** | 25 | 50 | $50\pi$ | $625\pi$ |

NOTE: **Leave answers 45–46 in terms of π.**

**45.** Find the length of a 135° arc in a circle with radius 3.   $\frac{9}{4}\pi$

**46.** A circle has radius 9. Find the area of a sector with a 10° arc.   $\frac{9}{4}\pi$

**Ch. 13**

**47–51.** True or False? Draw a sketch to illustrate each true statement. Sketch a counterexample for each false statement.

**48.** F (The intersection of 2 walls of a room is ‖ to the other 2 walls.)

**47.** Two planes perpendicular to the same line are parallel.   T

**48.** Two planes parallel to the same line are parallel.

**49.** Two lines perpendicular to the same plane are parallel.   T

**50.** Two lines parallel to the same plane are parallel.
   F (They may intersect or be skew.)

**52.** *Sketch of Proof:* By def., ∠*ABC* and ∠*XYZ* are plane ∠s of ∠*C*-$\overleftrightarrow{BY}$-*X*, and plane ∠s of a dihedral ∠ are ≅.

**53.** *Sketch of Proof:* By def., ∠*PQR* is a plane ∠ of ∠*P*-$\overleftrightarrow{SQ}$-*R*. But, since $(PQ)^2 + (QR)^2 = (PR)^2$, △*PQR* is a rt. △ and ∠*PQR* is a rt. ∠. So ∠*P*-$\overleftrightarrow{SQ}$-*R* is a rt. dihedral ∠, and the planes are ⊥.

**51.** Three parallel lines are coplanar.
   F (Consider lateral edges of triang. prism.)

**52.** Given: Dihedral ∠*C*-$\overleftrightarrow{BY}$-*X*, planes *ABC* and *XYZ* are ⊥ to $\overleftrightarrow{BY}$.

   Prove: ∠*ABC* ≅ ∠*XYZ*

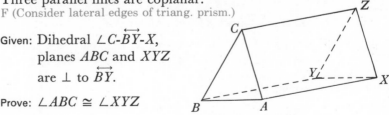

**53.** Given: Dihedral ∠*P*-$\overleftrightarrow{SQ}$-*R*, plane *PQR* ⊥ $\overleftrightarrow{SQ}$, $(PQ)^2 + (QR)^2 = (PR)^2$

   Prove: Plane *PQS* ⊥ plane *RQS*

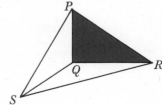

**54–60.** Find the volume of each figure.

**54.** right triangular prism, height 3 m, base edges of length 2 m $3\sqrt{3}\ \text{m}^3$

**55.** right circular cylinder, radius 42 cm, height 6.5 mm $1146.6\pi\ \text{cm}^3\ \text{or}\ 1\,146\,600\ \text{mm}^3$

**56.** oblique prism, height 13, square base with perimeter 12 $117$

**57.** oblique circular cylinder, radius $\frac{2}{3}$, height 12 $\frac{16}{3}\pi$

**58.** circular cone, radius 6, height 2 $24\pi$

**59.** triangular pyramid, height 9, base area $7\sqrt{2}$ $21\sqrt{2}$

**60.** sphere, radius 2.1 $12.348\pi$

**61–62.** Find the lateral area and the surface area of each figure.

**61.** prism in Exercise 54 $18\ \text{m}^2,\ (18 + 2\sqrt{3})\ \text{m}^2$

**62.** cylinder in Exercise 55

**62.** $54.6\pi\ \text{cm}^2\ \text{or}\ 5460\pi\ \text{mm}^2,$ $3582.6\pi\ \text{cm}^2\ \text{or}$ $358\,260\pi\ \text{mm}^2$

**63.** Find the surface area of a sphere with radius 11. $484\pi$

**64.** GIVEN: A pyramid of height $h$ whose base is a rhombus with diagonals of lengths $d_1$ and $d_2$
   PROVE: The volume $(V)$ of the pyramid is equal to $\frac{1}{6}h\,d_1 d_2$.

**64.** *Sketch of Proof:* By the Volume Thm. for Pyramid, $V = \frac{1}{3}Bh$. By the Area Thm. for a Rhombus, $B = \frac{1}{2}d_1 d_2$. Substituting, $V = \frac{1}{6}hd_1 d_2$.

**65–68.** Given $A(-1, -2)$, $B(9, 5)$, $C(3, 7)$, and $D(-3, 2)$,

**65.** Draw quadrilateral $ABCD$ in the coordinate plane.

**66.** Find the coordinates of the midpoint of $\overline{BD}$. $(3, 3\frac{1}{2})$

**67.** Find the length of $\overline{AB}$. $\sqrt{149}$

**68.** Find the slope of $\overline{CB}$. $-\frac{1}{3}$

**69–71.** Refer to quadrilateral $ABCD$ in Exercises 65–68. Find the standard form of the equation of a line that

**69.** contains $B$ and $C$ $x + 3y = 24$

**70.** contains $A$ and is parallel to $\overleftrightarrow{BC}$ $x + 3y = -7$

**71.** contains the midpoint of $\overline{AD}$ and is perpendicular to $\overleftrightarrow{AD}$ $x - 2y = -2$

**72–75.** Graph each on a separate pair of axes.

**72.** $(y - 3) = -\frac{2}{3}(x + 4)$

**73.** $5 \leq y < -1$

**74.** $5x + 6y \geq -12$

**75.** $x^2 + (y - 7)^2 = 64$

**76.** Using coordinates, prove that opposite sides of a parallelogram are congruent. HINT: Let $A(0, 0)$, $B(a, 0)$, $C(a + b, c)$, and $D(b, c)$ be the vertices of the parallelogram.

**76.** *Sketch of Proof:* By the distance formula, $AB = a = CD$ and $AD = \sqrt{b^2 + c^2} = BC$. So $\overline{AD} \cong \overline{BC}$ and $\overline{AB} \cong \overline{CD}$.

# POSTULATES

# NAMED THEOREMS

# CONSTRUCTIONS

## SYMBOLS

## SQUARES AND SQUARE ROOTS

| $n$ | $n^2$ | $\sqrt{n}$ | $n$ | $n^2$ | $\sqrt{n}$ | $n$ | $n^2$ | $\sqrt{n}$ |
|---|---|---|---|---|---|---|---|---|
| 1 | 1 | 1.000 | 51 | 2 601 | 7.141 | 101 | 10 201 | 10.050 |
| 2 | 4 | 1.414 | 52 | 2 704 | 7.211 | 102 | 10 404 | 10.100 |
| 3 | 9 | 1.732 | 53 | 2 809 | 7.280 | 103 | 10 609 | 10.149 |
| 4 | 16 | 2.000 | 54 | 2 916 | 7.348 | 104 | 10 816 | 10.198 |
| 5 | 25 | 2.236 | 55 | 3 025 | 7.416 | 105 | 11 025 | 10.247 |
| 6 | 36 | 2.449 | 56 | 3 136 | 7.483 | 106 | 11 236 | 10.296 |
| 7 | 49 | 2.646 | 57 | 3 249 | 7.550 | 107 | 11 449 | 10.344 |
| 8 | 64 | 2.828 | 58 | 3 364 | 7.616 | 108 | 11 664 | 10.392 |
| 9 | 81 | 3.000 | 59 | 3 481 | 7.681 | 109 | 11 881 | 10.440 |
| 10 | 100 | 3.162 | 60 | 3 600 | 7.746 | 110 | 12 100 | 10.488 |
| 11 | 121 | 3.317 | 61 | 3 721 | 7.810 | 111 | 12 321 | 10.536 |
| 12 | 144 | 3.464 | 62 | 3 844 | 7.874 | 112 | 12 544 | 10.583 |
| 13 | 169 | 3.606 | 63 | 3 969 | 7.937 | 113 | 12 769 | 10.630 |
| 14 | 196 | 3.742 | 64 | 4 096 | 8.000 | 114 | 12 996 | 10.677 |
| 15 | 225 | 3.873 | 65 | 4 225 | 8.062 | 115 | 13 225 | 10.724 |
| 16 | 256 | 4.000 | 66 | 4 356 | 8.124 | 116 | 13 456 | 10.770 |
| 17 | 289 | 4.123 | 67 | 4 489 | 8.185 | 117 | 13 689 | 10.817 |
| 18 | 324 | 4.243 | 68 | 4 624 | 8.246 | 118 | 13 924 | 10.863 |
| 19 | 361 | 4.359 | 69 | 4 761 | 8.307 | 119 | 14 161 | 10.909 |
| 20 | 400 | 4.472 | 70 | 4 900 | 8.367 | 120 | 14 400 | 10.954 |
| 21 | 441 | 4.583 | 71 | 5 041 | 8.426 | 121 | 14 641 | 11.000 |
| 22 | 484 | 4.690 | 72 | 5 184 | 8.485 | 122 | 14 884 | 11.045 |
| 23 | 529 | 4.796 | 73 | 5 329 | 8.544 | 123 | 15 129 | 11.091 |
| 24 | 576 | 4.899 | 74 | 5 476 | 8.602 | 124 | 15 376 | 11.136 |
| 25 | 625 | 5.000 | 75 | 5 625 | 8.660 | 125 | 15 625 | 11.180 |
| 26 | 676 | 5.099 | 76 | 5 776 | 8.718 | 126 | 15 876 | 11.225 |
| 27 | 729 | 5.196 | 77 | 5 929 | 8.775 | 127 | 16 129 | 11.269 |
| 28 | 784 | 5.292 | 78 | 6 084 | 8.832 | 128 | 16 384 | 11.314 |
| 29 | 841 | 5.385 | 79 | 6 241 | 8.888 | 129 | 16 641 | 11.358 |
| 30 | 900 | 5.477 | 80 | 6 400 | 8.944 | 130 | 16 900 | 11.402 |
| 31 | 961 | 5.568 | 81 | 6 561 | 9.000 | 131 | 17 161 | 11.446 |
| 32 | 1 024 | 5.657 | 82 | 6 724 | 9.055 | 132 | 17 424 | 11.489 |
| 33 | 1 089 | 5.745 | 83 | 6 889 | 9.110 | 133 | 17 689 | 11.533 |
| 34 | 1 156 | 5.831 | 84 | 7 056 | 9.165 | 134 | 17 956 | 11.576 |
| 35 | 1 225 | 5.916 | 85 | 7 225 | 9.220 | 135 | 18 225 | 11.619 |
| 36 | 1 296 | 6.000 | 86 | 7 396 | 9.274 | 136 | 18 496 | 11.662 |
| 37 | 1 369 | 6.083 | 87 | 7 569 | 9.327 | 137 | 18 769 | 11.705 |
| 38 | 1 444 | 6.164 | 88 | 7 744 | 9.381 | 138 | 19 044 | 11.747 |
| 39 | 1 521 | 6.245 | 89 | 7 921 | 9.434 | 139 | 19 321 | 11.790 |
| 40 | 1 600 | 6.325 | 90 | 8 100 | 9.487 | 140 | 19 600 | 11.832 |
| 41 | 1 681 | 6.403 | 91 | 8 281 | 9.539 | 141 | 19 881 | 11.874 |
| 42 | 1 764 | 6.481 | 92 | 8 464 | 9.592 | 142 | 20 164 | 11.916 |
| 43 | 1 849 | 6.557 | 93 | 8 649 | 9.644 | 143 | 20 449 | 11.958 |
| 44 | 1 936 | 6.633 | 94 | 8 836 | 9.695 | 144 | 20 736 | 12.000 |
| 45 | 2 025 | 6.708 | 95 | 9 025 | 9.747 | 145 | 21 025 | 12.042 |
| 46 | 2 116 | 6.782 | 96 | 9 216 | 9.798 | 146 | 21 316 | 12.083 |
| 47 | 2 209 | 6.856 | 97 | 9 409 | 9.849 | 147 | 21 609 | 12.124 |
| 48 | 2 304 | 6.928 | 98 | 9 604 | 9.899 | 148 | 21 904 | 12.166 |
| 49 | 2 401 | 7.000 | 99 | 9 801 | 9.950 | 149 | 22 201 | 12.207 |
| 50 | 2 500 | 7.071 | 100 | 10 000 | 10.000 | 150 | 22 500 | 12.247 |

# Manual and Tests
# Using Geometry

\* Permission is given to teachers of USING GEOMETRY to reproduce
these performance objectives and tests entirely or in part.

**LAIDLAW BROTHERS • PUBLISHERS**

**A Division of Doubleday & Company, Inc.**

RIVER FOREST, ILLINOIS

Irvine, California      Chamblee, Georgia      Dallas, Texas      Toronto, Canada

# Overview of Student's Text

USING GEOMETRY provides a straightforward approach to a comprehensive course in high-school geometry. The teacher will find the following features particularly useful.

■ **Concrete models** for geometric concepts are used widely, as are real-life applications of geometry. These appear not only in illustrations but also in the reading material and exercises, to help teach and to motivate.

■ **Concise, readable explanations** are supplemented with many graphic aids. Over 200 photographs and illustrations and over 1800 geometric diagrams are included.

■ **Three course levels**—minimum, regular, maximum—are built into the flexible textbook design. A summary of suggested class times for the three courses appears on page T4. Teacher's annotations on the student's pages give section-by-section class times as well as exercise assignment guides for all three course levels.

■ **Flexibility** is enhanced by the following treatment of content.

   ● **Proof.** Before students are asked to write proofs, practice is given in reading completed proofs and in supplying reasons. Early proofs written by students are based on congruent triangles. And triangle congruence is frequently the basis for later proofs, as is triangle similarity. The assignment guides adjust coverage of proof to minimum, regular, and maximum levels.

   ● **Constructions.** Geometric constructions are introduced in the first chapter, and thereafter they are included as special features in the exercise sets. This permits constructions to be taught as integral parts of the chapters or as a separate unit. (They may also be readily omitted.) A separate unit could be taught following Chapter 12. The list of construction page references on page 561 is a table of contents for this unit.

   ● **Solid geometry.** Three-dimensional concepts are integrated into the text, but not to the extent that the flow of plane geometry is affected. The bulk of the solid geometry is included in the second-semester portion of the text (in Chapters 8, 13, and 14). The major goals of this material are to develop spatial visualization and to derive the common formulas for volume and surface area.

   ● **Transformations.** A special section at the end of each chapter develops transformation concepts informally. These sections are essentially optional. But they are particularly helpful in providing readiness (size changes as a prelude to similarity, for example) and in reinforcing spatial visualization (congruent triangles as flip, slide, or turn images of each other, for example).

- Coordinate geometry. Coordinate ideas are, of course, used quite early to develop the concept of distance and the Ruler Postulate. But the coordinate geometry of the plane is developed in the last chapter as a preview of algebra two.

■ **Abundant exercises** in each section are graded as follows.

- "A" exercises are for oral classwork (though some or all of them may be assigned as written work for slower classes).

- "B" exercises are for individual written practice. Whenever possible, the "odds" and "evens" are parallel in content and difficulty, with the "odds" providing the regular practice and the "evens" remaining as backup exercises.

- "C" exercises are optional, for enrichment and student discovery.

■ **Frequent review material** includes

- Quick Quiz. These self-quizzes review a few sections at a time.

- Chapter Review. The review exercises are grouped by sections for easy omission of optional material.

- Chapter Test. In these self-tests the items are not grouped by sections in order to approximate a realistic test situation. Optional topics are restricted to the last test item or two.

- Cumulative Review. Four of these comprehensive reviews are included (following Chapters 3, 7, 10, and 15).

- Algebra Review. Students maintain algebra skills and, when necessary, review skills that will be used in upcoming geometry material.

■ **Optional special material** includes *Mini-Chapters* on such topics as repeating geometric designs and rubber-sheet geometry; *Geometry at Work*, highlighting career information and applications on the job; *Geometry Around You*, emphasizing consumer information and everyday applications; and other *Special Topics* (see page viii).

■ **End-of-book aids** consist of lists of postulates, named theorems, constructions, and symbols; an index; and answers to selected exercises. (Answers are given for the odd-numbered items in the "B" exercises, the Chapter Reviews, and the Algebra Reviews, as well as for all items in each Quick Quiz and Chapter Test.)

# Summary of Suggested Class Times*

| Chapter or Cumulative Review | Time Allotments in Days for | | | Possible Omissions |
|---|---|---|---|---|
| | Minimum Course | Regular Course | Maximum Course | These sections may be omitted. (See Teacher's Manual pages for notes on omissions.) |
| Ch. 1 | 11 | 11 | 11 | 1.9, 1.10 (p. T6) |
| Ch. 2 | 9 | 9 | 9 | 2.8 (p. T7) |
| Ch. 3 | 9 | 8 | 9 | 3.8 (p. T9) |
| Cum. Rev. 1–3 | 2 | 1 | 1 | |
| Ch. 4 | 10 | 10 | 11 | 4.10 (p. T11) |
| Ch. 5 | 12 | 11 | 11 | 5.10 (p. T13) |
| Ch. 6 | 11 | 10 | 9 | 6.8 (p. T15) |
| Ch. 7 | 10 | 9 | 7 | 7.6 (p. T16) |
| Cum. Rev. 1–7 | 3 | 2 | 2 | |
| | 77 | 71 | 70 | ◁ 1st Sem. Totals† |
| Ch. 8 | 5 | 6 | 6 | 8.5 (p. T17) |
| Ch. 9 | 9 | 8 | 8 | 9.7 (p. T18) |
| Ch. 10 | 12 | 9 | 10 | 10.9 (p. T20) |
| Cum. Rev. 8–10 | 2 | 1 | 1 | |
| Ch. 11 | 12 | 12 | 11 | 11.10 (p. T22) |
| Ch. 12 | 6 | 6 | 6 | 12.5 (p. T23) |
| Ch. 13 | 5 | 6 | 7 | 13.5 (p. T24) |
| Ch. 14 | 10 | 10 | 10 | 14.9 (p. T26) |
| Ch. 15 | 11 | 12 | 13 | 15.8, 15.10 (p. T28) |
| Cum. Rev. 8–15 | 4 | 2 | 2 | |
| | 76 | 72 | 74 | ◁ 2nd Sem. Totals† |

\* See annotations on student's pages for section-by-section suggestions.

† Some free time has been allowed for testing and flexibility.

# Notes to the Teacher

## Chapter 1     GEOMETRY: WHAT AND WHY?     Pages 1–42

*Overview:* This chapter is an introduction to (1) geometric figures and their models, (2) some basic vocabulary of geometry, and (3) geometry as a mathematical system.

The approach to geometry as a system (and to the nature of deductive reasoning) is low-keyed. Emphasis is given to the development of geometric intuition, the helpfulness of models, the use of algebra in geometry, and the importance of careful reasoning.

**1.1** In this section, the terms *point*, *line*, *plane*, and *space* are introduced. Models help to give students sound intuitions about these figures and about the relationships expressed by such terms as *intersect*, *intersection*, *contains*, and *is in*.

**1.2** When the real numbers and the points on a line are put in one-to-one correspondence, *distance* can be defined. A geometry in which distance is defined is called a *metric geometry*. (*Metric* as used here does not refer to the metric system of measurement.) Many properties developed in this course are metric properties that exist only because distance (length) and angle measure can be determined, at least in theory.

The *Cross-Number Puzzle*, page 9, provides practice for operations with integers.

**1.3** In this section the word *postulate* is introduced, but students will probably not yet appreciate the role of postulates in geometry. This role is discussed further in later sections.

**1.4** We have already defined a number of terms, but with the basic definitions in this section we also try to give students an idea of the role of definitions in a mathematical system. This role is also discussed further in later sections.

Emphasize that the definitions of *between*, *on opposite sides of*, and *on the same side of* require the points to be collinear.

**1.5** This section provides an introduction into the nature of the reasoning used in mathematics, particularly in geometry. We analyze this type of reasoning more thoroughly in Chapters 3 and 6.

The use of *counterexamples* is discussed here, but the term itself is reserved for later. The term *theorem* is introduced, and more is said about the role of postulates.

The *Algebra Review* on page 21 reviews skills used in Section 1.6.

**1.6** When the real numbers are put in correspondence with the points on a line, as in Section 1.2, the algebra of real numbers becomes part of the geometric system. This section reviews algebra that is needed later.

*Symbols*, on page 26, may be helpful for students who are intimidated by mathematical symbolism. Emphasize the advantages and the universality of symbols. Many students will already know the geometry symbols shown, some will figure them out, and others can learn them later.

**1.7** At first, reasoning is usually easier for students to follow in paragraph form than in other forms. But it is not intended that students master these paragraph proofs. Two-column proofs are introduced in Chapter 3 and are generally used from that point on to facilitate the writing of proofs by students.

In the text, the theorems and postulates are not numbered. Instead, most theorems and all postulates are assigned names. Some postulates and theorems are used so often that their names will be remembered without difficulty, while others can be referred to by name or by a brief statement, whichever is convenient.

*Point*, *line*, and *plane* are undefined, but we do know the models we want to use for them (see page 29). So we describe some of the properties of these figures by stating postulates about them, as on page 28.

The photographs on page 30 show models of some concepts from this section. Such models are included throughout the text. When they occur in exercises you do not assign, use them in class discussion.

**1.8** Generally, we try to state only a few postulates about geometric figures and to deduce other properties as theorems. This process is shown in this section. While the theorems in this section concern *existence* and *uniqueness*, these terms are not needed at this level. Instead, we can use equivalent terms as follows:

## Chapter 2   ANGLES   Pages 43–79

*Overview:* This chapter introduces angles and angle measure and defines pairs of angles as *adjacent*, *vertical*, *complementary*, *supplementary*, and so on. Equality of measures is used to define congruence of angles and of segments.

**2.1** The concepts of convex and nonconvex are used later to distinguish the *interior* and the *exterior* of an angle or a triangle and to define convex polygons and polyhedrons.

The *Algebra Review* on page 47 reviews skills used later in this chapter and in subsequent chapters.

existence ▶ at least one ⎫ exactly one,
uniqueness ▶ not more than one ⎭ determines

**1.9** Students usually enjoy constructing geometric figures. You may wish to teach this section now and use the construction exercises as you come to them in the text. On the other hand, constructions can be taught as a separate unit, in which case this section should be deferred until later. Such a unit might well be taught immediately after Chapter 12. (See the list of constructions on page 561.)

Omit this section if constructions are not to be taught at any point in the course.

**1.10** Omit this section if transformations are not being included in the course. Otherwise, it can be taught in all courses—minimum, regular, and maximum.

In this text, the sections on transformations do not constitute a course in transformational geometry. Rather, these topics reinforce ideas presented elsewhere in more traditional form, and they aid in developing spatial visualization.

**2.2** *Angle* can be defined in different ways. The definition used in this text is perhaps the simplest and is completely adequate for geometry. It excludes null (0°), straight (180°), and reflex angles because they would require special exclusion in some theorems. In later courses, the definition can easily be extended to *directed angle*, which also allows angles with negative measures.

In print, the symbol ∠ is not easily confused with the letter *L*. But in handwritten work, a convention such as ⊀ for "angle" or 𝓛 for the letter is helpful.

**2.3** Only degree measure of angles is introduced in the text. Other common units of angle measure, such as the *radian* and the *mil*, are not dealt with. In text diagrams, the degree symbol is always used for angle measure to distinguish the cases below.

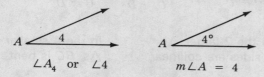

$$\angle A_4 \quad \text{or} \quad \angle 4 \qquad\qquad m\angle A = 4$$

In Exercises 7–10, students are asked to measure angles. Even the most accurate measurements may vary by a degree or two. Use this fact to emphasize that geometric figures have whatever measure we assign to them, regardless of how they are drawn. Students should realize that it is not always necessary to make an accurate drawing.

The *Algebra Review* on page 55 reviews skills used in Sections 2.4 and 2.5.

**2.4** Any figure that intersects a segment only at its midpoint is said to bisect the segment. Similarly, any figure (like a line or a plane) that contains the angle bisector and that intersects the angle *only* at its vertex can be said to bisect an angle.

Angles need not be adjacent to be supplementary, but to construct the supplement of an angle, it is sufficient to draw a ray opposite either side of the angle.

Constructions are introduced in Section 1.9 and thereafter appear only in the exercises. Exercises 31–34 on page 58 are the first such exercises. Construction exercises are listed separately in the assignment guides as on page 57.

**2.5** Most of the definitions in this section may already be familiar to students. Again, students should realize that angles need not be adjacent to be complementary.

**2.6** One of the most important concepts in geometry is that of *congruence*. Since we have a metric geometry, we define congruence in terms of measure.

Because the statements $\angle A \cong \angle B$ and $m\angle A = m\angle B$, as well as $\overline{AB} \cong \overline{CD}$ and $AB = CD$, are completely equivalent by definition, they may be interchanged whenever convenient. For most students it is best to emphasize this equivalence and not to require an explicit translation from one form to the other. Little is gained from such manipulation of symbols.

**2.7** The relationships in this section are established using simple algebra. They may be summarized as follows:

If two angles have the same measure,

(1) Their supplements have the same measure.

(2) Their complements have the same measure.

(3) If they are supplementary, they are both right angles.

Clearly, for any one angle,

(1) All supplements have the same measure.

(2) All complements have the same measure.

**2.8** Omit this section if transformations are not being included in the course. Otherwise it can be taught in all courses—minimum, regular, and maximum.

This section continues the informal discussion of transformations. Emphasis here is on transformations of angles and on the relationship between perpendicular bisectors and reflections.

*Reflections and Miniature Golf*, page 76, shows a simple application for reflections.

## Mini-Chapter: MOD ART    Pages 80–83

An almost endless variety of designs can be created using the methods shown.

The kaleidoscope grid was used on page 83 by considering the rows to be radiating from the corner. (Turn page 82 counterclockwise 45° to see the rows and columns more clearly.) The design could be changed by considering the columns to be radiating from the corner. (Turn page 82 clockwise 45°.)

Notice that six of the cells of the kaleidoscope grid on page 82 are triangles. These are regarded as distorted quadrilaterals.

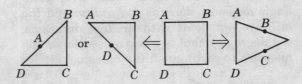

In the 2 larger △s, 2 sides are collinear.

In the 4 smaller △s, $\overline{BC}$ is bent.

Of course, there are other ways to use the triangles. If we think of $B$ and $C$ as coinciding in the smaller triangles, the patterns for 3 and 0 are all white, while the patterns for 1 and 2 are all color.

## Chapter 3    CONGRUENT TRIANGLES    Pages 84–120

*Overview:* This chapter introduces two very important topics:
(1) triangle congruence, and
(2) two-column proofs of theorems.

Models of congruent figures are so common in everyday experience that the geometric concept is easy for most students to understand. Also, triangle congruence proofs are generally quite simple and straightforward. Consequently, these proofs are used to introduce students to reading and writing two-column proofs.

Students are introduced to writing proofs very gradually in this text. They have already read proofs in paragraph form in Chapters 1 and 2. They have also completed one-step proofs by giving the reason supporting a conclusion (as on pages 70–71). Now they will learn to read and to follow the reasoning in simple two-column proofs and will practice supplying the reasons for statements in such proofs. Finally most, but not all, students can be expected to give both the statements and the reasons for simple proofs involving congruent triangles.

**3.1**  The statement of a hypothesis and its logical conclusion is a theorem. When such a statement is in if-then form, the parts are easily identified; students need to be able to rewrite statements in this form.

As early as the 16th century, circular diagrams were used to illustrate deductive reasoning (as on page 86). The Swiss mathematician Leonard Euler (1707–1783) did not invent these diagrams, but his use of them made the diagrams more widely known.

Later, the British logician John Venn (1834–1923) used similar circular diagrams. Venn diagrams provide for representation of universal and null sets and are used today in set algebra. However, the diagrams on page 86 are more appropriately called Euler diagrams, not Venn diagrams.

**3.2**  In this section proof is explained further, and the two-column form is introduced. Teachers tend to develop their own favorite variations of the two-column form of proof. In this text we try to steer a middle course so that you can adapt it to your own style and to the needs of your classes. In fact, the only absolute requirements for a proof are that the reasoning be correct and that the reader for whom it is written be able to follow the reasoning. (Students should generally be expected to write proofs for other students at the same level—not for the teacher.)

**3.3** The least-subtle proofs in geometry, and therefore the proofs most suitable for student practice, are those involving triangle congruence. As groundwork for those proofs, we first introduce the concepts of one-to-one correspondence of vertices and corresponding parts. These ideas are then used to make the transition from congruent segments and angles to congruent triangles.

The activities in Exercises 35–37 can be done in class with materials provided by the teacher, or they can be assigned as homework. If they are done in class, the better part of an extra day's class time is needed.

**3.4** It is possible to postulate SAS congruence for triangles and then to prove SSS and ASA congruence. But the proofs are somewhat subtle and difficult, so they interrupt the gradual introduction to proof that is so desirable. For this reason, we postulate all three congruence conditions at this time, and we immediately begin to use them.

Constructions are shown for SSS and SAS on page 100. The construction for ASA is in Exercise 24 on page 66. You may want to discuss that exercise at this time.

**3.5** The three postulates of the preceding section are used in this section to prove triangles congruent.

**3.6** This section emphasizes the use of triangle congruence to show that corresponding parts are congruent. This is the basis of many applications of congruent triangles.

**3.7** Students do not suppose that because all collies are dogs, all dogs are collies. And yet it is a common error to think of similarly related mathematical statements (converses) as equivalent. Throughout this text, the work with converses is developed carefully and gradually. See the notes for Sections 4.2 and 6.2, pages T10 and T14.

The term *corollary* is also introduced in this section. It indicates a theorem whose proof is almost trivial because it follows so easily from a previous statement. The *corollary* label is really quite arbitrary.

The theorems here are the first to include the phrase *in a plane*, which is not needed
(1) when the subject of a statement is already restricted to a plane by definition, postulate, or a previously proved theorem (an angle and its bisector, for example).
(2) when a statement is true for figures that need not be coplanar (congruent angles, for example).

**3.8** This section on transformations can be used in a maximum course, but it should be omitted in a minimum or regular course.

Under any transformation that preserves distance and angle measure, a triangle and its image are congruent. Thus, transformation geometry gives a mathematically acceptable interpretation to Euclid's intuitive concept of superposition.

The *Cumulative Review* on pages 121 and 122 is one of four cumulative reviews in this text. These cumulative reviews provide a midsemester review and an end-of-semester review for each semester. Since the material on transformations is optional and constructions will be handled differently in different classes, neither of these topics is included in the cumulative reviews.

*Overview:* In this chapter we state the parallel postulate that characterizes Euclidean geometry. This leads to a consideration of the various pairs of angles formed by two lines and a transversal, as well as to the Angle Sum Theorem for Triangles.

Parallel lines also lead naturally to the introduction of parallelograms, of special parallelograms, and of trapezoids and to the development of their properties.

**4.1** The Parallel Postulate stated on page 125 is often called Playfair's Postulate, after the Scottish mathematician John Playfair (1748–1819). Euclid's original postulate was, of course, equivalent (see the Mini-Chapter on pages 442–444). Over the years, Playfair's Postulate has become the one most frequently used. It is much less wordy than Euclid's version.

Indirect proof is introduced in this section, but little work with indirect proofs is required of the students. We consider this form of proof again in Chapter 6.

**4.2** Parts **a** and **b** of the Alternate Interior Angles Theorem are converses (introduced on page 110). Later, in Chapter 6, we introduce if-and-only-if statements, which enable us to combine a statement and its converse into one theorem. Until that time, we continue to use the two-part form as on page 128. This approach gives students more familiarity with converses, and it emphasizes the requirement that *both* parts must be proved.

On page 129, auxiliary figures are introduced. This concept is developed gradually throughout the text (see particularly Section 6.6). For now, do not overemphasize this topic. However, you may wish to point out that the existence of an auxiliary figure

must be justified by a previous postulate, definition, or theorem.

**4.3** Again, the two-part theorems consist of converses.

Call attention to the Z form associated with alternate interior angles and to the F form associated with corresponding angles.

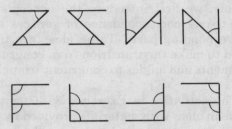

If you have previously discussed the phrase *in a plane* (see the notes for Section 3.7, page T9), it might be interesting for students to consider the reasons for its inclusion in the last two theorems on page 133. The first of these two theorems is not true in space. The second is true in space, but this more general form cannot yet be proved (see page 452).

The *Algebra Review* on page 135 reviews skills used in Section 4.4.

**4.4** The photograph on page 137 presents a model for the proof which follows it. The photo shows how a paper "triangle" can be torn and its angles rearranged along a straight line. The proof of the Angle Sum Theorem for Triangles does the tearing and rearranging in a theoretical sense.

There are other proofs possible for the Angle Sum Theorem. For example, another proof would make use of the fact that in the figure on page 137, $\angle A$ and $\angle C_{23}$ are supplementary.

**4.5** The key to many proofs about parallelograms lies in the choice of which lines to regard as parallels and which as transversals. If students have difficulty visualizing the parallels and transversals, have them make a separate drawing for each case being considered. Such drawings for the proof on page 141 follow.

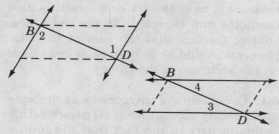

**4.6** This section discusses techniques for "planning" a proof. But perhaps the best method of developing planning skills is to give students opportunities to write proofs.

Call attention to this planning technique: Since the hypothesis and the conclusion are interchanged in converses, looking at the steps of a proof in reverse will frequently, though not always, give a clue to the proof of the converse.

**4.7** The proof of the Triangle Midline Theorem should be omitted in a minimum course and discussed carefully in other courses.

**4.8** It is important for students to realize that the properties of parallelograms—whether given by the definition or proved—apply to each of the special parallelograms also. They do not have to be proved again for these figures. The rectangle and the rhombus are parallelograms with one added condition each. A figure that meets both of these added conditions is a square (a rectangular rhombus).

*Kites and Arrows*, page 152, will interest many students. Kites and arrows may be distinguished not only by whether their diagonals intersect but also by the fact that a kite has a convex interior while an arrow has a nonconvex interior.

**4.9** This section illustrates how a theorem sometimes develops. First, a simple, restricted statement is proved. Then a slightly broader statement is proved. Finally, the proof is extended to the most general case. Students may be surprised to know that this evolutionary development of a theorem has sometimes taken centuries.

Notice that our definition of *trapezoid* excludes parallelograms. Also, while the segment joining the midpoints of the non-parallel sides of a trapezoid is sometimes called the *median*, this segment corresponds directly to the *midline* of a triangle. So we use the same term in both cases.

**4.10** This section on transformations can be used in a maximum course, but it should be omitted in a minimum or regular course.

Three distinct relationships between parallelism and slides (translations) are discussed in this section.
(1) Each line (ray, segment) is parallel to its slide image.
(2) Segments joining points to their slide images are parallel.
(3) Parallelism is preserved by slides.

Notice that with our definition of parallel lines, the first two relationships hold only when a line and its slide image do not coincide. When geometry is developed using a transformational approach, parallelism is usually defined so a line can be parallel to itself. Then the three statements above are true without exception.

*Overview:* Two types of polygons—triangles and quadrilaterals—were studied in earlier chapters. This chapter extends this study to polygons in general, covering the vocabulary and such properties as perimeter, angle measure, and congruence.

Later in the chapter we return to triangle congruence and right triangle congruence, and the entire topic is conveniently summarized on page 189. Also covered are the vocabulary and properties of special triangles and of isosceles trapezoids.

**5.1** The common names of the various *n*-gons are listed on page 165. In origin, all of these names but one (quadrilateral) refer to the number of angles determined by the figure, and all but two (triangle and quadrilateral) derive from the Greek. If we were consistent, we would replace the first two names with *trigon* and *tetragon* or, if just these two are to remain Latin in origin, we would use *triangle* and *quadrangle*.

We can generalize the discovery in Exercise 27 as follows: Suppose as many diagonals as possible are drawn from one vertex of a convex *n*-gon. A diagonal cannot be drawn from that vertex to itself or to the other endpoints of the two sides which meet at that vertex. So $n - 3$ diagonals can be drawn from *one* vertex. There are *n* vertices, so it seems that $n(n - 3)$ diagonals can be drawn—but this counts each diagonal twice, once at each end. So there are actually $\frac{1}{2}n(n - 3)$ diagonals.

**5.2** The perimeter of a polygon is independent of the angle measures and the number of sides. This can be demonstrated by making models whose sides are joined loosely at the vertices. As the shape of the model is changed, the area of its interior changes, the sizes of its angles change, and the height

changes; but the perimeter remains the same. Also, the sides can be bent, forming new vertices and increasing the number of sides, but the perimeter is constant.

**5.3** In surveying a closed course (polygonal and convex in shape), the interior angle at each turning point (vertex) is measured using surveying instruments. When this measure is recorded, its supplement is also computed and recorded. At the end of the course, the fact that the sum of the supplements should be 360 serves as one check on the accuracy of the survey.

**5.4** Congruence of polygons lacks the wide applicability of congruence of triangles. This is due in part to the fact that the former is usually more difficult to establish. However some special cases, such as the SAS Theorem for Parallelograms on page 174, are easily proved. (And this theorem could be followed by the corollaries SS Theorem for Rectangles, SA Theorem for Rhombuses, and S Theorem for Squares.)

**5.5** The far-reaching results of the Parallel Postulate can be found even here, where the AAS Theorem is proved, in effect, as a corollary of a corollary of the Angle Sum Theorem for Triangles.

The AAS and ASA Theorems, combined, have the effect that if two angles and *any* side of one triangle are congruent to the corresponding parts of another triangle, then the triangles are congruent. (The same *cannot* be said for two sides and *any* angle.)

**5.6** The work so far presented has concerned triangles in general and right triangles. This section defines other special categories of triangles and proves certain properties of isosceles and equilateral triangles and isosceles trapezoids.

**5.7** Since all right angles are congruent, the AAS and ASA Theorems, as applied to right triangles, produce the HA Theorem and the LA Theorem, while the SAS Postulate results in the LL Theorem.

The HL Theorem shows that side-side-angle, while it is not generally a congruence, does hold for right triangles.

The right triangle congruence theorems have this effect:

(1) If an acute angle and any side of one right triangle are congruent to the corresponding parts of another right triangle, the triangles are congruent.

(2) If any two sides of one right triangle are congruent to the corresponding parts of another right triangle, the triangles are congruent.

**5.8** This section provides practice in choosing, from all the triangle congruence theorems available, the one that applies to a particular situation, as well as practice in writing triangle congruence proofs.

**5.9** This section contains additional practice in applying the triangle congruence theorems, but the figures are complicated by the fact that the triangles overlap.

**5.10** Omit this section if transformations are not being included in the course. Otherwise, it can be taught in all courses—minimum, regular, and maximum.

Line symmetry can be exploited in many amusing and practical ways. It can be used, for example, in making paper snowflakes, inkblot designs, origami figures, clothing patterns, some letters of the alphabet, and strings of paper dolls.

## Mini-Chapter: REPEATING DESIGNS        Pages 200–203

There is currently an upsurge of interest in the work of the Dutch artist Maurits C. Escher (1898–1972). His subjects include such obviously mathematical ones as spheres, spirals, Moebius strips, and polyhedrons, as well as the plane tesselations we refer to on these pages.

A toy that has always been popular consists of sets of colored tiles of various

shapes that fit together to form plane tesselations. But now you can even buy sets of Escher-type "creatures" for this purpose. Escher's prints have also been made into ordinary jigsaw puzzles.

Another form of plane tesselation enjoying a revival is the patchwork quilt. Probably some enterprising needleworker has already made an Escher quilt.

## Chapter 6        MORE ABOUT PROOFS        Pages 204–237

*Overview:* This chapter contains a more detailed analysis of several topics introduced earlier, shows how they apply to proof, and extends some of them. Topics revisited are if-then statements, converses, definitions, indirect proofs, and auxiliary figures.

**6.1** This section continues the analysis of if-then statements (conditionals) begun in Chapter 3. True if-then statements are separated into (1) *postulates* (which are accepted as true without proof) and (2) *theorems* (in which we prove that if the hypothesis is true, then the conclusion is true).

In fact, any if-then statement is true unless the hypothesis is true and the conclusion is false. Students do not deal with *If false, then true* or *If false, then false* statements in geometry, and they seldom deal with them in daily life. So the discussion is confined to the cases *If true, then false* and *If true, then true*.

**6.2** This section returns to the discussion of converses (introduced on page 110), emphasizing the need to prove both statements. The use of *if and only if* to combine converses, when both are true, is illustrated by the Angle Bisector Theorem (page 210) and by restating earlier theorems involving converses (Exercises 21–24).

Point out that either hypothesis may be stated first when converses are combined in if-and-only-if statements (biconditionals). In other words,

these are equivalent $\begin{cases} X \text{ if and only if } Y. \\ Y \text{ if and only if } X. \end{cases}$

So the example on page 209 could also be written

$a = b$ if and only if $a + c = b + c$

**6.3** This section contains further material on definitions (first mentioned on page 14). Here, we emphasize that a good definition must be either an if-and-only-if statement or the equivalent of one. Until now, all definitions in the text have been stated in an equivalent form—without using *if and only if*. From now on, however, if-and-only-if form is used occasionally, especially when it results in an economy of wording.

**6.4** Unfortunately, students are probably exposed daily to more faulty patterns of reasoning than to good ones. Far too much advertising is based on invalid arguments, but so also are private decisions, public debates, and even peer discussions.

Avoid the temptation to convert this lesson to one in symbolic logic. Instead, help students to develop the ability to detect faulty reasoning in ordinary arguments. Good examples of bad reasoning should easily be obtainable, and they could be used to make an effective bulletin-board display.

**6.5** Indirect reasoning was introduced in Section 4.1, page 124. While this is a common form of reasoning in everyday life, it is a particularly powerful tool in mathematics. It is based on the simple rule of logic that if all possible alternatives are known and all but one of them are proved false, the remaining one is true. Of course, it is necessary to have an exhaustive list of the possible alternatives. For example,

**coplanar lines:** parallel—intersecting
**angles:** right—acute—obtuse

The *Algebra Review* on page 224 reviews skills used in Chapter 7.

**6.6** Past conditioning leads students to feel that if one answer to an exercise is right, a different answer is wrong. It is important to free them of this fallacy.

By now, students should realize that to have a good proof, they need not write the steps in exactly the same order or in the same symbols as everyone else. However, as more theorems become available to use as reasons, there are more ways a proof might be written. Whether an argument is a proof or not depends only on its internal logic. The favorite recreation of some mathematicians is to look for new ways to prove old theorems.

The caution to not put too many conditions on an auxiliary figure is important, and learning to choose the most useful condition takes experience. But once an auxiliary figure is introduced, *any* provable properties of the figure may be used.

Students who do the constructions on page 228 should be encouraged to discover the concurrency theorems for themselves before going on to Section 6.7. By doing Exercises 26–28 all on one figure, students might also discover Euler's theorem about collinear points of concurrency. Some related constructions are described in the notes for Sections 11.1 and 11.6, pages T21–T22.

**6.7** The angle bisectors and the medians are always concurrent at a point in the interior of the triangle. But for the perpendicular bisectors of the sides and the lines containing the altitudes, the points of concurrency may be on, inside, or outside the triangle.

The four points of concurrency have standard names.

| for the lines containing ▼ | the point of concurrency is called ▼ |
|---|---|
| the medians | the centroid |
| the angle bisectors | the incenter |
| the perpendicular bisectors of the sides | the circumcenter |
| the altitudes | the orthocenter |

**6.8** This section on transformations can be used in a maximum course, but it should be omitted in a minimum or regular course.

This section points out that a formal course in transformational geometry would have the same basic elements and the same types of proofs as a course without transformations. Transformations simply give us an additional tool for proving theorems.

## Chapter 7  GEOMETRIC INEQUALITIES        Pages 238–260

*Overview:* Length and angle measure are real numbers, and the real numbers have *order*. This property gives us a basis for comparing geometric figures in statements referred to as *geometric inequalities*.

The theorems in this chapter describe what happens when sides or angles of a triangle are noncongruent or when two triangles are noncongruent. The chapter provides many opportunities to review concepts of inequality from algebra.

**7.1** This section reviews the properties of inequality of real numbers and the algebra of inequalities. The three pairs of equivalent statements at the top of page 240, which result from the trichotomy of real numbers, are important for indirect proofs of geometric inequalities.

*Putting It Another Way*, on page 241, can be used to reemphasize the universality of

mathematical symbols. The more that words are replaced by mathematics symbols in an article or a book, the less "translating" it needs to be readable in other languages.

**7.2** The trichotomy of the real numbers leads to a trichotomy of geometric inequalities. So either two segments or angles are *congruent* or one is *longer* (*larger*) or *shorter* (*smaller*) than the other. As with congruence and equality of measure, the equivalence of the geometric inequality and the inequality of measure should be emphasized.

Using the definitions of $<$ and $>$, any postulate, theorem, or definition that involves a sum of measures provides us with an opportunity to prove an inequality. (Though four inequalities result from each equation, they are completely equivalent.)

At one time in the teaching of Euclidean geometry, the *definition of between* and the

*Angle Addition Postulate* were lumped together in a postulate that said *the whole is equal to the sum of its parts.* The resulting inequalities were then combined in a second postulate that said *the whole is greater than any one of its parts.*

The *Algebra Review* on page 244 reviews skills used in Chapter 9 and subsequent chapters.

**7.3**  The theorems in this section are rather obvious, and some students will wonder why they must be proved. But to make these statements a part of the system, we must either postulate them or show that they result from what has gone before. Given a choice, the latter is preferable mathematically.

**7.4**  If these theorems seem obvious to students, emphasize that this simply demonstrates how well geometry describes the familiar physical world and why it can therefore be so useful. You may want to point out that the statement *x is between 12 and 2,* at the bottom of page 250, can be written $12 > x > 2$ or $2 < x < 12$.

**7.5**  The pendulum and derrick models are so common that students should readily understand the concepts behind the theorems in this section. A hinge is another good model for the theorem on page 253.

**7.6**  This section on transformations can be used in a maximum or regular course, but it should be omitted in a minimum course.

When a ball is rolled on a smooth horizontal surface with no obstacles, it tends to take the shortest path from its starting position to its final position (see the theorem on page 251). We prove in this section that a ball rebounding from a barrier also takes the shortest path.

The technique of aiming at the reflection image of a ball's destination was also used in *Reflections and Miniature Golf*, page 76. Both applications assume that no "English" is applied to influence the ball's path.

The *Cumulative Review* on pages 261–264 can be used as an end-of-semester review for the first semester.

## Chapter 8    PERPENDICULAR LINES AND PLANES    Pages 265–285

*Overview:* Some basic three-dimensional concepts and their models were introduced in earlier chapters, but this is the first chapter that is actually about *space (solid) geometry.* The chapter covers the basic properties of lines perpendicular to planes. (Planes perpendicular to other planes are not covered until Chapter 13.)

Despite the fact that they are surrounded by three-dimensional models, most students find the geometry of space more difficult than plane geometry. Encourage students to find or make models of figures that they have trouble visualizing.

**8.1**  This section introduces the definition of *perpendicular line and plane.* The model shown will satisfy the students' intuition, but the definition itself may be less obvious.

To answer Exercise 3, we have to reason like this: If $\ell \perp s$, they intersect. But $\ell$ intersects plane $P$ only at $F$, and $F$ is not on $s$. So $\ell$ and $s$ don't intersect and can't be perpendicular.

The *Algebra Review* on page 269 reviews skills used in Chapter 9 and subsequent chapters.

**8.2**  A simpler condition for perpendicularity of a line and a plane is needed than the one provided by the definition. The Basic Theorem for Perpendiculars provides that condition; but the proof is long, and students will need some help with it.

**8.3**  The postulates on page 273 are easy for students to accept, and the proof of the theorem is short and easy to understand. The Perpendicular Bisecting Plane Theorem is directly analogous to the Perpendicular Bisector Theorem on page 110. Have students restate it in two parts before considering the proof.

**8.4**  The proofs of some theorems are more difficult to understand than the theorems themselves. This is certainly true of the theorem on page 278. The proof of the theorem on page 279 is simple by contrast.

Again the distance between two figures (in this case a point and a plane) is the length of the shortest segment joining them. This is also the case for two points (pages 11 and 251), for a point and a line (page 247), for parallel lines (page 142), and for parallel planes (page 453).

**8.5**  This section on transformations can be used in a maximum or regular course, but it should be omitted in a minimum course.

Reflections in space are the kind that students are most familiar with. Any object and its mirror image provide a model of the preservation properties on page 282. In particular, the fact that the mirror image of a right-hand glove looks like a left-hand glove demonstrates that reflections reverse orientation.

## Chapter 9    AREAS OF POLYGONS    Pages 286–319

*Overview:* In a metric geometry, the real numbers play an important role in the description of geometric figures. (For example, length describes a segment, degree measure describes an angle, and perimeter describes a polygon.) In this chapter, we consider that real-number description of a polygonal region called its *area*. Students are familiar with many applications of area.

The formula for the area of a rectangle is postulated and then used to develop the area formulas for many other plane figures. (Area of regular polygons is postponed until Chapter 12, where it is applied to develop the area formula for circles.)

After a review of the algebra of square roots, area is used to establish the Pythagorean Theorem, and its converse is also proved. Finally, certain relationships involving special right triangles are proved.

**9.1**  The postulates on page 287 are quite obvious to students because of their wide practical use, and the formulas on page 288 are also familiar.

The area of the rectangle on page 288 is the number of nonoverlapping square units needed to cover the rectangle and can be found by counting. (The formula is simply an efficient way to do the counting.) This idea can be difficult to apply to other regions, so we develop a formula in each case based on formulas already developed.

**9.2**  The only difficulty students are likely to have in this section is in visualizing the *base* of a figure in a position other than at the "bottom." Emphasize that any side of a triangle or a parallelogram can be called the *base*, but in this context we use the term to refer to a side for which we know the corresponding height.

**9.3** These area formulas may be less familiar to students than the earlier ones. The trapezoid could be separated into a parallelogram and a triangle, but more algebraic manipulation would be required to derive the same formula. The formula for the area of a parallelogram applies also to a rhombus, so there are two formulas for the area of a rhombus. Both of them also apply to a square.

**9.4** This section is a review of the arithmetic of square roots. Point out that final results should be expressed in simplest radical form (unless an approximation is called for) but intermediate results may be more convenient in another form.

We make no distinction between $\frac{\sqrt{6}}{2}$ and $\frac{1}{2}\sqrt{6}$. Both are in simplest form. The only basis for choosing between them might be the use to which the result is to be put.

The *Algebra Review* on page 303 reviews skills used in Sections 9.5 and 9.6.

**9.5** Long before the time of Pythagoras, the relationship between the hypotenuse and the legs of certain right triangles was used as a basis for forming right angles. But the Greeks were apparently the first to generalize the relationship and to prove it for all right triangles.

If $a$, $b$, $c$, and $k$ are positive integers and $a^2 + b^2 = c^2$, then $(a, b, c)$ is called a *Pythagorean triple* and $(ka, kb, kc)$ is also a Pythagorean triple. In general, if $m$ and $n$ are any positive integers and $m > n$, then $(m^2 - n^2, 2mn, m^2 + n^2)$ is a Pythagorean triple. If $m$

and $n$ are also relatively prime and not both odd or both even, this relationship can be used to generate all primitive Pythagorean triples (all triples whose members are relatively prime).

If the numbers of a Pythagorean triple are lengths of corresponding sides of *any three similar figures*, the sum of the areas of the two smaller figures equals the area of the third figure.

The *Wheel of Theodorus*, page 308, can be drawn as easily as it can be constructed, so it is suitable even for classes that have not done constructions.

**9.6** The isosceles right triangle and the 30-60-90° triangle are particularly useful because if the length of one side is known, the lengths of the other sides can be determined without trigonometry. These triangles occur frequently in connection with other common figures—as when we draw diagonals in a square, altitudes in an equilateral triangle, or diagonals in a regular hexagon.

**9.7** The material in this section is not related to the rest of this chapter but is a transformational preview of the next chapter, which deals with similar polygons.

Omit this section if transformations are not being included in the course. Otherwise, it can be taught in all courses—minimum, regular, and maximum.

The *Algebra Review* on page 316 reviews skills used in Chapter 10 and subsequent chapters.

## Mini-Chapter: RUBBER-SHEET GEOMETRY    Pages 320–323

Many of the properties of geometric figures considered in this course are metric properties (see the notes for Section 1.2, page

T5). The material here gives students an opportunity to work with some interesting nonmetric properties.

*Overview:* Next to congruence, similarity is probably the simplest property for students to visualize and to prove. Certainly they are familiar with models of similar figures and should have a good intuitive grasp of the concept of "same shape, different size." Similarity is the basis of all scale representations, without which industry and technology would have a difficult time indeed.

The chapter begins by reviewing ratio and proportion. Then *similar polygons* are defined, and theorems for proving triangles similar are developed. Conditions for triangle similarity are summarized on page 350. The chapter concludes by considering both proportional segments intercepted by parallels and areas of similar polygons.

**10.1**  Ratios and proportions are the numerical tools by which similarity of geometric figures is described and proved. This section is a review of the algebra of ratios and proportions. On page 325 a *proportion* is defined as a *true* statement that ratios are equal. So we will call such a statement a proportion if and only if it is true.

Two of the most useful properties in this section are cross multiplication and the property by which any two equations can be used to set up a proportion. They will be used many times in this chapter.

**10.2**  Emphasize the analogies between congruence and similarity, especially the importance of correspondence. The theorem on page 330 shows that congruence is, in fact, a special case of similarity. Students might find it helpful to think of the congruence symbol ($\cong$) as a combination of the similarity symbol ($\sim$) and the equality symbol ($=$). So $\cong$ figures are $\sim$ figures whose corresponding parts have $=$ measures.

**10.3**  As we did with congruence, we rapidly abandon the definition of similarity as unwieldy and develop shortcuts for proving triangles similar. But first, students must be convinced that we can postulate AAA similarity. (Use additional models if necessary.) It immediately follows from AAA that AA is sufficient.

**10.4**  There are four triangle congruences: SAS, SSS, ASA, and AAS. In this section we prove SAS and SSS similarity theorems and point out that ASA and AAS meet the conditions for AA similarity. Emphasize that SSA is not sufficient for either congruence or similarity, except for right triangles.

Similar triangles are used for indirect measurement in Exercises 31–36.

**10.5**  Two of the right triangle congruences, HA and LA, do not have analogous similarity theorems because they meet the conditions for AA similarity. However, LL and HL similarity theorems are established in this section.

The right triangle relationships involving the altitude to the hypotenuse are important. To avoid cumbersome wording, we use *geometric mean* in two senses—as a length and as the segment that has that length.

The construction of the *geometric mean* of two lengths is shown on page 347. In panel 3, $A'M = MD' = \frac{1}{2}(AB + CD)$, which is the *arithmetic mean* of $AB$ and $CD$. But $MD' = MT$, so we can use right $\triangle MB'T$ to show that the arithmetic mean of two unequal numbers is greater than the geometric mean. (If the numbers are equal, the means are equal.) For more on the construction of various means, see *The Mathematics Teacher* for March 1973, March 1974, and January 1977.

**10.6** In this section, students are expected to choose, from all the triangle similarity theorems available, the one that applies to a particular situation.

**10.7** The construction on page 355 uses a ratio with integer components. But the Proportional Segments Theorem can be used with any ratio whose components can be "constructed." (For example, given a unit, the construction on page 347 can be used to "construct" square roots of whole numbers.)

For Exercise 1 on page 353, have students use $e$ as the unit of measure. First, lay the edge of a piece of paper along transversal $r$ and mark off a segment of length $d$. Then see how many times the segment of length $e$ can be laid off between the marks. Repeat for the segment of length $f$. A similar method can be used for Exercise 2, but the unit of measure is one half the length of the shorter segment.

*The Golden Ratio* may interest some students. Point $C$ separates $\overline{AB}$ in this ratio if $\frac{BC}{AC} = \frac{AC}{AB} = \frac{1+\sqrt{5}}{2}$. To locate $C$ on $\overline{AB}$,

(1) Find the midpoint of $\overline{AB}$.
(2) Construct $\overline{BD} \perp \overline{AB}$ so that $BD = \frac{1}{2}AB$.
(3) On $\overline{DA}$, locate $E$ so that $DE = DB$.
(4) On $\overline{AB}$, locate $C$ so that $AC = AE$.

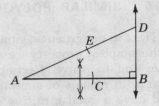

A rectangle with sides of lengths $AC$ and $AB$ would be a *Golden Rectangle*. (Information on this topic might also be found under *Divine Proportion*, *Mean and Extreme Ratio*, or *Golden Section*.)

**10.8** In general, we can compare the areas of two similar figures by squaring the ratio of *any two corresponding linear measures* associated with those figures. (We can likewise compare volumes of similar solids by cubing such a ratio.)

**10.9** This section on transformations can be used in a maximum course, but it should be omitted in a minimum or regular course.

Any combination of shape-preserving transformations is a similarity transformation. If students have difficulty imagining a transformation that is not a similarity transformation, refer again to page 38. Another good example is a transformation that stretches a figure in only one direction.

## Mini-Chapter: TRIGONOMETRY       Pages 365–372

The sine, cosine, and tangent functions are defined here as ratios of two sides of a right triangle. Because each ratio depends on the sizes of the angles of the triangle, each is a function of angle measure. But because the acute angles of a right triangle have measures between 0 and 90, the trigonometric functions are limited to this domain. In later mathematics courses, students will find that this domain can be extended by using slightly different definitions.

In some classes, you may want to have students use Exercises 1–5 on page 366 to discover that $\sin x = \cos (90 - x)$. They can then see the logic to the term *cosine* (sine of the complement). Additional relationships that might be explored are given by

$$\tan x = \frac{\sin x}{\cos x} = \frac{1}{\tan (90 - x)}$$

The exercises at the bottom of page 366 are good calculator exercises.

While all students should learn to use the table on page 368, you might have them compare calculator results with table results for the exercises on page 367. Using the table, discuss the ranges of the sine, cosine, and tangent functions.

Trigonometry has a wide variety of applications. We have chosen some that are particularly suited to this level. Have students use the table or calculators, as you prefer. For Exercises 13 and 17, page 371, point out the advisability of using the given data, not data derived in Exercises 12 and 16.

The *Cumulative Review* on pages 373–374 can be used as a midsemester review for the second semester.

## Chapter 11    CIRCLES AND SPHERES

**Pages 375–417**

*Overview:* This chapter exploits the analogy between circles in a plane and spheres in space by presenting parallel developments of the vocabulary and of the theorems on tangents and chords.

This is followed by more extensive material for circles, including arcs and the relationships of arcs to the angles that intercept them. Product theorems for some segments related to a circle are covered, and a section is also included on *locus*.

**11.1**  This section covers the basic terms relating to circles and spheres, which are already somewhat familiar to students. It may be helpful for them to know that *secant* is from a Latin word meaning "to cut" and *tangent* is from a word meaning "to touch."

The construction on page 378 works for any three noncollinear points. Clearly, the three points could be vertices of a triangle. In this case, $D$ is the *circumcenter* of the triangle (see the notes for Section 6.7, page T15).

**11.2**  Let $\overline{AB}$ be a chord of $\odot C$ and let $\ell$ be coplanar with $\odot C$. Consider these possibilities:

(1)  $\ell \perp \overline{AB}$
(2)  $\ell$ bisects $\overline{AB}$
(3)  $\ell$ contains $C$

It may be that none of these are true. Or it may be that exactly one of them is true. But the Chord Theorem shows that if any two of them are true, then all three are true.

*Congruent circles*, like congruent segments and angles, are defined in terms of a related measure. Ask students to state each part of the Congruent Chords Theorem separately.

**11.3**  Caution students to distinguish carefully between *tangents to a circle* and *tangent circles*. You may want to point out that not only circles but other curves may have lines tangent to them.

To visualize the relationships shown on pages 383 and 384, students may find it helpful to imagine the line as moving in relation to a circle and to imagine the smaller circle as moving in relation to the larger circle. Then the figures will pass through each of the stages illustrated.

Another help to visualization might be to imagine a circle rolling along a line tangent to it. Clearly, there is exactly one line tangent to the circle at each point on the circle. But if two circles are tangent and we imagine one of them being blown up like a (plane) balloon, we see that there are infinitely many circles tangent to another circle at a point on it.

**11.4** Make the most of the analogy between circles and spheres, particularly for such things as the Chord Theorem for Spheres. Either a line or a plane may be tangent to a sphere. Again, the idea of moving figures may help students to visualize the relationships shown on page 388.

*Great Circles of the World*, page 392, and *Circling the Globe*, page 397, illustrate the importance of the geometry of the sphere to the study of geography.

**11.5** A circle can be measured in two ways: in arc degrees (360) and in linear units (see Section 12.2, page 424). Similarly, an arc can be measured in arc degrees and in linear units (see Section 12.4). Emphasize that although the degree measure of an angle must be between 0 and 180, the degree measure of an arc is between 0 and 360. This is important when using the Addition Postulates.

Ask students to state each part of the Congruent Arcs Theorem separately.

**11.6** The measure of an arc has been defined in terms of the measure of its central angle (or of the central angle of the corresponding minor arc). There are also important relationships between the measure of an arc and certain other angles that intercept it. In this section, emphasis is on inscribed angles and the arcs they intercept.

The construction on page 402 shows how to circumscribe a triangle about a circle. If the triangle were given, the circle could be inscribed in it by locating the *incenter* (see the notes for Section 6.7, page T15).

**11.7** In this section, the relationship between an inscribed angle and the arc it intercepts is used to establish relationships between certain other angles and the arcs they intercept.

**11.8** The third theorem in this section can be expressed in terms of proportions as follows: *If a tangent segment and a secant segment intersect in the exterior of a circle, the tangent segment is the mean proportional to the secant segment and its external part.* The first two theorems can also be stated in terms of proportions, but this would require the concept of inverse proportions, which is not introduced in this text.

**11.9** At one time, *locus* was defined as the path of a point moving according to a given rule or condition. As the idea of the motion of the point was abandoned, it became clear that a locus is simply a geometric figure or a set of points. In fact, in every exercise in this section, we could replace *locus of points* with *set of all points* or *figure containing those points and only those points*. However, since the term *locus* is still used with some frequency, this section is included to acquaint students with its meaning.

**11.10** This section on transformations can be used in a maximum course, but it should be omitted in a minimum or regular course.

As with any transformation of the plane, a *turn* (or *rotation*) maps the plane onto itself. Except under a 360° turn or the equivalent, only one point—the center of the turn—is its own image. The image of any other point can be found using the method on page 413.

A model of a plane rotation can be made by taking a photographic time exposure of the night sky. In the photograph, each star will trace an arc around the celestial pole. The degree measure of each arc is the same and represents the magnitude of the turn. (The arc *length*, however, depends on the distance of the star from the pole.)

*Overview:* In this chapter, *circumference* and *area* of a circle are developed as *limits* of the perimeters and areas of the regular inscribed polygons.

Then, the *length of an arc* whose degree measure is known and the *area of its sector* are defined as fractional parts of the circumference and area of a circle.

**12.1** In this section, the vocabulary of regular inscribed polygons is introduced, and the formula for the area of a regular polygon is developed.

The constructions on pages 422 and 423 are based on the Perpendicular Bisector and Angle Bisector Theorems on pages 110 and 210. However, the centers of the inscribed and circumscribed circles are the same, so the first construction can actually be used to construct both circles.

**12.2** *Limit* is used in this section to introduce the idea of length (*circumference*) of a circle in linear units. (See the notes for Section 11.5, page T22.) The discussion is purposely kept intuitive and simple and does not digress into the theory of limits.

The number $\pi$ turns up in some surprising places in mathematics. But its most basic definition is the one given on page 425. Like $\sqrt{2}$ and $\sqrt{3}$, the number $\pi$ is irrational and cannot be expressed exactly by any fraction or repeating decimal. In fact, $\pi^2$ is also irrational, which is not the case for $(\sqrt{2})^2$ and $(\sqrt{3})^2$.

The instructions for purely computational exercises call for an exact result in terms of $\pi$. In applications, an approximation for $\pi$ is given. You may want to provide more practice by having students give all answers both exactly and as approximations.

**12.3** The area of a circular region can be thought of as the limiting value of the areas of the inscribed *or* the circumscribed polygons. The areas of the polygons in the two sequences approach the area of the circle from opposite directions. In this section, we use only the inscribed polygons.

**12.4** Since circles can be measured in linear units, arcs can also be measured in linear units. (See the notes for Sections 11.5 and 12.2, pages T22–T23.) The formula is based on the proportion

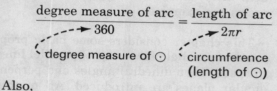

$$\frac{\text{degree measure of arc}}{360} = \frac{\text{length of arc}}{2\pi r}$$

$$\text{degree measure of} \odot \qquad \text{circumference (length of } \odot )$$

Also,

$$\frac{\text{degree measure of arc}}{360} = \frac{\text{area of sector}}{\pi r^2}$$

$$\text{degree measure of} \odot \qquad \text{area of } \odot$$

In other words, an arc that extends $\frac{1}{3}$ of the way around a circle with radius $r$ has degree measure $\frac{1}{3} \cdot 360$ and linear measure $\frac{1}{3} \cdot 2\pi r$, and it determines a sector whose area is $\frac{1}{3}\pi r^2$.

**12.5** This section on transformations can be used in a maximum course, but it should be omitted in a minimum or regular course.

A spoked wheel such as a bicycle wheel or a Ferris wheel is a good model for a figure with turn symmetry. Since a rectangle has turn symmetry for a 180° turn, it also has point symmetry. Capital letters that can be printed so that they have point symmetry are H, I, N, O, S, X, and Z. There are also some words that can be printed to be point-symmetric, such as MOW, SIS, and pod. Students might have fun looking for others.

This mini-chapter considers the history of Euclidean and non-Euclidean geometries and points out a few important differences. While this material is not technical in nature, its understanding requires a certain amount of maturity and experience with geometry. For this reason it has been deferred until well into the second semester, and in most classes it should not be attempted any sooner.

## Chapter 13    PARALLEL LINES AND PLANES    Pages 445–470

*Overview:* Remember that intuition and visualization are more difficult for most students when considering figures in space. Encourage students to work with models to help them visualize the figures in the theorems and exercises.

This chapter considers some basic properties of parallel planes and of parallel lines in space. Then dihedral angles and perpendicular planes are introduced. All of this material is helpful in defining and visualizing solid figures in Chapter 14.

**13.1** Discuss carefully the properties illustrated at the top of page 446. Models may readily be found using the walls, ceiling, and floor of the classroom and their intersections.

Before assigning Exercises 11–18, you may want to review counterexamples for if-then statements on page 205.

**13.2** Models for the theorems in this section are very easy to find or to make. Exploit the similarity, in both wording and content, of these theorems to the corresponding plane theorems in Chapter 4. The chart below shows the related theorems.

| Chapter 13 | Chapter 4 |
|---|---|
| p. 451 | p. 125 |
| p. 452, 1st theorem | p. 133, 2nd theorem |
| p. 452, 2nd theorem | p. 133, 3rd theorem |
| p. 453 | p. 142, 3rd theorem |

**13.3** Since a half plane does not contain its edge (see page 45), the face of a dihedral angle is defined as a half plane *and* its edge. Ruled index cards are useful for making models of dihedral angles. Fold a card so the edge of the dihedral angle is perpendicular to the rules on the card. The rules form plane angles of the dihedral angle, suggesting the theorem on page 458.

The need for perpendicularity in the definition of *plane angle* can be shown by making several oblique cuts into the fold of the card and sliding another card into each cut. The resulting angles should be obviously noncongruent.

**13.4** The theorems in this section are readily modeled using two index cards cut like eggcrate dividers. Make a cut halfway across each card, perpendicular to the rules. Slide each card into the slot on the other card and turn the cards so the dihedral angles formed are any size you wish. Set the cards on a flat surface so they are both perpendicular to it. This model can now be used to explore the definition of *perpendicular planes* as well as to illustrate both theorems in this section.

**13.5** This section on transformations can be used in a maximum course, but it should be omitted in a minimum or regular course. The ideas involved in slides and turns in space are easy to visualize, so special models are probably not needed.

*Overview:* At times in the past, geometry has been taught in two courses, *plane geometry* and *solid geometry.* By combining the study of the geometry of two and three dimensions, we can build on the analogies between the two and make more effective use of models. In addition, time is saved that can be put to more productive use.

In this chapter we introduce the basic vocabulary for several solid figures. Then we develop the volume formulas for prisms, circular cylinders, pyramids, circular cones, and spheres. Formulas for surface area are developed for right prisms, right circular cylinders, regular pyramids, right circular cones, and spheres.

**14.1** Any closed three-dimensional figure whose faces are polygonal regions is a polyhedron. Polyhedrons in space are analogous to polygons in a plane. A good source of information on making models of polyhedrons is *Polyhedron Models for the Classroom*, by Magnus J. Wenninger (NCTM).

**14.2** Many common models of polyhedrons are right prisms—rectangular boxes and flat-topped buildings, for example.

Emphasize the following progression:

| measure | units | dimensions |
|---------|-------|------------|
| length | linear | 1 |
| area | square | 2 |
| volume | cubic | 3 |

Remind students that linear measures must all be expressed in like units before they are used to compute area or volume.

The Volume Postulate and the Volume Postulate for a Rectangular Prism are analogous to the Area Postulate and the Area Postulate for a Rectangle, pp. 287–288.

**14.3** The two postulates on page 478 correspond to the second and third postulates on page 287.

On pages 478–479, the Volume Theorem for a Right Triangular Prism is developed in order to get at the more general Volume Theorem for a Right Prism.

**14.4** Another figure for which it is quite simple to find models is the right circular cylinder. Besides the ubiquitous "tin" can, there are silos and even hotels and office buildings made in this shape; other models are pipes, hoses, and so on. This is a very important figure for applications.

The comparisons asked for in Exercises 21, 22, 25, and 26 are not most easily done by computing volumes. Rather, in Exercise 21, compare $\pi \cdot 7 \cdot 7 \cdot 5$ to $\pi \cdot 5 \cdot 5 \cdot 7$ by removing common factors and comparing the remaining factors (7 and 5). Likewise, for Exercise 22, compare $\pi \cdot \frac{(7.8)(7.8)}{4}(8.2)$ to $\pi \cdot \frac{(8.2)(8.2)}{4}(7.8)$. (Removing common factors, compare 7.8 to 8.2.)

For Exercise 25, compare $\pi \cdot 7^2 \cdot 6$ to $\pi \cdot (3.5)^2 \cdot 6$ by writing $\pi \cdot 7^2 \cdot 6 = \pi \cdot (3.5 \cdot 2)^2 \cdot 6 = \pi \cdot (3.5)^2 \cdot 4 \cdot 6$. Now remove common factors, leaving the comparison of 1 to 4. (Since $A$ holds 1 gallon, $B$ holds 4 gallons.)

For Exercise 26, compare $\pi \cdot 3^2 \cdot 12$ to $\pi \cdot 6^2 \cdot 6$ by removing common factors, leaving the comparison of 1 to 2. Then use this result to answer the question.

**14.5** In this section, we use Cavalieri's Postulate to develop the completely general formulas for the volumes of a prism and a circular cylinder. It is more difficult to find models and applications for oblique solids than for right and regular solids, but modern art and sculpture are good sources of such models.

**14.6** The Egyptian pyramids and ice-cream cones are probably the most obvious models for square pyramids and right circular cones. Models of oblique forms would be more difficult to find.

Plastic models may be used to contrast the volumes of a right circular cylinder and a right circular cone with the same radius and height, as well as that of a regular pyramid and a right prism with equal base areas and the same height. The comparison can be accomplished either by pouring the contents of one hollow model into another or by using a solid model of the smaller figure to displace part of the contents of the hollow cylinder or prism model.

**14.7** Which measure of a solid is of most interest depends on whether you are going to fill the solid or paint it. We have so far dealt with the measure involved in filling it. This section deals with the measure involved in painting it—the surface area.

For each solid in this section, total surface area is computed in two steps. The area of the sides or lateral surface (the lateral area) is found first; then the area of the base or bases is added to this.

For the *Algebra Review* on page 502, note that *simplest radical form* does not distinguish between $\frac{-3 \pm \sqrt{6}}{3}$ and $-1 \pm \frac{1}{3}\sqrt{6}$, for example. So the answers for Exercises 6–9 and 12 may be written correctly either way.

**14.8** Again, plastic models may be used to demonstrate that the volume of a sphere with radius $r$ is equal to the sum of the volumes of a cylinder and a cone, each with radius and height $r$.

Exercises 28–30 on page 507 present another use for Cavalieri's Postulate. Previously, each solid to which we applied the postulate had a constant cross-sectional area. In this case, the cross-sectional area of each solid is a function of $h$. However, since those areas are equal for each $h$, Cavalieri's Postulate applies.

**14.9** This section on transformations can be used in a maximum course, but it should be omitted in a minimum or regular course.

Point out that if a figure has line symmetry, it also has plane symmetry when considered as a figure in space. Visualizing planes of symmetry of solids can be quite challenging. Use models freely.

## Mini-Chapter: PLATONIC SOLIDS    Pages 513–514

The discovery of the five regular polyhedrons is lost in prehistory. Plato described them, but historians agree that he probably learned about them from the Pythagoreans. However, at least three of the five were known in Egypt and other parts of the world before the time of the Pythagoreans.

There are crystals in the forms of tetrahedrons, hexahedrons, and octahedrons. Skeletons of microscopic sea animals have been found that have the shapes of dodecahedrons and icosahedrons. These polyhedrons are also used in a variety of ways in art and technology.

*Overview:* The modern era in mathematics began with the development, in the 17th century, of analytic geometry and the calculus. French mathematicians René Descartes and Pierre de Fermat, building on the groundwork laid by others, are responsible for the emergence of analytic geometry, in which geometric figures are described algebraically and algebraic statements are pictured geometrically.

The chapter gives students a glimpse of the added power gained by joining the two disciplines. The coordinate plane is introduced and is used to develop these topics: distance and midpoint formulas, slopes and equations of lines, and locus. Coordinate proofs are also introduced.

**15.1** Section 1.2 showed how a line is coordinatized using real numbers. This section shows how a plane is coordinatized using ordered pairs of real numbers. Space can also be coordinatized, using ordered triples of real numbers. At this point, we run out of geometric models, but we do not run out of algebra; mathematicians speak as easily of $n$-dimensional spaces, coordinatized using ordered $n$-tuples, as they do of the familiar space of high-school geometry.

A common model for the coordinate plane is a city laid out in a grid pattern. Any location in the city can be described by giving its distance east or west and north or south of some central point.

**15.2** *Distance* is not defined any differently in this section than in Section 1.3. However, instead of coordinatizing the line through two given points, as described in the Ruler Placement Postulate, we compute the distance between the points by using their plane coordinates and the Distance Formula.

Emphasize that either of two given points can be the $P$ of the theorem and the other point $Q$. Notice that since $(-n)^2 = n^2$, no harm is done to the Distance Formula by computing $(x_2 - x_1)^2 + (y_1 - y_2)^2$.

**15.3** The Midpoint Formula is based on simple, straightforward reasoning. If students understand its development, they will have no trouble recalling it. Notice the use of the second theorem from page 154 to establish that $M$ is indeed the midpoint of $\overline{PQ}$ in the figure on page 524.

You may want to elaborate on this statement from page 523:

Since $-2 < x < 4$, $x + 2 > 0$ and $4 - x > 0$.

If $M$ is on $\overline{PQ}$, then $-2 < x < 4$. Rewriting,

| | | |
|---|---|---|
| $-2 < x$ | and | $x < 4$ |
| $x > -2$ | and | $4 > x$ |
| $x + 2 > -2 + 2$ | and | $4 - x > x - x$ |
| $x + 2 > 0$ | and | $4 - x > 0$ |

**15.4** Unlike the Distance Formula, the Slope Formula requires that both coordinates of *one* point be subtracted from the corresponding coordinates of the *other* point.

Emphasize the distinction between *no slope* and *zero slope*. The popular idea of zero as representing *nothing* or *none* works against understanding in this situation.

**15.5** According to the Straight Line Postulate, two points determine a line. So if we can graph the points, we can graph the line. On the other hand, if we have certain information about a line, we can write its equation. In this section, we develop the equation of a line for which the slope and the coordinates of one point are known. Of course, if coordinates of two points are known, the slope can be found.

In the Point-Slope Theorem, we refer to *the* equation of a line. A line can, in fact, be described by any number of equations, but these equations are all equivalent. On page 532, six equivalent equations are given in Example 1 and the discussion following it. The last equation of the six is identified as being in *standard form*.

In this text, we use a relaxed standard form, since we do not require that the operation sign be $+$ or that the coefficient 1 be written. In other words, we accept $x - 2y = 5$ as being in standard form, rather than requiring $1x + (-2)y = 5$.

**15.6** It is not necessary to rewrite every linear equation in point-slope form in order to graph the line. In fact, it may be easier to find the coordinates of two points by substituting values for one variable or the other. Or, it may be convenient to rewrite the equation in a form that reveals the slope and the $y$-coordinate of the point at which the line intersects the $y$-axis (the *y-intercept*). Both techniques are covered in this section. Care must be taken to read the sign of the $y$-intercept correctly.

**15.7** Relationships between lines in a plane can be analyzed by comparing their slopes, but there must be *two distinct* lines with equal slopes for parallelism. For example,

$$y = \tfrac{1}{2}x + 6 \qquad \text{and} \qquad y - 4 = \tfrac{1}{2}(x + 4)$$

do not describe parallel lines with slope $\tfrac{1}{2}$. They describe the same line.

Also emphasize that if the slopes of two lines have product $-1$, the lines are perpendicular. But every horizontal line is perpendicular to every vertical line, and their slopes have *no product* because one of them has *no slope*.

**15.8** This section on coordinate proofs can be used in a maximum or regular course but should be omitted in a minimum course.

In this section, we analyze the convenient placement of figures in a coordinate plane. Another way to do this is to think of imposing the coordinate grid on the plane of the figure. Then the problem is to place the origin and to align the axes for greatest convenience.

Analytic geometry makes many otherwise cumbersome proofs simple. Students who are better at algebra than at geometry will appreciate this. Do not let them think, however, that all geometric theorems are more easily proved by algebraic methods. Some proofs are simpler using the so-called "synthetic" geometry of Euclid.

**15.9** A locus is, after all, a set of points, and we have been describing linear sets of points in the earlier sections. However, a locus need not be a line. In this section, two other types of locus are explored.

A locus of the first type can be described by an inequality. The graph of a locus of the second type is a circle. In this section, we deal only with equations of circles in *standard form*, so the center and the radius of the circle are obvious without algebraic manipulation of the equation.

**15.10** This section on transformations can be used in a maximum course, but it should be omitted in a minimum or regular course.

A transformation can be defined as a rule by which to find the coordinates of the image of any given point in the plane. This definition emphasizes the fact that the transformation affects the entire plane. Of course, the defining rule also gives the coordinates of each point in the image of any given figure in that plane.

The *Cumulative Review* on pages 556–559 can be used as an end-of-semester review for the second semester.

# Performance Objectives

This list of course goals may be reproduced for use by students of USING GEOMETRY. Objectives preceded by ○ refer to constructions or transformations.

**Chapter 1**   The student can do the following:

**1.1**   □ Pick out models for points, lines, and planes from common surroundings.

□ Identify points, lines, and planes in geometric diagrams, and draw such diagrams.

□ Recognize the symbols used to name points, lines, and planes.

**1.2**   □ Draw a number line and label integer and rational points that are given.

**1.3**   □ Recognize the symbol used to stand for the distance between two points.

□ Find the distance between two points on a number line, given their coordinates.

**1.4**   □ In geometric diagrams, pick out collinear and coplanar points, a point between two others, and two points on the same side of or on opposite sides of a third.

□ Recognize the symbols used to name segments and rays.

□ Identify the endpoints and midpoint of a segment, the endpoint of a ray, and opposite rays.

**1.5**   □ Given an appropriate situation, describe an example which would show that a conclusion reached by inductive reasoning is not correct.

□ Given a postulate and a hypothesis, state an appropriate conclusion.

**1.6**   □ Recognize examples of basic algebraic properties (of operations and equality).

**1.7**   □ Select the definition, postulate, or theorem that shows a given conclusion about points, lines, and planes is correct.

**1.8**   □ Given a statement containing "exactly one," restate it by using "determine," and vice versa.

□ Choose which theorem lets you reach a stated conclusion about intersecting lines and planes.

**1.9**   ○ Tell the difference between a drawing and a construction.

○ Construct a segment of a given length.

**1.10**   ○ Given two appropriate figures in a plane, tell if one is the reflection (flip), slide, turn, or size-change image of the other.

**Chapter 2**   The student can do the following:

**2.1**   □ Tell if a figure is a convex set.

□ Given an appropriate figure, tell if two points are on the same side or on opposite sides of a line in a plane or of a plane in space.

**2.2**   □ Use the symbols for naming angles and triangles.

□ Identify sides, vertices, interiors, and exteriors of angles and triangles.

**2.3**   □ Use a protractor to measure angles and to draw angles of given measures.

□ Identify adjacent angles.

□ Apply the Angle Addition Postulate to find measures of appropriate angles.

**2.4**   □ Identify the bisector of an angle, and find the measures of the angles formed when an angle is bisected.

□ Given the measure of an angle, find the measure of its supplement.

○ Construct the bisector of an angle.

**2.5** ☐ Identify acute, obtuse, and right angles, perpendicular lines, and the perpendicular bisector of a segment.

☐ Given the measure of an angle, find the measure of its complement.

○ Construct the perpendicular bisector of a segment and a perpendicular to a line at or from a given point.

**2.6** ☐ Use statements about congruence of segments (or angles) interchangeably with statements about equality of their measures.

☐ Use the basic properties of congruence of segments and angles.

○ Construct an angle congruent to a given angle.

**2.7** ☐ Determine that two angles are congruent by identifying them as supplements or complements of congruent angles or as vertical angles.

☐ Recognize that two supplementary and congruent angles are right angles and that two perpendicular lines form four right angles.

☐ Choose the theorem that supports a stated conclusion about angles.

**2.8** ○ Recognize that reflections, slides, and turns preserve betweenness, collinearity, distance, and angle measure and that reflections reverse orientation.

○ Given a figure and its reflection image, draw the reflecting line.

○ Given a simple figure (point, segment, line, triangle) and a reflecting line, draw the reflection image.

Chapter 3   The student can do the following:

**3.1** ☐ Identify the hypothesis and conclusion of an if-then statement.

☐ Change a statement to if-then form.

☐ Draw an Euler diagram to illustrate an if-then statement.

**3.2** ☐ State the reasons needed to complete a two-column proof.

**3.3** ☐ Given a congruence statement like $\triangle ABC \cong \triangle DEF$, identify all pairs of congruent parts.

☐ Given two triangles with the corresponding congruent parts marked, write a congruence statement like $\triangle ABC \cong \triangle DEF$.

**3.4** ☐ Identify which postulate—SSS, SAS, or ASA—can be used to prove two triangles congruent, given certain information.

○ Construct a triangle, given three sides or two sides and the included angle.

**3.5** ☐ State the reasons needed to complete a two-column proof that two triangles are congruent.

**3.6** ☐ State the reasons needed to complete a two-column proof that two angles or segments are congruent because they are corresponding parts of congruent triangles.

**3.7** ☐ Recognize that a point on the perpendicular bisector of a segment is equidistant from the endpoints of the segment.

☐ Recognize that in a plane, two points equidistant from the endpoints of a segment determine its perpendicular bisector.

**3.8** ○ Use reflections, slides, and turns to show how two congruent triangles can be made to coincide.

Chapter 4   The student can do the following:

**4.1** ☐ Recognize that two parallel lines determine a plane and that in a plane, two lines perpendicular to a third line are parallel.

☐ Recognize that we assume there is *exactly one* parallel to a line through a point not on it.

○ Use perpendicular lines to construct a line through a given point, parallel to a given line.

**4.2** ☐ Given two lines and a transversal, use alternate interior (or exterior) angles to determine if the lines are parallel.

☐ Given two parallel lines and a transversal, use alternate interior (or exterior) angles to find measures of other angles.

○ Use alternate interior angles to construct a line through a given point, parallel to a given line.

**4.3** ☐ Use corresponding angles (or interior angles on the same side of a transversal) to determine if two lines are parallel.

☐ Given two lines are parallel, use corresponding angles (or interior angles on the same side of a transversal) to find measures of other angles.

**4.4** ☐ Use the Angle Sum Theorem for Triangles and the Exterior Angle Theorem to find the measures of angles.

**4.5** ☐ Name a quadrilateral and identify its parts.

☐ Using properties of parallelograms, tell which segments are congruent and which angles are congruent or supplementary.

○ Construct a parallelogram, given two consecutive sides and an angle.

**4.6** ☐ Recognize that a quadrilateral is a parallelogram if opposite sides are congruent, if two sides are parallel and congruent, or if the diagonals bisect each other.

**4.7** ☐ Find measures of segments and angles by using the fact that the midline of a triangle is parallel to the third side and is half as long.

**4.8** ☐ Use properties of special parallelograms (rectangle, rhombus, and square) to find measures of segments and angles.

**4.9** ☐ Find measures of segments by using the fact that parallel lines which intercept congruent segments on one transversal also intercept congruent segments on every other transversal.

☐ Recognize that the midline of a trapezoid is parallel to the bases and half as long as the sum of the bases.

○ By construction, separate a segment into a given number of congruent segments.

**4.10** ○ Draw the slide image of a simple figure (triangle or quadrilateral).

**Chapter 5**  The student can do the following:

**5.1** ☐ Tell if a figure is a polygon.

☐ Name a polygon and identify its parts.

☐ Tell if a polygon is convex and identify types of polygons by the number of sides.

**5.2** ☐ Find the perimeter of a polygon, given the measures of its sides.

☐ Use the formulas for finding perimeters of rectangles and regular polygons.

○ Construct a regular hexagon with sides of a given length.

**5.3** ☐ For a convex polygon, find the sum of the measures of its interior angles and of its exterior angles.

☐ For a regular polygon, find the measure of each interior and each exterior angle.

**5.4** ☐ Recognize that two congruent polygons have all the parts of one congruent to the corresponding parts of the other.

☐ Use the SAS Theorem for parallelograms in proving them congruent.

**5.5** ☐ Use the AAS Theorem in proving triangles congruent.

**5.6**  ☐ Identify triangles as scalene, isosceles, and equilateral, and as acute, obtuse, right, and equiangular.

☐ Identify the bases, legs, and base angles of isosceles triangles and trapezoids.

☐ Use the properties of special triangles and of isosceles trapezoids to find measures of segments and angles.

**5.7**  ☐ Use the HA, LA, LL, and HL Theorems in proving right triangles congruent.

**5.8**  ☐ Use the various congruence postulates (SSS, SAS, ASA) and theorems (AAS, HA, LA, LL, HL) in proofs.

**5.9**  ☐ Use the various congruence postulates and theorems in proofs involving overlapping triangles.

**5.10**  ○ Identify the symmetry lines of a figure.

**Chapter 6**  The student can do the following:

**6.1**  ☐ Find a counterexample for a false if-then statement.

☐ Restate a theorem in if-then form.

**6.2**  ☐ Tell whether an if-then statement is true or false; then state the converse and tell whether it is true or false.

☐ Restate an if-then statement and its converse in if-and-only-if form.

**6.3**  ☐ Restate a definition in if-and-only-if form.

**6.4**  ☐ Recognize that affirming the hypothesis and denying the conclusion are valid patterns of reasoning, but denying the hypothesis and affirming the conclusion are not.

**6.5**  ☐ State the reasons needed to complete an indirect proof.

**6.6**  ☐ Identify the medians and altitudes of a triangle, and use these figures in proofs.

○ Construct the medians and altitudes of a triangle.

**6.7**  ☐ Recognize that for any triangle, each of these sets of figures is concurrent: the perpendicular bisectors of the sides, the angle bisectors, the medians, and the lines containing the altitudes.

☐ Find measures of segments by using the fact that the medians are concurrent at a point that is two thirds the distance from each vertex to the midpoint of the opposite side.

**6.8**  ○ State the reasons needed to complete a proof involving transformations.

**Chapter 7**  The student can do the following:

**7.1**  ☐ Use the definitions of $<$ and $>$ to translate equations into inequalities, and vice versa.

☐ Write equivalent statements by using the fact that for any real numbers $a$ and $b$, either $a < b$, $a = b$, or $a > b$.

☐ Solve inequalities.

**7.2**  ☐ Compare the measures of segments or angles by using the definition of *between*, the Angle Addition Postulate, and the Exterior Angle Inequality Theorem.

**7.3**  ☐ Compare the measures of two sides (or angles) of a triangle, given information about the opposite angles (or sides).

☐ Recognize that the shortest segment from a point to a line is the perpendicular segment.

**7.4**  ☐ Use the triangle inequality to tell if three numbers can be lengths of the sides of a triangle.

**7.5**  ☐ Given two noncongruent triangles with two sides of one congruent to two sides of the other, compare the included angles from information about the opposite sides, and vice versa.

**7.6**  ○ Given two points on the same side of a line, draw the shortest path from one of the points to the line, then to the other point.

**Chapter 8** The student can do the following:

**8.1** ☐ Recognize that a line ℓ is perpendicular to a plane *P* if and only if they intersect and ℓ is perpendicular to every line in *P* that contains the point of intersection.

**8.2** ☐ Use the Basic Theorem for Perpendiculars and given information to tell if a line is perpendicular to a plane or to a line in that plane.

**8.3** ☐ Recognize that through a given point, there is exactly one plane perpendicular to a given line as well as exactly one line perpendicular to a given plane.

☐ Identify the perpendicular bisecting plane of a segment as the figure containing all points and only those points equidistant from the endpoints of the segment.

**8.4** ☐ Use the facts that two lines perpendicular to the same plane are coplanar and that the shortest segment from a point to a plane is the perpendicular segment.

**8.5** ○ Recognize that points in space can be reflected over a plane, much like points in a plane can be reflected over a line.

**Chapter 9** The student can do the following:

**9.1** ☐ Use the formulas for finding areas of rectangles and squares.

**9.2** ☐ Use the formulas for finding areas of parallelograms and triangles.

**9.3** ☐ Use the formula for finding areas of trapezoids and the formula for finding areas of rhombuses from the lengths of the diagonals.

**9.4** ☐ Find the square roots of common perfect squares, and use a square-root table.

☐ Simplify radicals for square roots.

**9.5** ☐ Given a right triangle and the lengths of two sides, use the Pythagorean Theorem to find the length of the third side.

☐ Use the Converse of the Pythagorean Theorem to tell if a triangle is a right triangle.

**9.6** ☐ Use the properties of isosceles right triangles and 30-60-90° triangles to find the lengths of their sides.

○ Construct a 30-60-90° triangle.

**9.7** ○ Given the center and magnitude, draw the size-change image of a simple figure (segment, angle, triangle).

**Chapter 10** The student can do the following:

**10.1** ☐ Reduce ratios to lowest terms.

☐ Use basic properties of proportions to write equivalent proportions and to solve proportions.

**10.2** ☐ Given two similar polygons and the measures of some of their parts, find the ratio of similarity and the measures of other parts.

**10.3** ☐ Use the AA Similarity Theorem in proving triangles similar.

**10.4** ☐ Use the AA, SAS, and SSS Similarity Theorems in proving triangles similar.

**10.5** ☐ Use the AA, LL, and HL Similarity Theorems in proving right triangles similar.

☐ Find lengths of segments by using the geometric-mean relationship that exists between the altitude to the hypotenuse and the sides of a right triangle.

○ Construct the geometric mean of two segments.

**10.6** ☐ Use the various similarity theorems (AA, SAS, SSS, LL, HL) in proofs.

**10.7** ☐ Find lengths of segments by using the fact that parallel lines intercept proportional corresponding segments on any two transversals.

○ By construction, separate a segment into segments in a given ratio.

**10.8** ☐ Given the ratio of corresponding segments of similar polygons, find the ratio of their areas, and vice versa.

**10.9** ○ Recognize that under any combination of reflections, turns, slides, and size changes, a triangle is similar to its image.

**Chapter 11**  The student can do the following:

11.1  ☐ Identify radii, diameters, chords, and secants of circles and spheres.

○ Construct the circle containing three given noncollinear points.

11.2  ☐ Identify the interior and exterior of a circle.

☐ Use the Chord Theorem and the Congruent Chords Theorem in proofs.

11.3  ☐ Recognize that a circle and line can have 0, 1, or 2 points of intersection, and the same is true of two circles.

☐ Identify a tangent to a circle, externally and internally tangent circles, concentric circles, and common external and internal tangents.

○ Construct a tangent to a circle at or from a given point.

11.4  ☐ Recognize that a sphere and plane can have 0 points or 1 point of intersection, or they can intersect at a circle.

☐ Identify the interior and exterior of a sphere, as well as great and small circles of a sphere.

☐ Find perpendiculars and measures of segments by using the Tangent Plane Theorem and the Chord Theorem for Spheres.

11.5  ☐ Identify central angles, minor and major arcs, and semicircles.

☐ Find the measures of arcs from measures of central angles, and vice versa, and use the Arc Addition Postulate.

11.6  ☐ Identify inscribed angles and intercepted arcs.

☐ Find measures of inscribed angles from measures of intercepted arcs, and vice versa.

○ Construct a triangle circumscribed about a circle.

11.7  ☐ Find measures of angles formed by chords, secants, and tangents from measures of intercepted arcs, and vice versa.

11.8  ☐ Find lengths of segments by using the relationships between products of lengths of segments of chords, secants, and tangents.

11.9  ☐ Given the condition that a locus of points must satisfy, draw and describe the figure.

11.10  ○ Draw the turn image of a simple figure.

**Chapter 12**  The student can do the following:

12.1  ☐ Identify radii, apothems, and central angles of regular polygons, as well as inscribed and circumscribed regular polygons.

☐ Find the measure of a central angle of a regular polygon, given the number of sides.

☐ Use the formula for finding areas of regular polygons.

○ Construct a circle circumscribed about (or inscribed in) a given regular polygon.

12.2  ☐ Use the formula for finding circumferences of circles.

12.3  ☐ Use the formula for finding areas of circles.

12.4  ☐ Use the formulas for finding lengths of arcs and areas of sectors of circles.

12.5  ○ Tell if a figure has point or turn symmetry.

○ Given a simple figure, draw its reflection image over a point.

**Chapter 13**  The student can do the following:

13.1  ☐ Recognize that a third plane intersects two parallel planes at two parallel lines and that a line perpendicular to one of two parallel planes is perpendicular to the other.

☐ Recognize that two planes are parallel if both are perpendicular to the same line or both are parallel to the same plane.

13.2  ☐ Use facts about parallel lines and planes in proofs.

**13.3**  ☐ Identify dihedral angles and plane angles of dihedral angles.

**13.4**  ☐ Identify right dihedral angles and perpendicular planes.

☐ Recognize that if a line is perpendicular to plane $p$, then every plane containing that line is perpendicular to plane $p$.

☐ Name a plane by using three noncollinear points in the plane.

**13.5**  ○ Identify models of slides and turns in space.

**Chapter 14**  The student can do the following:

**14.1**  ☐ Identify vertices, edges, faces, dihedral angles, the interior, and the exterior of a polyhedron.

☐ Tell if a polyhedron is convex.

**14.2**  ☐ Identify the parts of a right prism.

☐ Use the formula for finding volumes of right rectangular prisms.

**14.3**  ☐ Use the formula for finding volumes of right prisms.

**14.4**  ☐ Identify the parts of a right circular cylinder.

☐ Use the formula for finding volumes of right circular cylinders.

**14.5**  ☐ Extend earlier formulas to finding volumes of oblique prisms and circular cylinders.

**14.6**  ☐ Identify the parts of pyramids and circular cones.

☐ Use the formulas for finding volumes of pyramids and circular cones.

**14.7**  ☐ Use the formulas for finding lateral areas and surface areas of right prisms, regular pyramids, and right circular cylinders and cones.

**14.8**  ☐ Use the formulas for finding volumes and surface areas of spheres.

**14.9**  ○ Identify the symmetry planes of a solid.

**Chapter 15**  The student can do the following:

**15.1**  ☐ Determine the coordinates of points in the coordinate plane.

☐ Graph points, given their coordinates.

**15.2**  ☐ Use the distance formula to find the distance between two points, given their coordinates.

**15.3**  ☐ Use the midpoint formula to find the coordinates of the midpoint of a segment, given the coordinates of its endpoints.

**15.4**  ☐ Find the slope of a line, given the coordinates of two points.

☐ Graph a line, given its slope and one point.

**15.5**  ☐ Graph a line, given its equation in point-slope form.

☐ Find the equation of a line in point-slope form and standard form, given its slope and one point.

☐ Find the equation of a line in standard form, given two points.

**15.6**  ☐ Graph a line by using its equation to find the slope and $y$-intercept or to find any three points.

☐ Given a linear equation, change it to slope-intercept form and state the slope and $y$-intercept of the graph.

**15.7**  ☐ Use slopes to tell if two lines are parallel, perpendicular, or neither.

☐ Find the equation of a line by using given facts and the relationship between slopes and perpendicularity (or parallelism).

**15.8**  ☐ Write a coordinate proof using a given figure (triangle or quadrilateral).

**15.9**  ☐ Graph a locus, given the algebraic condition that the points satisfy.

☐ Write an algebraic condition for a locus, given a verbal description.

**15.10**  ○ Draw the image of a polygon in the coordinate plane, given the coordinates of the vertices of the polygon and a coordinate description of the transformation.

# Tests

NOTE: Test items marked * refer to optional material that may have been omitted from the course.

## Test for Chapter 1   Geometry: What and Why?

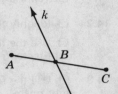

Ex. 1–10

1–10. Refer to the figure. Name an example of

1. two planes

2. two intersecting lines

3. three collinear points

4. line in plane $b$

5. segment containing $V$

6. intersection of two lines

7. endpoint of $\overrightarrow{RS}$

8. point coplanar with $R$, $V$, $S$

9. intersection of $\overleftrightarrow{TV}$ and $b$

10. two opposite rays

11. If $a < 5$ and $5 < b$, then $a\ (<,\ =,\ >)\ b$.

12. Find: **a.** $|\tfrac{1}{2}|$   **b.** $|5 - 8|$

13–17. Refer to the figure. Line $k$ intersects $\overline{AC}$ at $B$.

13. $B$ is _____ $A$ and $C$.

14. $AC$ is the _____ between $A$ and $C$.

15. $AB + $ _____ $= AC$

16. If $AB = BC$, then $B$ is the _____ of $\overline{AC}$.

17. If $B$ is the midpoint of $\overline{AC}$, then $k$ _____ $\overline{AC}$.

Ex. 13–17

18. If the coordinates of $X$ and $Y$ are $-5$ and 4, then $XY = $ _____.

19. A _____ is a statement accepted as true without proof.

20. Using examples to reach a conclusion is _____ reasoning.

21. Using postulates and definitions to reach a conclusion is _____ reasoning.

22. Exactly one means "at least one but _____."

23. A _____ states a hypothesis and its logical conclusion.

24. Two points determine a _____.

25. Exactly one _____ contains two intersecting lines.

26. *Postulate:* A person who studies geometry uses logical reasoning.

   *Hypothesis:* Susan studies geometry.

   *Conclusion:* _____

27. What postulate explains why a three-legged table doesn't rock from leg to leg?

* 28. The figure resulting from a transformation is called the _____.

## Test for Chapter 2   Angles

**1–6.** True or False?

1. A plane separates space into two half spaces.

2. The exterior of a triangle is a convex set.

3. Vertical angles can be adjacent angles.

4. In a plane, if $\overleftrightarrow{XY} \perp \overleftrightarrow{YZ}$, then $\overleftrightarrow{XZ}$ cannot be perpendicular to $\overleftrightarrow{YZ}$.

5. Every right angle has a measure of 90.

6. An obtuse angle can be the complement of another angle.

7. $\angle R \cong \angle S$ means $m \angle R$ _____ $m \angle S$.

8. If $\overline{LM} \cong \overline{NO}$ and $\overline{NO} \cong \overline{PQ}$, then $\overline{LM} \cong$ _____ .

**9–15.** Refer to the figure. $\overrightarrow{DF}$ and $\overrightarrow{BE}$ intersect $\overleftrightarrow{AC}$ at $B$.

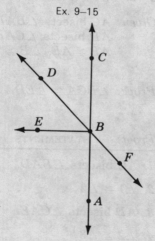

Ex. 9–15

9. Points $D$ and $F$ are on _____ sides of $\overleftrightarrow{AC}$.

10. $m \angle ABE + m \angle EBD = m \angle$ _____ .

11. If $\angle EBD \cong \angle DBC$, then _____ is the bisector of $\angle$ _____ .

12. If $\overrightarrow{BE} \perp \overleftrightarrow{AC}$, then $\angle$ _____ and $\angle$ _____ are complementary.

13. $\angle ABD$ and $\angle FBC$ are both supplementary to $\angle$ _____ , so $\angle ABD$ _____ $\angle FBC$.

14. If $\angle ABE$ _____ $\angle EBC$, then they are right angles.

15. If $\overleftrightarrow{BE}$ is the perpendicular bisector of $\overline{AC}$, then $B$ is the _____ of $\overline{AC}$.

**16–21.** Refer to the figure for Exercises 9–15. If $\overrightarrow{BE} \perp \overleftrightarrow{AC}$ and $m \angle EBD = 47$, find the measure of each angle.

16. $\angle ABE$          17. $\angle DBC$          18. $\angle ABF$

19. $\angle FBC$          20. $\angle ABD$          21. $\angle FBE$

**\*22.** $\triangle R'S'T'$ is the reflection image of $\triangle RST$. Is $R'S' = RS$?

# Test for Chapter 3    Congruent Triangles

1. Change the following statement to if-then form: All triangles have three sides.

2. Draw an Euler diagram for the statement in Exercise 1.

3. List all six congruence statements about angles and sides that follow from $\triangle ABC \cong \triangle XYZ$.

4. In a plane, if $R$ and $S$ are equidistant from $X$ and $Y$, then $\overleftrightarrow{RS}$ is the _____ of $\overline{XY}$.

5–7. Which postulate could be used to show that the given triangles are congruent?

5. 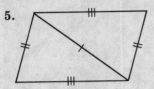    6. 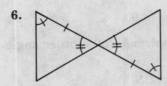    7.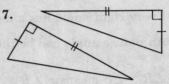

8–15. Give a reason for each statement in the following proof:

Given: $\overrightarrow{AC}$ bisects $\angle BAD$,
   $\overrightarrow{AD}$ bisects $\angle CAE$,
   $\overline{AB} \cong \overline{AE}$, $\angle B \cong \angle E$

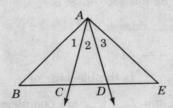

Prove: $\angle BCA \cong \angle EDA$

Proof:

| STATEMENTS | REASONS |
|---|---|
| 1. $\overrightarrow{AC}$ bisects $\angle BAD$. | 1. __8.__ |
| 2. $\angle 1 \cong \angle 2$ | 2. __9.__ |
| 3. $\overrightarrow{AD}$ bisects $\angle CAE$. | 3. __10.__ |
| 4. $\angle 2 \cong \angle 3$ | 4. __11.__ |
| 5. $\angle 1 \cong \angle 3$ | 5. __12.__ |
| 6. $\overline{AB} \cong \overline{AE}$, $\angle B \cong \angle E$ | 6. __13.__ |
| 7. $\triangle ABC \cong \triangle AED$ | 7. __14.__ |
| 8. $\angle BCA \cong \angle EDA$ | 8. __15.__ |

16. Are the triangular roof trusses in the figure the same size and shape? Why?

Ex. 16

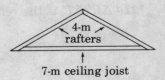

*17. Refer to the figure for the proof above. Tell if a slide, a turn, or a reflection is needed to make $\triangle ABC$ and $\triangle AED$ coincide.

# Test for Chapter 4    Parallel Lines in a Plane

**1.** Two parallel lines determine a _____.

**2.** Through a point not on line $\ell$, there is (no, at least one, exactly one) line parallel to $\ell$.

**3–8.** In the figure, $\ell \parallel r$.

**3.** $\angle 1$ and $\angle 2$ are (corresponding, alternate interior) angles.

**4.** If $m \angle 6 = 87$, $m \angle 5 = $ _____.

**5.** If $m \angle 7 = m \angle 4$, $\ell \parallel$ _____.

**6.** If $m \angle 2 + m \angle 3 = $ _____, $r \parallel n$.

**7.** If $r \parallel n$, $a = b$, and $c = 10$, $d = $ _____.

**8.** If $s \perp \ell$, $m \angle 5 = $ _____.

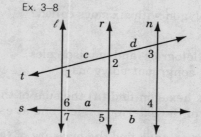

Ex. 3–8

**9–14.** In the figure, $AE = EB$.

**9.** If $AD = DC$, _____ $\parallel$ _____.

**10.** $m \angle 1 = m \angle 4 + m$ _____.

**11.** If $m \angle 3 = 90$, $m \angle 2 + m \angle 4 = $ _____.

**12.** If $\overline{ED} \parallel \overline{BC}$ and $BC = 10$, $ED = $ _____.

**13.** If $\overline{ED} \parallel \overline{BC}$, _____ is a trapezoid.

**14.** $m \angle 2 + m \angle 3 + m \angle 4 = $ _____.

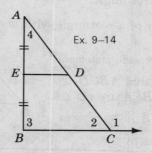

Ex. 9–14

**15–24.** Refer to the figure. $WXYZ$ is a parallelogram.

**15.** $\overline{YW}$ is a _____ of $WXYZ$.

**16.** $\triangle XYW \cong$ _____

**17.** $\overline{XW} \cong$ _____

**18.** $\overline{XY} \parallel$ _____

**19.** $m \angle XYZ + m$ _____ $= 180$

**20.** $m \angle XYZ = m$ _____

**21.** $\overline{YV} \cong$ _____

**22.** If $m \angle XYZ = 90$, $WXYZ$ is a _____.

**23.** If $\overline{XZ} \perp \overline{YW}$, $WXYZ$ is a _____.

**24.** If $\overline{XY} \perp \overline{YZ}$ and $\overline{XY} \cong \overline{YZ}$, $WXYZ$ is a _____.

Ex. 15–24

**\*25.** Slides (do, do not) preserve orientation.

# Test for Chapter 5    Polygons

**1–2.** Use the figures below.

a.   b.   c.   d.

**1.** Which figures are polygons?

**2.** Which figures are not convex polygons?

**3.** What is a polygon with six sides called?

**4.** If a triangle is equilateral, can it be a scalene triangle?

**5.** Can a parallelogram and an isosceles trapezoid be congruent polygons?

**6.** Can a right triangle also be an isosceles triangle?

**7.** For a convex hexagon find **(a)** the sum of the interior angles and **(b)** the sum of the exterior angles, one at each vertex.

**8.** For a regular octagon find the measure of **(a)** each interior angle and **(b)** each exterior angle.

**9.** Find the perimeter of a rectangle with $w = 3.2$ m and $\ell = 5.9$ m.

**10–15.** Give a reason for each statement.

*Given:* Isosceles trapezoid $ABCD$, $\angle CED$ and $\angle BFA$ are rt. $\angle$s.

*Prove:* $\triangle CED \cong \triangle BFA$

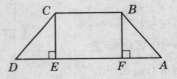

*Proof:*

| STATEMENTS | | REASONS |
|---|---|---|
| 1. $ABCD$ is an isosceles trapezoid. | 1. | **10.** ___ |
| 2. $\overline{CD} \cong \overline{BA}$ | 2. | **11.** ___ |
| 3. $\angle D \cong \angle A$ | 3. | **12.** ___ |
| 4. $\angle CED$ and $\angle BFA$ are rt. $\angle$s. | 4. | **13.** ___ |
| 5. $\triangle CED$ and $\triangle BFA$ are rt. $\triangle$s. | 5. | **14.** ___ |
| 6. $\triangle CED \cong \triangle BFA$ | 6. | **15.** ___ |

**16.** *Given:* $\overline{SV} \cong \overline{VT}$, $\angle R \cong \angle U$

*Prove:* $\triangle RST \cong \triangle UTS$

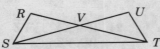

Ex. 17

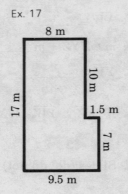

**17.** Find how many running meters of foundation must be poured for the house by finding the perimeter of the given figure.

**\*18.** How many symmetry lines does a regular hexagon have?

## Test for Chapter 6   More About Proofs

**1–2.** Describe a counterexample that shows the statement is false.

**1.** If two angles have a common vertex, they are vertical angles.

**2.** If two lines have no points in common, they are skew lines.

**3–4.** Write *true* or *false* for each statement. Then write the converse and tell if it is true or false.

**3.** If two angles are vertical angles, the angles are congruent.

**4.** If two angles are supplementary, the sum of their measures is 180.

**5.** Write an if-and-only-if statement for the following:
A right triangle is a triangle with exactly one right angle.

**6.** Write two true statements from the following:
Points are coplanar if and only if they are in the same plane.

**7–8.** Write *valid* or *faulty* for each argument. Then name the pattern of reasoning.

**7.** If $x = 3$, then $x^2 = 9$.
$x \neq 3$
So $x^2 \neq 9$.

**8.** If $\triangle ABC \cong \triangle XYZ$, then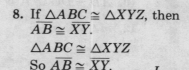
$\overline{AB} \cong \overline{XY}$.
$\triangle ABC \cong \triangle XYZ$
So $\overline{AB} \cong \overline{XY}$.

**9–13.** Give a reason for each step in this indirect proof.

*Given:* $\triangle KLM$, $\overline{MN} \not\cong \overline{NK}$

*Prove:* $\overline{LN}$ is not a median of $\triangle KLM$.

*Proof:*

| STATEMENTS | | REASONS |
|---|---|---|
| *1.* Assume $\overline{LN}$ is a median of $\triangle KLM$. | 1. | **9.** _____ |
| *2.* $N$ is the midpoint of $\overline{MK}$. | 2. | **10.** _____ |
| *3.* $\overline{MN} \cong \overline{NK}$ | 3. | **11.** _____ |
| *4.* But, $\overline{MN} \not\cong \overline{NK}$. | 4. | **12.** _____ |
| *5.* So, $\overline{LN}$ is not a median of $\triangle KLM$. | 5. | **13.** _____ |

**14.** For any triangle, which lines are concurrent? Those containing

**a.** the altitudes         **b.** the sides         **c.** the medians

**\*15.** If $\angle R'$ is the reflection image of right $\angle R$ over line $k$, then $\angle R'$ is a _____ angle.

# Test for Chapter 7    Geometric Inequalities

**1–5.** Which symbol, $<$, $=$, or $>$, should replace the ⫴ ?

1. If $x$ is not greater than $y$, then $x$ ⫴ $y$ or $x$ ⫴ $y$.

2. If $s = t + 5$, then $s$ ⫴ $t$.

3. If $m\angle A$ ⫴ $m\angle B$, then $\angle A$ is smaller than $\angle B$.

4. If $\overline{FG}$ is shorter than $\overline{HI}$, then $HI$ ⫴ $FG$.

5. For $\triangle PQR$, $PQ + QR$ ⫴ $PR$.

6. If $\overline{XY} \perp k$ at $Y$, then $XY$ is the _____ from $X$ to line $k$.

7. Solve:     **a.** $\frac{7}{8}t < 42$          **b.** $x + 8 < 17$

8. Can a triangle have sides with the given lengths?

   **a.** 5, 12, 7          **b.** 9, 13, 11          **c.** 8, 17, 6

**9–22.** Refer to the figures. Which symbol, $<$, $=$, or $>$, should replace the ⫴ ?

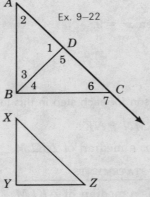

Ex. 9–22

9. $AB + BC$ ⫴ $AC$

10. $AD + DC$ ⫴ $AC$

11. $m\angle 7$ ⫴ $m\angle 2$

12. $m\angle 3$ ⫴ $m\angle 5$

13. $m\angle ABC$ ⫴ $m\angle 3$

14. If $m\angle 5 > 90$, $m\angle 7$ ⫴ 90.

15. If $BD > DC$, $m\angle 6$ ⫴ $m\angle 4$.

16. If $m\angle 2 > m\angle 3$, $AD$ ⫴ $BD$.

17. If $\overline{BD} \perp \overline{AC}$, $BD$ ⫴ $AB$.

18. If $m\angle 5 = 90$, $BC$ ⫴ $DC$.

19. If $\overline{AD} \cong \overline{DC}$, $m\angle 5 = 94$, and $m\angle 1 = 86$, then $BC$ ⫴ $AB$.

20. If $\overline{AB} \cong \overline{BC}$ and $m\angle 3$ ⫴ $m\angle 4$, then $D$ is closer to $A$ than to $C$.

21. If $\overline{XY} \cong \overline{BD}$, $\overline{XZ} \cong \overline{BC}$, and $m\angle X < m\angle 4$, then $DC$ ⫴ $YZ$.

22. If $\overline{XY} \cong \overline{BD}$, $\overline{YZ} \cong \overline{DA}$, and $XZ > BA$, then $m\angle Y$ ⫴ $m\angle 1$.

Ex. 23

● ball

● $E$

*23. In a game of pool, you want the cue ball to bounce off side $s$ of the table before stopping at point $E$. At what point should you aim?

## Test for Chapter 8    Perpendicular Lines and Planes

**1–12.** In the figure, $A$, $B$, and $C$ are in plane $p$; $D$, $E$, and $F$ are not.

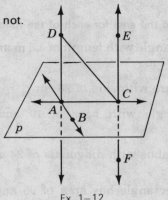

Ex. 1–12

1. If $\overrightarrow{AD} \perp \overrightarrow{AC}$ and $\overrightarrow{AD} \perp \overrightarrow{AB}$, $\overrightarrow{AD} \perp$ _____.

2. If $\overrightarrow{AD} \perp p$ and $\overleftrightarrow{CE} \perp p$, $\overrightarrow{AD}$ and $\overleftrightarrow{CE}$ are _____.

3. If $\overrightarrow{AD} \perp p$, $\overrightarrow{AD}$ is _____ to $\overrightarrow{AC}$ and $\overrightarrow{AB}$.

4. If $\overleftrightarrow{CE} \perp p$, $CE$ is the _____ from $E$ to $p$.

5. If $\overrightarrow{AD} \perp p$, $AD \ (<, =, >) \ DC$.

6. If $\overrightarrow{AD} \perp p$, $m \angle DAC =$ _____.

7. If $p$ is the _____ plane of $\overline{EF}$, then $AE = AF$.

8. If $\overleftrightarrow{CE}$ is not perpendicular to $p$, is it possible for $\overleftrightarrow{CE}$ to be perpendicular to $\overleftrightarrow{AC}$?

9. If $\overleftrightarrow{CE} \perp p$, is it possible for $\overleftrightarrow{CE}$ to be perpendicular to $\overline{DC}$?

10. How many planes through $E$ are perpendicular to $\overleftrightarrow{CE}$?

11. How many lines through $B$ are perpendicular to $p$?

12. How many planes contain $D$, $E$, $C$, and $A$ if $\overrightarrow{AD} \perp p$ and $\overleftrightarrow{CE} \perp p$?

**13–16.** Complete this proof.

*Given:* $r$ and $n$ intersect at $\overleftrightarrow{YS}$,
$\quad\quad X$ is in $n$, $T$ is in $r$,
$\quad\quad \overline{XY} \perp r$, $\overline{YT} \perp \overleftrightarrow{YS}$

*Prove:* $\overline{YT} \perp n$

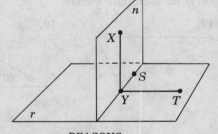

*Proof:*    STATEMENTS

| | REASONS |
|---|---|
| 1. $\overline{XY} \perp r$ | 1. **13.** _____ |
| 2. $\overline{XY} \perp \overline{YT}$ | 2. **14.** _____ |
| 3. $\overline{YT} \perp \overleftrightarrow{YS}$ | 3. **15.** _____ |
| 4. $\overline{YT} \perp n$ | 4. **16.** _____ |

***17.** If two lines are parallel, will their reflection images in space be parallel?

## Test for Chapter 9 Areas of Polygons

**1–7.** Find the area for each of the following:

1. rectangle with length of 4.3 m and width of 2.7 m
2. parallelogram with base of 73.5 cm and height of 4 m
3. square with side of 26 cm
4. right triangle with legs of $3\frac{1}{2}$ and 9
5. triangle with base of 19 and height of 5
6. trapezoid with bases of 25 and 17 and height of $8\frac{2}{3}$
7. rhombus with diagonals of 24 and 21

8. A rectangle has area of 95 and length of 15. Find its width.

9. A triangle has area of 72 and height of 18. Find the length of its base.

10. Find the area of the shaded region at right. All angles are right angles.

Ex. 10

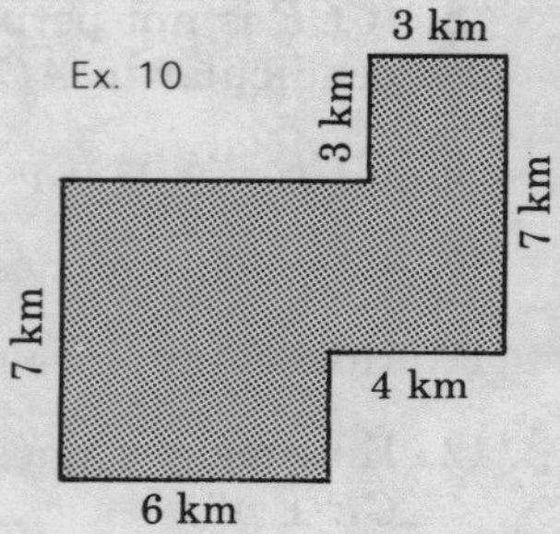


**11–14.** Simplify each radical.

11. $\sqrt{300}$ 12. $\sqrt{\frac{4}{5}}$ 13. $\sqrt{\frac{3}{16}}$ 14. $\sqrt{\frac{81}{36}}$

15. Can a right triangle have sides of lengths 7, 24, and 26?

**16–21.** Find the missing length(s) for each right triangle.

16.

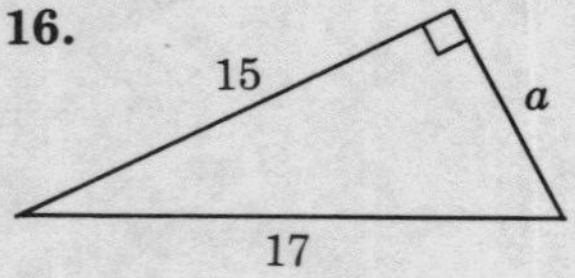


17.

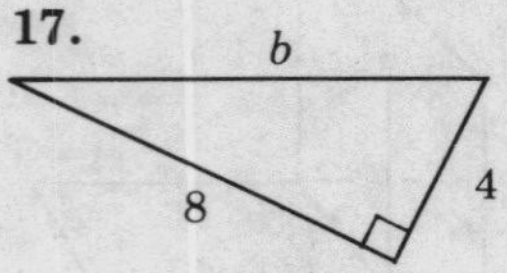


18.

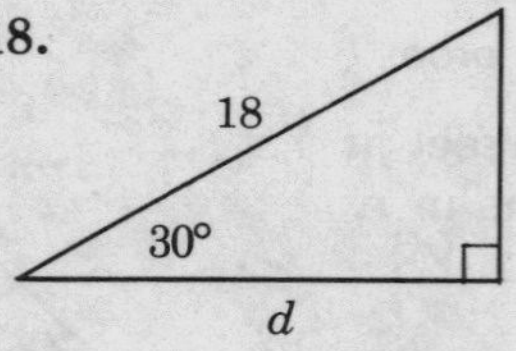


19.

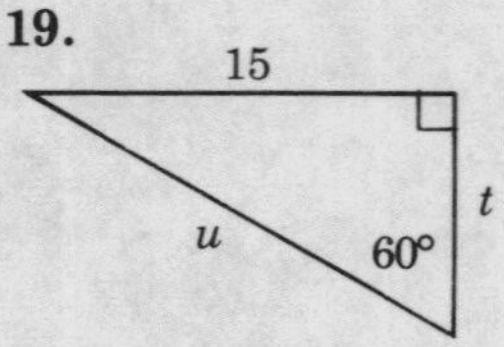


20.

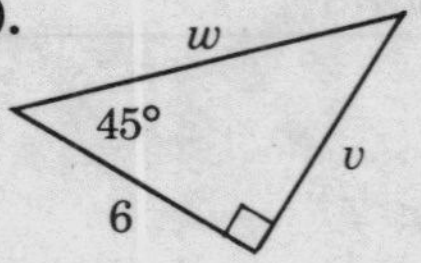


21.

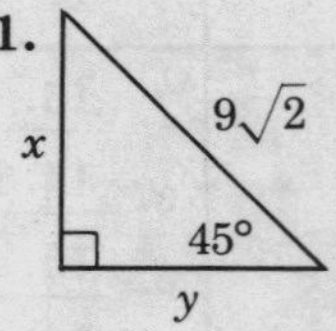


22. A rectangular warehouse door is braced with a metal rod as shown in the figure. The door is 8 ft high and 6 ft wide. How long is the rod?

Ex. 22

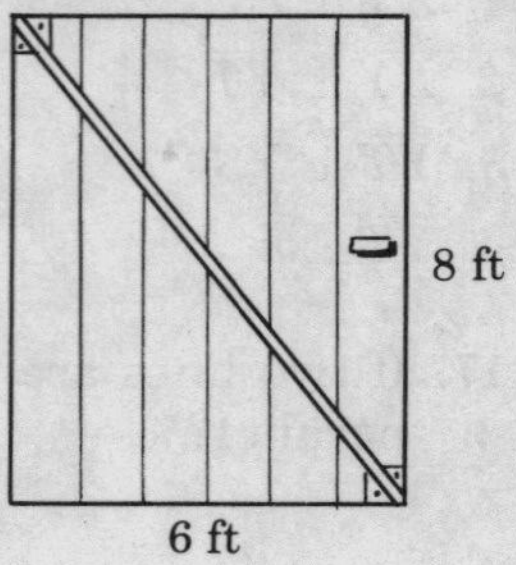


*23. $C$ is the center of a size change. $D'$ is the image of point $D$. Find the magnitude.

Ex. 23

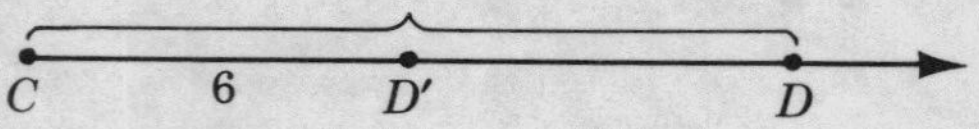

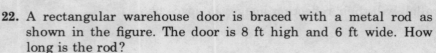

## Test for Chapter 10   Similar Polygons

**1–4.** Let $\dfrac{5}{x} = \dfrac{x}{12}$.

**1.** $\dfrac{5}{x}$ is a _____.

**2.** 5 and 12 are (means, extremes).

**3.** $\dfrac{12}{x} = $ _____

**4.** $x$ is the _____ of 5 and 12.

**5.** In similar polygons, corresponding _____ are congruent and corresponding _____ are proportional.

**6.** For $\triangle ABC \sim \triangle FGH$, if $AB = 6$ and $FG = 21$, the ratio of similarity is _____.

**7.** Solve: $\dfrac{3}{4} = \dfrac{c}{8}$

**8–11.** Using the figures and the given information, state which triangles are similar and the reason why they are similar.

Ex. 8–16

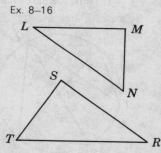

**8.** $\angle M \cong \angle S,\ \angle L \cong \angle R$

**9.** $\triangle LMN \sim \triangle RST,\ \triangle RST \sim \triangle XWY$

**10.** $\angle T \cong \angle N,\ \dfrac{ST}{MN} = \dfrac{RT}{LN}$

**11.** $\overline{LM} \perp \overline{MN},\ \overline{RS} \perp \overline{ST},\ \dfrac{LM}{RS} = \dfrac{LN}{RT}$

**12.** If $\triangle LMN \sim \triangle RST$, $\dfrac{LM}{RS} = \dfrac{7}{8}$, and $MN = 28$, $ST = $ _____.

**13–16.** For $\triangle VWX$, let $\overline{VW} \perp \overline{WX}$.

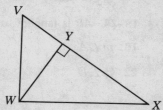

**13.** $\triangle VWX \sim$ _____ $\sim$ _____

**14.** If $VY = 4$ and $YX = 16$, then $WY = $ _____.

**15.** If $VW = 15$ and $VY = 9$, then $VX = $ _____.

**16.** If $\dfrac{\text{area } \triangle WYV}{\text{area } \triangle XYW} = \dfrac{9}{16}$, then $\dfrac{WV}{XW} = $ _____.

**17–18.** In the figure, $k \parallel \ell \parallel r \parallel n$.

Ex. 17–18

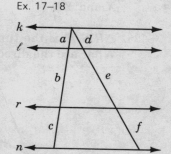

**17.** $b:a:c = $ _____

**18.** If $a:b:c = 1:3:2$ and $b = 6$, find $a$ and $c$.

**19.** *Given:* $\overline{AE} \parallel \overline{CD}$

*Prove:* $\dfrac{AE}{CD} = \dfrac{AB}{CB}$

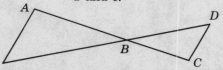

**20.** The shadow of a person, who is 1.8 m tall, is 4 m long when the shadow of a flagpole is 20 m. How tall is the flagpole?

**\*21.** A similarity transformation is any combination of what four kinds of transformations?

## Test for Chapter 11    Circles and Spheres

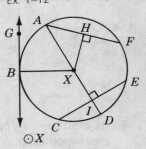

**1–12.** Refer to circle $X$ and sphere $Y$.

**1.** $\overline{YL}$ is a _____ of sphere $Y$.

**2.** $\overline{CE}$ is a _____ of $\odot X$.

**3.** $\overrightarrow{JK}$ is a _____ of sphere $Y$.

**4.** $\overleftrightarrow{BG}$ is a _____ of $\odot X$.

**5.** $G$ is in the _____ of $\odot X$.

**6.** $\overline{XA} \cong$ _____ $\cong$ _____

**7.** $\overline{AH} \cong$ _____

**8.** $\overleftrightarrow{BG} \perp$ _____

**9.** $\overline{CE} \cong \overline{AF}$ if _____ = _____ .

**10.** $\overset{\frown}{AED}$ is a _____ .

**11.** $\angle FAD$ is inscribed in _____ and intercepts _____ .

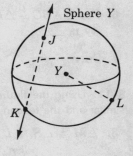

Sphere $Y$

**12.** The intersection of sphere $Y$ and a plane containing $Y$ is a (great, small) circle.

Ex. 13–18

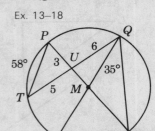

**13–18.** For $\odot M$, $m\overset{\frown}{PT} = 58$, $m\angle SQR = 35$, and $\overline{QS}$ is a diameter. Find:

**13.** $m\angle QRS$

**14.** $m\overset{\frown}{SR}$

**15.** $m\angle QMR$

**16.** $m\angle PUT$

**17.** $m\overset{\frown}{TSR}$

**18.** $UR$

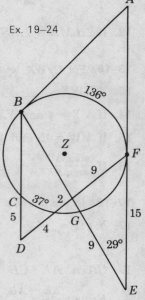

**19–24.** $\overleftrightarrow{AB}$ is tangent to $\odot Z$ at $B$, $\overleftrightarrow{AE}$ is tangent to $\odot Z$ at $F$. Find:

**19.** $m\angle A$

**20.** $m\overset{\frown}{FG}$

**21.** $\angle ABG$

**22.** $m\angle D$

**23.** $BE$

**24.** $BD$

**25.** In space, what is the locus of points equidistant from points $X$ and $Y$?

**\*26.** $\triangle R'S'T'$ is the turn image of $\triangle RST$ with center $C$. What are the direction and magnitude of the turn?

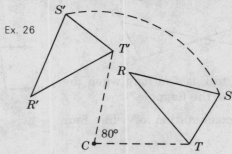

Ex. 26

# Test for Chapter 12    Regular Polygons and Circles

**1–2.** Refer to the square inscribed in $\odot C$.

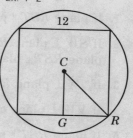

**1.** Find $CG$.

**2.** Find $CR$.

**3.** A regular hexagon has an inscribed circle of radius $7\sqrt{3}$. Find the radius of the hexagon.

**4.** If a regular polygon has a central angle with measure 24, how many sides does it have?

**5.** If a regular polygon has perimeter 58 and an apothem of length 3, what is its area?

**6.** Find the circumference of a circle with radius 8.5. Use 3.14 for $\pi$.

**7.** Find the diameter of a circle with circumference 176. Use $\frac{22}{7}$ for $\pi$.

**8.** Find the area of a circle with radius 9. Use 3.14 for $\pi$.

**9.** Find the radius of a circle with area 78.5. Use 3.14 for $\pi$.

**10.** Find the length of a 36° arc in a circle with radius 15. Leave answer in terms of $\pi$.

**11.** A circle has radius 10. Find the area of a sector with a 144° arc. Leave answer in terms of $\pi$.

**12.** If a circular tabletop with radius 60 cm is cut out of a square piece of wood 120 cm on a side, how much wood is wasted? Use 3.14 for $\pi$.

**13.** The hour hand on a clock is 5 cm long. How far does the outer end of the hour hand travel in 3 hours? Use 3.14 for $\pi$.

**\*14–17.** Which figures have point symmetry?

**14.**

**15.**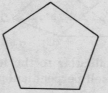

**16.**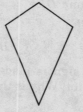

**17.**

# Test for Chapter 13    Parallel Lines and Planes

**1–6.** Refer to the figure. Give a reason for each statement.

1. If plane $RST$ ∥ plane $VWX$, $\overline{RS}$ ∥ $\overline{VW}$.

2. If $\overline{SW} \perp$ plane $RST$ and $\overline{SW} \perp$ plane $VWX$, plane $RST$ ∥ plane $VWX$.

3. If $\overline{TX} \perp$ plane $RST$, plane $a \perp$ plane $RST$.

4. If $\overline{VW} \perp$ plane $a$ and $\overline{RS} \perp$ plane $a$, $\overline{VW}$ ∥ $\overline{RS}$.

5. If plane $RST$ ∥ plane $VWX$ and $\overline{SW}$ and $\overline{TX}$ are perpendicular to plane $RST$, $SW = TX$.

6. If $\overline{SW}$ ∥ $\overline{RV}$ and $\overline{TX}$ ∥ $\overline{RV}$, $\overline{SW}$ ∥ $\overline{TX}$.

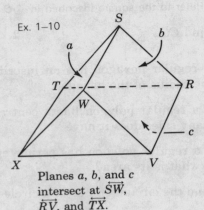

Ex. 1–10

Planes $a$, $b$, and $c$ intersect at $\overleftrightarrow{SW}$, $\overleftrightarrow{RV}$, and $\overleftrightarrow{TX}$.

7. $\angle R$-$\overleftrightarrow{SW}$-$X$ is a _____ angle.

8. If plane $VWX \perp \overline{TX}$, _____ is a plane angle of $\angle R$-$\overleftrightarrow{TX}$-$W$.

9. If plane $RST \perp$ plane $c$, $m \angle S$-$\overleftrightarrow{RT}$-$X =$ _____ .

10. If $\angle SRT$ and $\angle WVX$ are plane angles of $\angle \overleftrightarrow{RV}$, $\angle SRT$ _____ $\angle WVX$.

**11–13.** True or False?

11. If two planes are parallel, any line in one plane is parallel to the other plane.

12. If a line in one of two perpendicular planes is perpendicular to the line of intersection of the planes, it is perpendicular to the other plane.

13. Two planes perpendicular to a third plane are parallel.

14. *Given:* $\overline{CD} \perp \overline{AC}$, $\overline{CD} \perp \overline{BC}$,
            plane $ABC$ ∥ plane $DEF$

    *Prove:* $\overline{CD} \perp$ plane $DEF$

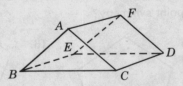

15. The post of a one-way sign is placed perpendicular to the level pavement of a parking lot. Why is the sign itself perpendicular to the pavement?

Ex. 15

*16. If $HIML$ is the slide image of $KJNO$, the magnitude of the slide is $(m \angle NOL, IJ, LM)$.

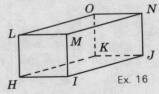

Ex. 16

T48    CHAPTER TESTS

## Test for Chapter 14   Solids

**1–6.** True or False?

1. Each face of a polyhedron is a polygonal region.

2. A lateral edge of a right prism is also an altitude of the prism.

3. The axis of an oblique circular cylinder is also an altitude of the cylinder.

4. A trapezoid can be the base of a regular pyramid.

5. The surface area of a solid is the measure of the amount of space enclosed by the solid.

6. The slant height of a regular pyramid is the height of one of its lateral faces.

**7–12.** Find the volume of each solid. Leave answers for Exercises 9–11 in terms of $\pi$.

7.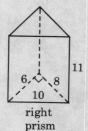
right
prism

8.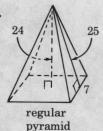
regular
pyramid

9.
right
circular
cone

10.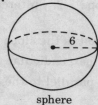
sphere

11. right circular cylinder whose radius is 9 and height is 17

12. cube whose edge is 8 cm long

13. Find the surface area for the following:
    **a.** right prism in Ex. 7      **b.** regular pyramid in Ex. 8

14. Find the lateral area of a right circular cylinder whose radius is 8 and height is $6\frac{1}{2}$. Leave answer in terms of $\pi$.

15. A 1-inch layer of dirt is to be spread on a rectangular garden plot that is 7 ft wide and 12 ft long. How many cubic feet of dirt will be needed?

16. An inflated plastic dome shaped like a hemisphere is being made to cover a swimming pool. If the radius of the dome is 6 m, how much plastic material is needed? Use 3.14 for $\pi$.

*17. How many symmetry planes does each of these solids have?
    **a.** right prism in Ex. 7      **b.** regular pyramid in Ex. 8

# Test for Chapter 15   Coordinate Geometry

**1–6.** Given $A(2, 9)$, $B(-5, 3)$, $C(-2, -3)$, $D(7, -1)$, and $E(11, 3)$,

1. Graph polygon $ABCDE$ in the coordinate plane.

2. Which of $A$, $B$, $C$, $D$, and $E$ are in the 1st quadrant?

3. Find the distance between $B$ and $C$.

4. Find the coordinates of the midpoint of $\overline{CD}$.

5. If $C$ is the midpoint of a segment with one endpoint at $B$, find the coordinates of the other endpoint.

6. Find the slope of **(a)** $\overline{BE}$ and **(b)** $\overline{AE}$.

**7–8.** Find, in standard form, an equation of the line described.

7. contains points $(5, 6)$ and $(-3, 8)$

8. slope $-2$, $y$-intercept 17

9. What is the slope of a line that is
   **a.** perpendicular to the graph of $y = \frac{2}{3}x$?
   **b.** parallel to the graph of $y = \frac{2}{3}x$?

Ex. 14

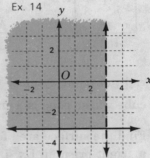

**10–13.** Graph each on a separate pair of axes.

10. $2x - 5y = 20$

11. $5 \le x \le 8$

12. $y < -\frac{3}{8}x + 2$

13. $x^2 + y^2 = 9$

14. Write an algebraic condition to describe the graph at right.

15. Find the equation of a circle with center at $(0, 4)$ and radius 6.

Ex. 16

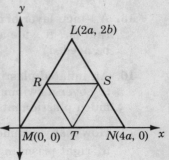

**\*16.** Prove that the segments joining the midpoints of the sides of an isosceles triangle form an isosceles triangle. HINT: Start by stating the *Given* and *Prove* in terms of the given figure.

**\*17.** A triangle has vertices at $X(-3, 0)$, $Y(9, 12)$, and $Z(6, -6)$. In the coordinate plane, draw the triangle and its image under this transformation: $(x, y) \rightarrow (\frac{1}{3}x, \frac{1}{3}y)$.

## Cumulative Test for Chapters 1–7

**1–8.** Refer to the figure at right.

1. $a$ and $b$ intersect at _____.

2. $W$ and $X$ are _____ of $\overline{WX}$.

3. $W$, $X$, and $Z$ determine a _____.

4. The intersection of $k$ and $\overrightarrow{VW}$ is _____.

5. If $W$ is the midpoint of $\overline{XV}$, then $XW =$ _____.

6. $\overrightarrow{WV}$ and _____ are opposite rays.

7. The intersection of $b$ and $k$ is _____.

8. $W$ is in plane _____ but not in plane _____.

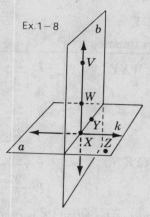

Ex. 1–8

9. If the coordinates of $L$ and $M$ are 8 and 15, $LM =$ _____.

10. A _____ is accepted as true without proof.

11. Definitions and postulates are used in _____ reasoning.

**12–18.** In the figure, $\overrightarrow{DA} \perp \overrightarrow{BE}$ at $D$, $\overrightarrow{CF}$ intersects $\overrightarrow{BE}$ at $D$.

12. Is the interior of $\angle ADF$ a convex set?

13. How many lines through $C$ are perpendicular to $\overrightarrow{BE}$?

14. Name **(a)** all obtuse angles and **(b)** all right angles.

15. Name two angles supplementary to $\angle BDC$.

16. If $m \angle FDE = 43$, find **(a)** $m \angle ADF$ and **(b)** $m \angle CDE$.

17. If $m \angle BDF = 134$, find $m \angle ADF$.

18. What theorem leads to the conclusion that $\angle BDC \cong \angle FDE$?

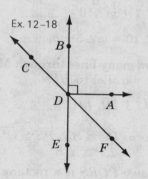

Ex. 12–18

19. Change the following statement to if-then form: Two perpendicular lines form four right angles.

20. List three congruence statements about sides that follow from $\triangle LMN \cong \triangle RST$.

21. In the given figure, $\ell$ is the perpendicular bisector of $\overline{PQ}$. Find values for $x$ and $y$.

Ex. 21

**22–27.** Give a reason for each statement.

Given: $\overrightarrow{XZ}$ bisects $\angle WXY$,
$\overline{XW} \cong \overline{XY}$

Prove: $\angle W \cong \angle Y$

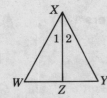

Proof:   STATEMENTS                          REASONS

1. $\overrightarrow{XZ}$ bisects $\angle WXY$.          1. _22._ ____

2. $\angle 1 \cong \angle 2$                      2. _23._ ____

3. $\overline{XZ} \cong \overline{XZ}$                     3. _24._ ____

4. $\overline{XW} \cong \overline{XY}$                     4. _25._ ____

5. $\triangle XWZ \cong \triangle XYZ$             5. _26._ ____

6. $\angle W \cong \angle Y$                      6. _27._ ____

**28–38.** In the figure, $\overline{LJ} \parallel \overline{HI}$ and $K$ is on $\overline{LJ}$.

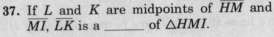

Ex. 28–38

**28.** $\angle 4$ and _____ are alternate interior angles.

**29.** $\angle 2$ and _____ are corresponding angles.

**30.** $HIKL$ is a _____.

**31.** If $\overline{LJ} \cong \overline{HI}$, $HIJL$ is a _____.

**32.** $m\angle 7 + m\angle 10 =$ _____

**33.** If $\angle 2 \cong$ _____, $\overrightarrow{LM} \parallel \overrightarrow{IJ}$.

**34.** $m\angle 10 = m\angle 5 + m$ _____

**35.** $m\angle 3 + m\angle 2 + m$ _____ $= 180$

**36.** How many lines through $M$ are parallel to $\overline{HI}$?

**37.** If $L$ and $K$ are midpoints of $\overline{HM}$ and $\overline{MI}$, $\overline{LK}$ is a _____ of $\triangle HMI$.

**38.** If $\overline{IJ} \perp \overline{HI}$, $\overline{IJ} \perp$ _____.

**39.** Given: $\overline{PQ} \cong \overline{SR}$, $\overline{PS} \cong \overline{QR}$,
$\angle P \cong \angle S$

Prove: $PQRS$ is a rectangle.

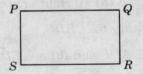

**40–43.** $ABCDEF$ is a regular hexagon. Find the following:

**40.** sum of its interior angles

**41.** sum of its exterior angles, one at each vertex

**42.** perimeter, if $AB = 12$

**43.** measure of each interior angle

**44–45.** For $\triangle ABC$ and $\triangle XYZ$, why is

**44.** $\overline{AB} \cong \overline{AC}$, if $\angle B \cong \angle C$?

**45.** $\triangle ABC \cong \triangle XYZ$, if $\angle A \cong \angle X$, $\overline{AC} \cong \overline{XZ}$, and $\angle B \cong \angle Y$?

**46.** Describe a counterexample for the following statement:
If two angles of a triangle are acute, the triangle is obtuse.

**47.** For the statement in Ex. 46, write the converse. Is it true?

**48.** What two true statements can be made from the following:
$x^3 = 8$ if and only if $x = 2$.

**49.** Which concurrence theorem does the figure at right illustrate?

Ex. 49

**50.** In a(n) _____ proof, you assume the opposite of the fact you want to prove.

**51.** *Given:* Rectangle $STWV$
   *Prove:* $\overline{VT} \cong \overline{SW}$

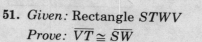

**52.** If $MN > SP$, then $\overline{MN}$ is _____ $\overline{SP}$.

**53.** If $\angle 1$ is _____ $\angle 2$, then $m\angle 2 > m\angle 1$.

**54.** Solve:    **a.** $s - 27 < 5$    **b.** $\frac{3}{4}t > \frac{15}{14}$

**55–64.** Refer to the figure. Which symbol, $<$, $=$, or $>$, should replace the ⦀?

Ex. 55–64

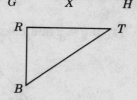

**55.** $m\angle 1$ ⦀ $m\angle 3$

**56.** $m\angle 3$ ⦀ $m\angle GFH$

**57.** $HF + FG$ ⦀ $HG$

**58.** $GX + XH$ ⦀ $GH$

**59.** If $m\angle 2 = 90$, $FH$ ⦀ $HX$.

**60.** If $\overline{FX} \perp \overline{GH}$, $FX$ ⦀ $GF$.

**61.** If $m\angle G > m\angle 4$, $GX$ ⦀ $FX$.

**62.** If $GX = XH$ and $m\angle 2 > m\angle 1$, $FG$ ⦀ $FH$.

**63.** If $\overline{BR} \cong \overline{GX}$, $\overline{TR} \cong \overline{FX}$, and $BT < GF$, $m\angle R$ ⦀ $m\angle 1$.

**64.** If $\overline{RB} \cong \overline{XH}$, $\overline{BT} \cong \overline{HF}$, and $m\angle B > m\angle H$, $RT$ ⦀ $XF$.

*65–68. True or False?

**65.** Reflections preserve angle measure.

**66.** To roll a ball along the shortest path from point $A$ to a wall to point $B$, you should aim for the reflection image of $A$ over the wall.

**67.** Refer to the figure for Ex. 55–64. If $\triangle FXH \cong \triangle TRB$, a slide and a turn can be used to make $\triangle FXH$ and $\triangle TRB$ coincide.

**68.** If $\triangle A'B'C'$ is the slide image of $\triangle ABC$, the magnitude of the slide is $AA'$.

## Cumulative Test for Chapters 8–15

**1–5.** Refer to the figure. $\overrightarrow{ST}$ and $\overrightarrow{SX}$ are in plane $b$.

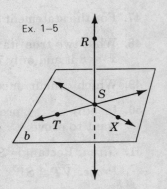

Ex. 1–5

**1.** If $\overrightarrow{RS} \perp \overrightarrow{ST}$ and $\overrightarrow{RS} \perp \overrightarrow{SX}$, then $\overrightarrow{RS} \perp$ _____.

**2.** If $\overrightarrow{RS} \perp b$, then $\overrightarrow{RS}$ is perpendicular to _____ lines in $b$ _____ S.

**3.** How many lines are perpendicular to $b$ at $X$?

**4.** If $\overrightarrow{RS}$ and another line $\ell$ are both perpendicular to $b$, are $\ell$ and $\overrightarrow{RS}$ coplanar?

**5.** Are all points in space equidistant from points $R$ and $S$ coplanar?

**6–9.** Find the area of each figure.

**6.** triangle with a base of length 8.5 m and height 1.2 m

**7.** parallelogram with a base of length $5\frac{1}{2}$ and height $2\frac{2}{3}$

**8.** trapezoid with height 8 cm and bases of lengths 5 cm and 42 mm

**9.** rhombus with diagonals of lengths 12 and 15

**10.** Simplify:   **a.** $\sqrt{27}$   **b.** $\sqrt{\frac{8}{9}}$   **c.** $\sqrt{\frac{16}{5}}$

**11.** Can a right triangle have sides of lengths 5, 11, and 12?

**12.** For $\triangle ABC$ at right, find $AB$ and $AC$.

**13.** For $\triangle QRS$ at right, find $QR$ and $QS$.

**14.** If $\frac{c}{6} = \frac{7}{d}$ and $c = 21$, find $d$.

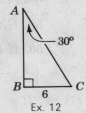

Ex. 12

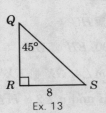

Ex. 13

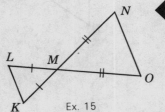

Ex. 15

**15.** Given: $KM = LM$, $OM = NM$

Prove: $\triangle KLM \sim \triangle ONM$

**16.** Given: $\overline{XY} \perp \overline{YZ}$, $\frac{XZ}{WX} = \frac{XY}{WY}$

Prove: $\angle Z \cong \angle YXW$

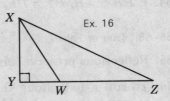

Ex. 16

**17–18.** Refer to $\triangle DEF$.

**17.** If $EG = 12$ and $DG = 18$, find $GF$.

**18.** If $GF = 3$ and $DG = 9$, find $EF$.

**19.** $a:b:c = 5:3:4$ and $a = 10$. Find $b$ and $c$.

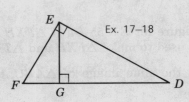

Ex. 17–18

**20–25.** In the figure, $\overrightarrow{LM}$ is tangent to $\odot A$ at $L$, $\overrightarrow{MP}$ is tangent to $\odot A$ at $N$, and $\overline{KN}$ is a diameter. Find:

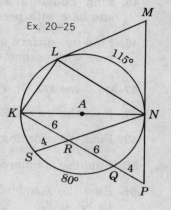

Ex. 20–25

**20.** $m\angle KLN$

**21.** $m\angle LNK$

**22.** $m\angle M$

**23.** $m\angle SRQ$

**24.** $RN$

**25.** $NP$

Ex. 26–27

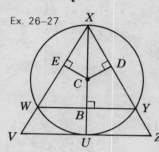

**26.** *Given:* $\odot C$, $\overline{CD} \perp$ chord $\overline{XY}$, $\overline{CE} \perp$ chord $\overline{XW}$, $CD = CE$

*Prove:* $\triangle WXY$ is isosceles.

**27.** *Given:* $\overline{ZV}$ tangent to $\odot C$ at $U$, diameter $\overline{XU}$, $\overline{YB} \perp \overline{XU}$ at $B$

*Prove:* $\triangle XBY \sim \triangle XUZ$

**28.** In space, what is the locus of points 6.5 cm from point $B$?

**29–31.** A regular hexagon is inscribed in $\odot P$. See figure. Find:

**29.** $PA$

**30.** $PB$

**31.** area of the hexagon

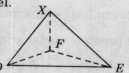

Ex. 29–31

**32–35.** Leaving answers in terms of $\pi$, find the following:

**32.** circumference of a circle with radius $3\frac{2}{3}$

**33.** area of a circle with radius 9

**34.** length of a $120°$ arc in a circle with radius 7.5

**35.** area of a sector with a $45°$ arc, in a circle with radius 12

**36–38.** True or False?

**36.** Two planes perpendicular to the same plane are parallel.

**37.** A line perpendicular to one of two parallel planes is perpendicular to the other.

**38.** Two planes parallel to the same plane are parallel.

**39.** *Given:* $\overrightarrow{XF} \perp$ plane $DEF$

*Prove:* $\angle X\text{-}\overleftrightarrow{EF}\text{-}D$ is a right dihedral angle.

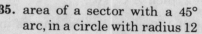

**40–44.** Find the volume of each figure. Leave answers in terms of $\pi$ for Exercises 42–44.

**40.** oblique prism, height 17 cm, square base with edge 8 cm

**41.** pyramid, height $6\frac{2}{3}$, base with area 54

**42.** circular cone, height 5.1, radius 2

**43.** circular cylinder, height 13, radius 5

**44.** sphere, radius 3

45. Find the lateral area of a regular pyramid with slant height 3 m and base with perimeter 30 m.

46. Find the surface area of a right prism with height 14 and square base with perimeter 20.

**47–51.** Given $X(2, 9)$, $Y(-4, 1)$, and $Z(-9, -3)$,

47. Find the length of $\overline{XY}$.    48. Find the slope of $\overleftrightarrow{YZ}$.

49. Find the coordinates of the midpoint of $\overline{XZ}$.

50. Find the standard form of the equation of $\overleftrightarrow{YZ}$.

51. Find the standard form of the equation of a line perpendicular to $\overleftrightarrow{YZ}$ at $Y$.

**52–55.** Graph each on a separate pair of axes.

52. $9x - 12y = 36$                53. $-6 < y < -1$

54. $y \geq \frac{5}{8}x + 7$                55. $x^2 + y^2 = 25$

**\*56–63.** True or False?

56. If $A'$ is the image of $A$ under a size change of magnitude 3, center $C$, and $AC = 2$, then $A'C = 6$.

57. If two lines are parallel, their reflection images in space will be parallel.

58. Similarity transformations preserve distance.

59. If $\triangle R'S'T'$ is the turn image of $\triangle RST$ in a plane, and the orientation of $\triangle RST$ is clockwise, the orientation of $\triangle R'S'T'$ is counterclockwise.

60. A regular pentagon has point symmetry.

61. Turns in space preserve coplanarity.

62. One symmetry plane of a right circular cylinder is the perpendicular bisecting plane of the axis of the cylinder.

63. Adding $-6$ to the $x$-coordinate of each point of a figure in the coordinate plane slides the figure 6 units to the right.

**\*64.** Using coordinates, prove that the segment joining the midpoints of two sides of a triangle is half as long as the third side. HINT: Start by stating the *Given* and *Prove* in terms of the given figure.

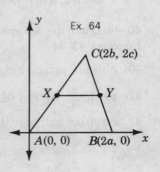
Ex. 64

# Answers to Tests

## Chapter 1

**1.** $a, b$ **2.** $\overrightarrow{RS}$, $\overrightarrow{TV}$ **3.** R, T, S **4.** $\ell$ **5.** $\overline{TV}$ **6.** T (or V) **7.** R **8.** T
**9.** V **10.** $\overrightarrow{TR}$, $\overrightarrow{TS}$ **11.** < **12. a.** $\frac{1}{2}$ **b.** 3 **13.** Between
**14.** Distance **15.** $BC$ **16.** Midpoint **17.** Bisects **18.** 9 **19.** Postulate
**20.** Inductive **21.** Deductive **22.** Not more than one **23.** Theorem **24.** Line
**25.** Plane **26.** Susan uses logical reasoning. **27.** Three noncollinear points determine a plane. **28.** Image

## Chapter 2

**1.** T **2.** F **3.** F **4.** T **5.** T **6.** F **7.** = **8.** $\overline{PQ}$
**9.** Opposite **10.** $ABD$ **11.** $\overrightarrow{BD}$; $EBC$ **12.** $EBD$; $DBC$ (or $ABF$)
**13.** $DBC$ (or $ABF$); $\cong$ **14.** $\cong$ **15.** Midpoint **16.** 90 **17.** 43 **18.** 43
**19.** 137 **20.** 137 **21.** 133 **22.** Yes

## Chapter 3

**1.** If a figure is a triangle, then it has three sides.

**2.**

figures
with 3 sides
triangles

**3.** $\angle A \cong \angle X$, $\angle B \cong \angle Y$, $\angle C \cong \angle Z$, $\overline{AB} \cong \overline{XY}$, $\overline{BC} \cong \overline{YZ}$, $\overline{AC} \cong \overline{XZ}$ **4.** $\perp$ bisector

**5.** SSS Post. **6.** ASA Post. **7.** SAS Post.

**8.** Given **9.** Def. of $\angle$ bis. **10.** Given **11.** Def. of $\angle$ bis.

**12.** $\angle$s $\cong$ to same $\angle$ are $\cong$. **13.** Given **14.** ASA Post.

**15.** Corres. parts of $\cong$ $\triangle$s are $\cong$. **16.** Yes; SSS Post. **17.** Reflection

## Chapter 4

**1.** Plane **2.** Exactly one **3.** Corresponding **4.** 87 **5.** $n$ **6.** 180
**7.** 10 **8.** 90 **9.** $\overline{ED}$; $\overline{BC}$ **10.** $\angle 3$ **11.** 90 **12.** 5 **13.** $EDCB$
**14.** 180 **15.** Diagonal **16.** $\triangle ZWY$ **17.** $\overline{YZ}$ **18.** $\overline{ZW}$ **19.** $\angle WXY$ (or $\angle YZW$)
**20.** $\angle ZWX$ **21.** $\overline{WV}$ **22.** Rectangle **23.** Rhombus **24.** Square **25.** Do

# Chapter 5

1. a, b, d        2. b, c        3. Hexagon        4. No        5. No        6. Yes

7. **a.** 720    **b.** 360    8. **a.** 135    **b.** 45    9. 18.2 m    10. Given

11. Def. of isos. trapezoid        12. Base ∠s of isos. trapezoid are ≅.        13. Given

14. Def. of rt. △        15. HA Thm.

16. *Proof:*

| STATEMENTS | REASONS |
|---|---|
| *1.* $\overline{SV} \cong \overline{VT}$ | *1.* Given |
| *2.* $\angle RTS \cong \angle UST$ | *2.* ∠s opp. ≅ sides of △ are ≅. |
| *3.* $\angle R \cong \angle U$ | *3.* Given |
| *4.* $\overline{ST} \cong \overline{ST}$ | *4.* Seg. is ≅ to itself. |
| *5.* $\triangle RST \cong \triangle UTS$ | *5.* AAS Thm. |

17. 53 m        18. 6

# Chapter 6

1. *Typical answer:* 2 adjacent angles        2. Parallel lines

3. T; If 2 ∠s are ≅, they are vert. ∠s; F

4. T; If the sum of the measures of 2 ∠s is 180, ∠s are supp.; T

5. A △ is a rt. △ if and only if it has exactly one rt. ∠.

6. If points are coplanar, they are in the same plane. If points are in the same plane, they are coplanar.

7. Faulty; denying the hypothesis

8. Valid; affirming the hypothesis        9. Assump. for ind. prf.        10. Def. of median

11. Def. of midpt.        12. Given        13. Prin. of Ind. Reas.        14. a, c        15. Right

# Chapter 7

1. =; <        2. >        3. <        4. >        5. >        6. Distance        7. **a.** $t < 54$    **b.** $x < 9$

8. **a.** No    **b.** Yes    **c.** No    9. >    10. =    11. >    12. <    13. >    14. >

15. >        16. <        17. <        18. >        19. >        20. <        21. >        22. >

23. At the reflection image of *E* over *s*

## Chapter 8

1. $p$    2. Coplanar    3. $\perp$    4. Distance    5. $<$    6. 90    7. $\perp$ bisecting

8. Yes    9. No    10. Exactly one    11. Exactly one    12. Exactly one    13. Given

14. Def. of $\perp$ line and plane    15. Given    16. Basic Thm. for $\perp$s    17. Yes

## Chapter 9

1. 11.61 m²    2. 29 400 cm² (or 2.94 m²)    3. 676 cm²    4. $15\frac{3}{4}$    5. $47\frac{1}{2}$    6. 182

7. 252    8. $6\frac{1}{3}$    9. 8    10. 67 km²    11. $10\sqrt{3}$    12. $\frac{2}{5}\sqrt{5}$    13. $\frac{1}{4}\sqrt{3}$    14. $\frac{3}{2}$

15. No    16. $a = 8$    17. $b = 4\sqrt{5}$    18. $c = 9, d = 9\sqrt{3}$    19. $t = 5\sqrt{3}, u = 10\sqrt{3}$

20. $v = 6, w = 6\sqrt{2}$    21. $x = y = 9$    22. 10 ft    23. $\frac{1}{2}$

## Chapter 10

1. Ratio    2. Extremes    3. $\frac{x}{5}$    4. Geometric mean    5. Angles; sides

6. $\frac{2}{7}$    7. $c = 6$    8. $\triangle LMN \sim \triangle RST$; AA Sim. Thm.

9. $\triangle LMN \sim \triangle XWY$; $\triangle$s $\sim$ to same $\triangle$ are $\sim$.    10. $\triangle LMN \sim \triangle RST$; SAS Sim. Thm.

11. $\triangle LMN \sim \triangle RST$; HL Sim. Thm.    12. 32    13. $\triangle VYW$; $\triangle WYX$    14. 8

15. 25    16. $\frac{3}{4}$    17. $e:d:f$    18. $a = 2, c = 4$

19. *Proof:*

| STATEMENTS | REASONS |
|---|---|
| 1. $\overline{AE} \parallel \overline{CD}$ | 1. Given |
| 2. $\angle A \cong \angle C, \angle E \cong \angle D$ | 2. If lines are $\parallel$, alt. int. $\angle$s are $\cong$. |
| 3. $\triangle ABE \sim \triangle CBD$ | 3. AA Sim. Thm. |
| 4. $\frac{AE}{CD} = \frac{AB}{CB}$ | 4. Def. of $\sim$ polygons |

20. 9 m    21. Reflections, turns, slides, and size changes

## Chapter 11

1. Radius    2. Chord    3. Secant    4. Tangent    5. Exterior    6. $\overline{XB}$; $\overline{XD}$

7. $\overline{HF}$    8. $\overline{BX}$    9. $X\overline{'}$; $XH$    10. Semicircle    11. $\overparen{FAD}$ (or $\overparen{FBD}$ or $\overparen{FCD}$); $\overparen{FD}$

12. Great    13. 90    14. 70    15. 110    16. 84    17. 122    18. 10

19. 44    20. 78    21. 107    22. $49\frac{1}{2}$    23. 25    24. 12

25. $\perp$ bisecting plane of $\overline{XY}$    26. Direction: counterclockwise, magnitude: 80

# Chapter 12

**1.** 6     **2.** $6\sqrt{2}$     **3.** 14     **4.** 15     **5.** 87     **6.** 53.38     **7.** 56

**8.** 254.34     **9.** 5     **10.** $3\pi$     **11.** $40\pi$     **12.** 3096 cm$^2$     **13.** 7.85 cm

**14.** Yes     **15.** No     **16.** No     **17.** Yes

# Chapter 13

**1.** 3rd plane intersects 2 ∥ planes at 2 ∥ lines.

**2.** 2 planes ⊥ to same line are ∥.

**3.** Plane containing line ⊥ to given plane is ⊥ to given plane.

**4.** 2 lines ⊥ to same plane are ∥.

**5.** ∥ planes are everywhere equidistant.

**6.** 2 lines ∥ to same line are ∥.

**7.** Dihedral     **8.** $\angle WXV$     **9.** 90     **10.** ≅     **11.** T     **12.** T     **13.** F

**14.** *Proof:*

| STATEMENTS | REASONS |
|---|---|
| 1. $\overline{CD} \perp \overline{AC}$, $\overline{CD} \perp \overline{BC}$ | 1. Given |
| 2. $\overline{CD} \perp$ plane $ABC$ | 2. Basic Thm. for ⊥s |
| 3. Plane $ABC$ ∥ plane $DEF$ | 3. Given |
| 4. $\overline{CD} \perp$ plane $DEF$ | 4. Line ⊥ to 1 of 2 ∥ planes is ⊥ to the other. |

**15.** Plane containing line ⊥ to given plane is ⊥ to given plane.

**16.** *IJ*

# Chapter 14

**1.** T     **2.** T     **3.** F     **4.** F     **5.** F     **6.** T     **7.** 264

**8.** 392     **9.** $100\pi$     **10.** $288\pi$     **11.** $1377\pi$     **12.** 512 cm$^3$     **13. a.** 312     **b.** 399

**14.** $104\pi$     **15.** 7 ft$^3$     **16.** 226.08 m$^2$     **17. a.** 1     **b.** 4

## Chapter 15

**1.**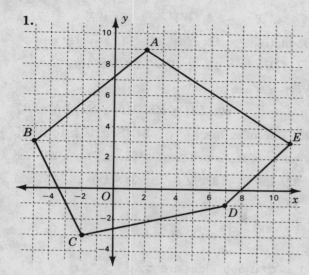

**2.** $A$, $E$

**3.** $3\sqrt{5}$

**4.** $(2\frac{1}{2},\ -2)$

**5.** $(1,\ -9)$

**6. a.** $0$   **b.** $-\frac{2}{3}$

**7.** $x + 4y = 29$

**8.** $2x + y = 17$

**9. a.** $-\frac{3}{2}$   **b.** $\frac{2}{3}$

*For Ex. 10–13, graphs are described.*

**10.** Line through $(10, 0)$ and $(0, -4)$

**11.** Solid lines through $(5, 0)$ and $(5, 5)$ and through $(8, 0)$ and $(8, 5)$ and the part of the plane between them.

**12.** Half plane below dashed line through $(0, 2)$ and $(8, -1)$

**13.** Circle with center $(0, 0)$, radius 3, and points at $(3, 0)$, $(0, -3)$, $(-3, 0)$, $(0, 3)$

**14.** $x < 3$ and $y \geq -3$

**15.** $x^2 + (y - 4)^2 = 36$

**16.** *Given:* Isos. $\triangle MNL$ with $M$ at $(0, 0)$ and $\overline{MN}$ on the $x$-axis; $R$, $S$, and $T$ are midpts. of $\overline{ML}$, $\overline{LN}$, and $\overline{MN}$.

*Prove:* $\triangle RST$ is isosceles.

*Proof:* 1. By the midpt. formula, $R$ is at $(a, b)$, $S$ is at $(3a, b)$, and $T$ is at $(2a, 0)$.

2. By the distance formula, $RT = \sqrt{a^2 + b^2}$, $ST = \sqrt{a^2 + b^2}$.

3. By substitution, $RT = ST$, and $\triangle RST$ is isos. by def. of isos. $\triangle$.

**17.** The vertices of the image are $X'(-1, 0)$, $Y'(3, 4)$, and $Z'(2, -2)$.

# Cumulative Test for Chapters 1–7

1. $\overleftrightarrow{XY}$     2. Endpoints     3. Plane     4. $X$     5. $WV$     6. $\overrightarrow{WX}$     7. $X$

8. $b; a$     9. 7     10. Postulate     11. Deductive     12. Yes     13. Exactly one

14. a. $\angle CDA, \angle BDF, \angle EDC$   b. $\angle BDA, \angle ADE$     15. $\angle BDF, \angle CDE$

16. a. 47   b. 137     17. 44     18. Vert. $\angle$s are $\cong$.

19. If 2 lines are $\perp$, they form 4 rt. $\angle$s.     20. $\overline{LM} \cong \overline{RS}, \overline{MN} \cong \overline{ST}, \overline{LN} \cong \overline{RT}$

21. $x = 21, y = 13$     22. Given     23. Def. of $\angle$ bis.     24. Seg. is $\cong$ to itself.

25. Given     26. SAS Post.     27. Corres. parts of $\cong \triangle$s are $\cong$.     28. $\angle 7$     29. $\angle 8$

30. Trapezoid     31. Parallelogram     32. 180     33. $\angle 5$     34. $\angle 6$     35. $\angle 1$

36. Exactly one     37. Midline     38. $\overline{LJ}$

39. *Proof:*

| STATEMENTS | REASONS |
|---|---|
| 1. $\overline{PQ} \cong \overline{SR}, \overline{PS} \cong \overline{QR}$ | 1. Given |
| 2. $PQRS$ is a $\square$. | 2. Quad. is $\square$ if opp. sides are $\cong$. |
| 3. $\angle P$ and $\angle S$ are supp. | 3. Consec. $\angle$s of $\square$ are supp. |
| 4. $\angle P \cong \angle S$ | 4. Given |
| 5. $\angle P$ and $\angle S$ are rt. $\angle$s. | 5. $\cong$ supp. $\angle$s are rt. $\angle$s. |
| 6. $PQRS$ is a rectangle. | 6. $\square$ with rt. $\angle$ is rectangle. |

40. 720     41. 360     42. 72     43. 120     44. Sides opp. $\cong \angle$s of $\triangle$ are $\cong$.

45. AAS Thm.     46. Any rt. or acute $\triangle$     47. If a $\triangle$ is obtuse, 2 $\angle$s of the $\triangle$ are acute. Yes

48. If $x^3 = 8$, then $x = 2$.     49. Altitude conc.     50. Indirect
If $x = 2$, then $x^3 = 8$.

51. *Proof:*

| STATEMENTS | REASONS |
|---|---|
| 1. $STWV$ is a rectangle. | 1. Given |
| 2. $\angle STW, \angle VWT$ are rt. $\angle$s. | 2. Rectangle has 4 rt. $\angle$s. |
| 3. $\triangle STW, \triangle VWT$ are rt. $\triangle$s. | 3. Def. of rt. $\triangle$ |
| 4. $\overline{ST} \cong \overline{VW}$ | 4. Rectangle is $\square$, and opp. sides of $\square$ are $\cong$. |
| 5. $\overline{TW} \cong \overline{TW}$ | 5. Seg. is $\cong$ to itself. |
| 6. $\triangle STW \cong \triangle VWT$ | 6. LL Thm. |
| 7. $\overline{VT} \cong \overline{SW}$ | 7. Corres. parts of $\cong \triangle$s are $\cong$. |

52. Longer than     53. Smaller than     54. a. $s < 32$     b. $t > \frac{10}{7}$

55. $>$     56. $<$     57. $>$     58. $=$     59. $>$     60. $<$     61. $<$

62. $<$     63. $<$     64. $>$     65. T     66. F     67. T     68. T

**1.** $b$    **2.** All; containing    **3.** Exactly one    **4.** Yes    **5.** Yes    **6.** 5.1 m²

**7.** $14\frac{2}{3}$    **8.** 36.8 cm²    **9.** 90    **10. a.** $3\sqrt{3}$    **b.** $\frac{2}{3}\sqrt{2}$    **c.** $\frac{4}{5}\sqrt{5}$    **11.** No

**12.** $AB = 6\sqrt{3}$, $AC = 12$    **13.** $QR = 8$, $QS = 8\sqrt{2}$    **14.** $d = 2$

**15.** *Proof:*

| STATEMENTS | REASONS |
|---|---|
| 1. $KM = LM$, $OM = NM$ | 1. Given |
| 2. $\dfrac{KM}{OM} = \dfrac{LM}{NM}$ | 2. Use given equations to write proportion. |
| 3. $\angle KML \cong \angle OMN$ | 3. Vert. $\angle$s are $\cong$. |
| 4. $\triangle KLM \sim \triangle ONM$ | 4. SAS Sim. Thm. |

**16.** *Proof:*

| STATEMENTS | REASONS |
|---|---|
| 1. $\overline{XY} \perp \overline{YZ}$ | 1. Given |
| 2. $\angle XYZ$, $\angle WYX$ are rt. $\angle$s. | 2. Def. of $\perp$ |
| 3. $\triangle XYZ$, $\triangle WYX$ are rt. $\triangle$s. | 3. Def. of rt. $\triangle$ |
| 4. $\dfrac{XZ}{WX} = \dfrac{XY}{WY}$ | 4. Given |
| 5. $\triangle XYZ \sim \triangle WYX$ | 5. HL Sim. Thm. |
| 6. $\angle Z \cong \angle YXW$ | 6. Def. of $\sim$ polygons |

**17.** 8    **18.** 6    **19.** $b = 6$, $c = 8$    **20.** 90    **21.** $32\frac{1}{2}$    **22.** 65

**23.** 130    **24.** 9    **25.** 8

**26.** *Proof:*

| STATEMENTS | REASONS |
|---|---|
| 1. $\overline{CD} \perp \overline{XY}$, $\overline{CE} \perp \overline{XW}$, $CD = CE$ | 1. Given |
| 2. $\overline{XY} \cong \overline{XW}$ | 2. In a $\odot$, chords equidistant from the center are $\cong$. |
| 3. $\triangle WXY$ is isos. | 3. Def. of isos. $\triangle$ |

**27.** *Proof:*

| STATEMENTS | REASONS |
|---|---|
| 1. Tangent $\overline{ZV}$, diameter $\overline{XU}$ | 1. Given |
| 2. $\overline{ZV} \perp \overline{XU}$ | 2. A radius is $\perp$ to a tangent at the pt. of tangency. |
| 3. $\overline{YB} \perp \overline{XU}$ | 3. Given |
| 4. $\overline{YB} \parallel \overline{ZV}$ | 4. In a plane, lines $\perp$ to same line are $\parallel$. |
| 5. $\triangle XBY \sim \triangle XUZ$ | 5. If line $\parallel$ to side of $\triangle$ intersects other 2 sides, $\sim \triangle$ is formed. |

**28.** Sphere $B$, with radius 6.5 cm    **29.** $5\sqrt{3}$    **30.** 10    **31.** $150\sqrt{3}$    **32.** $7\frac{1}{3}\pi$

**33.** $81\pi$    **34.** $5\pi$    **35.** $18\pi$    **36.** F    **37.** T    **38.** T

**39.** *Proof:*

| STATEMENTS | REASONS |
|---|---|
| 1. $\overleftrightarrow{XF} \perp$ plane $DEF$ | 1. Given |
| 2. Plane $XEF \perp$ plane $DEF$ | 2. Plane containing line $\perp$ to given plane is $\perp$ to given plane. |
| 3. $\angle X\text{-}\overline{EF}\text{-}D$ is a rt. dih. $\angle$. | 3. Def. of $\perp$ planes |

**40.** 1088 cm$^3$    **41.** 120    **42.** 6.8$\pi$    **43.** 325$\pi$    **44.** 36$\pi$    **45.** 45 m$^2$    **46.** 330

**47.** 10    **48.** $\frac{4}{5}$    **49.** $(-3\frac{1}{2}, 3)$    **50.** $4x - 5y = -21$    **51.** $5x + 4y = -16$

*For Ex. 52–55, graphs are described.*

**52.** Line through (4, 0) and (0, −3)

**53.** The part of the plane between dashed lines through (0, −6) and (5, −6) and through (0, −1) and (5, −1)

**54.** Solid line through (0, 7) and (−8, 2) and half plane above it

**55.** Circle with center (0, 0), radius 5, and pts. at (5, 0), (0, 5), (−5, 0), (0, −5)

**56.** T    **57.** T    **58.** F    **59.** F    **60.** F    **61.** T    **62.** T    **63.** F

**64.** *Given:* $\triangle ABC$ with $A$ at (0, 0) and $\overline{AB}$ on the $x$-axis; $X$, $Y$ are midpts. of $\overline{AC}$ and $\overline{BC}$.

*Prove:* $XY = \frac{1}{2}AB$

*Proof:* 1. By the midpt. formula, $X$ is at $(b, c)$ and $Y$ is at $(a + b, c)$.

2. By the distance formula, $XY = a$ and $AB = 2a$.

3. Multiplying both sides of $AB = 2a$ by $\frac{1}{2}$, $\frac{1}{2}AB = a$.

4. By substitution, $XY = \frac{1}{2}AB$.

1 2 3 4 5 6 7 8 9 10 11 12 13 14 15    7 6 5 4 3 2 1 0 9 8